SOCIAL REGISTER *Observer*

WINTER 2020, ISSUE LII

SOCIAL REGISTER ASSOCIATION
14 WALL STREET, NEW YORK, NY 10005
© COPYRIGHT 2019 BY THE SOCIAL REGISTER ASSOCIATION
WWW.SOCIALREGISTERONLINE.COM

Scully & Scully

CELEBRATING 85 YEARS ON PARK AVENUE

18k Gold with Diamonds

China Crystal Silver Fine Furniture Jewelry Gifts

Scully & Scully
Established 1934

504 Park Avenue
(between 59th and 60th Streets)
New York
800-223-3717
Please call for Catalogue
www.scullyandscully.com

18k White Gold, Aquamarines, Diamonds and Freshwater Pearls, Exclusively Ours.

Contents

Regular Features

Cover: *Attached*, 2018
Lorraine Shemesh (American)
oil on canvas
64" x 61 ½"
Courtesy of Lorraine Shemesh and Gerald Peters Gallery.
Photograph by Robert Puglisi.

Front Page: *Vigil*, ca. 1930
Marguerite Zorach (American, 1887-1968)
oil on canvas
32" x 26"
Courtesy of Gerald Peters Gallery.

Editor: Nicholas Prychodko
Art Director: Charles Sheblom
Associate Editor: Stephanie Hadik
Consulting Editors:
Pippa Biddle
Brantley Carter Bolling Knowles
D. Brenton Simons
Chase Reynolds Ewald
George H. McNeely IV
Rowan Jacobsen
Brian D. White

Director of Membership & Events
Alexandra Hoyle
Office: (646) 612-7323
Email: ahoyle@thesocialregister.org

Director of Advertising Sales
Lise Honoré
Office: (646) 612-7317
Cell: (415) 517-2013
Email: lhonore@thesocialregister.org

14 Wall Street, New York, NY 10005
Telephone: (646) 612-7310
Fax: (646) 612-7319
Email: SRObserver@thesocialregister.org
www.socialregisteronline.com

The Social Register Observer is published twice a year by the Social Register Association.

All rights reserved. Reproduction in whole or in part without written permission is strictly prohibited.

ISBN: 0-940281-33-3

TOP RIGHT: KINDRA CLINEFF; BOTTOM LEFT: A. EDGEWORTH; BOTTOM RIGHT: CLAIRE VAIL PHOTOGRAPHY

THE WINTER SHOW

A Benefit for
East Side House

5,000 Years of Art,
Antiques & Design

January 24
–
February 2
2020

Opening Night Party
January 23

Park Avenue Armory
New York City

thewintershow.org

Carl Milles, 1875-1955
Heraldic Lion, 1923
Gilded Bronze
Courtesy of Bernard Goldberg Fine Arts

2020 Loan Exhibition
Unrivaled: The Hispanic Society Museum & Library

Lead Sponsor
CHUBB®

Mr. and Mrs. Harrison Falb. The bride wore a gown by Amsale along with a custom veil, and her late father's family crest ring as her "something old."

Brittany Mack and Harrison Falb are married

Brittany Blair Mack, daughter of Mrs. Richard G. Himelrick (Mack—Roxanna M. Armstrong) of Paradise Valley, AZ, and the late Louis W. Mack III of La Jolla, CA, was married on September 29, 2018, to Harris Bentsen Falb, son of Mrs. Margaret R. Benson of Dallas, TX, and John H. Falb II, also of Dallas. The ceremony took place at the Nantucket United Methodist Church, followed by a reception at the White Elephant Hotel, overlooking Nantucket Harbor.

The bride, known as Blair, is the granddaughter of John S. Armstrong III of La Jolla, and the late Mrs. Armstrong (Margaret B. Morton), and of the late Mr. and Mrs. Louis W. Mack II (Martha Proctor), also of La Jolla. She is the stepdaughter of Mr. Himelrick. The bride is the great-great-granddaughter of John Samuel Armstrong, who founded Arizona State University in 1885 as the Territorial Normal School.

The groom, known as Bentsen, is the grandson of Mr. and Mrs. Calvin R. Bentsen (Mary M. Harris) of McAllen, TX, and of the late Mr. and Mrs. John H. Falb (Marjorie A. Odeneal) of Chicago.

The bride wore a gown by Amsale along with a custom veil, and as her "something old", wore her late father's family crest ring to remind her of his presence on such an important day. In addition to their wedding procession, the bride's cousin, Chapin Lewis, 1st Lieutenant in the U.S. Marine Corps, served as flag bearer immediately prior to her entry. Paying homage to the couple's Scottish roots, a bagpiper playing "Highland Cathedral" led the bride into the church.

Mrs. Falb is a graduate of Southern Methodist University. Mr. Falb also graduated from Southern Methodist University, and received an MBA from Wake Forest University.

MR & MRS FALB BY JORDI CABRE

"When I wanted to preserve and publish my family history, I went to the best source."

Nancy Sands Maulsby
Greenwich, Connecticut

— EST. 1845 —

Call Kathleen Mackenzie at 617-226-1256 or visit AmericanAncestors.org/sro

The couple took a wedding trip to India and the Maldives, and make their home in Chicago.

Lila Dupree and Daniel Adair are married

Lila Lancaster Seiler Dupree, daughter of Mrs. Frederick F. Dupree Jr. (Sunny A. Seiler) of Cambridge, MA, and the late Mr. Dupree, was married on September 15, 2018, to Daniel Lee Adair, son of Ms. Catherine A. Steiner-Adair and Fred L. Adair Jr., also of Cambridge. The ceremony took place in the garden of Wasget Cove, the bride's family home in Northeast Harbor, ME. A reception followed on Little Cranberry Island.

The bride is the granddaughter of the late Chief Justice and Mrs. Robert E. Seiler (Faye Poore) of Jefferson City, MO, and of the late Mr. and Mrs. Frederick F. Dupree (Caroline Henderson) of Knoxville, TN.

The groom is the grandson of Mr. and Mrs. Lee Steiner (Rosalind Roth) of Scarsdale, NY. He is also the grandson of Mr. and Mrs. Fred Adair (Martha Jordan) of Williamsburg, VA.

Mrs. Adair attended Milton Academy and is a graduate of Columbia University and London Academy of Music and Dramatic Arts. Mr. Adair also attended Milton Academy. He is a graduate of John's Hopkins University and received an MBA from Columbia.

The couple took a wedding trip to Botswana, Zambia, and Mozambique. They currently reside in Los Angeles.

Left: Mr. and Mrs. Daniel Adair about to depart from the wedding ceremony. The ceremony took place in the garden of Wasget Cove, the bride's family home in Northeast Harbor, ME.

MR & MRS ADAIR BY JENNIFER SMITH ALDERS PHOTOGRAPHY

Claire Chewning weds Claiborne Smith

Claire McNulty Chewning, daughter of Ms. Karen Beal Chewning of Georgetown, SC, and Lawrence Harris Chewning of Rocky Mount, NC, was married on June 15, 2019, to Claiborne Alexander Livingston Smith, son Mr. and Mrs. Blair Webster Smith (Catherine Stirling Cassidy) of New York and Georgetown. The ceremony took place at Saint Mary Our Lady of Ransom Catholic Church, followed by a reception at Winyah Indigo Society Hall, both in Georgetown.

The bride is the granddaughter of the late Mr. and Mrs. Frank Shouse Beal (Nancy McNulty) of Georgetown. She is also the granddaughter of the late Dr. and Mrs. Lawrence Harris Chewning Jr. (Dorothy Gillespie) of Spartanburg, SC.

The groom, known as Alec, is the grandson of Mrs. Arch Wilson Cassidy (Dolores Barnes) of Jacksonville, FL, and the late Mr. Cassidy. He is also the grandson of Mrs. Donald Kaye Smith (Sarah Elizabeth Glascock) of Vero Beach, FL, and Solomons Island, MD, and the late Mr. Smith.

Mrs. Smith attended Saint Mary's School in Raleigh, NC. She received a Bachelor's degree from Presbyterian College, as well as a Master's degree from Converse College. Mr. Smith attended Episcopal High School in Alexandria, VA, and is a graduate of the College of Charleston.

The couple took a wedding trip to Gasparilla Island, FL, and reside in Beaufort, SC.

MR & MRS SMITH BY KELLY JONES

Top: Mr. and Mrs. Claiborne Smith. The ceremony took place at Saint Mary Our Lady of Ransom Catholic Church, followed by a reception at Winyah Indigo Society Hall, both in Georgetown.

MR & MRS DAVIDSON BY KELI PHOTOGRAPHY

Philippa Biddle and Benjamin Davidson are married

Philippa Lloyd Biddle, daughter of Mr. and Mrs. Edward E. Biddle (P. Ridgely Horsey) of Katonah, NY, was married on June 1, 2019, to Benjamin Quittner Davidson, son of Mr. and Mrs. J. Matthew Davidson (Amy Clark) of Germantown, NY. The ceremony took place at Christ Church in Dover, DE, with a reception held at Ridgely House & Gardens, also in Dover.

The bride, known as Pippa, is the granddaughter of the late Mrs. Alexandra Leigh-Hunt (Horsey—Alexandra Leigh-Hunt) of Sag Harbor, NY, and the late Honorable Henry Ridgely Horsey of the Supreme Court of Delaware, who was of Rehoboth Beach, DE. She is also the granddaughter of the late Mrs. Barbara Ruth Noyes (Biddle—Barbara R. Noyes) of Ithaca, NY, and the late William Whelen Biddle of Seattle. The bride is a direct descendant of French writer and poet Louise de Vilmorin, and of American industrialist Henry Leigh Hunt. She is also a direct descendant of Nicholas Biddle, president of the Second Bank of the United States, and Anthony J. Drexel, founder of Drexel Morgan & Co. and Drexel University.

The groom is the grandson of the late Mrs. Judy Abbott of New York, and the late Richard Clark of Lake Forest, IL. He is also the grandson of Mrs. Joan Kaplan Davidson of New York and Germantown, and the late Crowe G. Davidson. The groom is a great-grandson of George Abbott, the Broadway producer and playwright responsible for hits including *Damn Yankees* and *The Pajama Game*, and also of Jacob M. Kaplan, former president of the Welch's Grape Juice Company and founder of the J.M. Kaplan Fund, a New York-based philanthropic fund focused on preservation, development, and innovation in the arts.

The wedding saw friends and family in "old-fashioned" attire, with guests in hats and morning suits making a colorful promenade as they walked from the historic colonial church to the reception, repeating a pattern the bride's parents' guests made 33 years ago, and which dates back centuries. Built in 1726, the Ridgely House is one of the oldest houses in the United States still in original private family ownership.

Mrs. Davidson attended Miss Porter's School and graduated from Columbia University. Mr. Davidson is a graduate of Bennington College.

The couple took a wedding trip to Marshall, NC, and currently reside in Germantown.

MR & MRS DAVIDSON BY KELI PHOTOGRAPHY

Opposite & Top: Mr. and Mrs. Benjamin Davidson. Friends and family dressed in "old-fashioned" attire, a family tradition dating back centuries.

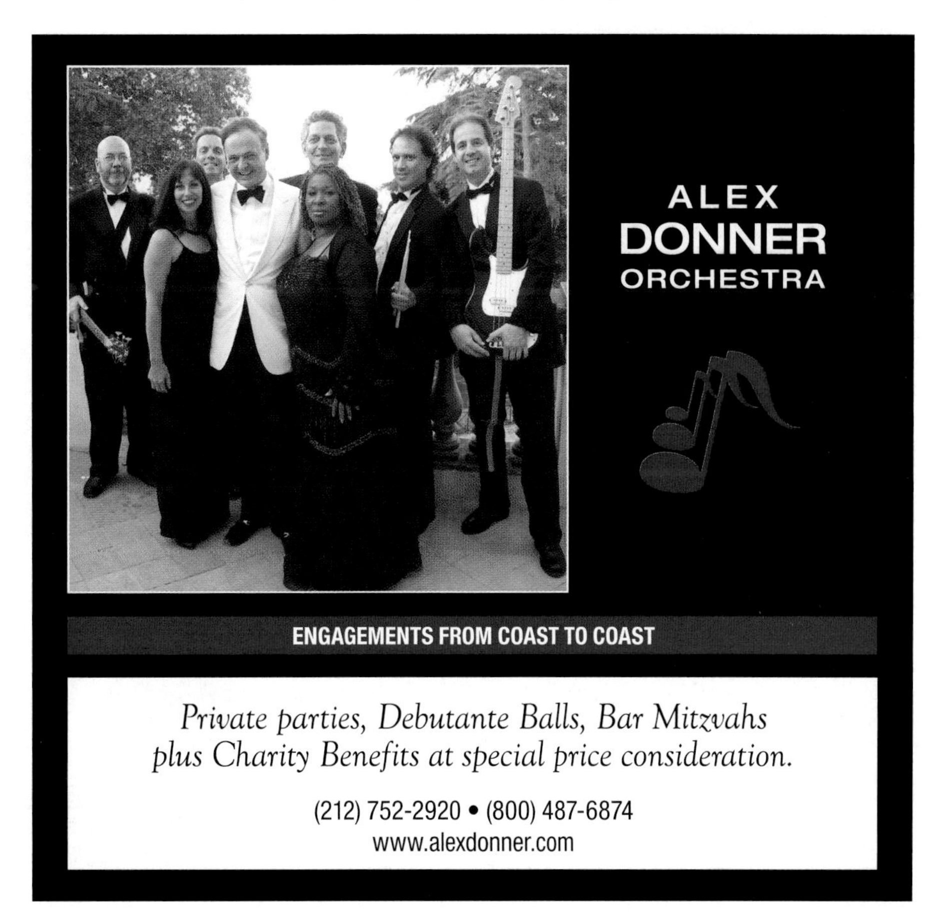

Opposite: Mr. Phillips Hamilton and Ms. Beatrice Schneider-Hamilton. The bride's family flew in from Berlin, Munich, Zurich, Seattle and Portland to celebrate and assist the bride in catering the event for 100 cherished guests.

Left: The bride arrived in a draft-horse carriage drawn through a pear tree allée lined with Tibetan prayer flags. Guests and their children were invited to play with toy steamboats and a petting zoo of pygmy goats.

Beatrice Schneider and Phillips Hamilton are married

Beatrice Sieglinde Schneider, daughter of Mrs. Sieglinde Erna Schneider of Bad Aibling, Germany, and the late Herman Karl Schneider of Kulmbach, Germany, married Phillips Howard Hamilton, son of the late Mrs. Alison

MR HAMILTON AND MS SCHNEIDER-HAMILTON BY HOLLY RUSSELL OF LADY AND THE LENS

Phillips Hamilton of Highland Park, IL, and the late Howard Laverne Hamilton of Ames, IA. A private wedding ceremony performed by the Hon. Karen Shields took place at the Alfred Caldwell Lily Pool in Chicago on June 25, 2019. A public ceremony and reception took place on June 29, 2019, at Grace Gables, the couple's home in Hebron, IN.

The bride is the granddaughter of Mrs. Franz A. Zinko (Erna Hupfauer) of Schonau-Tuntenhausen, Germany, and the late Mr. Zinko. She is also the granddaughter of the late Mr. and Mrs. Joseph Schneider (Johanna Katharina Pausch) of Munich, Germany.

The groom is the grandson of the late Mr. and Mrs. Charles Ray Phillips (Helen Bagoe) of Charlottesville, VA, and of the late Mr. and Mrs. Harry S. Hamilton (Gertrude R. Shibley) of Lone Tree, IA.

The bride's family flew in from Berlin, Munich, Zurich, Seattle and Portland to celebrate and assist the bride in catering the event for 100 cherished guests. She arrived in a draft-horse carriage drawn through a pear tree allée lined with Tibetan prayer flags. Guests and their children were invited to play with toy steamboats and a petting zoo of pygmy goats. At sundown, everyone assisted each other releasing hot air sky lanterns inscribed with their well-wishes.

Ms. Schneider-Hamilton is a graduate of the University of Illinois. Mr. Hamilton graduated from Princeton, Queens College, and the Eastman School of Music of the University of Rochester.

The couple took a wedding trip to the bride's family home in Bavaria, and to Lyon, France. They reside in Hebron and Chicago.

MR HAMILTON AND MS SCHNEIDER-HAMILTON BY HOLLY RUSSELL OF LADY AND THE LENS

Julia Fowkes marries Thomas Hasse

Above: Mr. and Mrs. Thomas Hasse. The ceremony and reception took place at Hotel Delos in Bandol, France.

Julia Clarke Fowkes, daughter of Mrs. William Wadsworth (Fowkes—Jane Clarke) of Tuxedo Park, NY, and William I. Fowkes of New York and New Fairfield, CT was married on July 6, 2019, to Thomas Thierry Hasse, son of Mr. and Mrs. Thierry G. Hasse (Clarisse M. Le Blay) of Mamaroneck, NY. The ceremony and reception took place at Hotel Delos in Bandol, France.

The bride is the granddaughter of the late Mr. and Mrs. Charles F. Clarke (Virginia Schoppenhorst) of Cleveland Heights, OH. She is also the granddaughter of the late Dr. and Mrs. Robert A. Fowkes Sr. (Angela M. Vescio) of Bronxville and Dobbs Ferry, NY. She is the stepdaughter of Mr. Wadsworth and of Stephen M. Smith.

The groom is the grandson of the late Mr. and Mrs. Roger Le Blay (Marie L. Bac) of Montoison, France, and Mr. and Mrs. Guy Hasse (Janine Paganessi) of Boulogne, France.

Mrs. Hasse attended Ethical Culture Fieldston School and is a graduate of the University of Michigan. Mr. Hasse attended Riverdale Country Day School and graduated from Duke University.

After a wedding trip to Indonesia, the couple make their home in New York.

Caroline Pires weds Peter Day

Caroline Margaret Pires, daughter of Ms. Colleen King and Edmund Pires of Bristol, RI, was married on July 20, 2019, to Peter Samson Day, son of Mr. and Mrs. Lee Day (Laura Globus) of New York. The ceremony and reception were held at Rosecliff Mansion in Newport, RI.

The bride is the granddaughter of the late Ms. Margaret La Riviere and Russell King of Barrington, RI, and of Mrs. Edmund Pires (Rose Santos) of Bristol, and the late Mr. Pires.

The groom, known as Samson, is the grandson of David Globus of New York and the late Mrs. Globus (Vivian Irwig). He is also the grandson of the late Mrs. Conway M. Day (Lacagnina—Conway MacLean) of Montecito, CA, and the late Lee G. P. Day Jr. of New Canaan, CT.

Mrs. Day is a graduate of Columbia University. Mr. Day graduated from Otis College of Art and Design.

The couple took a wedding trip to Portugal, and reside in West Hollywood, CA.

Opposite Page: Mr. and Mrs. Peter Day.

MR & MRS HASSE BY BUBBLEROCK

Go Confidently

At Van Liew Trust Company our clients want someone to look out for their investments today, as well as provide direction for them and their families tomorrow. Van Liew Trust offers portfolio management and trust services designed to meet individual financial goals. Our clients take comfort in knowing their assets will be managed as if they were our own.

VAN LIEW TRUST COMPANY

One Regency Plaza, Providence, Rhode Island 02903
Nine Memorial Boulevard, Newport, Rhode Island 02840
1-800-300-1116 www.vanliewtrust.com

Dorothy Hunter and Matthew Reardon are married

Dorothy Sachs Hunter, daughter of Mrs. Robert D. Hunter (Elizabeth I. Valsam) of Walpole, MA, and the late Mr. Hunter, was married on September 8, 2018, to Matthew James Reardon, son of Mr. and Mrs. Kevin Reardon (Amy Nakano) of Millis, MA. The ceremony and reception took place at Bullard Memorial Farm in Holliston, MA.

The bride is the granddaughter of the late Mrs. Donald Wheeler of Toronto, and the late Theodore W. J. Valsam of Needham, MA. She is also the granddaughter of the late Mr. & Mrs. George I. Hunter

Above: Mr. Matthew Reardon and Ms. Dorothy Hunter. The ceremony and reception took place at Bullard Memorial Farm in Holliston, MA.

MR & MRS REARDON BY PIZZUTI PHOTOGRAPHY

(Hazel F. Costa) of Boston. She is the step-granddaughter of the late Mr. Wheeler.

The groom is the grandson of the late Mr. and Mrs. Tsutomo Nakano of Toronto (Joan Hayashi) and of the late Mr. and Mrs. Arthur Reardon (Jeanne Cook) of Brighton, MA.

Ms. Hunter is a graduate of the University of Massachusetts Amherst and Northeastern University. Mr. Reardon graduated from Salem State University.

The couple took a wedding trip to Spain and reside in Cambridge, MA.

Parker Howe and John Sheptock Jr. are married

Parker Shedd Howe, son of Mr. and Mrs. Jonathan S. Howe (Victoria H. Muller) of South Pasadena, CA, married John Joseph Sheptock Jr., son of Mr. and Mrs. John J. Sheptock Sr. (Patricia Dockray) of Clifton, NJ. The ceremony and reception took place on May 9, 2019, at the Fairmont Orchid Hawaii in Kamuela, HI.

Mr. Howe is the grandson of Mr. and Mrs. George Muller (Virginia de Surville) of San Marino, CA, and of the late Mr. and Mrs. Charles S. Howe (Barbara Pielemeier) of La Jolla, CA.

Mr. Sheptock is the grandson of the late Mr. and Mrs. Roy V. Dockray (Ruth E. Boerner) of Boynton Beach, FL. He is also the grandson of Mr. and Mrs. John H. Sheptock (Dolores J. Mendello) of Totowa, NJ.

Mr. Howe graduated from Babson College. Mr. Sheptock is a graduate of Emerson College.

The couple took a wedding trip to Australia and make their home in Altadena, CA.

MSSRS HOWE & SHEPTOCK BY JOSH FLETCHER

PALM BEACH FINE PROPERTIES AND WALLY TURNER PRESENT

In-Town Mizner Villa "Costa Bella"

Just one property from the Atlantic is this outstanding 1920's Addison Mizner-designed residence on prestigious Dunbar Road. The house has been updated to today's luxury standards and offers 4 principal bedrooms plus 4 additional sea view guestrooms. Impeccable original details. Beach access steps away. The ultimate house for entertaining and gracious daily living. 111DunbarRoad.com

EXCLUSIVE

WALLY TURNER | 561.301.2060

Senior Global Real Estate Advisor

wally.turner@sothebyshomes.com

Operated by Sotheby's International Realty, Inc.

Sotheby's INTERNATIONAL REALTY

Lisa-Marie Mattas and Keith Steinmeyer are married

Lisa-Marie Irene Mattas, daughter of Mr. and Mrs. Paul Mattas (Kathleen Juhasz) of Orlando, FL, was married on April 13, 2019, to Keith Lewis Steinmeyer, son of Mr. and Mrs. Tomas Steinmeyer (Susan Kreul) of Colorado Springs, CO. The ceremony took place at Knowles Memorial Chapel in Winter Park, FL, with a reception at the Rice Family Ballroom of Rollins College.

The bride is the granddaughter of Mrs. Irene Juhasz (Irene Toth) of Toronto, Canada, and the late Mr. Frank Juhasz. She is also the granddaughter of the late Mr. and Mrs. John Mattas (Helen Lovasik) of Hartford, CT.

The groom is the grandson of the late Mr. and Mrs. Florian Kreul (Loretta Mary Foley) of Colorado Springs. He is the grandson of Mr. and Mrs. Jack Steinmeyer (Dorothy Canfield), also of Colorado Springs.

The bride wore a custom veil with over 1,000 Swarovski crystals, designed by her mother, a former Cartier designer. At the reception, guests enjoyed a string quartet with Hungarian music, cuisine, and wine from the vineyards of the bride's maternal grandfather's estate. A lifelong equestrian and competitive dressage rider, the bride founded Rollins Equestrian, an intercollegiate riding program which provides students of diverse backgrounds the opportunity to ride and compete in an intercollegiate hunter-jumper circuit.

Mrs. Steinmeyer is a graduate of Rollins College. Mr. Steinmeyer is a graduate of the University of Central Florida and received his JD from Florida State University.

Following a wedding trip to Sanibel Island, FL, the couple reside in Orlando.

Above: Mr. and Mrs. Keith Steinmeyer. The ceremony took place at Knowles Memorial Chapel in Winter Park, FL, with a reception at the Rice Family Ballroom of Rollins College.

Left: Mrs. Steinmeyer wore a custom veil with over 1,000 Swarovski crystals, designed by her mother, a former Cartier designer.

MR & MRS STEINMEYER BY ANDI MANS

Elizabeth McKnight and David Quinn are wed

Elizabeth Connelly McKnight, daughter of Mr. and Mrs. Stephen Hayward McKnight (Peggy L. Thomas) of Pittsburgh, was married on April 13, 2019, to David Benjamin Quinn, son of Mr. and Mrs. Joseph F. Quinn (Diane S. Juliar) of Newton, MA. The ceremony and reception took place at Indian Creek Country Club in Miami Beach, FL.

The bride, known as Libby, is the granddaughter of the late Mr. and Mrs. Robert J. Thomas (Peggy A. Crabtree) and of the late Mr. and Mrs. Roy Herd McKnight Jr. (Beatrice C. Bartlett), all of Pittsburgh.

The groom is the grandson of the late Mr. and Mrs. Benjamin Juliar (Rose Gershenson) of Detroit, and the late Mr. and Mrs. Joseph F. Quinn (Lois Anderson) of Baltimore.

The marriage ceremony was performed by Reverend Robert W. Asinger, a minister of the United Church of Christ, with the Reverend Dr. Barbara A. Asinger taking part. The bride wore a gown designed by Oscar de la Renta, complemented by a veil which had been worn by her mother.

Ms. McKnight is a graduate of Boston College and The Juilliard School. Mr. Quinn is a graduate of Boston College, from which he also received a law degree.

The couple took a brief wedding trip to Key West, FL, with a longer trip to Hawaii planned. They reside in New York.

Right: Mr. David Quinn and Ms. Elizabeth McKnight. The bride wore a gown designed by Oscar de la Renta, with a veil which had been worn by her mother.

MR QUINN & MS MCKNIGHT BY SUZANNE DELAWARE STUDIOS

Mary-Jane Castleton and Lee Snodgrass are married

Mary-Jane Castleton, daughter of Mr. and Mrs. Douglas J. Castleton (Kathryn Stringam) of Hyde Park, UT, was married on October 27, 2018, to Lee Linington Snodgrass, son of Mr. and Mrs. John D'Arcy Snodgrass (Toner—Ellen L. Carlson) of Locust Valley, NY. The ceremony and reception were held at the home of the groom's parents.

The bride is the granddaughter of the late Mr. and Mrs. Bryant Stringam (Ruby Anderson) of Lethbridge, Canada, and of the late Mr. and Mrs. Leon Castleton (Elaine Jones) of Malad City, ID.

The groom is the grandson of Mrs. Allan A. A. Flynn (Carlson—Judith L. Lee) of Locust Valley and West Palm Beach, and the late Eric G. Carlson of Plandome, NY. He is also the grandson of the late Dr. John J. Snodgrass (Laetitia McGreer) of Plandome. He is the stepgrandson of the late Mr. Flynn.

Mrs. Snodgrass graduated from Utah State University and received a Master's degree from Rice University. Mr. Snodgrass is a graduate of George Washington University.

The couple took a wedding trip to Paris and make their home in Sea Cliff, NY.

Left: Lucky is the bride the rain falls on. Mr. and Mrs. Snodgrass took a wedding trip to Paris.

MR & MRS SNODGRASS BY DAPHNE AND DEAN LLC

Lucy Coolidge and Zachary Trout are married

Jacqueline Langholtz weds William Taylor

Above: Mr. and Mrs. Zachary Trout. The ceremony took place at Holy Rosary Church, with the reception at The Willard Hotel, both in Washington, DC.

Right: Mr. and Mrs. William Taylor. The groom is a descendant of early Virginia colonist William Randolph, who settled on Turkey Island in the James River area around 1650.

MR & MRS TROUT BY MATTHEW D'AGOSTINO OF LOVE LIFE IMAGES; MR. & MRS. TAYLOR BY MAGALI DE VULPILLIERES

Lucy Read Coolidge, daughter of Mrs. Francis L. Coolidge (Marylouise E. Redmond) of Charlottesville, VA, and the late Mr. Coolidge, was married on April 27, 2019, to Zachary Ryan Trout, son of Mrs. Rick A. Morris (Trout—Kimberly Lukacs) of Fincastle, VA, and the late Dr. Robert G. Trout. The ceremony took place at Holy Rosary Church, with a reception at The Willard Hotel, both in Washington, DC.

The bride is the granddaughter of the late Dr. and Mrs. James W. Redmond of Milton, MA. She is also the granddaughter of the late Mr. and Mrs. Francis L. Coolidge Sr. of Boston and Washington.

The groom is the grandson of the late Mr. and Mrs. Joseph A. Lukacs of Pittsburgh, and of the late Mr. and Mrs. Howard Trout of Harrisburg, PA. He is the stepson of Mr. Morris.

Mrs. Trout is a graduate of Rhodes College and a received a JD from the University of Mississippi. Mr. Trout graduated from Wake Forest University and received a Master's degree from the University of Chicago.

Following a wedding trip to Australia, the couple reside in Washington.

Jacqueline Camille Langholtz, daughter of Mr. and Mrs. Harvey J. Langholtz (Danielle Moretti) of Williamsburg, VA, was married on June 1, 2019, to William Randolph Taylor, son of Ms. Sandra I. Mirkil (Taylor—Sandra Mirkil) of Charlottesville, VA, and Harrison W. Taylor of Keswick, VA. The ceremony took place at St. Paul's Memorial Church at the University of Virginia in Charlottesville, followed by a luncheon reception at Keswick Farm, home of the groom's father and stepmother.

The bride is the granddaughter of the late Mr. and Mrs. Nunzio Moretti (Gloria Koch) of Yonkers, NY. She is also the granddaughter of the late Mr. and Mrs. Leo Langholtz (Esther Popper) of Dobbs Ferry, NY.

The groom is the grandson of the late Mrs. Helen M. Hollerith of New York, and the late William I. Mirkil of Newtown Square, PA. He is also the grandson of the late Mrs. Mary M. Taylor of Charlottesville, and the late Harry W. Taylor of Tucson, AZ. He is the stepson of Mrs. Liza Nash Taylor.

The groom is a descendant of early Virginia colonist William Randolph, who settled on Turkey Island in the James River around 1650 and who, with his wife, Mary Isham, is known as the "Adam and Eve of Virginia." He is also the great-great-great-grandson of Joseph Newton Pew Sr., founder of Sun Oil Company.

Joined in celebration by family, the ceremony was led by Episcopal Rector Will Peyton with support by Catholic Deacon Chris Morash. Among the readings was the Sheva Brachot, read in both Hebrew and English by cousins of the bride. The groom's sister, Annabel Boyd Taylor, also offered a reading. The bride's sister, Gabrielle Marie Langholtz, was matron of honor. The groom's brother, Thomas Morehead Taylor, was best man.

Mrs. Taylor attended Walsingham Academy and is a graduate of the College of William & Mary and the University of Oklahoma. Mr. Taylor attended Suffield Academy and is a graduate of Hampden-Sydney College.

The couple took a wedding trip to Alaska and make their home in Charlottesville.

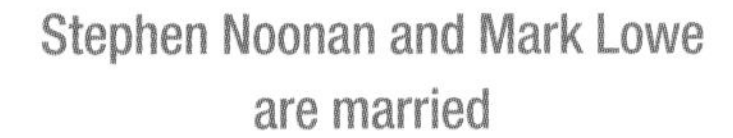

Stephen Noonan and Mark Lowe are married

Stephen Michael Noonan, son of Mrs. Thomas M. Noonan (Gabrielle H. F. Chadeayne) of Ladue, MO, and the late Mr. Noonan, married Mark Anthony Lowe, son of the late Mr. and Mrs. John J. Lowe (Elouise D. Gray) of Decatur, GA. The ceremony and reception took place on August 16, 2019, at the Harvard Club of New York City.

Above: Mssrs. Noonan and Lowe. The ceremony and reception took place at the Harvard Club of New York City.

Mr. Noonan is the grandson of the late Mr. and Mrs. Henry F. Chadeayne (Mildred R. Brady) of St. Louis, MO, and the late Mr. and Mrs. Raymond J. Noonan (Ellen V. O'Fallon), also of St. Louis.

Mr. Lowe is the grandson of the late Mr. and Mrs. John N. Gray (Clara B. Faigins) of Reynolds, GA. He is also the grandson of the late Mr. and Mrs. George Lowe (Mary E. Dean) of Boston.

Mr. Noonan is a graduate of Saint Louis University and received Master's degrees from Hunter College, Fordham University, and Mercy College. Mr. Lowe graduated from Harvard and received a JD degree from the University of Michigan, as well as Master's degrees from Endicott College and the University of Massachusetts.

The couple took a wedding trip to Iceland and reside in New York and Dorchester, MA.

Edited by Stephanie Hadik

Mary Catherine Burdine and James Hurrion

Ms. Mary Catherine Burdine, daughter of Mrs. Nick Uros (Burdine—Pamela C. Dorminey) of Augusta, GA, and Essley B. Burdine Jr. of Columbus, MS, is engaged to be married to Dr. James R. Hurrion, son of Mrs. Robert D. Hurrion (Judith E. Marshall) of Coventry, England, and the late Dr. Hurrion.

The bride-to-be is the granddaughter of Mrs. W. W. Dorminey (Betty McAlhany) of Augusta, and the late Mr. Dorminey. She is also the granddaughter of the late Mr. and Mrs. Essley B. Burdine (Doris Lykins) of Decatur, GA. She is the stepdaughter of Mrs. Essley Burdine Jr. (Kathryn Paul) and Mr. Uros.

The groom-to-be is the grandson of the late Mr. and Mrs. Reginald A. Marshall (Mavis Gould) of Cottingham, England. He is also the grandson of the late Mr. and Mrs. Sidney Hurrion (Salome Walls) of Croydon, England.

Ms. Burdine graduated from Washington and Lee University as well as the Massachusetts Institute of Technology. Dr. Hurrion is a graduate of Oxford.

A wedding is planned for 2020.

MSSRS NOONAN & LOWE BY FIFTH AVENUE DIGITAL PHOTOGRAPHY

Mallory Howe and David Molina

Amanda Thorne and John Harman Jr.

Brooke Block and Oliver Kennan

Mr. and Mrs. Jonathan S. Howe (Victoria H. Muller) of South Pasadena, CA, announce the engagement of their daughter, Mallory de Surville Howe, to David Mario Flynn Molina, son of Dr. and Mrs. Joseph M. Molina (Therese Flynn), also of South Pasadena.

The bride-to-be is the granddaughter of Mr. and Mrs. George Muller (Virginia de Surville) of San Marino, CA, and of the late Mr. and Mrs. Charles S. Howe (Barbara Pielemeier) of La Jolla, CA.

The groom-to-be is the grandson of the late Mr. and Mrs. Raymond P. Flynn (Mary M. Corbett) of San Diego, CA. He is also the grandson of the late Mr. and Mrs. Clarence D. Molina (Mary Saladini) of Long Beach, CA.

Miss Howe graduated from Amherst College. Mr. Molina is a graduate of California State University, Long Beach.

A wedding is planned for September 2020 in Malibu, CA.

Miss Amanda Lynn Thorne, daughter of Harry S. Thorne of Hudson, OH, and the late Mrs. Thorne (Beverly J. Grad), is engaged to be married to John Robert Harman Jr., son of Mr. and Mrs. John R. Harman (Gloria J. Cason) of Raleigh, NC.

The bride-to-be is the granddaughter of the late Mr. and Mrs. Alex L. Grad (Margaret Wagel) of Kent, OH. She is also the granddaughter of the late Mr. and Mrs. Harry Thorne (Ruth M. Marsalas) of Stow, OH.

The groom-to-be is the grandson of the late Mr. and Mrs. Samuel P. Cason Jr. (Gloria E. Gilbert) of Raleigh, and the late Mr. and Mrs. Glenn G. Harman (Sara F. McLean) of West Palm Beach.

Miss Thorne graduated from Ohio University and received a Master's degree from the University of North Carolina at Chapel Hill. Mr. Harman is a graduate of North Carolina State University.

A wedding is planned for May 2020 in Raleigh.

Mr. and Mrs. John D. Block (Hilary Cushing) of New York City and Millbrook, NY, announce the engagement of their daughter, Brooke Douglas Block, to Oliver James Johnson Kennan, son of Christopher J. Kennan of Millerton, NY, and the late Mrs. Elizabeth Ross Johnson of New York.

The bride-to-be is the granddaughter of the late Dr. and Mrs. Robert M. Cushing (Robin Fersten) of New York, and the late Mr. and Mrs. Lester Block (Ruth Harris) of Princeton, NJ.

The groom-to-be is the grandson of the late Mr. and Mrs. Robert Wood Johnson III (Betty Wold) and of the late Mr. and Mrs. George F. Kennan (Annelise Sorensen), all of Princeton.

Miss Block graduated from Hobart and William Smith College. Mr. Kennan is a graduate of Colorado College.

A wedding is planned for February 2020 in Montego Bay, Jamaica.

Edited by Stephanie Hadik

1. Caroline Ellison Grayson

Miss Grayson is the daughter of Mr. and Mrs. William E. Grayson (Laureen Buckert) of San Francisco. She was presented at the San Francisco Debutante Ball. She is a student at the University of California, Berkeley.

2. Chevalier Rice McWilliams

Miss McWilliams is the daughter of Mrs. Christopher A. M. Low (McWilliams—Deborah A. Spaeder) of New York, and John L. McWilliams IV of University Park, TX. She was presented at New York's Paas Festival Ball. She attends the University of Florida.

3. Katherine Ann Johnson

Miss Johnson is the daughter of Mr. and Mrs. David C. Johnson (Ann F. Snowden) of New York and Westerly, RI. She was presented at New York's Viennese Opera Ball. She is a graduate of Wellesley College.

4. Trinity Cassatt Polk

Miss Polk is the daughter of Mr. and Mrs. F. Lyon Polk III (Hilary B. Edson) of New York and Locust Valley, NY. She was presented at New York's Junior Assembly Ball. She is a student at the University of Virginia.

MISS GRAYSON BY DREW ALTIZAR; MISS MCWILLIAMS BY ANDREJ JACKAMETS PHOTOGRAPHY; MISS POLK BY BACHRACH

Wealth management with a genuine difference for 40 years.

THE HAVERFORD TRUST COMPANY

QUALITY INVESTING

haverfordquality.com

Above: Dr. Antell holds his Alumnus of the Year Award, presented to him for more than 40 years of outstanding service.

New York City plastic surgeon **Dr. Darrick E. Antell** was recently honored as the Alumnus of the Year by University School in Shaker Heights, OH, for his more than 40 years of outstanding service. Dr. Antell returned to his alma mater to receive this award and celebrate the 50th reunion of the class of 1969 on May 16, 2019. He was celebrated for his outstanding community service and good deeds to University School, including partnering with Squash Hall of Famer Jack Herrick ('56) and Jack Turben ('53) to provide new squash courts for the school. Dr. Antell has served on the school's Board of Trustees since 2000 and is currently a Life Trustee.

Capt. Sean D. Glendening returned from combat deployment with the U.S. Army's elite XVIII Airborne Corps on August 27, 2019. He was deployed in support of Combined Joint Task Force—Operation Inherent Resolve, the international counter-ISIS coalition. His tour of duty included missions in Iraq and Kuwait. For his service, Capt. Glendening was awarded the Joint Services Commendation Medal. He returned to his home in New York where he continues to practice as an attorney.

Top: Capt. Glendening (*second from left*) was awarded the Joint Services Commendation Medal for his service.

Above: Thomas Schlafly celebrates after the Blues won their first Stanley Cup in the 52-year history of the franchise.

Lt. Ryan B. Weddle is deployed as an intelligence, surveillance and reconnaissance (ISR) officer with the NATO Resolute Support mission based in Kabul. He also serves as the Secretary of the New Hampshire **Society of the Cincinnati** and was able to have the Cincinnati flag flown inside a compartment of this drone during strike missions in Afghanistan against the Taliban.

Left: Lt. Weddle *(left)* holds the Society of the Cincinnati flag which was flown inside a compartment of his drone during strike missions.

Thomas F. Schlafly joined the ownership group of the St. Louis Blues hockey team in 2012; seven years later he was in Boston when the Blues won their first Stanley Cup in the 52-year history of the franchise. It was a special thrill for Mr. Schlafly to hoist Lord Stanley's renowned Cup on the ice at Boston's TD Garden after the seventh and decisive game of the series on June 12, 2019. He notes that the Bruins' fans he encountered were gracious, and that he received lots of congratulatory messages from friends in Boston.

DR. ANTELL BY JWD PHOTO

Left: Gold's Dragoon Master of the House, David Loda.

Above: Squadron A in gold vs. Gold's Dragoons in scarlet.

ERIC L. HOYLE

The 10th annual Gold's Dragoons Polo Cup championship game was held on August 25, 2019, at the Fairfield County Hunt Club in Westport, CT. This yearly match between **Squadron A** and Gold's Dragoons took place on a pleasantly mild late-summer day. At halftime, the score was 2–2 and the divot stompers sprang into action while sipping champagne. Judges were also busy winnowing down the candidates for prizes including the best ladies' hat, as well as "top chap" for best-dressed male. Throughout the second half, the Squadron A team consistently produced strong offensive and defensive maneuvers leading to their victory with a score of 6–4. Gold's Dragoons' five-year run was over!

Originating in 1884 when 18 young equestrians joined together to form the New York Hussars, Squadron A was first a political club and then an exclusive cavalry troop known for its expert riding and elegantly ornate uniforms. The stylish Hussars quickly became a very popular addition to New York City parades and National Horse Show events. On April 2, 1889, the group was mustered into the National Guard as Squadron A, the first cavalry arm of the Guard of the State of New York. During World War II, its members became part of the 101st Cavalry Group that fought gallantly in Germany and Austria. Currently, as a volunteer, social and philanthropic organization, it provides a venue for men and women to continue, preserve and forward the traditions, memory and contributions of the Squadron and the cavalry.

Gold's Dragoons was formed in 1657 under Cromwell in Fairfield County, CT, to defend against the Dutch and the Pequots. In 1660, it came under Royal control with the restoration of King Charles II, and was incorporated into the charter of Connecticut in 1662. After the American Revolution, it faded from records until it was resurrected as a Connecticut militia cavalry troop in 1932. The Dragoons recruited members from the foxhunters at the Fairfield County Hounds and polo players at the Fairfield County Hunt Club.

The annual polo match with Gold's Dragoons is less a competition than a celebration of almost 90 years of good sportsmanship. It is also a vehicle to raise money for organizations focused on repaying the debt all Americans owe our military for their courageous and selfless service to our nation. This year's beneficiary was The Equus Effect in Sharon, CT, whose mission is to use equine therapy to give veterans in transition the tools they need to build healthy relationships at home and in their communities.

Above Right: Mr. and Mrs. William Andersen.

Right: (*l-r*) Patrick D. Smith, Adam P. Hess and Chester Burley, dressed for the occasion.

Below Left: Bubbly coming right up! Patrick D. Smith does the honors.

On May 17, 2019, **William M. Graves Jr.** was presented with the 2019 Individual Distinguished Service Award by the Florida Trust for Historic Preservation, a statewide partner of the National Trust for Historic Preservation. Mr. Graves, a national community activist, is the founder of Friends of Florida's Coasts, Friends of Winter Park, Friends of Windermere, and Friends of Cypress Gardens.

Col. Todd W. Burnley and his daughter, **Juniors Miss Catherine A. M. Burnley**, attended the Fairytale Princess Daddy-Daughter Royal Ball hosted by CenterPoint Legacy Theater in Centerville, UT, on September 14, 2019. The evening was part of the theatre's 7th annual celebration of all things fairytale: bravery, wisdom, wonder, love, family and the lessons and adventures found in books!

ALL IMAGES BY ERIC L. HOYLE EXCEPT BOTTOM RIGHT.

Above: Dinner is served in honor of Ms. Russell and Mr. Grillo after the annual meeting of The Order of Colonial Lords of Manors in America.

The Order of Colonial Lords of Manors in America held its 108th annual meeting on May 30, 2019, at the townhouse of **The National Society of Colonial Dames in the State of New York.** The evening featured a lecture on the storied history of Long Island's St. George's Manor by Barbara Russell, Town of Brookhaven historian. This expansive manor and in particular its 18th-century chatelaine, Revolutionary War spy Anna Smith Strong, were recently made internationally famous by the TV series *Turn*. Additionally, Michael J. Grillo, the living historian and museum educator at The Van Cortlandt House Museum, was awarded the 2019 Timothy Field Beard Memorial Award for Excellence in History Education in recognition of his 19 years of dedication in bringing the past to life via his hand-tailored period costumes. The Order also inducted its newest member, **Robb A. Allan**, representing the Manor of Tisbury on Martha's Vineyard, which was created by his ancestor Thomas Mayhew. After the meeting, attendees gathered in the downstairs dining room for a punch reception hosted by **Mrs. Robert Armstead Naud (M. P. Curran)** and Mrs. Caroline Brown, officers of The National Society of Colonial Dames in the State of New York, followed by a dinner served in honor of Ms. Russell and Mr. Grillo.

Miss Eryn Burr Cooper graduated summa cum laude from the University of Alabama in the spring of 2019, and was honored as Outstanding Senior by the university's National Alumni Association. Miss Cooper has accepted employment as an on-air news reporter with WTVC Channel 9 (ABC/FOX affiliates/networks) in Chattanooga, TN. She is the daughter of **Mr. and Mrs. Joshua J. Cooper (Alisa A. Nesmith)** of Vienna, VA.

Opposite Page: Col. Burnley with his little princess, Juniors Miss Catherine Burnley, at the Fairytale Princess Daddy-Daughter Royal Ball hosted by CenterPoint Legacy Theater in Centerville, UT.

Thomas Nicholas Khazzam, known as Nico, will travel to Brazil this winter to teach English as part of his Fulbright Scholarship. Nico is a 2018 graduate of Rollins College. Motivated by his love of teaching, he has traveled extensively to rural communities studying international development and human rights, including trips to the Dominican Republic, Costa Rica, and Tanzania, where he climbed Mount Kilimanjaro.

Presidential historian and bestselling author Douglas Brinkley was guest of honor at an elegant dinner for more than 100 members and guests of the **New England Historic Genealogical Society & American Ancestors** held on July 25, 2019—a beautiful summer evening at a private club in Brookline, MA. Dr. Brinkley, whose notable books include *Cronkite and American Moonshot: John F. Kennedy and the Great Space Race*, is a professor at Rice University, a CNN Presidential Historian, and a contributing editor at *Vanity Fair*. Speaking on "The Art of Presidential Biography" after a sunset

Right: Miss Eryn Burr Cooper with her proud parents, Mr. and Mrs. Joshua J. Cooper.

1. Ryan J. Woods shares a laugh with Douglas Brinkley (*left*).

2. Mrs. Michael Vitton, Mrs. Allen F. Maulsby and Mr. D. Brenton Simons.

3. Mr. and Mrs. George Passela.

4. Dr. Douglas Brinkley and Mr. Thomas Bailey Hagan.

drinks party on the club porch, he was interviewed by NEHGS Literary Events Director Margaret Talcott. He was presented a detailed genealogy of his family by NEHGS President & CEO **D. Brenton Simons**, who revealed his kinship to three presidents of the United States and other ancestors and notable kinsmen. After dinner, a Lifetime Achievement Award in History and Biography was conferred upon Dr. Brinkley by NEHGS Senior Vice President **Ryan J. Woods**. Guests included event patron and NEHGS Board Chairman **Mrs. Allen F. Maulsby** **(Geist—Nancy L. Sands)** and many others, among them former Chairman **David H. Burnham; Sara S. Champion; Dr. Francis de Marneffe; Bradford F. Egan; Mr. and Mrs. Gerard A. Halpin III (Mary Lee Swift); Dr. and Mrs. Gary P. Kearney (Susan Hickcox); G. Marshall Moriarty; Mrs. John O. Parker (Olivia C. Hood); Mr. and Mrs. George W. Passela (Elizabeth McCaslin); John S. Reidy; Austin V. Shapard; Mr. and Mrs. Marshall L. Stocker (Alexandra E. Sanderson); Thomas W. Thaler; Jonathan B. Treat II; David M. Trebing; Mr. and Mrs. Michael S. Vitton (Elizabeth Buswell); Mr. and Mrs. Eric N. Ward (Sarah E. Rainwater);** and **Mrs. Ryan J. Woods (Karen K. Hoffmann).**

Left: A seersucker set: Mr. David H. Burnham, *Genealogy Roadshow* (PBS) co-host Mary Tedesco, and Mr. Marshall Stocker.

A group of SR members recently crossed the Atlantic for Queen Charlotte's Ball, held in London on September 7, 2019. Among those attending were **Michael A. Halperson; Ann Sims Haugen; Kenneth A. Kraft; Ronald E. Padgett; Elizabeth A. Stuart; Mr. and Mrs. Douglas S. VanDerzee (Carrie S. Konop); Cedric W. Vogel;** and **Richard M. Yates.** The debutante event, which took place at Lancaster House, supports Smile Train, a non-profit organization providing free corrective cleft surgery in 87 countries,

Above: Dr. Richard Paul and Mr. George Marshall Moriarty were two of the more than 100 members and guests of the NEHGS & American Ancestors function in Brookline.

Above Right: Mr. and Mrs. Douglas S. VanDerzee with Mr. Ronald E. Padgett (*right*) attended the Queen Charlotte's Ball in London in September.

training local doctors and providing hospital funding for the procedures.

Mr. and Mrs. Robert S. Roberson (Barbara C. Drane) enjoyed a visit to London this past June, which included catching up with friends, partaking in St. John's Day celebrations, visiting the city's great museums and attending sporting events, among them Royal Ascot. The five-day horse-racing event is considered one of the most anticipated events in the British summer's sporting and social calendar.

Lynn Forney Young, President General of the **National Society Daughters of the American Revolution**, has been appointed to The United States Semiquincentennial Commission, a national commission formed to plan commemorations and celebrations surrounding the 250th anniversary of the United States in July 2026. Members of the group will solicit ideas about how to mark the anniversary, meet at Philadelphia's Independence Hall to develop a plan, submit recommendations for the consideration of the President and Congress, and assist with the execution of the approved itinerary. Sixteen private citizens, eight members of Congress, and nine federal officials, including the Secretary of State, Librarian of Congress and Archivist of the United States, comprise the committee roster. Commissioner Young was appointed to serve by the Speaker of the U. S. House of Representatives.

Above: Mr. and Mrs. Robert S. Roberson at Royal Ascot.

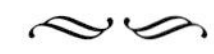

Left: Members of the U.S. Semiquincentennial Commission and partners gather inside Independence Hall in Philadelphia, Pennsylvania. The Commissioners were sworn in at the Commission's inaugural meeting on Friday, Nov. 16, 2018. (*Lynn Forney Young is front row, far right*).

TOP LEFT BY PEIRCE HARMAN; TOP RIGHT NEIL SPENCE PHOTOGRAPHY

Top: William Beggs IV, Lee Brozen, and Todd Schwebel.

Above: Lincoln 51 Band entertains at the Schwebel/Beggs soirée.

Below Left: Mr. and Mrs. Allen G. Carter Jr.

Below Right: Mrs. Edward W. Horner Jr. (Constance L. Forbes)

Society designer **Todd D. H. Schwebel** and his partner, **William Beggs IV**, hosted a garden party on July 21, 2019 at their beautifully restored Chicago residence before leaving the city for Vertefeuille, their summer home in Murray Bay, Quebec. Well known for their old-fashioned hospitality, Todd and William's guests enjoyed homemade hors d'ouevres and finger sandwiches while listening to the sounds of the popular Lincoln 51 Band, which played everyone's favorite hits from Frank Sinatra to Tina Turner. Dancing ensued!

Those attending included **Mrs. Dallas S. Boschen (Jetta A. Hawryluk); Mrs. Jonathan M. Bross (Sophia W. Poulos); Mr. and Mrs. Allen G. Carter Jr. (Mary S. Charles); Mr. and Mrs. Dwight M. Cleveland (Maria-Gabriela Franco Abarca); Mrs. Mary Jo Field (Ward—Simpson—Mary Jo Laflin); Donald H. J. Hermann; Mr. and Mrs. Edward W. Horner Jr. (Constance L. Forbes); Mr. and Mrs. Leland E. Hutchinson (Jean E. Perkins); Jonathan Janott; Ms. Anna L. Forstmann Kealy; James M. Kinney and Brian D. White; Edmund H. Lester; William H. Parke; Stratford Shields; Mr. and Mrs. Richard C. Spain (Nancy L. Mavec); Mrs. S. Zachariah Sudler (Violet L. Danilovic); Oscar S. Tatosian**; and **Mr. and Mrs. Thatcher Waller Jr. (Ellen W. MacRae).**

On Thursday, July 25, 2019, the **Sons of the Revolution in the State of New York** celebrated their second annual Tavern Night in the cozy Nichols Room at Fraunces Tavern. Now in its third year, the event was well-attended by both Sons and prospective members, as well as guests from many other hereditary organizations in New York. Guests enjoyed conversations about their summer activities to date and hatched plans for the upcoming fall over cocktails and hors d'oeuvres. This year's Tavern Night marked a special milestone in the history of the New York Society: Three hundred years ago, in 1719, construction began on the building that would come to be known as Fraunces Tavern. Throughout the history of the building, it has served as a tavern, the site of George Washington's farewell dinner for his officers, and the offices of the fledgling Department of State. Now under the stewardship of the New York Society, Fraunces Tavern welcomes tens of thousands of visitors from around the world each year.

To commemorate this special occasion, the Color Guard of the SRNY presented the Society with a special gift of a gleaming silver punch bowl; with no small degree of pomp and circumstance, it was ceremoniously carried into the room by the Color Guard, led by **Adam P. Hess** and **Eric L. Hoyle**. A special grog ceremony under the supervision of "grogmaster" **David A. Disi** was held to mix a revolutionary punch to properly dedicate the bowl. Each potent ingredient was chosen to represent a certain individual who contributed to "that vast event" that led to the founding of our nation. The chair of the Younger Members Committee of the Colonial Dames of America, **Miss Lauren Rose**, presented the Society with a lovely silver spoon, which was quickly put to use in the mixing of the grog. New York Society President **Peter C. Hein** gave a final tasting of the punch. Having deemed it not yet fit for human consumption, he corrected its shortcomings by adding a bottle of Champagne. The grog was declared most delicious and eminently suited to toasting, which elicited many a loud "huzzah!" from the assembled guests. Several new members were then inducted, and immediate Past President **Ambrose M. Richardson III** was presented with his past president's medal. All in attendance enjoyed a lighthearted evening with friends both new and old, and look forward to seeing the punch bowl in service many a time in the years to come.

The **22nd Annual Ronny Maher Memorial Polo Match** was held on July 19, 2019, on Ladew Field at the Maryland Polo Club near Monkton, MD. Founded by **Ronald L. O'D. Maher Jr.**, son of the match's namesake, and his cousin, Mary Bee, the event benefits the R. Adams Cowley Shock Trauma Center at the University of Maryland Medical Center. Five hundred thirty guests enjoyed a buffet dinner, silent auction, and a spectacular polo match between Dovecote and Bad Ass Polo— with Dovecote coming out on top by one goal. At halftime, guests were treated to champagne at the traditional divot stomp, and had the opportunity to meet the Monkton Hall Basset Pack, which was in attendance with masters Elizabeth McKnight and Keri Smyth. After the trophy presentation, guests reveled to the sound of the Party Rockers, a nine-piece band from Washington, DC. Ronny Maher was an avid horseman and enthusiast of the sports of polo and foxhunting. He suffered a spinal cord injury during a hunt on Thanksgiving Day in 1996 and was taken to "Shock Trauma," as it is known, one of the leading trauma centers in the U.S., treating over 8,000 patients annually. Held as a yearly thank-you for all the center did for Mr. Maher and his family after his injury, the event has raised approximately $750,000.00 for the hospital to date.

Above: (*l-r*) Angel Nimikos, Arabella Knox Brockett, and Thomas Huber

Below: (*l-r*) Maxwell Hempt, Tommy Huber, and George Krabbe.

Edited by Stephanie Hadik

ROBERT KELLER

New Additions to the SR Family

Left: Miss Sofia Lily Dionne. Born September 17, 2018, to parents Mr. and Mrs. Dino Dionne (Michelle Lily).

Right: Miss Emmanuela Chevers Lengler Wood was born August 28, 2018, to Mr. and Mrs. Richard H. M. Wood (Karina Lengler) in São Paulo, Brazil.

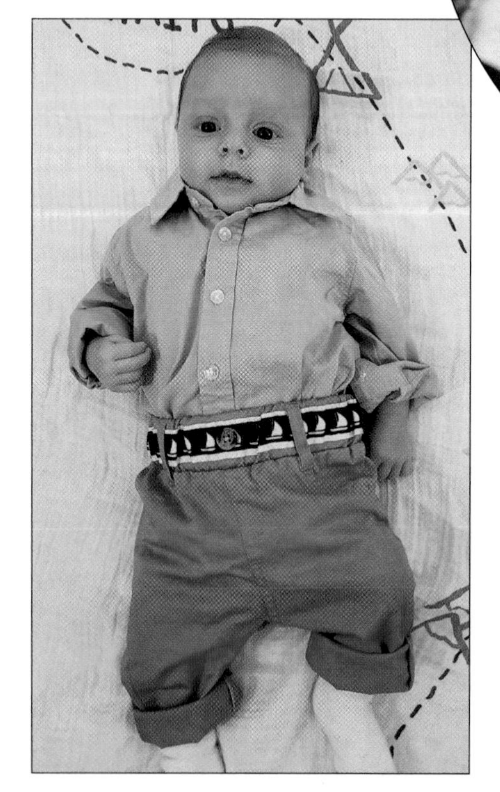

Above: Master Emerson Wooden Dupree was born on October 13, 2018, to Mr. Andrew Chapin S. Dupree and Ms. Franca Sara Kraenzlin. The announcement was submitted by his grandmother, Mrs. Frederick F. Dupree Jr.

Left: Master Achille Lindsay Grieco was born on July 2, 2019, to Mr. and Mrs. Matthew V. Grieco (Sarah L. Depew).

Right: Master Robert Warren Gebhardt was born to Mr. and Mrs. Jeffrey W. Gebhardt (Melissa A. Iredell) on May 10, 2019.

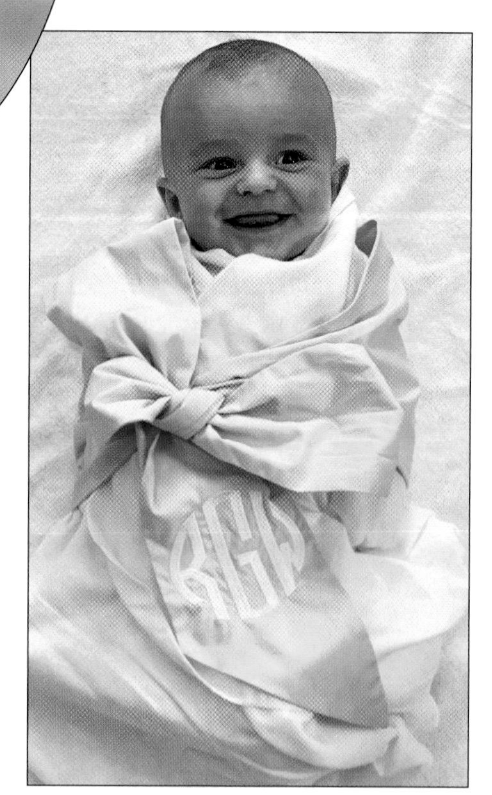

First Two Reciprocal Clubs Announced

The River Club
447 East 52nd Street
New York, NY 10021

Reciprocal Privileges Include:
- Overnight accommodations.
- Dining privileges.
- Use of full-service members Bar.
- Invitations to select River Club events and receptions.

The Explorers Club
46 East 70th Street
New York, NY 10021

Reciprocal Privileges Include:
- Use of Club premises.
- Use of full-service members Bar.
- Invitations to Explorers Club events.
- Access to over 30 chapters worldwide.

Reciprocal Clubs and Associations

Please check our website regularly for a complete guide to reciprocity and for updated information. Additional reciprocal agreements with premier clubs in the U.S. and abroad are anticipated.

www.socialregisteronline.com

First Two Foundations Donate to Social Register Foundation

Special thanks to our first two foundations for their generous contributions:

- The William H. Donner Foundation (New York)
- The Mary Alice Fortin Foundation (Palm Beach)

Special thanks to our many individual donors, host committee donors and association donors for their generous contributions.
We could not do this without you.

Ways To Make a Donation:

Checks may be mailed to:

Social Register Foundation
14 Wall Street
New York, NY 10005

Credit cards, please contact:
AHoyle@SocialRegisterFoundation.org
or call: (646) 612-7323

All gifts are tax deductible to the full extent of the law.

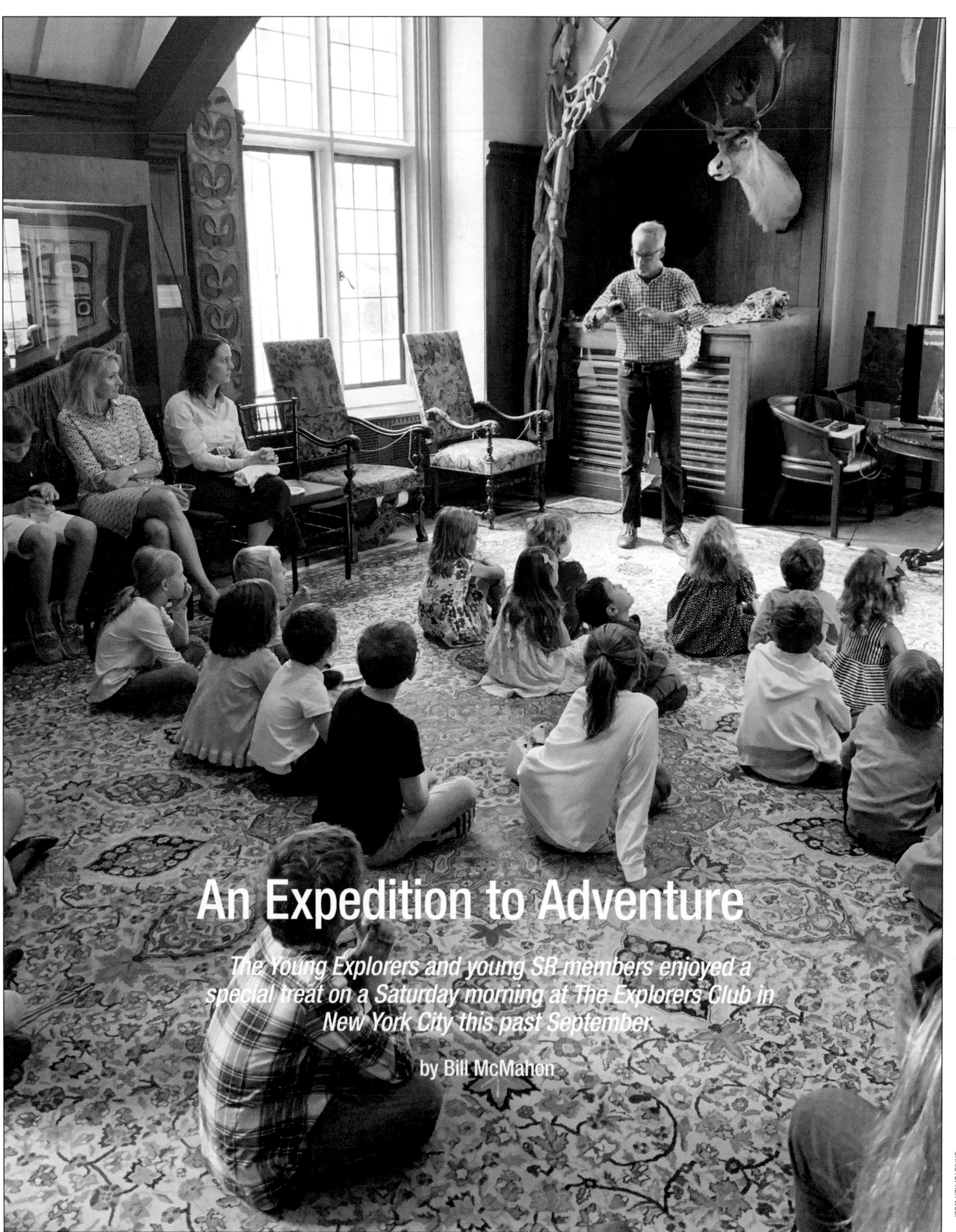

An Expedition to Adventure

The Young Explorers and young SR members enjoyed a special treat on a Saturday morning at The Explorers Club in New York City this past September.

by Bill McMahon

CHRISTOPHER WOLF

AQUANAUT AND author Richard E. Hyman, who was a diver with Jacques-Yves Cousteau, regaled the youngsters, as well as their parents and grandparents, with exciting tales of his far-flung adventures on the famous ship *Calypso*. Enlivened with photos and videos, his presentation showcased the beauty and wonder of the undersea world, the excitement of exploration and discovery, and the importance of curiosity and education about the natural world. He took viewers on an engaging behind-the-scenes tour of the *Calypso* and its crew, giving them a vivid picture of life aboard the ship. Long on adventure but short on creature comforts, it was a rugged life for Cousteau and his frogmen, but one that they embraced wholeheartedly, as Mr. Hyman's account vibrantly illustrated. Undersea creatures, in all their diversity, beauty, and exoticism were on ample display, eliciting murmurs of awe from children and adults alike.

The presentation was interactive, allowing the children an opportunity to learn more about the ship and how it worked, along with designing their own underwater environments. Paper and crayons became the vehicles to unleash the youngsters' imaginations, and their fanciful creations reflected both what they had learned that morning, and their vision of what life undersea might look like.

A question-and-answer session engaged the children's imaginations, who asked whether pirates are real (yes, but they don't talk or dress like pirates in popular culture, although they do steal things, like two outboard motors from the *Calypso*), do ghost ships exist (no), and how to pee in a wetsuit (very carefully).

The Club provided a buffet table of healthy snacks for the children, including fresh fruit, granola bars, mini-scones, juice, and plenty of water, which was roundly appreciated. The event took place on the fifth-and-a-half floor library, a truly impressive setting that enchanted young and old alike. One parent commented that her husband had taken their older child to the Hamptons, but she had kept their youngest in the city expressly for this occasion, which she thought would be a special time for her little one. She was delighted with the presentation.

Mr. Hyman's book *Frogmen* pays homage to Cousteau, a legendary explorer, oceanographer and environmentalist. Cousteau invented the aqualung, which he called "the Self-Contained Underwater Breathing Apparatus"—or in short, SCUBA—and the regulator that controls the flow of oxygen. This was a revolution for undersea divers, making it possible for them to swim more freely and to greater depths, no longer dependent on breathing air through tethers. Cousteau made more than 100 films and was a three-time Academy Award winner, as well as winning the Palme d'Or at the Cannes Film Festival for his documentary *The Silent World*. He received 40 Emmy nominations for his television specials. He was a recipient of the U.S. Presidential Medal of Freedom and the National Geographic Society's Special Gold Medal, a Commander of the Legion of Honour, and was inducted into the Television Hall of Fame.

Mr. Hyman is the executive director of FutureFrogmen.org, which has the mission of inspiring and supporting multidisciplinary education about Earth's aquatic environments through exploration and leadership development. He is also a distinguished

CHRISTOPHER WOLF

visiting professional at Fairfield University, focused on innovating programs around environmental ethics and social entrepreneurship. The series is sponsored by the Center for Applied Ethics, an inter-school program that integrates interdisciplinary courses, seminars, lectures, colloquia, and workshops. This unified approach to ethical conduct raises student awareness of the moral dilemmas of their chosen fields of practice. He has been a keynote and guest speaker at Harvard, MIT, University of Miami, The Explorers Club, and Woods Hole Oceanographic Institute.

Among the wonders on display at the historic Explorers Club are many taxidermy mounts of creatures great and small, donated by, among others, President Theodore Roosevelt. These historic objects are relics of a time before the advent of photography, when it was believed this was the best way to educate people about the natural world. Also exhibited are the many Explorers flags, 202 in all, that were taken on expeditions ranging from Thor Heyerdahl on his Kon-Tiki voyage to the miniature flag carried to the moon on Apollo 11.

The Explorers Club, founded in 1904, promotes the advancement of field research, through the scientific exploration of land, sea, air, and space. Members have been responsible for many historic firsts—first to the North and South Poles, first to the summit of Mount Everest, first to the deepest point in the ocean, and first to the surface of the moon. The Club supports current expeditions through funding, online information, and member-to-member consultation. It also maintains research collections, including a library and map room, to preserve the history of the club and assist those interested and engaged in exploration and scientific research. Famous members, past and current, include astronauts Neil Armstrong, Buzz Aldrin and John Glenn, television anchorman Walter Cronkite, President Theodore Roosevelt, marine biologist Sylvia Earle, geologist and former astronaut Kathryn D. Sullivan, and filmmaker James Cameron. SR

CHRISTOPHER WOLF

JESUS SANTOS

The Social Register Bids Aloha to Spring

By Judy Carmack Bross

Sunny skies and 75-degree temperatures in Chicago set the tone for the annual spring cocktail party for members of the Social Register Association.

HELD IN the magnificent apartment of longtime SR members **Catharine and David Hamilton**, Aloha Spring!, honoring the Social Register Foundation, drew over 140 members, many traveling from around the country to attend. Rum cocktails greeted guests as they were welcomed in the grand foyer by **Christopher R. Wolf**, the association's chairman, while Chicago SR Committee Chairman, **Brian D. White**, presented each member with a special "SR" lapel pin.

White introduced Wolf, who thanked the Hamiltons as well as the evening's sponsors and host committee members **Edward** and **Kate Rutledge**, White and **James M. Kinney**, and **Ryan S. Ruskin** and **Michael C. Andrews** for their support of the SR Foundation and generous contributions to make the evening possible, and Koloa Rum Company for its premium aged spirits. Wolf then spoke briefly about well-received progress and future plans and observed, "It's heartwarming to hear the expressions of support for the foundation's mission, which reflects the commitment to the SR community."

Guests were delighted as the party flowed from room to room through the apartment with magnificent 18th-century paneling from a French château, mingling over drinks and hors d'oeuvres while enjoying the residence's breathtaking lakefront views. "What a fantastic way to spend a spring evening. The setting is just beautiful, and it's wonderful to support the foundation while

catching up with friends and meeting new people as well," said one member.

White later noted, "How fun it was that after the party, many of us arrived for dinner at a nearby club, and three-quarters of the guests in the dining room had all just come from the party! It's wonderful to see the SR bring us all together...the world keeps getting smaller and smaller."

Now, as the Chicago SR Committee prepares to plan for a future fête, everyone's first question is: *Where will it be next year?* SR

JESUS SANTOS

7

8

9

10

1. William Parke; Rick Spain; Tobin Richter and George Vincent.

2. Ed Rutledge; Kate Rutledge; Christopher Wolf; Lyndsay Pond White; Brian White; Ryan Ruskin and Michael Andrews.

3. Laura Berardocco and Tony Lamonia

4. Jonathan Janott and William Parke.

5. Nathan and Melinda Swift; Janet Owen and Peggy Snorf.

6. Susie Kealy; Jean Perkins and Libbet Richter.

7. Mary Conrad and Sandra Thomas.

8. Kristin and Louis Margaglione.

9. David and Catharine Hamilton.

10. Robert, Eunice and Violette Buhler.

11. Ray Drymalski; Kathy Fox and Bill Fox.

12. Sargent M. McC. Collier; Amanda and John Rutledge and Brian D. White.

11

JESUS SANTOS

12

1

2

3

A Social Register Association Fête In Cincinnati

The Queen City rolled out the red carpet of hospitality to SR members and prospective members from Ohio and Kentucky, as Cincinnati hosted its inaugural "Social Register Fête," on the evening of June 1, 2019.

Evoking the traditions of High Society past while bringing a modern twist, guests at the black-tie event were treated to a cocktail hour and sit-down dinner, as well as lively dancing to the swinging sounds of the Kim Kelly Orchestra. The sophisticated revelry took place in the grand surrounds of a private club, nestled in a historic neighborhood of the City.

The happenings and guests flowed freely through the lovely venue, as the party and night progressed, commencing with a receiving line of Fête Committee Co-Chairs **Mr. and Mrs. Douglas S. VanDerzee** and **Dr. and Mrs. John E. Mitakides**, along with Fête Committee Members **Mr. William T. Konop** and **Mr. Ronald E. Padgett**, joining Social Register Association Chairman **Christopher R. Wolf** and his wife, **Lise Honoré-Wolf**, in welcoming the attendees. The assembled guests next moved into the club's formal living room, where lively banter and the greeting of friends, old and new, helped set the tone for the evening. The warm sunny weather allowed for those gathered to move to the garden patio for drinks, before heading to the elegant formal dining room for a sumptuous meal and more camaraderie. After dinner, attendees shifted to the pillar-lined dance hall area, beneath a starlit glass-domed ceiling, to enjoy the band and dancing late into the night.

Special attention was paid to detail in the SR theme of the table decorations, with place settings adorned by miniature Social Register cover-style menu cards, a logo napkin tag and black glossy boxes containing an SR membership pin for each guest—these pins being donned within minutes by delighted attendees.

Prior to dinner, SR Chairman Christopher R. Wolf acknowledged the Cincinnati Fête Committee for their efforts, before treating the guests to a talk about the historic context and modern relevance of the Social Register. Mr. Wolf detailed the SR's efforts to be member-centered, through the

JGR PHOTOGRAPHY

creation of reciprocal agreements with other organizations and by increased acknowledgement of member happenings through the *Observer* magazine. He also explained the importance of the Social Register Foundation, which will not only preserve the group's history, but will also become a focal point for member participation as its programs develop. The remarks also touched on how the Social Register is becoming more inclusive, as a reflection of modern times, while still being a bastion of the traditional values of polite society, individual accomplishment, as well as recognition of multi-generational family contributions to society and culture. Evidence of the binding sense of community fostered by the SR could be seen in the event's large attendance, with guests representing a cross-section of civic, philanthropic and cultural leadership, from both long established and emerging families.

According to event Co-Chair **Jane Mitakides**, "One of the most exciting aspects of the Fête was the response from outside our area, with guests coming from as far away as New York, Texas, Maryland, Missouri and Washington DC, which says a great deal about the Social Register community." Equally pleased and surprised by the breadth of support was Co-Chair **Carrie Van Derzee**, who says, "It was amazing to see come to fruition the idea that I had a couple of years ago, to connect current and potential SR members from Ohio and Kentucky, but I had no idea people from throughout the country would attend!"

Proceeds from the Cincinnati Fête benefitted the Social Register Foundation. Key to the event's success was corporate sponsorship. Mr. Jack Olshan, General Manager of Hotel Covington, an Aparium Boutique Hotel, donated a suite for the Wolfs as well as local

JGR PHOTOGRAPHY

1. Douglas and Carrie VanDerzee.

2. Ryan Burnette *(left)* and Lt. Cdr. Richard Yates.

3. Joan Montenegro (*left*); Janet Moland and Lise Honoré-Wolf .

4. Elizabeth K. Bigelow Moore and William Konop.

5. *(l-r):* Ronald Padgett; William Konop; Carrie VanDerzee; Douglas VanDerzee; Lise Honoré-Wolf; Christopher Wolf; Jane Mitakides; John Mitakides.

6. *(l-r):* Andrew Mitakides; Alexis Mitakides; Ashton McRae; Cassie Brand and Richard Yates.

4

5

6

transportation. Michelle Krumpelman of Biltmore Estate Wines arranged for a donation to the Social Register Foundation, as well as wine for the dinner tables. Adding to the night's excitement, four lucky guests chosen at random received tickets donated by Biltmore Estate Wines to visit the Estate in Asheville, NC.

Though formal events and dinner dances are becoming rarer, Committee Member William Konop believes "the enthusiastic embrace of a black-tie dinner dance, with guests of varying ages, proves that the spirit of modernized High Society is alive and well—and that the SR will be its galvanizing force for years to come."

The appetite for another Cincinnati event was universal. Summing the experience up best, Committee Member Ronald Padgett declared, "What a pleasure to enjoy a sophisticated evening and mingle with friends in common cause for the Social Register Foundation," adding, "All in attendance agree that we have to do this again—and we will!"

Other current SR members in attendance included **Mr. and Mrs. Prescott Bigelow III (Juanita A. Walter)**; **Mr. and Mrs. David W. Campbell II (Cheryl D. Nichols)**; **Mrs. Thomas A. Konop (Virginia A. Reed)**; **Mr. and Mrs. Andrew J. Mitakides (Alexis L. Roy)**; **Mr. and Mrs. William Moland (Janet Robinson)**; **Mrs. Melody Sawyer Richardson**; **David I. Sanders Jr.**; **Mr. and Mrs. Ethan T. Stanley (Doreen A. Haus)**; and **Cedric W. Vogel**. SR

1. Greg and Becky Jones.

2. (*l-r*): David W. Campbell II; Virginia Konop; Cheryl Campbell.

3. The program and SR membership pin gift box table setting.

JGR PHOTOGRAPHY

SOCIAL REGISTER & VILLA TAVERNA

Spring Cocktail Party

Celebrating our members and the many who are members of both

THE SOCIAL Register Association held its second formal gathering on the West Coast on May 10, 2019, in partnership with the Villa Taverna at their exclusive private dining club in San Francisco. Approximately 100 invitees enjoyed an evening of comradery, cocktails, and conversation at the historic building in the heart of the city's Financial District.

The spring cocktail party was a chance for members of the Social Register Association and Villa Taverna, many of whom belong to both organizations, to socialize over drinks and hors d'oeuvres, delighting in the company of each other in the beautiful surroundings of the club. Those attending hailed from not only San Francisco, but also Marin County, Silicon Valley and Northern California, and even from Los Angeles and Seattle. Multiple generations were also represented, ranging in age from their twenties to their nineties, providing a collegial atmosphere full of fun and interesting conversations among a well-dressed room. One attendee even sported a family ring originally worn by Ward McAllister, co-creator with *the* Mrs. Astor of "The Four Hundred" list of New York society published in 1892, to honor the occasion.

The club had a wonderful hostess greeting everyone upon arrival, with waiters in white dinner jackets presenting

Above Left: (*l-r*) Charles M. Hambleton with Karen Mondoux and Lise Honoré-Wolf.

Above Right: Ms. Sally Yu.

Below Left & Right: The spring cocktail party was a chance for members of the Social Register Association and Villa Taverna to socialize in the beautiful surroundings of the club.

an array of small bites to guests as they mingled. "Though spacious, the atmosphere of Villa Taverna is so welcoming and may I even add, cozy!" commented one guest, clearly enamored with the beautiful surroundings.

William E. Grayson, President of Villa Taverna, graciously welcomed everyone on the mild spring evening, giving a wonderfully detailed speech on the club and its storied history. Christopher R. Wolf, Chairman of the Social Register, also welcomed everyone, and followed with an entertaining and informative summary of the recent developments at the Social Register.

The Villa Taverna was established in 1958 by Italian Consul General Pierluigi Alvera as a cultural dining club to promote close ties with Italy. Named in homage to the United States

"It was great to run into old friends and make some new ones in a unique setting. There was such a warm, welcoming tone to the gathering and it was fun to hear about the history of Villa Taverna and new directions for the Social Register. I really appreciate the SR's push to bring people together and create convivial events; my daughter attended the recent New York event and had some great conversations. I'm looking forward to the next one, wherever it's held!"
—Chase Reynolds Ewald

SARAH ARNOLD PHOTOGRAPHY

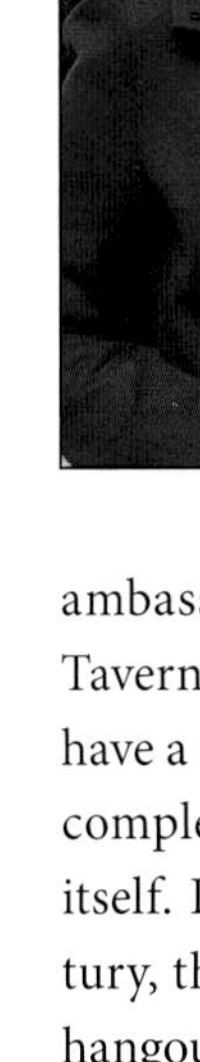

ambassador's residence in Rome, Villa Taverna and the alley in which it resides have a rich and varied history as diverse, complex, and artful as San Francisco itself. In the early part of the 20th century, the neighborhood was a bohemian hangout for famed local painters, writers, and sculptors such as Jack London, Mark Twain, Diego Rivera and Frida Kahlo, who resided within the upstairs apartments for most of the 1930s.

Villa Taverna quickly gained the attention of prominent businessmen, politicians, and notable San Francisco families upon its founding. Known for its discrete, stylish ambience, it has successfully maintained a fine marriage of traditional Italian food—for which it was originally known—and inspired San Francisco nouvelle cuisine. The modern era of the club has welcomed the addition of the handsomely renovated Club Room Bar, a fascinating array of historical speakers, musical performances, and a selection of rare and sought-after wines. Excellent food and plentiful drinks at a historic location, coupled with good company, made for a memorable evening of fellowship among the distinguished group of guests. SR

Above Left: Gretchen Kimball, William Grayson, and Arlene Inch.

Above Right: Christopher R. Wolf (*l*) with Jeffrey L. Bleich.

Right: Genie Callan (*l*) with her daughter, Leslie Callan.

Below Left: Excellent food and plentiful drinks at a historic location, coupled with good company, made for a memorable evening of fellowship.

Below Right: Kit Tobin (*l*) and Sally Fay Cottingham.

SARAH ARNOLD PHOTOGRAPHY

Abbott, Katharine Stanley-Brown
Cobblestones & Ice Cream Cones: A Trip to Nantucket in Rhymes

Filled with warm nostalgia, this charming collection of playful verse rekindles seaside memories for both the young and young-at-heart, old-timers and newcomers to the island alike. A delightful way to discover what makes Nantucket so special and beloved by all who fall under its shimmering spell.

Abbott, 2019, 51 pp.
$15.00, hardcover.
ISBN: 978-0578498423

Argenti, Nicolas
Remembering Absence: The Sense of Life in Island Greece

Drawing on research conducted on Chios during the sovereign debt crisis that struck Greece in 2010, the author follows the lives of individuals who symbolize the transformations affecting this Aegean island. As witnesses to the crisis discuss their lives, their current anxieties and frustrations are expressed in terms of past crises that have shaped the dramatic history of Chios. The author utilizes unpublished correspondence from survivors of the Massacres of 1822 and their descendants and reflects on oral family histories as he explores the ways in which a body of memory and a cultural experience came to be shared.

Indiana University Press, 2019, 330 pp.
$35.00, paperback
ISBN: 978-0253040657

Baker, Ian A.
Tibetan Yoga: Principles and Practices

A visual presentation of Tibetan yoga, the hidden gem at the heart of the Tibetan Tantric Buddhist tradition, which explains its core principles and practices with illustrated instructions. This guide explores esoteric practices less familiar to practitioners of yoga in the West, including lucid dream yoga, and draws on scientific research and meditative traditions to explain Tibetan yoga from not only a biological perspective, but from anthropological and historical points of view as well.

Inner Traditions, 2019, 292 pp,
$40.00, hardcover.
ISBN: 978-1620559123

Carter, Charles Carroll; DiGiacomantonio, William C.; and Scott, Pamela
Creating Capitol Hill: Place, Proprietors, and People

An in-depth look at the founding of the U.S. Capitol which uses family papers from relatives of Mr. Carter, a direct descendant of one of the nation's founding families, as part of its vast wealth of well-researched information. Accompanied by beautiful and rare illustrations, it tells the Capitol's story from the beginning, traversing forward through the decades to contemporary times.

The U.S. Capitol Historical Society, 2018, 304 pp.
$65.00, hardcover.
ISBN: 978-1513634050

Cleveland, Dwight M.
Cinema on Paper

A gorgeously presented compilation of a pre-eminent private collection of film posters. Including iconic films as well as cult classics, the artwork presented spans over a century of cinema, and includes an array of genres, from dramas and comedies, to Westerns and science fiction thrillers.

Assouline, 2019, 192 pp.
$95.00, hardcover.
ISBN: 978-1614288756

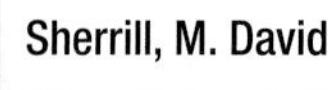

Sherrill, M. David
Dice, Cubes & Gentlemen

A detailed history of backgammon, both in society and at New York's Union Club, which played a pivotal role in the transition of the old game to its modern incarnation. The rules, etiquette, and traditions of the game are explained at great length, in what is the perfect guide for both the novice and seasoned player alike.

Union Club, 2018, 244 pp.
Hardcover.
No ISBN

Sweet, David A. F.
Three Seconds in Munich: The Controversial 1972 Olympic Basketball Final

The true story of one of the most controversial finishes in Olympic sport history: the 1972 gold-medal contest between the world's two superpowers at the time, the United States and the USSR. The flouting of rules and a referee making illegal allowances and late fouls is set against the hostage crisis that forever marked these Games. The author interviews numerous American players, relating the horror of terrorism, the costs of the players' decision to shun their medals, and the pain of losing what is arguably the most controversial championship game in sports history to a despised rival.

University of Nebraska Press, 2019, 264 pp.
$29.95, hardcover.
ISBN: 978-0803299962

Edited by Stephanie Hadik

The label attached to the back of this photograph reads as follows: Paris—May 31, 1929, Eleanora Sears, veteran Boston Society woman hiker, who, after finishing a hike of 42 ½ miles from Fontainebleau to her Parisian hotel, said she "felt fine". On her hike Miss Sears took only tea from a thermos bottle. Her time for the distance was eight hours and 35 minutes.

[INTERNATIONAL NEWSREEL PHOTO]

The Sportsman and the Writer

Gene Tunney's son Jay reflects on the famous prizefighter's life and his unlikely friendship with George Bernard Shaw

by Judy Carmack Bross

As AUTHORS and journalists, new Social Register members Kelly and Jay Tunney join the lengthy list of accomplished artists you'll find as you turn the pages of our directory. Citizens of the world who now reside in Chicago, this branch of the Tunney family returns to the Social Register after an absence of more than 90 years. Social Register Chairman Christopher Wolf couldn't be happier about it. Jay's mother, Polly Lauder, was a cousin of Andrew Carnegie; his father was the boxer Gene Tunney, who beat Jack Dempsey in September 1927 in what was called "The Battle of the Long Count," which confirmed his title as the heavyweight boxing champion of the world.

Paradoxically, it was the elder Tunneys' marriage that accounts for the gap in the listing of the Tunney family. At the time they were wed, in 1926, pugilism was one of the professions, such as show business

Above: The Tunney Family, (*l-r*) daughter Teressa R. Tunney; Jay Tunney; Kelly Tunney, Jay's wife of 51 years; daughter-in-law Elizabeth Tunney; and son Jonathan R. Tunney.
Front row: Granddaughters Evelyn (*left*) and Ava.

CAROL DE ANDA

Above: Polly's favorite picture from Gene's boxing days. He holds a speed bag, used in training, in 1928. [TUNNEY COLLECTION]

Previous Page: The newly-wed Tunneys, 1930, in Palm Beach, Florida. [AP IMAGES/ASSOCIATED PRESS]

and dentistry among others, generally excluded from representation in the Social Register. This unwritten rule resulted in the newlyweds' discreet omission — however well publicized by the society press—following the appearance of their marriage notice. Inconsistently applied from the beginning, this policy has long since fallen by the wayside.

While the Social Register Association has evolved over the years along with the society it reflects, what has not changed, Mr. Wolf assures us, is its "commitment to maintaining the high standards traditionally employed in selecting its membership, as well as its commitment to recognizing prominence in multiple fields of endeavor." According to these criteria, both Mr. and Mrs. Tunney certainly merit inclusion in the Social Register.

Jay is the author of numerous articles and essays; his work has been published by the *New York Times Magazine*, the *Asian Wall Street Journal*, the *Hartford Courant*, the *Annual of Bernard Shaw Studies*, and *The Independent Shavian*. He is Vice President of the International Shaw Society. Kelly, his wife, was a war correspondent in Vietnam and the first woman the Associated press sent into a war zone following World War II. She subsequently served as vice president of the Associated Press.

Gene Tunney's youngest son, Jay, an international entrepreneur who once searched for oil in Burma and later had the happy opportunity to introduce ice cream to South Korea, wrote a powerful book about his father, whom he described as a "self-made man with a driving iron will and the determination to better himself. He was the embodiment of fighter courage, intelligence and morality." *The Prizefighter and the Playwright* focuses on the friendship between Tunney and George Bernard Shaw, and Jay is now working on a play and a possible TV documentary on the same subject.

"Dad had started life as a poor Irish boxer from the Hell's Kitchen, then a part of Greenwich Village, and he was desperate to become respectable. In those days, people quoted the great classics of Shakespeare, Shaw, Lord Byron, Keats, Shelley and Yeats. Dad really got into it. He was invited to lecture at Yale. He spent much time with the writer Thornton Wilder. At night he would listen to the music of Enrico Caruso and by day he was determined to make himself into a learned man. Dad was an extreme example of a person wanting to better himself, to have more in life than he had at the beginning. His own father died young, a longshoreman with many unresolved anger issues.

"He married my mother, Polly Lauder, who was a niece of Andrew Carnegie and grew up in Greenwich, Connecticut. They were married for 50 years. Polly, who lived for many years in Stamford, Connecticut, died in 2008. She is buried beside her husband, who died in 1978, once the most famous man in the world. Although she was very tender, soft-spoken, and loved poetry, the secret was that she wanted to marry a warrior, not just some lawyer that her parents expected her to marry.

"My mother was absolutely the most private person who ever walked the face of the earth and when I first suggested that I write a book about my father she really resisted, but we reached a compromise, She thought that Shaw's and Dad's friendship was the solution. She played a vital role until she died 12 days before her 101st birthday."

This, according to Jay, is how the Shaw-Tunney friendship began:

"When Shaw came to London from Ireland at age 20, he looked like a timid little rabbit, but he went on to become England's greatest orator and playwright.

"He loved boxing and he loved winners. He wrote about the sport in his fourth novel, *Cashel Byron's Profession,* and was in dialogue with Tunney about starring in a movie based on the book. Shaw believed that, no matter what your obstacles, if you tried harder and harder your own willpower could overcome them.

"Dad felt that if Shaw could raise the bar of boxing in fiction, he could raise it further in real time by his unmatched display of scientific and moral boxing, by outthinking and outmaneuvering his opponents and by persevering until he won. Gene closed his career with an unsurpassed boxing record of 77 wins and one loss, retiring undefeated as heavyweight boxing champion of the world, the first fighter to do so.

"My father, while maintaining his scruples in a scoundrel's arena, elevated the quality of the audience in the roaring 1920s to include men of politics, business and social stature, and women of refinement—a first in boxing history. His nickname was "Gentleman Gene," as he often spoke publicly about character, clean living, and the importance of education and books. My father was a different type of sportsman who combined physical and spiritual dimensions. He went on to marry the woman he loved, and to achieve two new careers, one as a man of letters, the other as a businessman.

"It was as if he had stepped right out of Shaw's sketchbook. With Cashel as a subliminal role model, Gene had permitted himself to envision a gentleman's life beyond the ring as a realistic alternative and not a pipe dream. Even more significantly, Shaw's novel allowed Gene to consider the idea of marriage above his social class, to a woman beyond his world, and to live happily ever after, as Cashel Byron had done."

The Tunney-Shaw connection was an enduring one.

"They would meet periodically in London, Europe, and Jerusalem after they first vacationed together with their wives in Veliki Brijun, the largest island in the Brijuni archipelago in the northern Adriatic.

"Dad had an encyclopedic mind and he worshipped what Shaw, who was 41 years older, had made of himself. Many years later, in 1950, along with friends William Randolph Hearst, Marion Davies, Gertrude Lawrence, Upton Sinclair and Albert Einstein, my father helped establish the first U.S. Shaw Society."

Although Jay never met Shaw, he did meet Ernest Hemingway and knew many other of his father's other favorite friends, including Thornton Wilder, Somerset Maugham, John Marquand, Lowell Thomas and Prescott Bush, grandfather and father of presidents. He took 10 years to write his book about his father, has lectured around the world on the long-lasting friendship between the two legends, and has been a member of the Governor's Council of the Shaw Festival in Ontario and organized international Shaw conferences.

Above: Sitting for a rare posed portrait in Paris were Thornton Wilder and Tunney (*front*) with F. Scott Fitzgerald (*center back*) between two unidentified friends. [TUNNEY COLLECTION]

Writing about his father's boxing career, Jay noted that his father, engrossed in a book, was almost late to his Chicago re-match with Dempsey, which was dubbed "The Fight of the Century":

"In an upstairs bedroom of a house in downtown Chicago, the heavyweight champion lay stretched out on the bed for an hour and a half, slowly reading the last two chapters of Somerset Maugham's *Of Human Bondage*, a novel that explores the intellectual and emotional development of an orphan raised by a pious uncle.

"None of these literary traits endeared him to sportswriters or boxing fans who rooted for Dempsey and booed what they considered Tunney's pretensions. His choices did win him entrée into a world of words and ideas where he was at home."

During the week before the fight, trains pulling private and Pullman cars had converged on Chicago carrying Hollywood entertainers, European royalty, bankers, industrialists and politicians, greats and near-greats, sports fans, czars of the underworld, the son of the Duke of Marlborough, who came by private rail coach with Harold Vanderbilt, and Princess Xenia of Greece.

"By 4 pm, six hours before the fight, tens of thousands of people swarmed across Michigan Avenue, making it almost impossible to walk the sidewalks of the Loop. Grant Park had been cleared of people and 6000 police set up a cordon four blocks from the arena. More than 50 million people, the largest broadcast audience ever, tuned into their radios.

"It had only been in boxing's recent history that a law was introduced that a fighter had to go to his own corner when his opponent was down. Dempsey stood over Dad when he was knocked down in the seventh round, and told the referee: 'I stay.'

"The fact that my father was so well conditioned, that he made his legs so strong by running five miles backwards every day, saved the day. He won the world championship, and the million-dollar prize, because he was quicker and faster

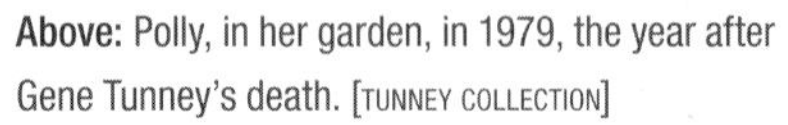
Above: Polly, in her garden, in 1979, the year after Gene Tunney's death. [TUNNEY COLLECTION]

Below: Tunney and Shaw smile for the camera while Charlotte chats with friends. Tunney wrote on the picture that they were attending pony races. [TUNNEY COLLECTION]

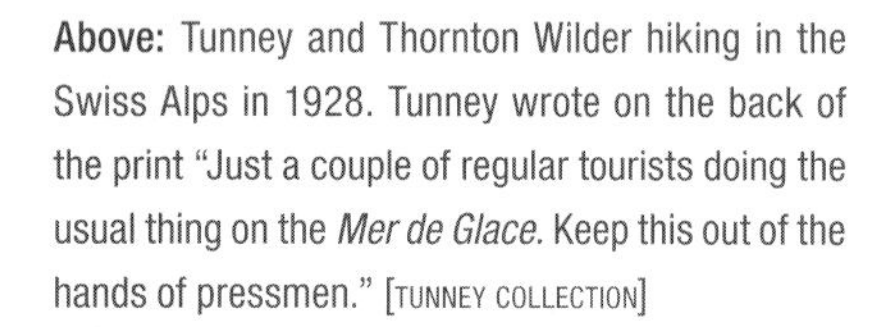
Above: Tunney and Thornton Wilder hiking in the Swiss Alps in 1928. Tunney wrote on the back of the print "Just a couple of regular tourists doing the usual thing on the *Mer de Glace*. Keep this out of the hands of pressmen." [TUNNEY COLLECTION]

and more intellectual than any fighter. Many gave him no credit. They said the reading made him a poser and men said he was too good looking for his own good. Dad felt very humiliated by the sports writers who influenced the fans, he never got over it. But he did set the finest record in boxing history."

His father was "trying to find the answers to life, the answers to happiness," according to Jay. Much of that came through his family and their life together in Stamford, Connecticut. His family of three sons and one daughter was very important to him and he was delighted that they went to top universities—two to Stanford and one to Yale. His son John served as a U.S. Senator from California. Son Gene served as a district attorney in Sonoma County, California. Jay's career allowed him to travel the world as an entrepreneur.

Jay recalled that, as he was growing up, "privacy is what my parents worshipped although they were not recluses. During the late 1800s through the end of WW II, it was not considered in good taste to show off one's attributes or possessions. There was dignity in humility and people of class often avoided showing off. In addition, my parents had an addiction for reading poetry and classical works of literature.

"Both were congenial and participating members of society who enjoyed occasional private dinner parties where they could set forth their ideas in conversation. They loved to travel and enjoyed being in the company of others who were informed

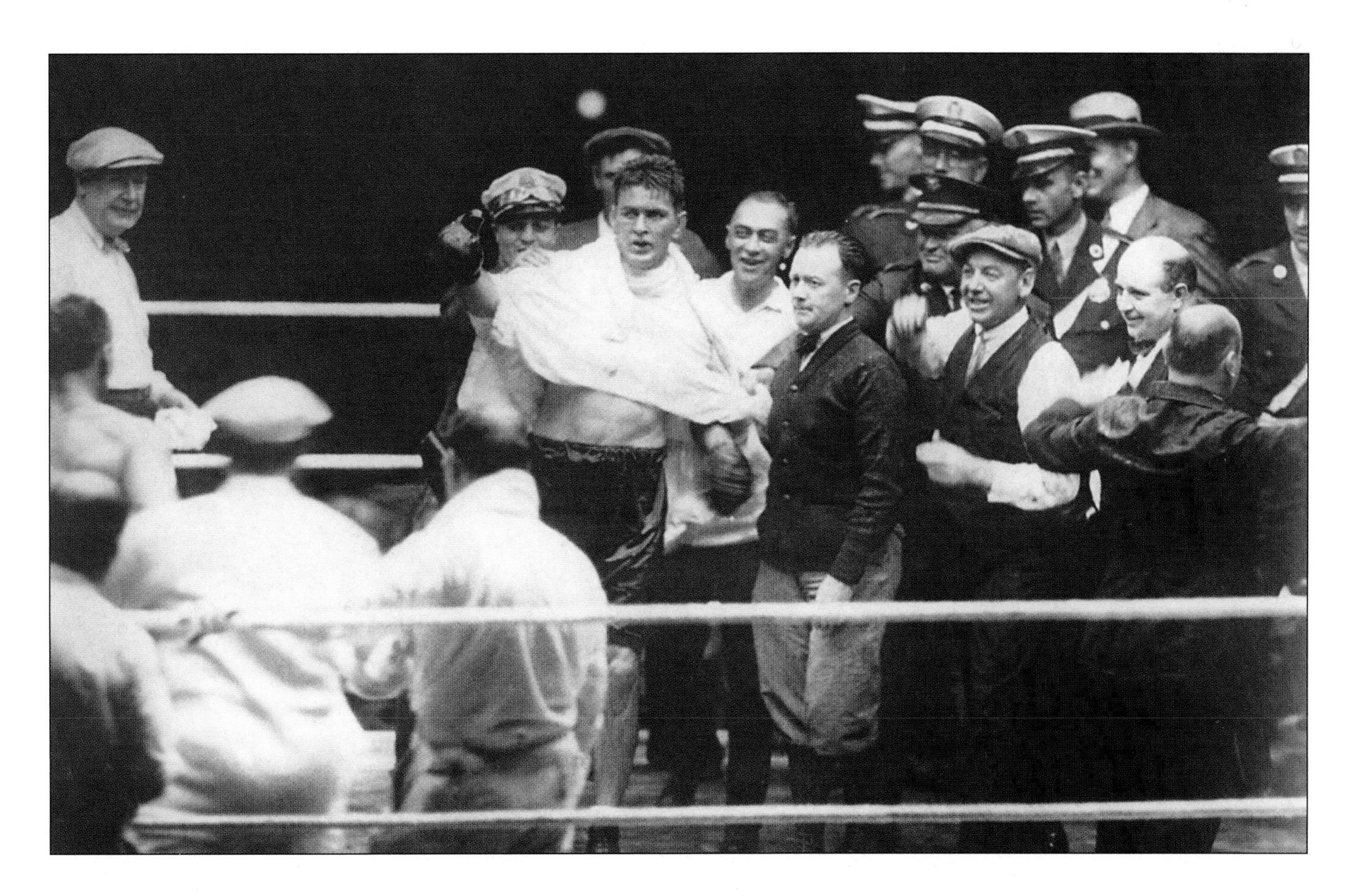

Above: Tunney, the new Heavyweight Champion of the World, moments after winning the 1926 decision. Dempsey is visible at far left, facing Tunney. [TUNNEY COLLECTION]

by travel, good food, fine music and an abundant life. They enriched everyone who came near them.

"Shaw taught my father, and my father taught me, and I have ingrained it in my children, that although money and fame were not important, these traits could triumph in a brutal and unfair world."

Jay shared one final reflection on his father:

"There's been no one else I've ever known who had the gigantic personality of my father, the conviction in what he believed, and the sheer courage to carry it out no matter what the odds."

He concluded with some recollections about his mother, Polly Lauder Tunney:

"My mother grew up on a grand estate on Lake Avenue in Greenwich, Connecticut, the daughter of George Lauder Jr. and Katherine Rowland. Her grandfather George Lauder was first cousin and a close business partner of Andrew Carnegie. Her father was a philanthropist and yachtsman who served for a time as commodore of the Indian Harbor Yacht Club. She went to Versailles for a semester in college and after high school took the traditional European tour with a godmother. *Endymion,* her father's 136-foot schooner, once held the record for the fastest transatlantic passage ever made. Upon his death, he donated the land that would become Island Beach—off of which he used to anchor his schooner—to the town of Greenwich.

"Although Mother loved poetry and books, she had another side to her: adventure and the love of exploring distant lands. Her first memories of travel were at age 3, when she visited Dornoch and Skibo, the former home of Andrew Carnegie. She remembered the sundial and playing in the heather in the gardens.

"She lived her entire married life with my father on an estate overlooking a large pond and reservoir in the forested hills of North Stamford, not far from her ancestral home in Greenwich. She liked it for its long private drive, the hilltop location which allowed a vista for miles, and because as a young woman she and her Rockefeller friends and cousins next door had ridden horseback through the same trails she walked as a widow. She knew and cared for every tree, every bird on the estate, and devoted immense time and money to preserving the land."

Whatever the differences in their origins, or the trajectories their lives took before their marriage, it is undeniable that Gene and Polly Tunney perfectly complemented each other. It is also very likely that, had their union occurred a generation or two later, they would, like their son and his wife, have occupied a well-deserved space in the Social Register.

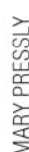

A Tale of Two Garden Clubs

The Nantucket Garden Club and the Garden Club of Palm Beach: "Both have a high level of intensity and involvement, in a very short period of time. Both do much for their communities."

by Marion Laffey Fox

When Gretchen Riley heads to Nantucket from Philadelphia each summer, her diary is filled with reminders of responsibilities associated with membership in the Nantucket Garden Club. The respected Garden Club of America floral design and horticulture judge has been an active member of the club since 2006. "I am actually a member of four garden clubs, but thoroughly enjoy all the remarkable things the Nantucket club is able to accomplish in such a short season of eight weeks a year." Stressing that the "hard work is very fulfilling," Riley says, "we annually give back over $60,000 to the community in scholarships and grants."

The accomplishments of hundreds of garden clubs across the country are nothing short of astonishing—there are 200 affiliated clubs with 18,000 participants under the umbrella of the Garden Club of America alone—whose projects involve beautification, conservation, preservation, scholarships, or something unique to a specific location. But within that overview, the feats of two "seasonal" clubs merit special applause. The Nantucket Garden Club, in GCA's Zone 1, is in full swing from May through August. The Garden Club of Palm Beach, in Zone VIII, operates from December to May.

On Nantucket, the group of 123 dedicated women cares so deeply about the island they spend an inordinate amount of time tending to its multifaceted needs. Of the entire membership, only around 20 live there year-round, yet when most members are back home, on-islanders

MARY PRESSLY

cheerfully tackle tasks such as refreshing seasonal plantings in the Main Street fountain and decorating a holiday tree for the Festival of Trees at the Nantucket Historical Association's Whaling Museum. They also deal with details involved in the Annual Daffodil Show that celebrates spring every April.

Founded in 1953 by a small group of summer residents who were interested in gardening and preservation of Nantucket's unique wildflowers, the club would prove to be a bonanza for the storied island. By the end of the 1954 season, the fledging group planted attractive trees and shrubs around an austere nursing home for aged and indigent island residents. The modest but heartfelt gift of $1,350 was such a resounding community-wide success, members voted to landscape seven barren acres around the newly-completed Nantucket Cottage Hospital. The ambitious project softened the site, cheered patients and solidified the presence of the club. "Since our inception, plants, flowers and horticulture contributed to the beauty of Nantucket and always support conservation initiatives that protect the island's fragile historic environment," says president Gail McRobie.

This dedication begins with a year of provisional membership during which new candidates are expected to take on maintenance of certain projects and attend mandatory meetings. Carrie Griffith of Newtown, PA, is one of six current "provisionals." "Although we have summered here 25 years, I look forward to serving in this capacity, to learn the ropes of the club and do whatever needs doing," she says. These responsibilities and learning opportunities ensure that members become versed in the history, lore and vagaries of this windswept outpost 25 miles off the Massachusetts coast, where gardeners face unique weather challenges including salt spray and erosion, strong prevailing winds, cool summer temperatures, and Gulf Stream-warmed winters.

The meetings also create a useful forum for reportage of 21 committees that focus on multiple island projects, such as the Annual House & Garden Tour, always held in the first week of August, which attracted over 1,500 visitors in 2018. Since it funds most of their projects, it is

Above: Mary Pressly, arriving at the Preview Party, was awarded Best in Show for Botanical Arts and several creative awards. She also designed the centerpiece for the Garden Club of Palm Beach biennial 2019 GCA Flower Show.

Right: A moss-covered Volkswagen Beetle greeted attendees at the 2015 Hort Couture: A GCA Flower Show presented by The Garden Club of Palm Beach at The Society of the Four Arts.

Opposite: An old-fashioned assortment of summer flowers and fruit is transformed into beguiling arrangements for a festive outdoor porch party on Nantucket.

MARY PRESSLY

Above: Palm Beach Garden Club member Ginny Parker strides into the O'Keefe Gallery at the Society of the Four Arts to refresh her arrangement in the Gold Leaf Flower Show in 2019, a day after it won the Class 2 Blue Ribbon.

Right: A block from the ocean, a vertical garden of 11 different species and over 10,000 plants has become a visual horticultural triumph, covering a once blank wall on the Saks Fifth Avenue store on Palm Beach's famous Worth Avenue.

monumentally important to scholarship funding. The latter includes five to six $5,000 scholarships to Nantucket High School graduates for advanced study in horticulture, landscaping, environmental studies or conservation. In addition, there is a lengthy list of grants that benefit island nonprofits, as well as the biannual Flower Show, annual Community Daffodil Show and biannual Art with Blooms Gallery Walk.

One of its most visible recent projects involved landscaping of Sankaty Head Light after its famous move in 2007. "The lighthouse has been a revered beacon on Nantucket since 1850, and was the brightest light in New England," says McRobie, "so when it was in danger of falling into the sea because of relentless erosion, the Sconset Trust acquired it from the U.S. Coast Guard and moved it 405 feet northwest of its original location to safer ground." When landscaping for the new but barren site was addressed, the Nantucket Garden Club jumped in, allotting $50,000 over two years to the project. Today, the iconic red-and-white-and-black lighthouse remains a stalwart symbol of the island, but now is charmingly framed by appropriately natural native scrub oaks, underplanted with hardy shrubs and plants. In spring, the site is alive with more than 11,000 yellow, orange, pink and white dancing daffodils, including a new species named "Sankaty Light."

Laura and Bill Buck are ardent supporters of Sankaty Light, as well as countless island initiatives. They have been coming here since the late 1980s, when they first stepped on Nantucket's shores. "We had never been here before, and were captivated by everything, including its whaling history, rose-covered cottages, historic preservation and conservation ethos," says Laura. Today, her spectacular organic cottage garden has become a stellar example of "responsible horticulture."

Mary Randolph Ballinger feels fortunate to be a member of both the Nantucket and Palm Beach clubs. She says "the two clubs are similar in that they are seasonal island clubs that have a high level of intensity and involvement, in a very short period of time, such as popular house tours, and spectacular flower shows. Both clubs have some similar and different geographical issues, such as erosion, climate change and sea level rise. Currently, island ecology is a big concern for us, and we have invited speakers on risks to butterflies and bees, on harbor health and cleanliness, shellfish protection measures and other challenges for plants and fauna."

The Garden Club of Palm Beach was founded on March 28, 1928, during a gathering of 15 women at the residence of Mrs. John S. Phipps. Mrs. Frederick E. Guest is credited with the original idea of organizing it, and the meeting was attended by famous residents such as Mrs. Edward T. Stotesbury, Mrs Barclay Warburton and Mrs. Marion S. Wyeth. Like its sister club almost 1,500 miles north, its mission focused on horticulture, the environment,

conservation and civic improvement.

The enthusiastic group plunged into ambitious tasks from its inception. In January 1929, after severe hurricane damage to the Lake Trail was assessed, minutes from the March 22 meeting state: "The Garden Club members realize that they must shoulder some Civic responsibility and are keenly interested in the betterment of both the Trail and Royal Palm Way as a start in that direction." During that year, membership was increased to 43, and the club's first Flower Show was staged. More importantly, the grandiose idea of creating an overall Town Plan was adopted and the firm of Bennett, Parsons and Frost of Chicago was hired to create it. Resolute members contributed over $10,000 to cover the expenses of the plan which was completed in 1930 and presented to the Town of Palm Beach."

Throughout the 1930s the young club made enormous strides. In 1931, it was admitted to membership in The Garden Club of America and in 1935, after a remarkably successful Flower Show, the

Above: Bill and Laura Buck's seaside garden is an example of responsible horticulture where bountiful borders and window boxes wordlessly illustrate the advantages of green gardening.

club was able to finance the planting of three blocks of Royal Palm Way with Royal Palm trees. In 1938, it contributed to construction of The Four Arts building, then designed and planted demonstration gardens, intended to show newcomers to the area how a small space could become an attractive garden in the humid, semitropical climate.

During ensuing years, The Garden Club of Palm Beach became an increasingly powerful voice. In the elegant walkways and fountains of the gardens of the Society of the Four Arts, patroness Edith Robb Dixon's generosity created spectacular gardens around the Fitz Eugene Dixon Education Building, and Mr. and Mrs. William Pannill underwrote the Pannill Pavilion, considered the crown jewel of the overall garden design.

Today the club thrives and consistently gives back to the town in especially powerful ways because one of its members attends town meetings to determine important issues to which it might lend a hand. In 2010, this involvement translated into two highly visible road beautification projects: the lyrical garden at the Southern Oasis Traffic Circle, with plants that serve as an example of species that thrive in this particular climate. A few minutes away eight Kaleidoscope Flower Beds on Royal Poinciana Way depict the advantage of xeriscape landscaping. The following year, the club was a major funder of the Living Wall, a vertical garden on Saks Fifth Avenue store, that was part of the 2011 Worth Avenue Restoration Project.

Although both clubs radiate selfless enthusiasm for their particular islands, everyone is in agreement that whether they adore cottage gardens abloom with purple hydrangeas and pink climbing roses, or regal palms above exotic orchids, their collective work is so successful because it fosters companionship, camaraderie and lasting friendships. SR

Challenging the Present with an Eye to the Future

The River Club Remains New York's Top Family Club

by Jack Smith

SINCE ITS completion in 1931, the art deco building that rises above the East River between 52nd and 53rd Streets has earned fame for sheltering the cream of Manhattan society. River House is famously discreet and from the beginning housed an elegant five-story private club: The River Club. The club's 1932 membership list resonated with the names of the great American families of the era: Astors, Roosevelts, Vanderbilts, Rockefellers, Morgans, Pulitzers and du Ponts, among others. It was intended to be a social club, completely divorced from business; bringing business papers into the club was frowned upon. As longtime member and former president Tom McCarter recalls, it was unabashedly select. "When I first joined the board, all the governors knew each other and came from families who knew each other."

For all the prestige that accrued to membership, The River Club wasn't a place where people went to bask in the awareness of their elevated status. As *Town & Country* magazine advised in an article from 1931, "It is an active place, as distinguished from a sedentary eating, talking, reading club. It is created for people who like to do things."

From the outset, the style of governance was patrician yet benign. The first board of governors had decreed that there would be "no rules for the club that are not absolutely necessary." While it stood at the apex of New York society, The River Club was devoid of the rigid taboos that marked some New York clubs.

Unlike the clubs elsewhere in America and Europe, which were designated to be either men's clubs or women's clubs and dominated by one sex or the other, The River Club was co-ed; of those first fifteen members on the board, seven were women. It's a pattern that continues to this day. "As long as I can remember it's been 50-50," says board member Nicky Grant. "Today I'm the board member in the family."

Mrs. Grant recalls her first day as a member. "I joined in 1994 as a summer member. On my first day at the club I went to the pool and sat on the terrace and had lunch. It was all very relaxed, a departure from the stifling ambiance of the old-fashioned London clubs. Of course, we were on our best behavior. It was wonderful to join The River Club. It wasn't a "drink after work" kind of place, it was a place for the whole family."

Her fellow board member Celeste Rault agrees. "There is a strong sense of community about this place, especially during the holidays. Christmas is especially fun with the members and staff all getting involved. The nice thing is, nobody comes here with an agenda or attempts to promote a point of view. I suppose we're all rather like-minded."

For Mrs. Rault, the club's significance was illustrated several years ago when she and some of the other parent members organized a series of events at the club called the "Twenty Somethings." "The idea was, our children had made so many friends from The River Club. Now they were coming back from Deerfield or Buckley or Groton and wanted to get back in touch. The place that meant the most to them was The River Club and it has been a great success."

Likewise, the club now offers dances for 5th- and 6th- graders as well as etiquette classes. "The point is, we're more than a men's or women's club, we're caretakers of a fabulous tradition."

The core of this tradition—and the symbol of enduring change—was tennis. Tom McCarter recalls the times he used to spend on the club's courts. "The club has always been associated with some of the greatest tennis players of all time, such players as Bill Talbert, Sidney Wood, Ham Richardson, and Gene Scott. Thanks to my being a member of The River Club I could say I had played them, though I really couldn't hold my own against them. They just let me hit the ball with them but it was a thrill, knowing that I was playing on the same court with some of the best players in the world. Later, as I got older, my interests shifted and the club became a place to make and meet friends. Even though, at 90, I no longer play, it's a treat to watch from the sidelines."

According to legend, one reason why the players are so good is that the courts they play on are without peer. The porous Har-Tru courts are impeccably maintained, the courts are completely separated, and surrounded by real walls. There is plenty of space around the courts, the lighting and sound are perfect and the ceilings are high. "You can hit a high lob and play all out," says Tennis Director Paul Saputo.

Members all have their own favorite places within the club. One of McCarter's is the River Suite, which looks out over the river. "You know, this place is not what you might expect of a club; there's not a lot of dark, heavy wood. It's light and airy, more like an oasis within the city. First-time visitors say they never imagined a place like this. It's an extreme privilege to be invited to The River Club. Something happens when you walk through the door."

"It's like walking into an extension of your own home; it's a very personal space. As long as I've been here our vision for the club has been shaped by our members' family lives," says club president Andrés Coles. "Once it was all tennis, now there's a lot of interest in squash and golf, sports they'll play all their lives. We always had good squash players, but now we use the latest high-tech practice techniques. I-squash is one of these. There are only a few of these elaborate laser-driven devices in the city and we have one of them."

Though there is no golf course at the club, it makes the sport available to members via state-of-the-art golf simulators and an inter-club program in which club members compete annually for the Shea Cup against four other clubs, The Brook, Knickerbocker Club, Union Club, and The Links.

"We have close to 200 kids in our tennis program, 50 or 60 in golf, and a like number in swimming. We have 70-80 children in squash—some of the city's best elite youth squash players training for top collegiate level teams. Next we're going to introduce paddle tennis. It's an obvious next step," said Mr. Coles.

With five children, Andrés Coles gets plenty of use out of the club's tennis

Opposite: An artist's concept of the River Club building.

Top: "...this place is not what you might expect of a club; there's not a lot of dark, heavy wood."

Right: One of longtime member and former president Tom McCarter's favorite places is the River Suite and Library, which looks out over the river.

RIGHT: KARRIEM SIMMONS; TOP: A. EDGEWORTH

courts. "I especially enjoy hitting balls with my children. We pay attention to the kids; this is the premier family club and kids are the catalyst of change. If there is something new, they'll pick up on it and want it and make it popular. We're watching pickle ball, to see what happens there. Will it remain a practice game or will it catch on like paddle tennis? For that matter, it wasn't that long ago that squash was in decline. But no longer."

"Squash is having a renaissance at The River Club," says former president Charles Berry, who captained the squash team while at Yale. "It's one of the few places in New York where boys and girls can play this wonderful sport." Today, he says, even tennis devotees recognize the sport as a great way to develop racquet skills, footwork, and hand-eye coordination. "Contrary to the old belief, playing squash does not hurt a tennis swing."

The club's squash program is likely to become even more prominent with the recent addition of Chris Walker, Director of Squash. He's one of the biggest names in the game, a four-time World Champion and former Men's and Women's U.S. National Coach (2004-2013). Mr. Walker has also been ranked No. 1 in the World in Hardball Doubles and No. 4 in the World in Singles.

"There are so many reasons why this club is special for me and so many of our members, so much of my life has revolved around the club," continued Charles Berry. "When I think of The River Club, I think of holiday meals over the years; rehearsal dinners and weddings,

Top: & Center: The Main Dining Room.

Center: Kathryn Berry (*right*) with her son Nicholas Berry, daughter-in-law Molly, and her grandchildren — three generations of River Club members.

Left: The recently renovated saltwater pool.

anniversary parties; memorial receptions for both of my parents. The intergenerational aspect of the club is one of the greatest pleasures. My parents met playing tennis here in 1946; our two sons are members and our granddaughter is learning to swim here. Inter-club match play is a growing and particularly sociable and enjoyable feature."

The rigors of running The River Club keeps Brendan Slaven, the club's general manager, in touch with his peers in other clubs. "We have reciprocal arrangements with about 20 premier clubs in this country and around the world, including clubs like Polo de Paris in Paris, Hurlingham Club in London, and Lyford Cay Club in the Bahamas. We can offer top-notch golf through these arrangements."

"The club is well-positioned for a bright future," observed Andrés Coles. "We have a strong, enthusiastic board. We raised a great deal of money from our supportive members, through subscriptions and reasonable assessments, to extensively renovate and transform our unique clubhouse while respecting its long history. This included a complete renovation of our sports floor (two new international squash courts, new gym, new locker

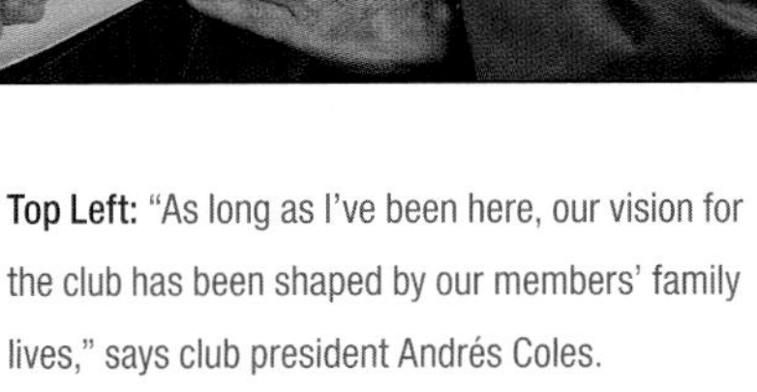

Top Left: "As long as I've been here, our vision for the club has been shaped by our members' family lives," says club president Andrés Coles.

Top Center: Nicky Grant, board member.

Top Right: Former president Tom McCarter.

Above: Former president Charles Berry.

Left: General manager Brendan Slaven.

Far Left: Board member Celeste Rault: "There is a strong sense of community about this place, especially during the holidays."

Above Left: Paul Saputo, tennis director and head professional, teaching a children's clinic.

Above Right & Center: "There are so many reasons why this club is special for me and so many of our members"—Charles Berry.

Below: "It's like walking into an extension of your own home"—Andrés Coles.

TOP RIGHT & BOTTOM: A. EDGEWORTH CENTER: THEIK SMITH

rooms, new golf simulators, renovated saltwater pool, renovated tennis courts), as well as beautiful redecorating and refurbishing of our primary public rooms. Our decorator is Tom Sheerer, who has done beautiful work at Lyford Cay, the Jupiter Island Club, Fishers Island, Maidstone and Piping Rock, and has a good understanding of how to preserve the tradition and style of the club's spacious rooms while brightening and modernizing them. Our architect, Randy Gerner, did a masterful job of reworking spaces throughout the club efficiently and tastefully. It's an exciting time for the club."

Tom McCarter shares club president Andrés Coles' enthusiasm. He smiles approvingly while considering all the changes and the enduring prestige of the River Club, as the one certainty he is sure of is: "You'll never have a future if you don't challenge the present." SR

The Pilgrim Four Hundredth

Commemorating Four Centuries of *Mayflower* Heritage in 2020

by D. Brenton Simons

THROUGHOUT THE year 2020, the eyes of the world will turn to the legendary saga of the *Mayflower*, her some 108 identified passengers and crew, and their 66-day voyage as the 400th anniversary of the arrival of that vessel on American shores is commemorated through high-profile events in the United States, the United Kingdom, and The Netherlands, and in cooperation with the Wampanoag Nation.

According to various estimates, up to 10% of all living Americans—some 20 to 35 million people—can trace their ancestry to a *Mayflower* passenger, although the vast majority of these descendants are unaware of their family connections to the Pilgrims. For all Americans, whether they are descended from a Pilgrim or not, the epic story of the Separatists and their compatriots is critical to understanding early American history, the democratic nature of our government, and the tradition of Thanksgiving, a celebration derived from the harvest festival in early Plymouth Colony. The importance of the Mayflower Compact, and its formative role in our democracy, will be a focus of 2020 and form a central part of the commemorations in all three countries.

Just as the Pilgrim story influenced our national identity in the aforementioned ways, it is also enshrined in the worlds of art, prose, and music—from the folkloric "Courtship of Miles Standish" by Henry Wadsworth Longfellow to the whimsical "Anything Goes" by Cole Porter:

Times have changed
And we've often rewound the clock
Since the Puritans got a shock*
When they landed on Plymouth Rock.
If today
Any shock they should try to stem
'Stead of landing on Plymouth Rock,
Plymouth Rock would land on them.

**Porter erred in calling the Pilgrims "Puritans," rather than "Separatists."*

In 2020, histories of the oft-called "Saints and Strangers" who settled at

Plymouth will be recounted; greater access to the genealogies of millions of Americans will be provided, including sources for some of the most socially prominent families in America; and in this anniversary year Americans will learn about valiant men, women, and children who experienced great privations and untold hardships to forge new lives in a new land—William Bradford, William Brewster, John Alden, Priscilla Mullins, Edward Winslow, Myles Standish, Mary Chilton, John Howland, Richard Warren, Peregrine White, and many others. Likewise, commemorative activities will also examine the impact of the settling of New England upon indigenous populations, especially the Wampanoag nation, in new ways and through other eyes.

In addition to commemorative events to be held in 2020, groundbreaking scholarship will be published on Pilgrim history (including a new edition of Governor William Bradford's history *Of Plimoth Plantation*), exclusive lineage sources will be made available online, and tours will be guided by leading historians and genealogists in the "Pilgrim Trail"—from Provincetown on Cape Cod, site of the first landing of the Pilgrims, to Boston. Other tours will visit historic locations in England and The Netherlands, for those wishing to learn more about the story of the Separatists, their struggles for freedom, and all the individuals and families of the *Mayflower* who helped forge new opportunities in America and shape our nation in significant ways.

A host of organizations, museums, cultural centers, and lineage societies are involved in 2020 commemorative events, and several are taking the lead in sponsoring activities around this historic milestone, including, most especially, the nation's founding genealogical institution: AmericanAncestors.org, known widely as the New England Historic Genealogical Society (NEHGS), in Boston (which, coincidentally, will celebrate its 175th anniversary in 2020). Today, this nonprofit organization provides genealogical coverage of the entire country for more than 260,000 members with 1.4+ billion records online. It assists Americans of all backgrounds in learning about their ancestry, with services ranging from research for hire to publishing impeccably produced, bespoke family histories. The creation of this institution almost two hundred years ago has allowed for countless millions of Americans to explore their heritage in ways not possible elsewhere and, as a result, its work has forever influenced the way people see history and themselves.

Founded in 1845, the Society's first member was John Quincy Adams, a descendant of *Mayflower* passengers John Alden and Priscilla Mullins, and today the New England Historic Genealogical

Above: D. Brenton Simons, CEO of the NEHGS, makes remarks at the opening ceremony of the April 17, 2019 Boston Commemoration of the *Mayflower* 2020 400th Anniversary, pictured with Christopher C. Child in Pilgrim attire.

Previous Page: A 10-foot model of the *Mayflower*, a permanent exhibit outside the NEHGS.

Society maintains a world-class research center in Boston and serves as a research partner to, and anchor location of, the popular PBS television series *Finding Your Roots with Henry Louis Gates, Jr.* (The Society's connections with the Social Register Association are considerable. On Thursday, October 4, 2018, the organization hosted a cocktail reception for Boston-area members of the Social Register Association in its oak-paneled Treat Rotunda in Boston's historic Back Bay. Serving as hosts were NEHGS President and CEO **D. Brenton Simons**, Board Chairman **Mrs. Allen F. Maulsby (Geist—Nancy L. Sands)**, and immediate past Board Chairman **David H. Burnham**.)

In June 2019, the New England Historic Genealogical Society led a tour, on which members of the Social Register Association were invited, to the Netherlands: "The Pilgrim Escape to Leiden," where a small group of guests and invited VIPs learned about the Pilgrim flight to Amsterdam in 1608 and their subsequent move to Leiden in 1609. Visiting locations associated with

PIERCE HARMAN

the Pilgrims, the group learned about their lives there, and, ultimately, the Pilgrim departure from Delftshaven to Southampton on the *Speedwell* in 1620, and then their transfer to, and departure on, the *Mayflower*. In 2020, when NEHGS will offer an exclusive tour in England, where the group will visit Plymouth and other Pilgrim-related sites.

In April 2020, NEHGS and the Social Register Association will host a dinner gala in Boston for former UK Prime Minister The Rt Hon Sir John Major KG CH to commence the 400th anniversary commemorations (more details to be announced soon). Other dignitaries will include the Earl and Countess of Devon, patrons of Mayflower 400, a UK-based partner.

Among the New England Historic Genealogical Society's most notable 2020 activities are the development of *Mayflower*-themed resources at AmericanAncestors.org, including free public access to detailed biographies of all known *Mayflower* passengers and crew members; an online gallery of present-day descendants, who may submit their own photographs and stories; and, for NEHGS members, use of lineage materials developed in an exclusive collaboration with the General Society of Mayflower Descendants (GSMD). Another major online resource being developed for 2020 in a partnership between NEHGS, GSMD, and FamilySearch, will make available a wealth of lineage information to those who are experiencing a new or renewed interest in identifying and verifying their genealogical relationships to the *Mayflower* Pilgrims. It will provide unprecedented access to some 100,000 lineage applications of accepted GMSD members—along with more than a million supporting documents. These applications, which date from 1896, offer a veritable treasure trove of verified research on *Mayflower* descendants.

PIERCE HARMAN

AmericanAncestors.org will present images of applications—from submitters born at least 100 years ago—and all supporting documentation. Each application includes a four-page form listing the applicant's lineage from a *Mayflower* passenger ancestor, as well as supporting materials that prove the line of descent. The material will be made searchable and include names, dates, and relationships, so researchers will be able to make connections to recent generations of *Mayflower* descendants.

One of the leading international sponsors of 2020 commemorations is Plymouth 400 (www.Plymouth400inc.org), a not-for-profit formed in Massachusetts

Top: Wampanoag Nation dancers perform at New England Historic Genealogical Society's April 17, 2019 event launching the 400th Anniversary Commemoration of the *Mayflower* landing.

Above: Visitors at the Origins and Legacy of the *Mayflower* Exhibit at NEHGS.

to lead the planning and execution of 400th anniversary commemorations. It has brilliantly organized the efforts of numerous partnering organizations, including Plimoth Plantation, the Pilgrim Monument and Provincetown Museum, Pilgrim Hall Museum, and many others, for a series of signature events in 2020 exemplifying themes of exploration,

Some Prominent Mayflower Descendants

Being descended from a *Mayflower* passenger has long been a source of pride to many families, and the Pilgrims are found among the ancestors of socially prominent Americans, including many members of the Social Register Association, and historical figures.

New York *Mayflower* descendants include brothers Nelson A. Rockefeller and David Rockefeller; Society leader Mrs. Stuyvesant Fish; Louis Comfort Tiffany; John Hay Whitney; Harry Payne Whitney, husband of Gertrude Vanderbilt; J.P. Morgan, Jr., and his son, Henry Sturgis Morgan (founder of Morgan Stanley); and the Cushing sisters, originally of Boston: Barbara "Babe" Cushing, wife of CBS founder William S. Paley, Mary "Minnie" Cushing, wife of William Astor, and Betsey Cushing, who first married James Roosevelt, and secondly John Hay Whitney.

From Boston, *Mayflower* descendants include several Brahmin families, such as the Cabots and Saltonstalls, as well as one branch of the Kennedy family. Notable Chicagoans descended from the Pilgrims include Brooks McCormick of International Harvester, the Armours, and the Swifts. California *Mayflower* descendants include the Crockers of San Francisco and the Chandlers of Los Angeles. Other well-known descendants include decorator Elsie DeWolfe and authors Cleveland Amory and George Plimpton, as well as presidents and presidential families, such as the Adamses, Franklin D. Roosevelt and his cousin Alice Roosevelt Longworth, Ulysses S. Grant, and the Bushes.

Mrs. Ashbel P. Fitch (Elizabeth A. Cross), wife of the New York City politician and president of The Trust Company of America, was an early member of the Mayflower Society, and her son, Ashbel P. Fitch, Jr. (the present author's great-grandfather), thought so highly of his *Mayflower* antecedents that an early 20th-century cartoon depicted him as stepping from a vessel named *Mayflower* onto Plymouth Rock.

Top Left, Right & Center: Details from an illustration of a *Mayflower*-themed Family Register at NEHGS.

Bottom Left & Right: Details from an illustration of a *Mayflower*-themed Family Register at NEHGS.

Bottom Center: Circa 1920 embroidery of the *Mayflower*, NEHGS Fine Art Collection.

innovation, religious freedom, self-governance, immigration, and thanksgiving. The *Mayflower II*, which has undergone a multi-million-dollar restoration, will sail to Boston Harbor for "Mayflower Sails" events in the spring of 2020 and, over the course of the anniversary year, be explored by tens of thousands of visitors. Serving as an iconic centerpiece of the 2020 commemorations, this vessel is a full-scale reproduction of the ship that brought the Pilgrims to America. A smaller model of the original *Mayflower* is on view at the New England Historic Genealogical Society in Boston. Also scheduled by Plymouth 400 are an international opening ceremony on April 24, 2020, in Plymouth, MA; a ceremony at the State House in Boston on September 14, 2020; and, in the autumn of 2020, an indigenous history conference and powwow in Bridgewater, MA, that will "address the legacy of the colonization experienced by Wampanoag and other Native people."

For all Americans, this commemoration provides an opportunity to examine our early history, better understand a root of our democracy, and provide avenues for learning more about the lives and times of all our ancestors, whatever their origins. The moving story of the Pilgrims will offer inspiration and pride, and for families, including many of those in the Social Register Association, this quadricentennial anniversary will speak to traditions and values of a special heritage we hold dear. ℞

ALL IMAGES COURTESY OF NEHGS

Earl Fain IV

Earl Fain IV, 56, of Charleston, SC, died on July 31, 2019.

Born on November 1, 1962, to Mr. and Mrs. Earl Fain III (Kelly Erwin), Baron, as he was known, spent most of his formative years growing up in Dallas, TX. Baron attended Deerfield Academy and graduated from The University of the South. He received a master's degree from the University of Virginia. Baron met and married Courtenay Haden McCormick in 2006. Their son, Taliaferro "Tradd" Fain, was born in 2010.

From July of 1992 until his death, Baron worked for nearly three decades at Ben Silver, where he specialized in providing custom items that required a detailed understanding of heraldry, vexillology, institutions of higher learning and military traditions.

Baron was a member, leader or founder of a significant number of fraternal, social and patriotic societies, a few of which include the Carolina Yacht Club, the Charleston Club, the Caledonian Club of Charleston, the Royal Society of St. George, the Most Venerable Order of the Hospital of Saint John of Jerusalem, and the Sons of the American Revolution.

He served honorably for many years in the signal corps of the South Carolina State Guard, and attained the rank of staff sergeant. Baron enjoyed traveling and brought home stories—and many flags—from all over the globe. His deep intellectual curiosity directed him in many directions, including becoming a founder of the *Charleston Mercury* newspaper. Baron was a devoted member of St. Philip's Church and belonged to many Anglican groups, including the Prayer Book Society.

He was dedicated to history and tradition, but Baron will most be remembered for his strong faith, his love for his family and his devoted friendship and genuine interest in others.

William H. Painter

William Hall Painter, 91, passed away on October 28, 2018, in Yarmouth Port, MA.

Bill, as he was known, was born May 2, 1927, in Pittsburgh, PA, to Mr. and Mrs. John Littleton Dawson Painter (Eleanor Hall). The Painter family had been involved in the steel industry before the turn of the century and in the brokerage business in Pittsburgh thereafter. The Hall family had lived in in Maryland and Pennsylvania since the 1600s. He attended St. Paul's School and was a 1949 graduate of Princeton University. He also graduated from Harvard Law School in 1954.

A member of the New York Bar, Bill was a law professor for most of his professional life, teaching at the University of Illinois and George Washington University. He was the chief counsel to a U.S. House of Representatives Committee studying the securities industry from 1971 to 1972, and was the author of dozens of books and articles. His expertise was in corporate law, securities law and tax. He was a member of the American Bar Association and the American Law Institute, and of the Cosmos Club in Washington and the Capitol English Setter Club.

Bill's hobbies included reading a wide range of literature, collecting first editions of English literature, and showing his beloved English Setters Tasha, Tasha II, George, and Nikka.

He is survived by his wife of 62 years, Marion Homer Painter. They were married at St. George's Church in New York City in July of 1956. His sons Richard William Painter of Minneapolis, and Edward Homer Painter of New York, as well as five grandchildren also survive him. Finally, but not least, Bill is survived by his beloved English Cocker Spaniel, Boswell.

A funeral service was held in Massachusetts on November 10, 2018, at St. Mary's Episcopal Church Barnstable. He was buried at Woodside Cemetery in Yarmouth Port.

James F. Scharnberg

James Fagan Scharnberg, 80, of Malvern, PA, passed away peacefully on January 27, 2019, following a long and courageous battle with cancer.

Jim, as he was known, was born on February 21, 1938, in Newport, AR, to the late Mr. and Mrs. Oliver H. Scharnberg (Lady E. Watson). He grew up on a large cattle farm in Arkansas that was in his family for several generations. Jim graduated from Yale's School of Art and Design in 1959.

Following graduation, Jim embarked on a long and successful career in graphic design and advertising, working for a number of large firms and corporations in New York City and Philadelphia before setting up his own private firm. Aside from his professional design work, Jim was also well known for his fine art drawings and paintings, as well as his cartoon illustrations.

He was a distinguished huntsman and developed a passion for the ancient sport of hunting with foot hounds. While living and working in New York, he was a founding member of the Gracie Mansion Foot Hounds and hunted with Mayor Lindsay and his terriers in one of the only hunting packs based in Manhattan during the 20th century.

Back in Philadelphia, Jim began hunting with Skycastle French Hounds. He became a key staff member and was elected Master of Basset Hounds for Skycastle in 1987. For 32 years, Jim guided the Skycastle pack and its large "field" of subscription members across some of the most beautiful countryside in Chester County, PA. Jim worked tireless to preserve open space and served on numerous committees and advisory boards providing guidance on dog care issues and environmental issues to Pennsylvania's governor and state legislature.

Jim was a member of the Franklin Inn Club, the Philadelphia Club, the Countrymen's Alliance, St. Anthony's Hall, the Society of Colonial Wars, and the Pennsylvania Society Sons of the Revolution. A few months before his passing, he had discovered a veteran of the War of 1812 in his ancestry. His application to the Society of the War of 1812 in the Commonwealth of Pennsylvania had been acted upon favorably by the Society, but unfortunately, Jim passed before receiving notification of his election.

Jim was the beloved husband of the late Patricia Colladay Scharnberg and the late Marsha Gray Laubenstein Knight-Scharnberg; and loving father of Eric Scharnberg, Alex Scharnberg, and Gwendolyne Knight.

Samuel W. Meek Jr.

Samuel Williams Meek Jr. died peacefully at his home in Palm Beach on Tuesday, February 26, 2019.

Born in New York on May 9, 1925, Sam, as he was known, grew up in London and Greenwich, CT. He attended Greenwich Country Day School and Deerfield Academy, and was a graduate of Yale and the University of Virginia Law School.

Sam served stateside as a Marine lieutenant in WWII and captain in reserves during the Korean War. He then joined National City Bank and later, Morgan Guaranty Trust. His career took him to Palm Beach, where he worked at the First National Bank of Palm Beach, and then as counsel to Cummings and Lockwood and Simses and Associates.

Sam was a lifelong Episcopalian and served as a knight in the Venerable Order of St. John of Jerusalem. A skilled racquets player, marksman, skier and fly fisherman, he especially enjoyed his time at the Mastigouche Fish and Game Club in Quebec. His greatest abiding passion was his family: his beloved late wife Marjorie; sisters Susan Meek McCabe, Priscilla Meek Christy, and the late Elizabeth Meek Jeffery; four children; 13 grandchildren; a great-grandson and a stepdaughter. A service and interment was held at Christ Church in Greenwich on May 25, 2019.

William C. von Raab

William Conrad von Raab, lawyer and former government official, died in Charlottesville, VA, on February 20, 2019.

Willy, as he was known, was born in New Rochelle, NY, to Mr. and Mrs. Frederick von Raab (Regina Whalen), and was raised in Roslyn, NY. He received a BA from Yale in 1963 and an LLB from the University of Virginia in 1966.

During the Nixon Administration, Willy worked as a director at the Cost of Living Council. He later was vice president of Administration and Finance at New York University. In 1981, he returned to Washington as the commissioner of the United States Customs Service during the Reagan Administration. In his later years, living on his farm in Madison, VA, Willy was active on numerous boards and with the Piedmont Environmental Council.

Willy was a member of the Virginia Bar Association, the Bar Association of the City of New York, The District of Columbia Bar Association and the Bar of the Supreme Court of the United States. He was also a member of the Brook Club and the Racquet and Tennis Club in New York, as well as White's in London.

Willy is survived by his wife of 20 years, Lucy S. Rhame, as well as his children from two previous marriages, daughter Alexandra Lambert von Raab, along with her daughters Luisa and Adrian Raby; and son Nicholas Christian von Raab.

A memorial service was held at the Piedmont Episcopal Church in Madison on April 16, 2019.

Daniel P. Redmond

Daniel Pierson Redmond, M.D. (COL, USA, Ret.), passed away in Bethesda, MD, on July 27, 2018, surrounded by two of his children after suffering a stroke. He was 76 years old.

Daniel was born February 3, 1942, in Tulsa, OK, to Mr. and Mrs. John Franklin Redmond. Dan attended Darien High School in Darien, CT, and was a graduate of Rice University and the University of Texas Southwestern Medical Center. After medical school, Dan undertook his clinical training in internal medicine at Dallas Veterans' and Parkland Memorial Hospitals, followed by a third year at the University of Toronto St. Michael's Hospital. While working in Parkland's emergency room Dan met his future wife, Suzanne, who was a nurse there. He spent two additional years as a fellow at University of Pittsburgh School of Medicine.

Upon completing medical school, Dan was commissioned in the Army Reserve and entered active duty as a major in 1973. His initial assignment was at the Walter Reed Army Institute of Research. He was promoted to lieutenant colonel in 1978, and continued his Army service until 1980, when he accepted a position at the University of Oklahoma Tulsa Medical College. Dan later returned to the Army and rejoined his colleagues at Walter Reed, where he resumed his work researching issues involving deployment stress, sleep, and cognitive performance. He participated in several temporary field assignments to gather knowledge of sleep and activity patterns. After an interesting career, Dan retired from active duty as a Colonel in 2003.

Dan was a proud member of the Society of Colonial Wars, which he and his son Sean joined together in 2009, one of few father and son duos to do so at the same time.

Dan was preceded in death by his parents, his beloved wife Suzanne, and his brother Richard C. Redmond. He is survived by his sons Matthew, Sean, and Rev. Nicholas Redmond, as well as his daughter Bonnie Lindsly, and three grandchildren. He was laid to rest with full military honors at Arlington National Cemetery on January 10, 2019.

Adrienne Gignoux

Adrienne Morton Smith Gignoux passed away peacefully at her home in London on January 15, 2019. She was 72 years old.

Adrienne was born in Sharon, CT, on July 16, 1946, to Mr. and Mrs. James Morton-Smith (Katrina Spaulding). She was raised in New York, where she attended Chapin School and subsequently Wheaton College in Massachusetts. Adrienne moved to London in 1971, where she settled with her family.

Adrienne was passionate about politics and international affairs and pursued this interest by being a member of Chatham House. She travelled extensively throughout the Middle East, Central Asia, China and Latin America. Adrienne kept her links with the United States through membership in the Colony Club of New York and frequent trips to visit family in Montecito, CA.

Adrienne never failed to light up a room with her smile and enthusiasm. She will be remembered for her gift of hospitality, her generosity of spirit and her enthusiasm to live life to the fullest. Being a grandmother was one of Adrienne's greatest joys. She is survived by her children, Consuela Sharrocks, Camilla Speck, and Alan Gignoux; her half-brother Crane Kirkbride; and her grandchildren.

Robin B. Martin

Robin Bradley Martin, 70, passed away wrapped in the love of his wife and children on March 21, 2019, after losing a valiant fight with mesothelioma. Robin left this world at peace, with no regrets and having accepted his fate.

Robin was born on February 12, 1949, to the late Mr. and Mrs. Alastair Martin (Edith Park) of New York. He was a great-grandson of Henry Phipps, and of Mr. and Mrs. Bradley Martin (Caroline Cornelia Sherman), whose 1897 fancy dress ball ("The Bradley-Martin Ball") marked the end of the Gilded Age.

Robin grew up in Glen Head, NY. He attended The Green Vale School and The Choate School, and graduated from the Rensselaer Polytechnic Institute. His professional career began with a stint as Regional Coordinator for the Committee to Re-Elect the President during the 1972 Nixon campaign. He later co-founded Deer River Group, LLC, which bought and sold commercial radio and television stations.

Racket sports were Robin's love. As a child, he learned to play tennis on the courts at his grandfather's estate. Later, he tried his hand at squash, and won the Club Championship and Senior Club Championship at the Metropolitan Club many times. Robin next took up court tennis. He was a member of the board of the United States Court Tennis Preservation Foundation and a member of the National Tennis Club.

Robin climbed Aconcagua, the highest peak in South America, and was an avid biker. He and his wife spent four weeks traveling through Southeast Asia just five months before he passed away. A favorite pastime of his was piecing together elaborate wooden jigsaw puzzles, a hobby he shared with his father and his children.

Robin held numerous positions and sat on the boards and committees of many organizations, including the Washington Hospital Center; the District of Columbia Board of Education; the Corcoran Gallery of Art; Smithsonian Institution; Town of Palm Beach United Way; Palm Beach Civic Association; the Gerald R. Ford Presidential Foundation; Rensselaer Polytechnic Institute; and St. Albans School.

He was a member of the Chevy Chase Club, the Knickerbocker Club, the Everglades Club, the Bath and Tennis Club, and the Rolling Rock Club. Robin was also a past president of The Metropolitan Club of the City of Washington, and a member of the Society of the Cincinnati, the Sons of the American Revolution, the Baronial Order of Magna Carta, the General Society of Mayflower Descendants, and a pending member of the Society of Colonial Wars.

Those who knew Robin will always remember his ever-present Panama hat floating down the street wherever he went. He is survived by his wife, Jocelyn White Martin; daughter, Catherine Martin Jain; and sons, Christopher and Dana Martin.

Edited by Stephanie Hadik

Social Register®
Locator
Winter 2020

VOLUME V

The *Locator* is an index to all heads of entry listed in the *Social Register* and is an essential aid in locating the names of new acquaintances as well as those of old friends. US listings are arranged by state, city and postal code, and then by the surname of the head of entry. International listings appear by country and city, in alphabetical order.

The 2020 *Locator* should be used in conjunction with the Winter 2020 *Social Register.*

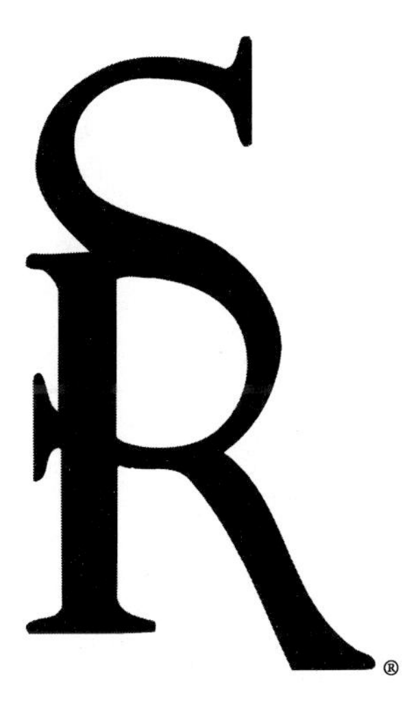

SOCIAL REGISTER ASSOCIATION
14 WALL STREET, NEW YORK, NY 10005

SRService@thesocialregister.org
Telephone: (646) 612-7310
www.socialregisteronline.com

© Copyright 2019 by THE SOCIAL REGISTER ASSOCIATION
0-940281-33-3

Let us in education dream of
an aristocracy of achievement
arising out of
a democracy of opportunity.

— Thomas Jefferson—
1743-1826

Table of Contents

US Listings

To nominate a candidate for the Social Register Association, please email: SRCommittee@thesocialregister.org

ZIP Code zones of the United States

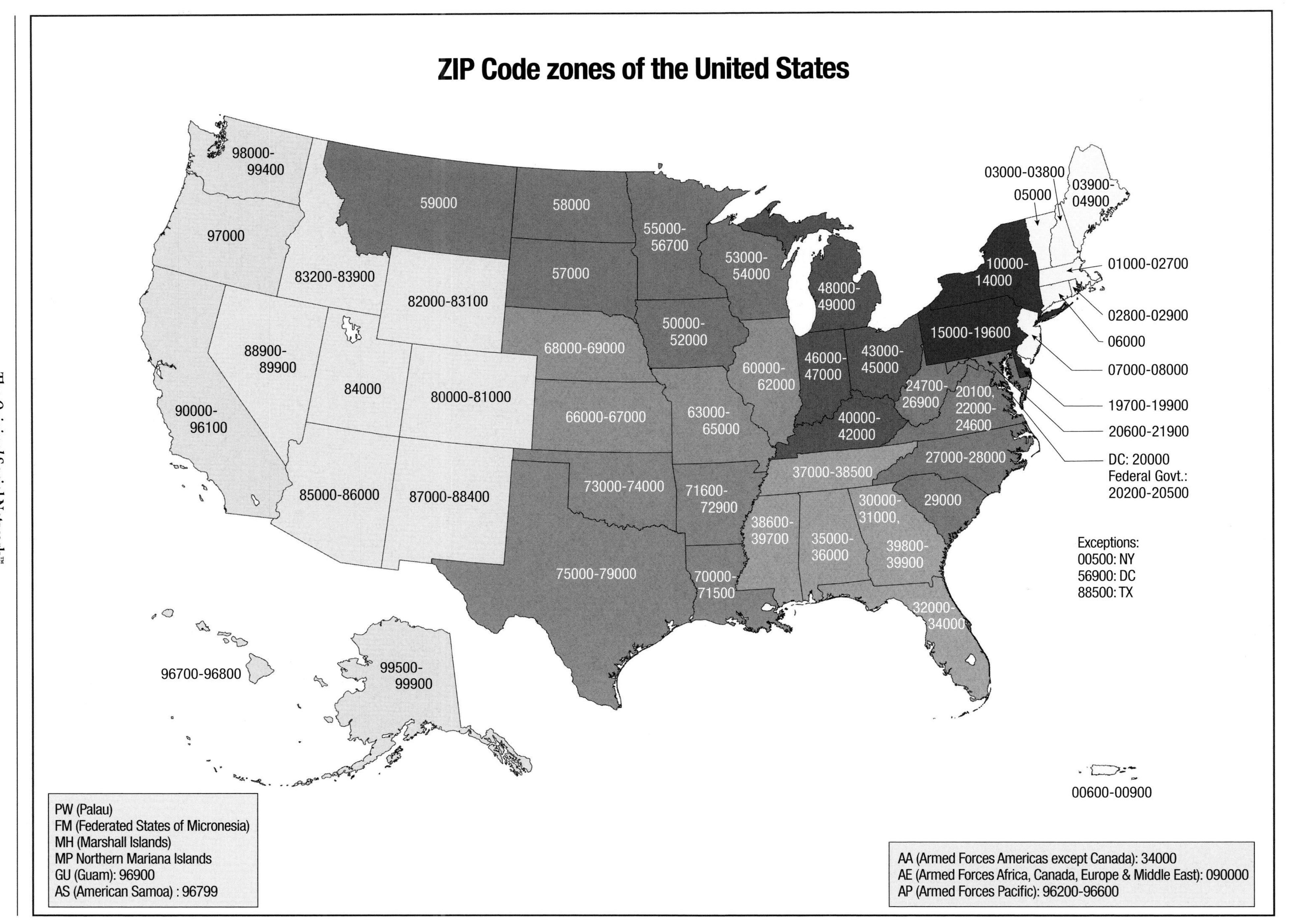

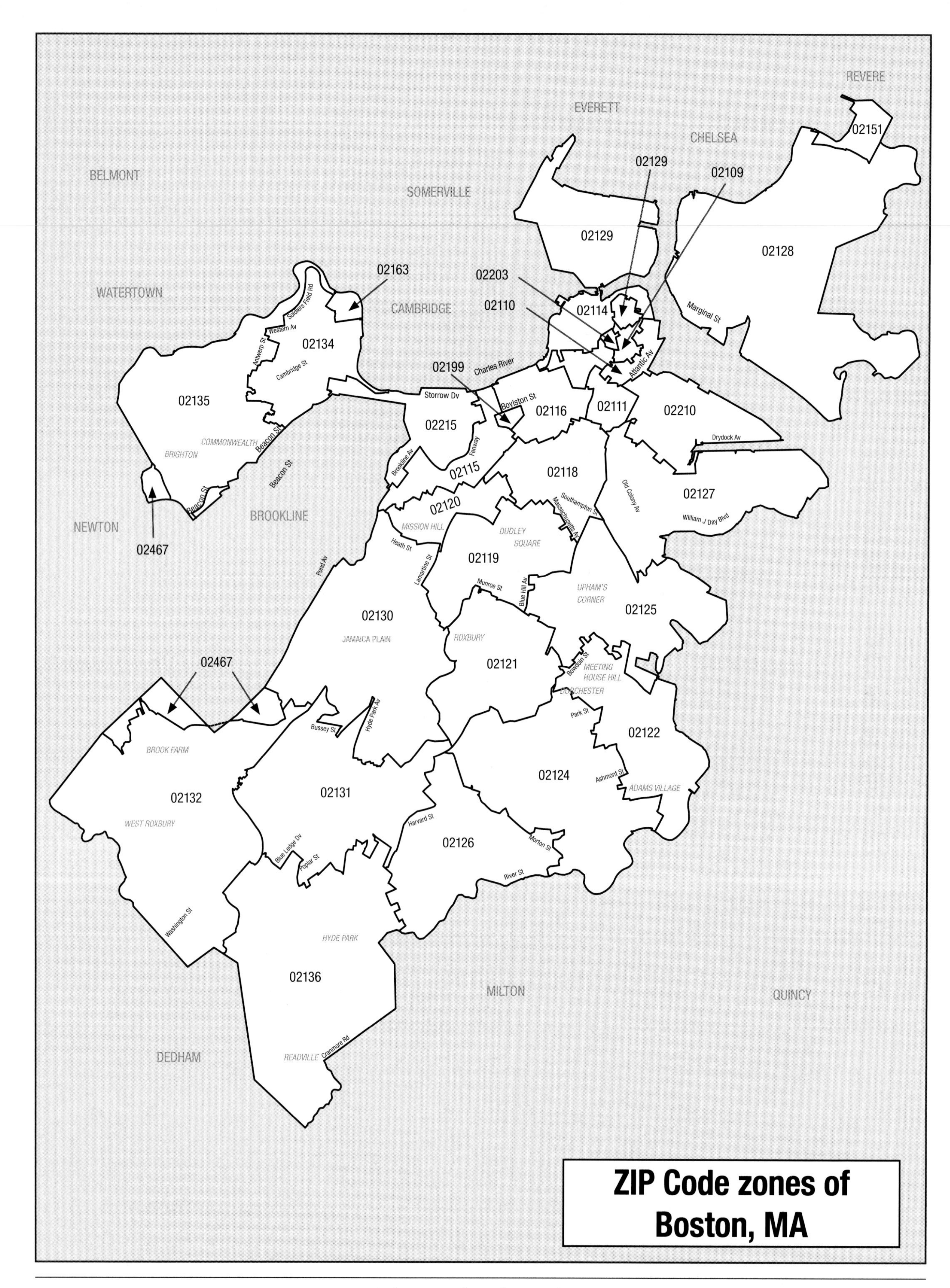

ZIP Code zones of Boston, MA

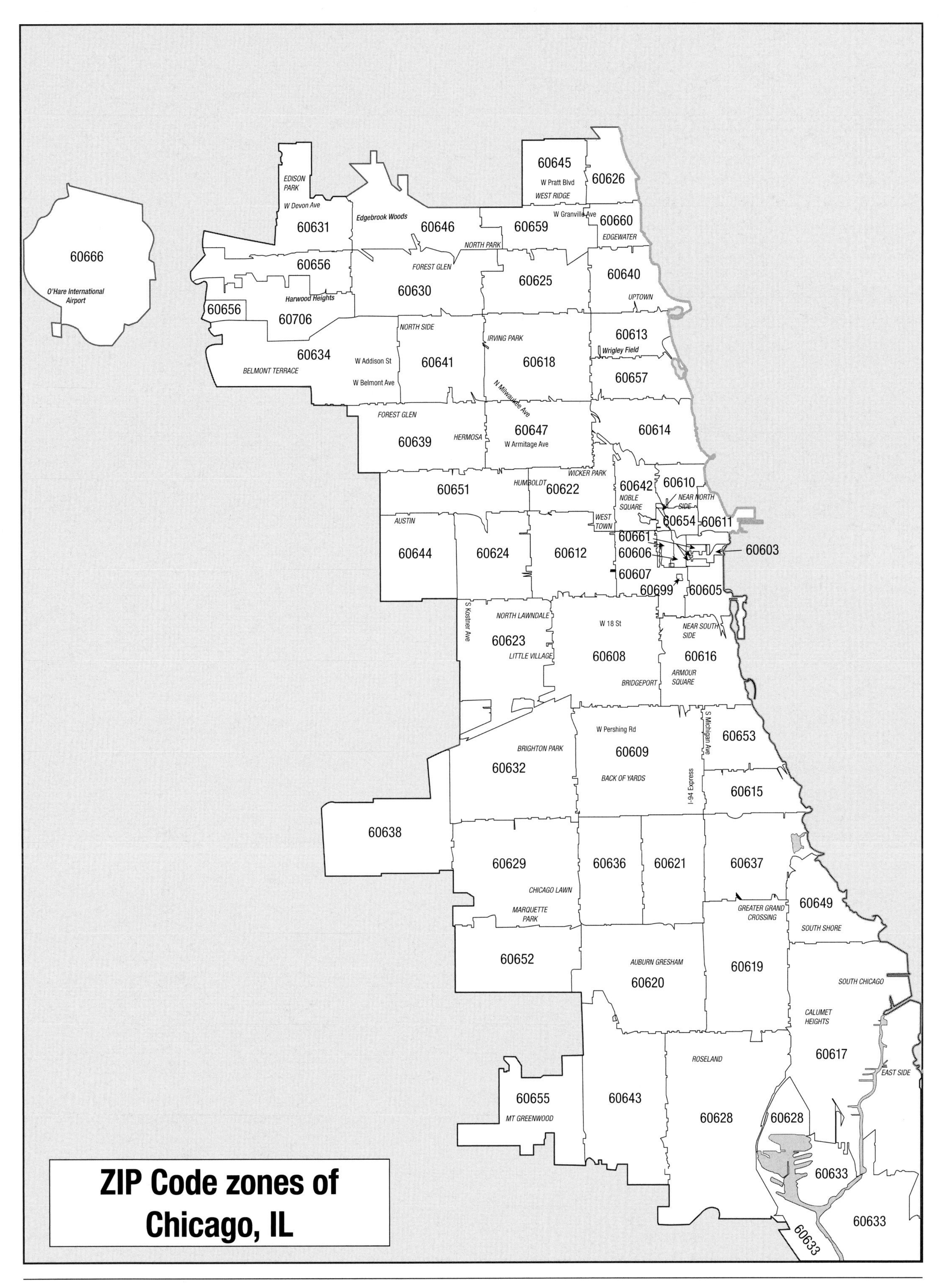
60666
O'Hare International Airport
EDISON PARK
W Devon Ave
60631
60656
60656
Harwood Heights
60706
60634
BELMONT TERRACE
W Addison St
W Belmont Ave
Edgebrook Woods
60646
FOREST GLEN
60630
NORTH SIDE
60641
60645
W Pratt Blvd
WEST RIDGE
60626
W Granville Ave
60660
EDGEWATER
60659
NORTH PARK
60625
60640
UPTOWN
IRVING PARK
60618
60613
Wrigley Field
60657
N Milwaukee Ave
FOREST GLEN
60639
HERMOSA
60647
W Armitage Ave
60614
WICKER PARK
60651
HUMBOLDT
60622
60642
NOBLE SQUARE
60610
NEAR NORTH SIDE
60654
60611
AUSTIN
60644
60624
60612
WEST TOWN
60661
60606
60607
60603
60699
60605
S Kostner Ave
NORTH LAWNDALE
60623
LITTLE VILLAGE
W 18 St
60608
BRIDGEPORT
NEAR SOUTH SIDE
60616
ARMOUR SQUARE
S Michigan Ave
60653
W Pershing Rd
BRIGHTON PARK
60632
60609
BACK OF YARDS
I-94 Express
60615
60638
60629
CHICAGO LAWN
MARQUETTE PARK
60636
60621
60637
60649
GREATER GRAND CROSSING
SOUTH SHORE
60652
AUBURN GRESHAM
60620
60619
SOUTH CHICAGO
CALUMET HEIGHTS
60617
EAST SIDE
ROSELAND
60655
MT GREENWOOD
60643
60628
60628
60633
60633
60633
ZIP Code zones of
Chicago, IL

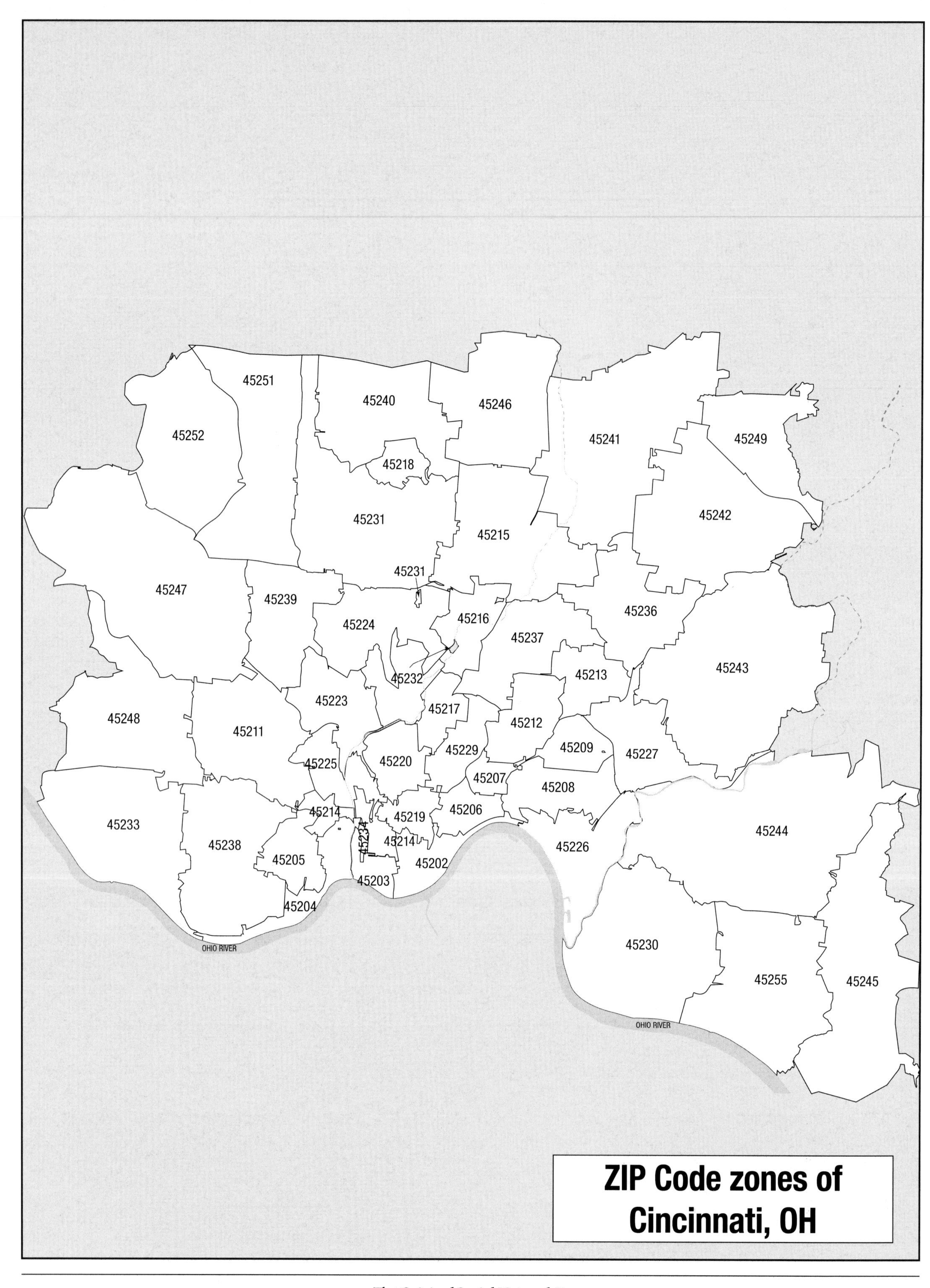
45251
45240
45246
45252
45241
45249
45218
45231
45215
45242
45247
45231
45239
45216
45236
45224
45237
45243
45232
45213
45223
45217
45248
45211
45212
45229
45209
45227
45225
45220
45207
45208
45214
45219
45206
45233
45238
45234
45214
45244
45205
45202
45226
45203
45204
OHIO RIVER
45230
45255
45245
OHIO RIVER
ZIP Code zones of
Cincinnati, OH

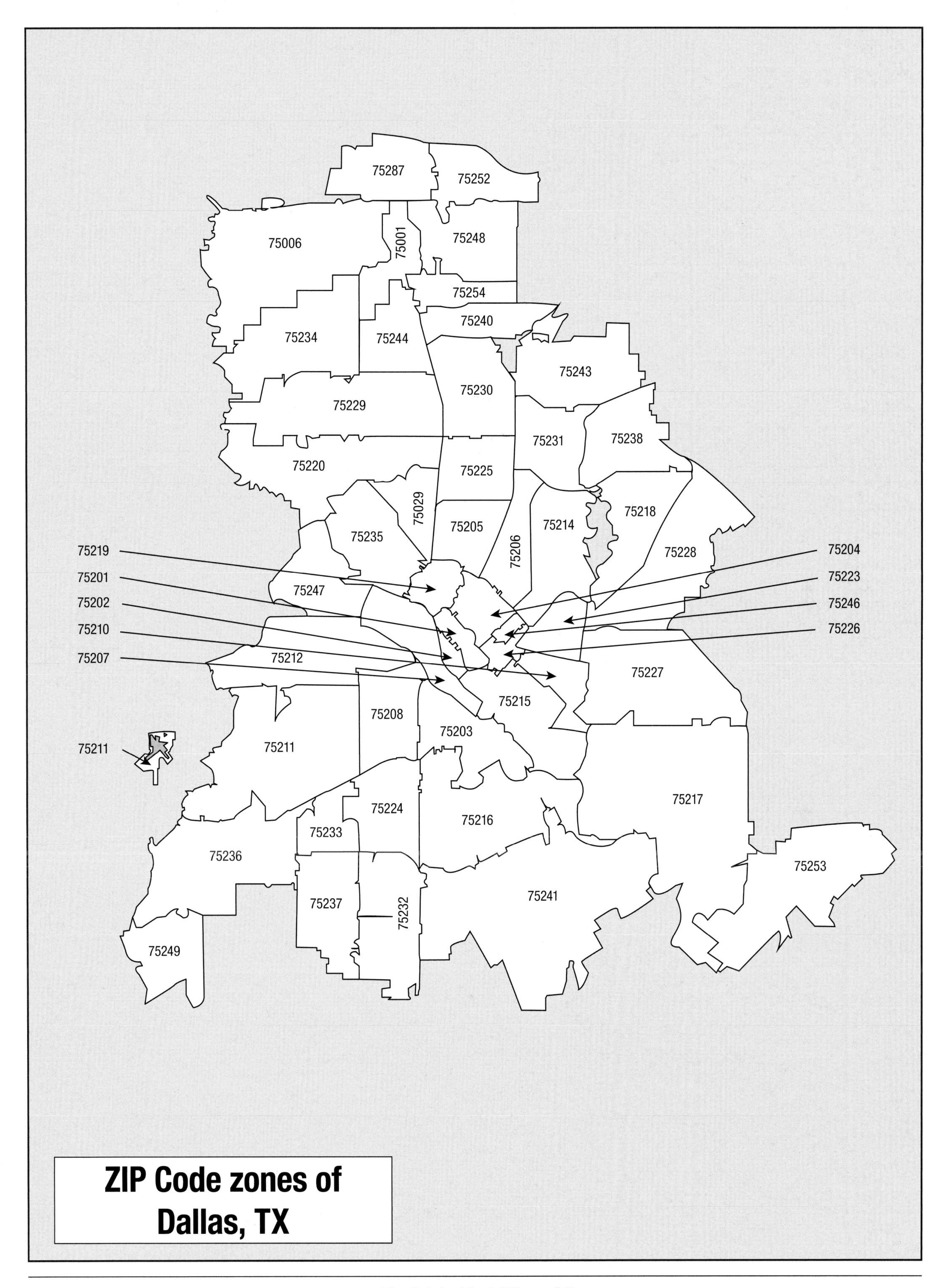
75287
75252
75006
75001
75248
75254
75240
75234
75244
75243
75230
75229
75231
75238
75220
75225
75029
75218
75205
75214
75235
75206
75228
75219
75201
75202
75210
75207
75204
75223
75246
75226
75247
75212
75227
75215
75208
75203
75211
75211
75217
75224
75216
75233
75236
75253
75241
75237
75232
75249
ZIP Code zones of
Dallas, TX

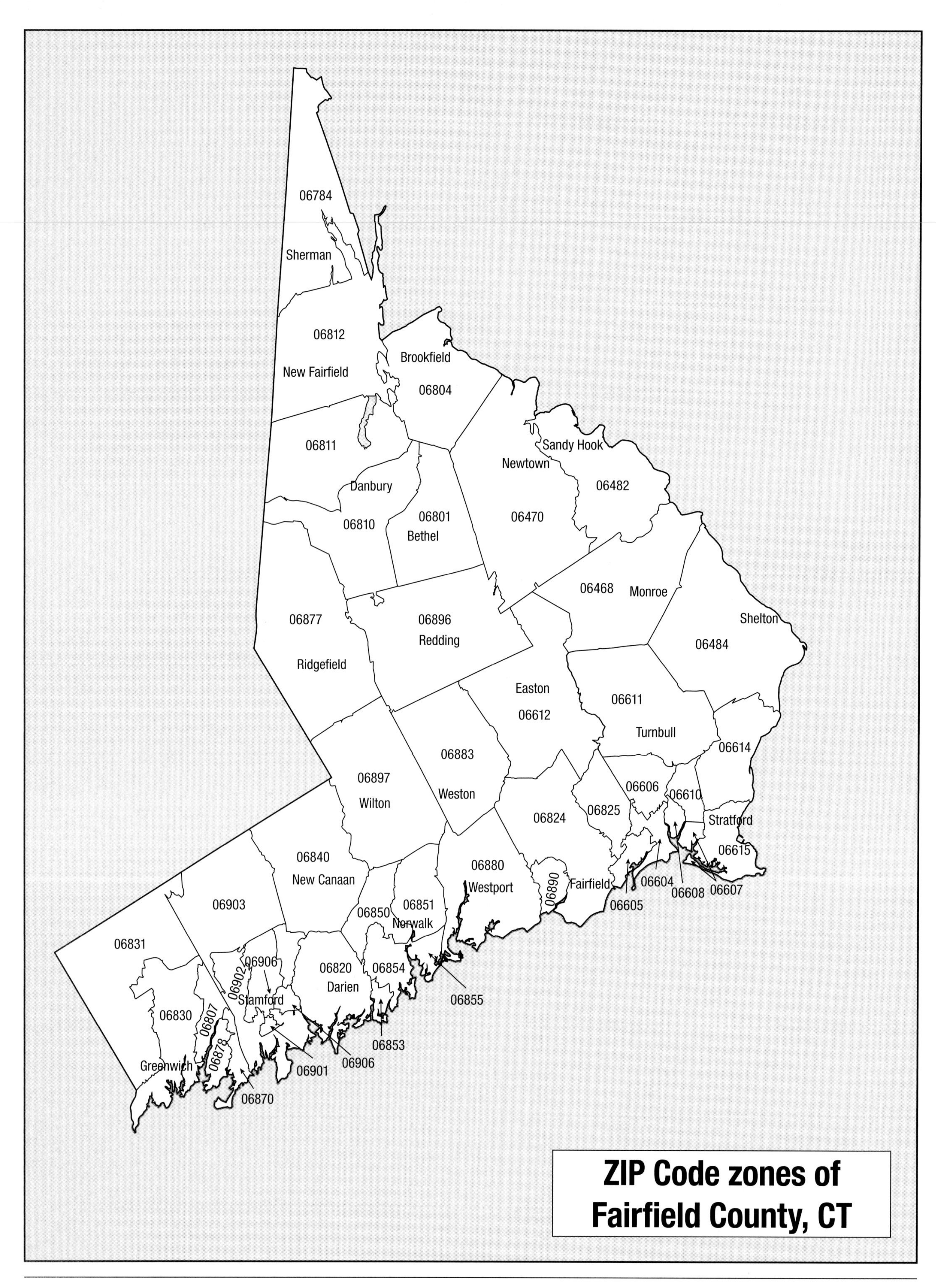
06784
Sherman
06812
New Fairfield
Brookfield
06804
06811
Sandy Hook
Newtown
06482
Danbury
06801
06470
06810
Bethel
06468
Monroe
06877
06896
Shelton
Redding
06484
Ridgefield
Easton
06611
06612
Turnbull
06614
06883
06897
06606
06610
Wilton
Weston
06824
06825
Stratford
06615
06840
06880
New Canaan
Westport
06890
Fairfield
06604
06608
06607
06903
06851
06605
06850
Norwalk
06831
06906
06820
06854
06902
Darien
Stamford
06855
06830
06807
06878
06853
Greenwich
06901
06906
06870
ZIP Code zones of
Fairfield County, CT

ZIP Code zones of Houston, TX

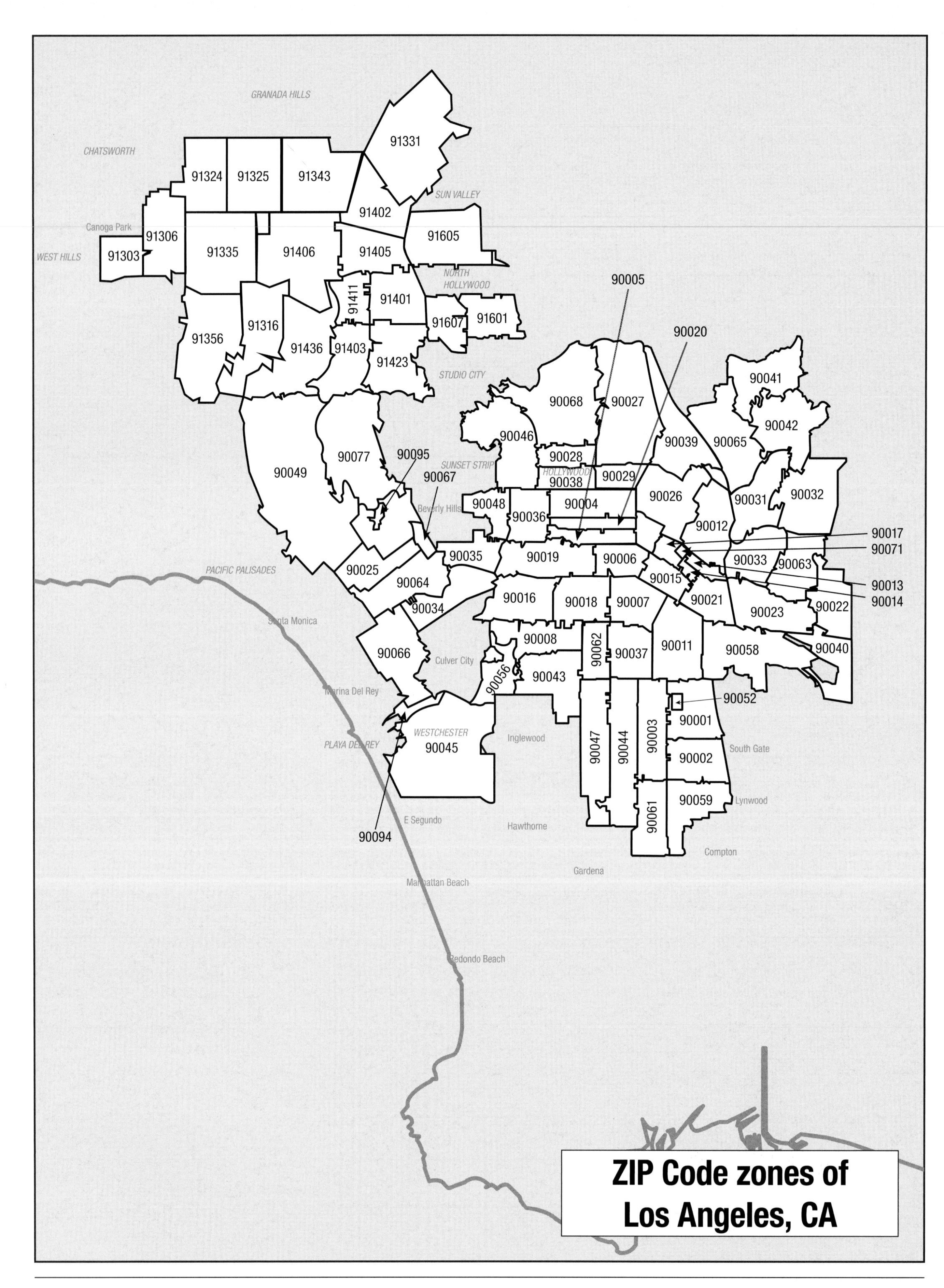
GRANADA HILLS
CHATSWORTH
Canoga Park
WEST HILLS
SUN VALLEY
NORTH HOLLYWOOD
STUDIO CITY
SUNSET STRIP
HOLLYWOOD
Beverly Hills
PACIFIC PALISADES
Santa Monica
Culver City
Marina Del Rey
PLAYA DEL REY
WESTCHESTER
Inglewood
E Segundo
Hawthorne
Gardena
Compton
South Gate
Lynwood
Manhattan Beach
Redondo Beach
91331
91324
91325
91343
91402
91306
91303
91335
91406
91405
91605
91411
91401
91607
91601
91356
91316
91436
91403
91423
90005
90020
90041
90068
90027
90042
90046
90039
90065
90028
90038
90029
90077
90095
90049
90067
90048
90036
90004
90026
90031
90032
90012
90017
90071
90035
90019
90006
90033
90063
90025
90015
90013
90014
90064
90016
90018
90007
90021
90023
90022
90034
90008
90062
90037
90011
90058
90040
90066
90056
90043
90052
90001
90045
90047
90044
90003
90002
90059
90061
90094
ZIP Code zones of Los Angeles, CA

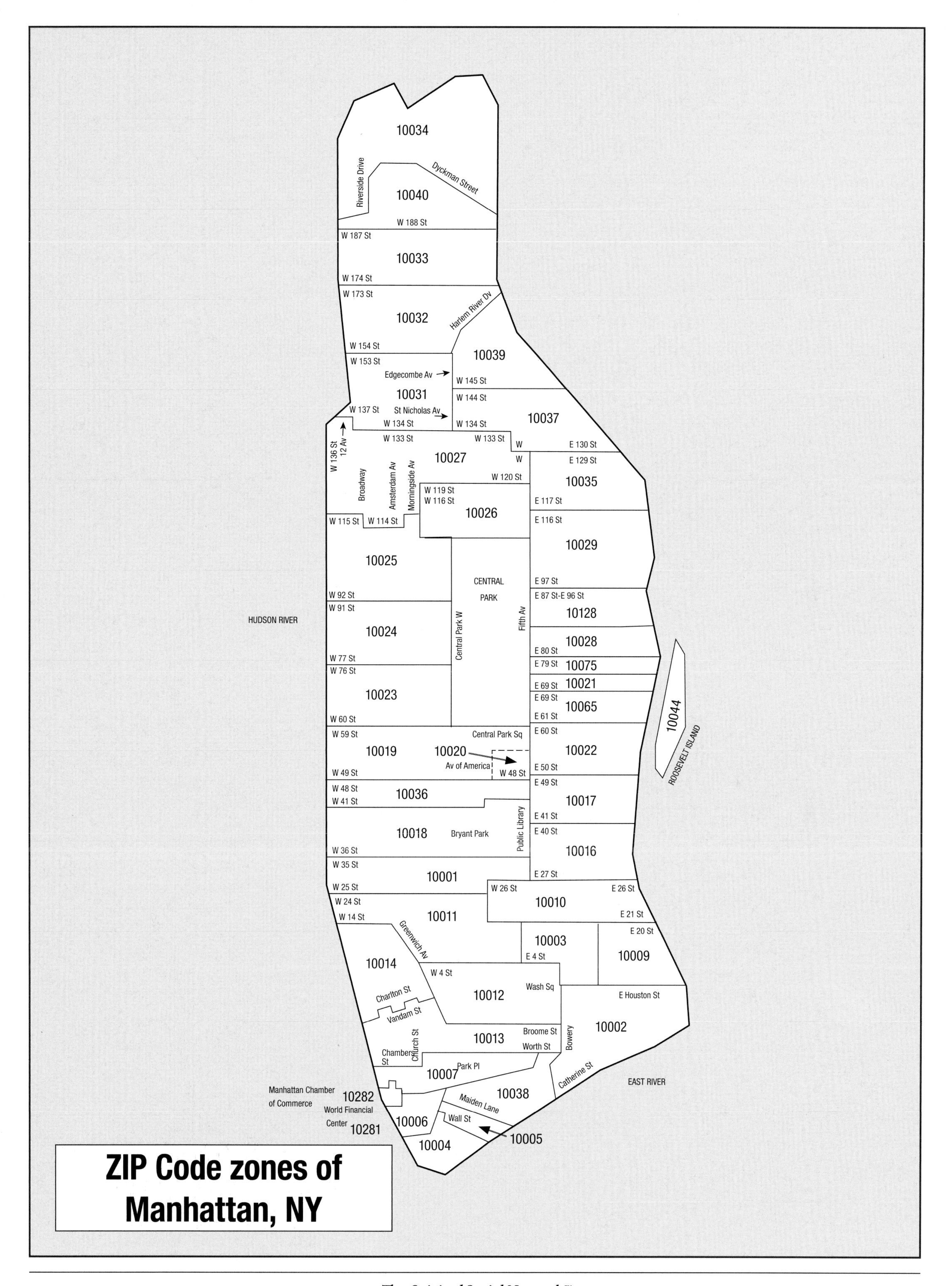
10034
Riverside Drive
Dyckman Street
10040
W 188 St
W 187 St
10033
W 174 St
W 173 St
10032
Harlem River Dv
W 154 St
W 153 St
10039
Edgecombe Av
W 145 St
10031
W 144 St
W 137 St
St Nicholas Av
W 134 St
W 134 St
10037
W 133 St
W 133 St
W
E 130 St
W 136 St
12 Av
10027
W
E 129 St
Broadway
Amsterdam Av
Morningside Av
W 120 St
10035
W 119 St
W 116 St
E 117 St
10026
W 115 St
W 114 St
E 116 St
10029
10025
CENTRAL
PARK
E 97 St
W 92 St
E 87 St-E 96 St
W 91 St
10128
HUDSON RIVER
10024
Central Park W
Fifth Av
10028
E 80 St
W 77 St
E 79 St
10075
W 76 St
E 69 St
10021
E 69 St
10023
10065
10044
W 60 St
E 61 St
W 59 St
Central Park Sq
E 60 St
10019
10020
10022
ROOSEVELT ISLAND
Av of America
W 49 St
W 48 St
E 50 St
W 48 St
E 49 St
10036
W 41 St
10017
Public Library
E 41 St
10018
Bryant Park
E 40 St
W 36 St
10016
W 35 St
E 27 St
10001
W 25 St
W 26 St
E 26 St
W 24 St
10010
W 14 St
10011
E 21 St
Greenwich Av
E 20 St
10003
10009
E 4 St
10014
W 4 St
Wash Sq
10012
E Houston St
Charlton St
Vandam St
10002
Church St
10013
Broome St
Bowery
Chambers St
Worth St
Park Pl
10007
Catherine St
EAST RIVER
Manhattan Chamber of Commerce
10282
10038
Maiden Lane
World Financial Center
10006
Wall St
10281
10005
10004
ZIP Code zones of Manhattan, NY

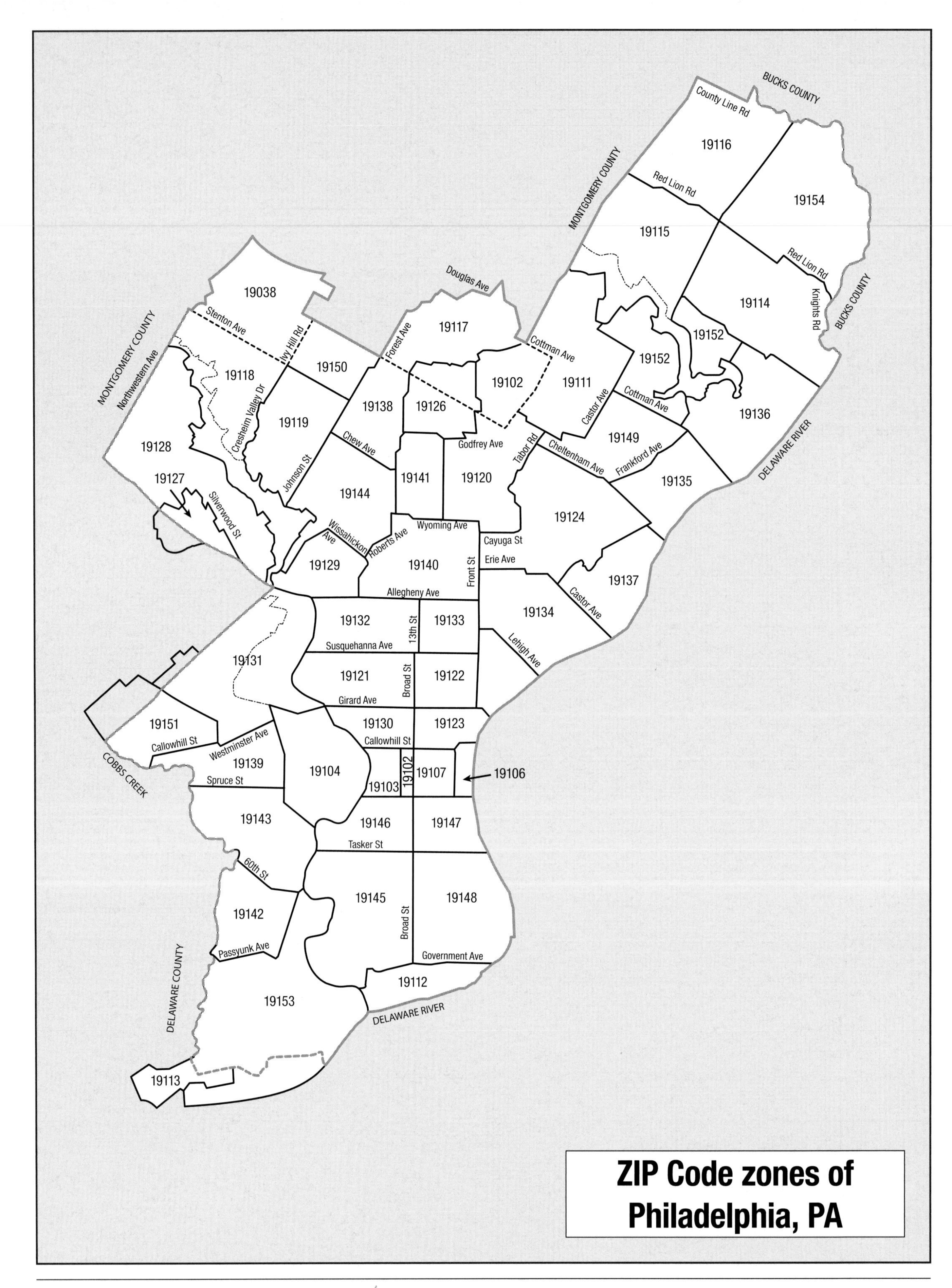

ZIP Code zones of Philadelphia, PA

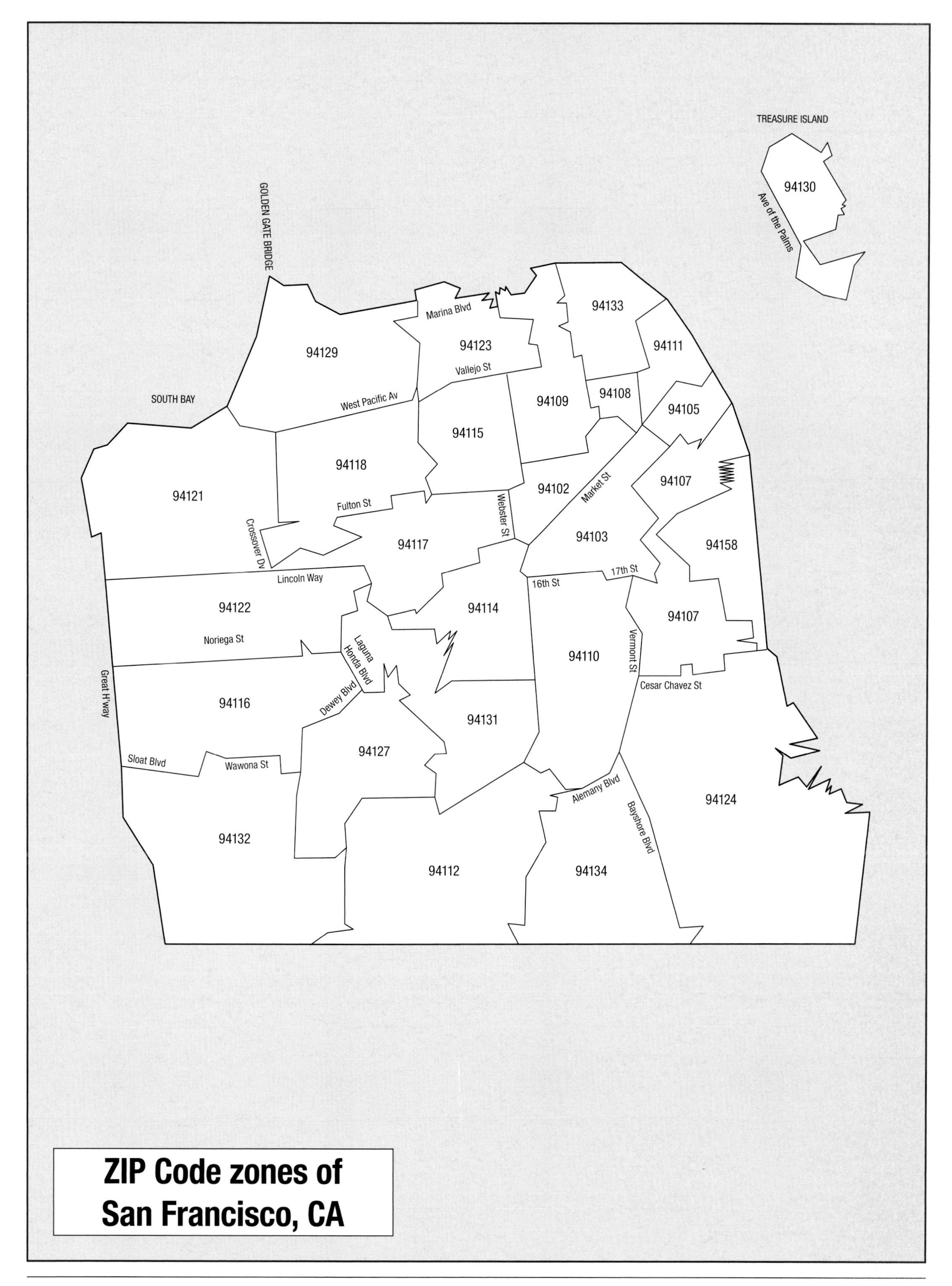

ZIP Code zones of San Francisco, CA

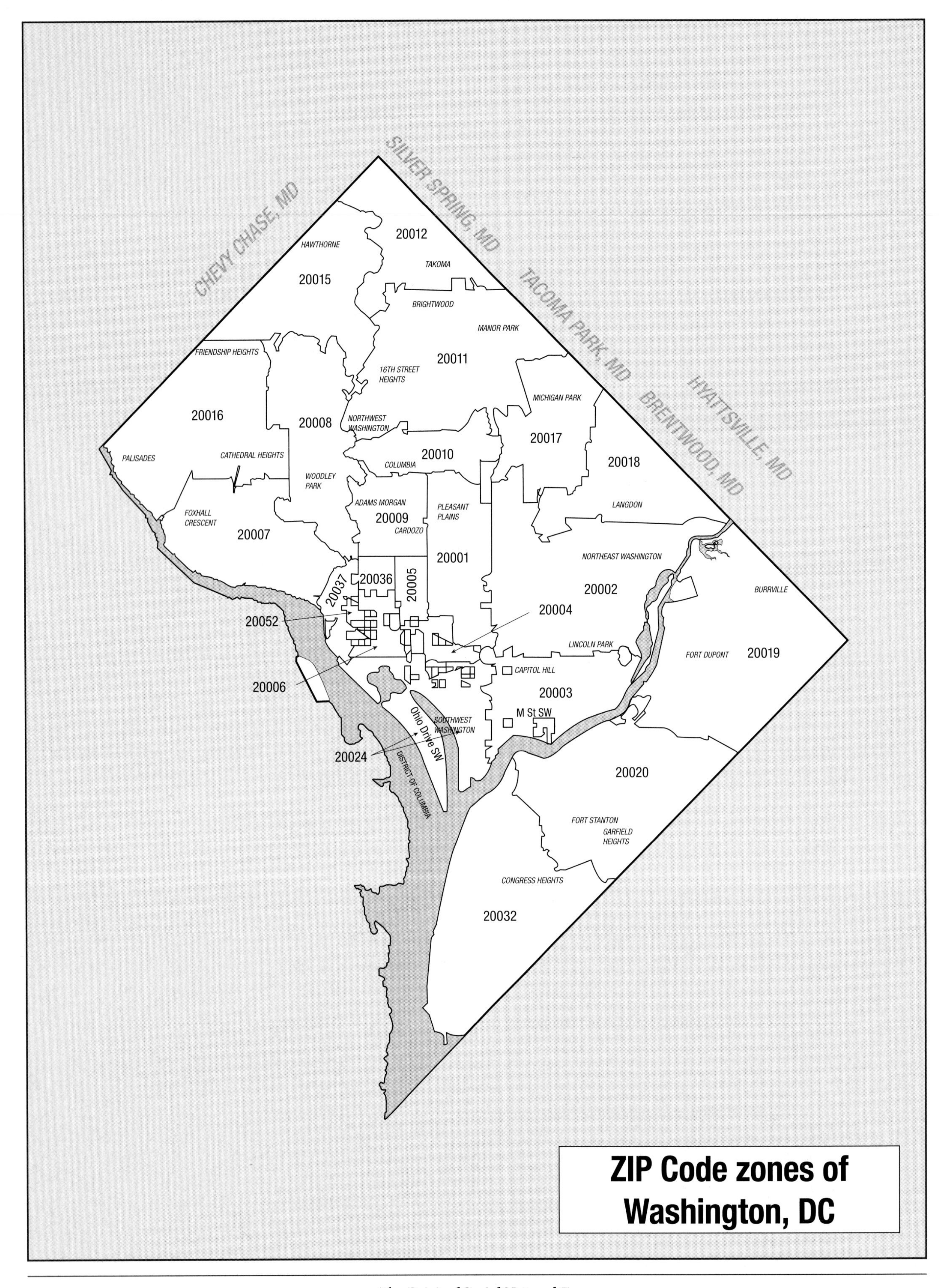

ZIP Code zones of Washington, DC

ALABAMA

Alexander City............ 35010......... Sizemore MR & MRS James M JR
Anniston.................... 36207......... Howell LTC (RET) & MRS Charles S
Auburn....................... 36830......... Raines MR & MRS Victor K
Bay Minette............... 36507......... Van Antwerp MR & MRS Thomas B
Birmingham............... 35209......... Reque MISS Susan B
Birmingham............... 35209......... Smith MR & MRS Lathrop W 3D
Birmingham............... 35209......... Walters MR & MRS D Matthew JR
Birmingham............... 35213......... Barnett MR & MRS Michael F JR
Birmingham............... 35213......... Boehme MR & MRS Robert A
Birmingham............... 35213......... Boulware MR & MRS Thomas M III
Birmingham............... 35213......... Davis MR & MRS Scott D
Birmingham............... 35213......... Driscoll MR & MRS David M
Birmingham............... 35213......... Fairley MRS James Vardaman
Birmingham............... 35213......... Featheringill MRS William W
Birmingham............... 35213......... Flowers MR & MRS Samuel R
Birmingham............... 35213......... Hill MRS S Richardson JR
Birmingham............... 35213......... Karpeles MRS Leo M JR
Birmingham............... 35213......... Livingston MR & MRS James A 3D
Birmingham............... 35213......... Livingston MRS James A JR
Birmingham............... 35213......... Mellen MR & MRS Henry L 3D
Birmingham............... 35213......... Pharo MR & MRS Andrew B E
Birmingham............... 35213......... Ramsay MR & MRS Erskine II
Birmingham............... 35213......... Randolph MR & MRS Richard R III
Birmingham............... 35213......... Randolph MR & MRS Richard R IV
Birmingham............... 35213......... Randolph MR & MRS Ryland M
Birmingham............... 35213......... Reich MR & MRS David R
Birmingham............... 35213......... Scribner MR & MRS Charles IV
Birmingham............... 35213......... Simpson MRS Sandra S
Birmingham............... 35213......... Slaughter MR & MRS B Hanson
Birmingham............... 35213......... Smith MR & MRS Lathrop Winchester JR
Birmingham............... 35213......... St John MRS Warren Jackson
Birmingham............... 35213......... Weatherly MR & MRS Robert S JR
Birmingham............... 35213......... Wrinkle MR & MRS John N
Birmingham............... 35223......... Carmichael DR & MRS James Donald
Birmingham............... 35223......... Clayton MR & MRS Charles Trueheart JR
Birmingham............... 35223......... Collins MR & MRS Stephen G
Birmingham............... 35223......... Cooper MR & MRS N Lee
Birmingham............... 35223......... De Buys MR & MRS J Forrester 3D
Birmingham............... 35223......... DeBardeleben MR & MRS Newton H JR
Birmingham............... 35223......... Hobbs MR & MRS David W
Birmingham............... 35223......... Inskeep MR & MRS Steven R
Birmingham............... 35223......... Johnson MRS Crawford T 3D
Birmingham............... 35223......... Lineberry MR & MRS William D
Birmingham............... 35223......... Lynn MR George Gambrill
Birmingham............... 35223......... Marks MR & MRS C Caldwell
Birmingham............... 35223......... Rhett MR & MRS W Warren B
Birmingham............... 35223......... Shepherd MR & MRS Everett JR
Birmingham............... 35223......... Straus MR & MRS Michael S
Birmingham............... 35223......... Tilson REV & MRS Martin Robert
Birmingham............... 35223......... Vowell MR & MRS J Scott
Birmingham............... 35242......... Brown MRS Sally P
Birmingham............... 35242......... Corts DR & MRS Thomas E
Birmingham............... 35242......... Farquhar MR & MRS William E JR
Birmingham............... 35242......... Goozée MR & MRS Stevan K
Birmingham............... 35242......... Lee MR & MRS John R
Birmingham............... 35242......... Marvin MR & MRS Timothy S
Birmingham............... 35243......... Carmichael MR & MRS Beatty P
Birmingham............... 35243......... Erdreich MR & MRS Stanley M JR
Birmingham............... 35243......... Massey MRS Richard W JR
Birmingham............... 35243......... Naughton MR & MRS Albert S
Birmingham............... 35243......... Trimmier MR & MRS C Stephen
Birmingham............... 35243......... Vaughan DR & MRS William P
Birmingham............... 35244......... Moore MR & MRS S Harbaugh III
Chapman.................... 36015......... McGowin MRS Norman Floyd JR
Chapman.................... 36015......... Miller MR & MRS James Rumrill 3D
Daphne...................... 36526......... Peterson MR John H
Decatur...................... 35601......... Peeples MR Josef C
Eufaula...................... 36027......... Wise MR John S JR
Fairhope.................... 36532......... Beresford MR & MRS Peter G
Fairhope.................... 36532......... De Masi HON Piero & Whiting MRS Sharrilyn A
Fairhope.................... 36532......... Payson MR Parker L
Fairhope.................... 36532......... Poillon MRS Arthur J
Gadsden.................... 35901......... Ryle MR & MRS John M
Haleyville.................. 35565......... McDougal MR & MRS Brent P
Hazel Green.............. 35750......... Coberly CAPT (RET) Daniel L
Huntsville.................. 35801......... Christian MR & MRS Donald L JR
Huntsville.................. 35816......... Holland DR & MRS Lawrence R
Huntsville.................. 35824......... Lucas MR & MRS Richard H JR
Mobile........................ 36601......... Snider MR & MRS Ronald A
Mobile........................ 36602......... Edington MR & MRS Robert Sherard
Mobile........................ 36604......... Klotz MR & MRS John W
Mobile........................ 36604......... Sanders MR & MRS David L
Mobile........................ 36605......... Whiddon DR & MRS Frederick P
Mobile........................ 36606......... McPhillips MR & MRS J Manning
Mobile........................ 36607......... Cooper MR & MRS David J
Mobile........................ 36607......... Leland MR & MRS Thomas Mikell JR
Mobile........................ 36607......... McGehee MR & MRS Thomas C
Mobile........................ 36607......... McGowin MRS Nicholas S
Mobile........................ 36607......... Smith MR & MRS James Dale
Mobile........................ 36608......... Hardie MR & MRS William H JR
Mobile........................ 36608......... Hayes MR & MRS J Walter
Mobile........................ 36608......... Horst MR & MRS Jesse B
Mobile........................ 36608......... Ladd MR & MRS G Russell 3D
Mobile........................ 36608......... Rutherford DR & MRS Charles L JR
Mobile........................ 36608......... Smith MR & MRS T Gunter
Mobile........................ 36608......... Underwood MR & MRS Walter A
Mobile........................ 36609......... Brock MR & MRS G Porter JR
Mobile........................ 36633......... Cooper MR Angus R 2D
Montgomery.............. 36105......... Johnson MR & MRS William H III
Montgomery.............. 36106......... Benkwith DR & MRS Sanders M
Montgomery.............. 36106......... Dorrough MR & MRS Richard H
Montgomery.............. 36106......... Engelhardt DR & MRS M Bonner
Montgomery.............. 36106......... Griffen MR Thomas K
Montgomery.............. 36106......... Hill MR & MRS William I 2D
Montgomery.............. 36106......... Hubbard MR & MRS Charles C
Montgomery.............. 36106......... Jackson MRS Douglass G
Montgomery.............. 36106......... Jordan MR & MRS George E
Montgomery.............. 36106......... May DR & MRS (DR) Stuart T 3D
Montgomery.............. 36106......... McPhillips MR & MRS Julian L JR
Montgomery.............. 36106......... Miles MR & MRS Paul W
Montgomery.............. 36106......... Patton MR & MRS Stuart T
Montgomery.............. 36106......... Reid MR & MRS Bruce S
Montgomery.............. 36106......... Reynolds MRS J Donald
Montgomery.............. 36106......... Rinehart MR & MRS Edmon L
Montgomery.............. 36106......... Rinehart MR & MRS Robert B
Montgomery.............. 36106......... Schrier DR & MRS Michael D
Montgomery.............. 36106......... Smith MR & MRS H Houghton
Montgomery.............. 36106......... Westcott MR & MRS John A JR
Montgomery.............. 36106......... Wood MRS George M JR
Montgomery.............. 36107......... Gant MR William Eugene 3D
Montgomery.............. 36109......... Nachman MR & MRS M Roland JR
Montgomery.............. 36111......... Amberg MR & MRS Richard H JR
Montgomery.............. 36111......... Babcock MR & MRS Charles D
Montgomery.............. 36111......... Brightwell MR & MRS Charles Pope III
Montgomery.............. 36111......... Eskridge MR & MRS William I
Montgomery.............. 36111......... Haigler MR & MRS Charles B III
Montgomery.............. 36111......... Haigler MRS Charles Brightman JR
Montgomery.............. 36111......... Hill MR & MRS T Bowen 3D
Montgomery.............. 36111......... Hobbs MRS Truman McG
Montgomery.............. 36111......... Horner MRS C Scudday

To nominate a candidate for the Social Register Association, please email: SRCommittee@thesocialregister.org

Montgomery, AL—Phoenix, AZ

Montgomery	36111	Jones DR & MRS John Allen 3D
Montgomery	36111	Kyser MR & MRS E Kyle JR
Montgomery	36111	Kyser MR & MRS Emery K
Montgomery	36111	Lancaster MR W Lloyd JR
Montgomery	36111	Lawson MR & MRS Thomas S JR
Montgomery	36111	McCall MRS Doy Leale JR
Montgomery	36111	Rawlings MR & MRS Phillip O
Montgomery	36111	Reese MR & MRS Pickett R
Montgomery	36111	Rice MR & MRS L Rushton
Montgomery	36111	Schloss MR & MRS B Stephen
Montgomery	36111	Schloss MRS Samuel L
Montgomery	36111	Sellers MR & MRS William B
Montgomery	36111	Torbert MR & MRS Clement C 3D
Montgomery	36111	Weiss MR & MRS John Ward
Montgomery	36116	Duggar DR & MRS Roger S
Montgomery	36116	Pickett MRS George B JR
Montgomery	36116	Trotman MR John McN SR
Montgomery	36117	Johnson MR Robert C JR
Montgomery	36117	Lott MR & MRS John Benjamin
Mountain Brook	35213	Cooper MR & MRS Robert E
Mountain Brook	35213	Cox MR & MRS John Edward
Mountain Brook	35213	Shaw MR & MRS George L
Mountain Brook	35213	Starling MR & MRS Marion Jefferson 3D
Mountain Brook	35216	Gregg MR & MRS Timothy W
Mountain Brook	35223	Bethea MR & MRS Edward P
Mountain Brook	35223	Goings MR & MRS Harold H
Mountain Brook	35223	Long MR & MRS Thad G
Mountain Brook	35223	Lynn MR Henry S JR
Mountain Brook	35223	Slaughter MR & MRS William M
Mt Brook	35223	Selfe MRS Edward M
Opelika	36801	Torbert MR & MRS Clement C JR
Pelham	35124	Griffin MR & MRS James H
Pike Road	36064	Cook DR & MRS William Jesse JR
Pike Road	36064	Schloss MR & MRS S Adam
Point Clear	36564	Hearin MISS Ann B
Point Clear	36564	Speir MRS (DR) Betty Ruth
Point Clear	36564	Thompson MR & MRS Terrence J JR
Point Clear	36564	Zieman MR & MRS Thomas T JR
Ramer	36069	Napier MRS John H III
Scottsboro	35768	Cannon MR & MRS Henry B JR
Spanish Fort	36527	Peterson MR & MRS Thomas B
Tuscaloosa	35401	Wolfe MR & MRS Richard P
Tuscaloosa	35405	Thomas DR James Henry
Tuscaloosa	35405	Wanstall MRS Robert E
Tuscaloosa	35406	Cook MRS Camille W
Tuscaloosa	35406	Nolan MR & MRS Robert C JR
Tuscaloosa	35406	Shaw MR & MRS Robert H JR
Tuscaloosa	36401	Rand DR & MRS (DR) Richard A
Vestavia Hills	35216	Gant MR & MRS Brooks Hammett

ALASKA

Anchorage	99501	Taylor MR Kneeland L
Anchorage	99501	Treadwell MR Louis Mead 2D
Anchorage	99502	Spencer DR & MRS Upshur M
Anchorage	99507	Ellsworth MR & MRS Kevin D
Anchorage	99508	Jordan MR & MRS Nicholas A
Anchorage	99515	Dreyer MRS Frank A
Ester	99725	Tiffany MR & MRS Henry D IV
Fairbanks	99709	Harbison MR & MRS Frederick H 2D
Girdwood	99587	Scott MR & MRS G Gordon
Homer	99603	Avant MR Grady M
Talkeetna	99676	Perkins MRS Grete L

ARIZONA

Amado	85645	Oswald MRS Frank G 3D
Buckeye	85396	Bradley MR & MRS Robert L JR
Carefree	85377	Renwick MR George W
Casa Grande	85122	Sugden MR & MRS Dennis M
Eagar	85925	Knox MR & MRS Andrew S
Flagstaff	86004	Beckley MR & MRS David C
Flagstaff	86004	Wainwright MR Peter S
Fountain Hills	85269	Redfield MRS Robert Latimer III
Green Valley	85614	Hillard MRS George O JR
Green Valley	85622	Haight MR & MRS George I II
Marana	85658	Lesher MR Stephen H
Munds Park	86017	Genrich MR & MRS Timothy W
Oro Valley	85737	Hellyer MR John T
Oro Valley	85755	Canton MR & MRS Anthony M
Oro Valley	85755	Chulick MR & MRS John J
Paradise Valley	85253	Bidwill MR & MRS William V JR
Paradise Valley	85253	Brosnahan MS Michele T
Paradise Valley	85253	Cluxton MR & MRS Harley E III
Paradise Valley	85253	Conklin MRS Samuel E Egerton
Paradise Valley	85253	Day MR & MRS John F
Paradise Valley	85253	Dorrance MR & MRS Bennett
Paradise Valley	85253	Firestone MR & MRS Nicholas S
Paradise Valley	85253	Firestone MRS Peter S
Paradise Valley	85253	Glascock MR & MRS Bonsal H
Paradise Valley	85253	Goodyear MR & MRS Frank H JR
Paradise Valley	85253	Hildebrandt MR David D
Paradise Valley	85253	Joaquim MR & MRS Richard Ralph
Paradise Valley	85253	Kuhle MR & MRS Richard J JR
Paradise Valley	85253	Lau DR & MRS Frederick T 2D
Paradise Valley	85253	Lenhardt MR & MRS David K
Paradise Valley	85253	Leslie MRS William M JR
Paradise Valley	85253	Lindsley MR & MRS Michael J
Paradise Valley	85253	Mathews MRS Robert F
Paradise Valley	85253	Mitten MR & MRS Roger C
Paradise Valley	85253	Oliphant MR & MRS Robert T
Paradise Valley	85253	Pakis MR & MRS Frederick M
Paradise Valley	85253	Perez-Vargas MR & MRS Antonio
Paradise Valley	85253	Pike MR Lawrence V & Bidwill MS Nicole L
Paradise Valley	85253	Reyno MR & MRS John E
Paradise Valley	85253	Rhoads MR & MRS Douglas C
Paradise Valley	85253	Salem MR & MRS Marc J
Paradise Valley	85253	Shields MR & MRS Charles W
Paradise Valley	85253	Shultz MS Susan
Paradise Valley	85253	Symington MR & MRS J Fife IV
Paradise Valley	85253	Sypher MRS (DR) Eleanor K
Paradise Valley	85253	Vanier MR & MRS Jay D
Paradise Valley	85253	Weil MR & MRS Louis A 3D
Paradise Valley	85253	Wick MRS Henry C III
Paradise Valley	85253	Winssinger HON Reginald A H & Armstrong-Winssinger MS Leila L M
Paradise Valley	85253	Wray MS Gay F
Patagonia	85624	Treherne-Thomas MRS Virginia
Pearce	85625	Jenkins MR Jonathan W
Phoenix	85001	Bidwill MR & MRS Patrick C
Phoenix	85004	Lentz MR Martin M
Phoenix	85012	Fenzl MR & MRS Terry E
Phoenix	85012	Righi DR & MRS David F
Phoenix	85012	Sexson MR & MRS Timothy J
Phoenix	85013	Cummings MR F Ramsdell
Phoenix	85013	de Blank MR & MRS Paul M B
Phoenix	85013	Scott MR & MRS Stephen H JR
Phoenix	85013	Spellman MR & MRS James Whitney
Phoenix	85014	Kahus MR & MRS Sean C
Phoenix	85014	Roman MR & MRS Stephen H

Phoenix, AZ—Tucson, AZ

Phoenix .... 85014 .... Savage MR & MRS Stephen M
Phoenix .... 85014 .... Thomas MR & MRS Jared E 2D
Phoenix .... 85014 .... Zacharias MR & MRS David L
Phoenix .... 85016 .... Dickinson MR & MRS Thomas W
Phoenix .... 85016 .... Fels COL & MRS John V
Phoenix .... 85016 .... Korrick MR & MRS Edgar L
Phoenix .... 85016 .... Lynch MR & MRS Richard E
Phoenix .... 85016 .... MacLean MR & MRS Charles C III
Phoenix .... 85016 .... Wendt MR & MRS Albert G
Phoenix .... 85018 .... Clements MR & MRS William W
Phoenix .... 85018 .... Clements MR John R
Phoenix .... 85018 .... Coppins MR & MRS J Burge
Phoenix .... 85018 .... Cronin MR Peter & Thiele MS Cynthia
Phoenix .... 85018 .... de Marneffe DR Peter L
Phoenix .... 85018 .... de Marneffe MRS Katrin B
Phoenix .... 85018 .... Finch MR & MRS Charles A
Phoenix .... 85018 .... Green MR & MRS Michael Preston
Phoenix .... 85018 .... Laflin MRS Louis E 3D
Phoenix .... 85018 .... Lewis MR Orme JR
Phoenix .... 85018 .... Oppedahl MRS Gillian C
Phoenix .... 85018 .... Schiffner MR & MRS Charles R
Phoenix .... 85018 .... Thorne MRS Niblack
Phoenix .... 85018 .... Wesley MR & MRS Timothy A
Phoenix .... 85018 .... White MR & MRS Edward A
Phoenix .... 85018 .... White MR & MRS Somers H
Phoenix .... 85020 .... Toberman MRS Beatrice B
Phoenix .... 85021 .... Fournier MRS Donald F
Phoenix .... 85021 .... Lemon MR & MRS L Gene
Phoenix .... 85021 .... Tait MR & MRS Thomas
Phoenix .... 85021 .... Tait MR & MRS William E
Phoenix .... 85021 .... Van Der Toorn MR Eric W
Phoenix .... 85023 .... Coghill MR & MRS W Thomas JR
Phoenix .... 85023 .... McKellar MRS Donald McC
Phoenix .... 85024 .... Carpenter MR & MRS Peter A
Phoenix .... 85024 .... McLeod MRS Norman C JR
Phoenix .... 85028 .... Fesler MRS Deborah A
Phoenix .... 85028 .... Stobs MRS Constance W
Phoenix .... 85028 .... Vietor REV & MRS Oliver R
Phoenix .... 85042 .... Hume MR Douglas A
Phoenix .... 85048 .... Yeager MR & MRS Raymond H JR
Phoenix .... 85050 .... Sumner MR & MRS William O
Phoenix .... 85064 .... Scott MR & MRS Stephen H
Prescott .... 86303 .... Nicholson MR & MRS Frederic A
Prescott Valley .... 86314 .... Hamilton MR David B
Scottsdale .... 85250 .... Culley MR & MRS Peter M
Scottsdale .... 85250 .... Russell MR & MRS Mark S
Scottsdale .... 85250 .... Wolfenden MRS John T
Scottsdale .... 85251 .... Agar MRS J H Michael
Scottsdale .... 85251 .... Livermore MR Robert S JR
Scottsdale .... 85251 .... Magoun MRS William C B
Scottsdale .... 85251 .... Martin MR & MRS R David
Scottsdale .... 85251 .... McKellar MR & MRS Winston P
Scottsdale .... 85251 .... Mellor MRS Mary-Audrey W
Scottsdale .... 85251 .... Rudd MRS Eldon
Scottsdale .... 85252 .... Duff MR & MRS Richard M JR
Scottsdale .... 85253 .... Donahoe MR & MRS Daniel J 3D
Scottsdale .... 85253 .... Theobald MR & MRS John C 2D
Scottsdale .... 85253 .... Trevor MRS Michele
Scottsdale .... 85254 .... Adams MR & MRS Charles A
Scottsdale .... 85254 .... Coles MR William A
Scottsdale .... 85254 .... Hughes MRS Erville W
Scottsdale .... 85254 .... Taylor MR & MRS W Stuart E
Scottsdale .... 85254 .... Wright MRS Sylvia A
Scottsdale .... 85255 .... Damon MR & MRS Robert A
Scottsdale .... 85255 .... Deupree MRS Richard R JR
Scottsdale .... 85255 .... Emerson MR & MRS Carter W
Scottsdale .... 85255 .... Gallún MRS Marjorie M
Scottsdale .... 85255 .... Henry MRS Samuel J JR
Scottsdale .... 85255 .... Metcalf MR Robert A
Scottsdale .... 85255 .... Wick MR & MRS Jared K
Scottsdale .... 85257 .... McClintic MR & MRS David W
Scottsdale .... 85258 .... Bentley MRS Leon F
Scottsdale .... 85258 .... Coffin MR Christopher K
Scottsdale .... 85258 .... Hildebrandt MRS Donald H
Scottsdale .... 85258 .... McCann MRS Donald Fraser
Scottsdale .... 85258 .... Stubbs MR & MRS Paul D
Scottsdale .... 85259 .... Murphy MR & MRS James R
Scottsdale .... 85260 .... Alexander MR & MRS Jason B
Scottsdale .... 85260 .... Treaccar MR & MRS Thomas H
Scottsdale .... 85260 .... Wilson MR & MRS John A
Scottsdale .... 85262 .... Dorr MR & MRS Williams P
Scottsdale .... 85262 .... Gray MRS Walter F
Scottsdale .... 85262 .... Lundy MR & MRS A Lee JR
Scottsdale .... 85262 .... Seeley MR & MRS James H JR
Scottsdale .... 85262 .... Verhamme MR & MRS Mark T
Scottsdale .... 85266 .... Carpenter MR Peter Rockefeller
Scottsdale .... 85266 .... Huber MR & MRS John Y IV
Scottsdale .... 85266 .... Peabody MR & MRS Endicott JR
Scottsdale .... 85267 .... Maulsby MR Allen F
Sedona .... 86336 .... Phillips MR Bradford L
Show Low .... 85901 .... Flail MR & MRS Charles M
Sierra Vista .... 85650 .... Cartwright MRS John W P
Sierra Vista .... 85650 .... Sutro MR & MRS Livingston D
Sonoita .... 85637 .... Mills MRS Marcey D
Surprise .... 85387 .... Walsh MR Richard K & Everett MS Sally
Tempe .... 85281 .... Lewis MR & MRS Joseph O
Tempe .... 85282 .... Trump MS Tacy S
Tempe .... 85284 .... Bidwill MR & MRS William V
Tubac .... 85646 .... Warren MR & MRS H Robert
Tucson .... 85704 .... Clark MS A Valer
Tucson .... 85704 .... Curry MRS Robert W
Tucson .... 85704 .... Houston DR & MRS William R M
Tucson .... 85704 .... McCaleb MR & MRS B Franklin JR
Tucson .... 85710 .... Shivers MR & MRS Samuel R 3D
Tucson .... 85715 .... Amos MR & MRS George H 3D
Tucson .... 85715 .... Amos MR & MRS Philip R
Tucson .... 85715 .... Brown MR & MRS Archibald M JR
Tucson .... 85715 .... Denny MRS Robert O
Tucson .... 85715 .... Dunn MISS Maryann W
Tucson .... 85715 .... Feulner MR & MRS George J
Tucson .... 85715 .... Hitchcock MS Peggy Mellon
Tucson .... 85715 .... Loring MRS Thacher
Tucson .... 85715 .... Shelby MR & MRS Thomas W
Tucson .... 85715 .... Studwell MR & MRS James R
Tucson .... 85715 .... Sundt MRS H Wilson
Tucson .... 85715 .... Terry DR & MRS Stephen
Tucson .... 85715 .... Wenaas MRS John E J
Tucson .... 85716 .... Amos MRS George H JR
Tucson .... 85716 .... Hallowell MR & MRS Roger H
Tucson .... 85716 .... Morales MR & MRS Michael E
Tucson .... 85716 .... Murphy MR & MRS Lewis C
Tucson .... 85716 .... Nelson MS Wendy
Tucson .... 85716 .... Odell MR & MRS Devin R
Tucson .... 85716 .... Sawyer MR S Prentiss
Tucson .... 85716 .... Sugiyama MR & MRS Alexandre B
Tucson .... 85718 .... Bell MRS G Graham
Tucson .... 85718 .... Dye MRS Anna-Marie
Tucson .... 85718 .... Frelinghuysen MR & MRS Frederick
Tucson .... 85718 .... Hard MR & MRS Michael W
Tucson .... 85718 .... Heine DR & MRS M Wayne
Tucson .... 85718 .... Holland MR & MRS Hudson JR
Tucson .... 85718 .... Luebbermann MR & MRS Henri A JR

Tucson, AZ—Belvedere, CA

Tucson 85718 Olyphant MR & MRS J V Bevan
Tucson 85718 Patterson MR & MRS Michael E
Tucson 85718 Patton MR & MRS James R JR
Tucson 85718 Pearson MR Theodore JR & Simbari DR Russell D
Tucson 85718 Pell MRS Herbert C 3D
Tucson 85718 Pew MR & MRS Thomas W III
Tucson 85718 Pew MR & MRS Thomas W JR
Tucson 85718 Scaife MR Curtis S
Tucson 85718 Sullivan MR & MRS Mark 3D
Tucson 85718 Weeks MR Ralph E & Harris MS Margherita Gale
Tucson 85719 Kinerk MR & MRS Burton J
Tucson 85719 Walker MRS Robert C JR
Tucson 85728 Lloyd MR John R
Tucson 85737 Bell MR & MRS James B
Tucson 85737 McClintock MR & MRS Edward A 3D
Tucson 85737 Tilton MR & MRS Webster III
Tucson 85739 Macy MR & MRS John H D JR
Tucson 85739 O'Shaughnessy MRS Lynn
Tucson 85743 Schmitz MR & MRS Richard D
Tucson 85743 Severson MR & MRS Edward E
Tucson 85745 Ely MS Kimberly D
Tucson 85747 Hodge MRS Andrew W
Tucson 85748 Schaefer DR & MRS (DR) John P
Tucson 85748 Voevodsky MR & MRS Peter
Tucson 85749 Rose MRS R Peter
Tucson 85749 Sutterley MRS Edmund L
Tucson 85750 Blacutt MR & MRS Sergio X
Tucson 85750 Demas DR & MRS Christopher P
Tucson 85750 Kamilli MR & MRS Robert J
Tucson 85750 Litsas MRS Ann P
Tucson 85750 Mitchell DR & MRS John Wright
Tucson 85750 Park MR & MRS David E JR
Tucson 85750 Smith MR & MRS Gerald K
Tucson 85750 Treadwell MRS George H JR
Tucson 85751 Franklin MR & MRS John O
Tucson 85751 Smallhouse MR & MRS David C
Tucson 85756 Connell MR & MRS Michael J
Vail 85641 Gibson MR & MRS Nicholas J
Wickenburg 85358 Petersen MR & MRS Erroll M
Wickenburg 85390 Armour MR & MRS A Watson 4TH
Wickenburg 85390 Stephens MR F Scott

ARKANSAS

El Dorado 71730 Ellzey MR & MRS Robert Theron JR
Eureka Springs 72632 Adamson MR Gary
Forrest City 72335 McCollum MR & MRS T Bonner
Harrison 72601 Churchill MRS W Philip
Hot Springs 71901 Tognazzini MRS Richard E
Hot Springs 71901 White MR & MRS David N JR
Hot Springs Village 71909 Ashley MR & MRS Edgar C
Little Rock 72201 Dillard MR & MRS William T 2D
Little Rock 72202 Wolfe MRS Jane Lee
Little Rock 72207 Dickinson MR & MRS Haskell L 2D
Little Rock 72207 Flake MR & MRS John J
Little Rock 72207 Ford MR & MRS Joe T
Little Rock 72207 Hurst MR & MRS Howard C
Little Rock 72207 Kumpuris DR & MRS Andrew G
Little Rock 72207 Levy MR & MRS Eugene P
Little Rock 72207 Miller MR & MRS Patrick D
Little Rock 72207 Moody JUDGE & MRS James Maxwell
Little Rock 72207 Norton DR & MRS George A
Little Rock 72207 Van Ness MR & MRS Lewis W
Little Rock 72211 Kelley MR & MRS Henry C JR
Little Rock 72211 Williamson DR & MRS Adrian 3D
Little Rock 72212 Gadberry MR & MRS James F
Little Rock 72223 McNulty MR & MRS T Stanley JR
Little Rock 72227 Brown JUDGE & MRS Robert L
Magnolia 71753 Partee MR & MRS W Calhoun JR
Magnolia 71753 Weiser MR & MRS Christian W
Tuckerman 72473 Farrar MRS Clayton A
Tuckerman 72473 Van Wyck MR & MRS F Bronson

CALIFORNIA

Agoura Hills 91301 Robinson MR & MRS Sanger P II
Alameda 94501 Bertozzi MRS Sheila K
Alameda 94501 Bowles MR & MRS Henry M JR
Alameda 94501 Jobson MR J Roger
Alameda 94501 Miller MR & MRS Victor B
Alameda 94501 Pedley MR Eric A
Alameda 94501 Stearns MR & MRS J Anthony
Alameda 94501 Stearns MRS John P
Alameda 94501 Youmans MR & MRS John Scott
Alamo 94507 Bowring MR & MRS Douglas B
Alamo 94507 Herron MR & MRS Ronald K
Alamo 94507 Logan MR & MRS Thomas D
Alamo 94507 Van Voorhees MR & MRS Tracy J
Albany 94706 Weems MISS (DR) Mathilde S
Alhambra 91802 Sateriale MR Robin A
Altadena 91001 Howe MR Parker S & Sheptock MR John J Jr
Altadena 91001 Hunter MR & MRS John L
Altadena 91001 Logan MR & MRS Francis D
Altadena 91001 Odell MRS I Gordon
Altadena 91001 Poe MR & MRS E Allan IV
Altadena 91001 Rosenfeld MR & MRS Michael A
American Canyon 94589 Maffey MR & MRS Rexford A JR
Aptos 95003 Beckett MR William J
Aptos 95003 Darling MR Peter & Gummere MS Elizabeth A
Aptos 95003 Gummere MR & MRS William 3D
Aptos 95003 Hanchett MRS Lewis E
Aptos 95003 Pervere MR Peter F
Aptos 95003 Tipping MR & MRS Bradley J
Aptos 95003 Tripp MR Stephen R 3d
Atherton 94025 Eddy MR & MRS Selwyn 2D
Atherton 94027 Dennehy MISS (DR) Virginia
Atherton 94027 Kelleher MR & MRS Warren F
Atherton 94027 Kubal MR & MRS Larry A
Atherton 94027 Little MR & MRS Gary R
Atherton 94027 Magruder MR & MRS (DR) Roy M
Atherton 94027 O'Reilly MRS Katharine W
Atherton 94027 Patterson MR & MRS Robert E
Atherton 94027 Pyne MR & MRS Russell B
Atherton 94027 Roberts MR & MRS George R
Atherton 94027 Sickel MR & MRS Edward T IV
Atherton 94027 Taft MR & MRS David D
Atherton 94027 Wollenberg MR David A
Bakersfield 93301 Meek MR & MRS George H
Bakersfield 93306 Burley REV Clarence A III
Bakersfield 93313 Mumford MR & MRS Lawrence C
Bakersfield 93386 Nickel MR & MRS James L
Bakersfield 93386 Nickel MRS George W JR
Balboa Island 92662 Allan MR & MRS David L
Ballard 93463 Walker MR & MRS David L
Bel Air 90007 Fairchild MRS (DR) Sherman Mills
Bel Air 90077 Smith MR Whitney Sudler
Bel Tiburon 94920 Helfet MR & MRS Anthony B
Bel Tiburon 94920 Merrill MR & MRS John O
Belmont 94002 Peña MRS Katherine D
Belvedere 94920 Beavers MR Carl D JR & Mujica-Beavers MRS Azita
Belvedere 94920 Cobb MR & MRS David A
Belvedere 94920 Di Gangi MS Marguerite T

Belvedere	94920	Draganic MRS Penelope
Belvedere	94920	Hachman MR & MRS Timothy D M
Belvedere	94920	Hofmann MR & MRS John R JR
Belvedere	94920	Kimball MRS William Rice
Belvedere	94920	Mitchell MRS Charles S
Belvedere	94920	Sann MR & MRS Ronald N
Belvedere	94920	Wheeler MRS Faith
Belvedere Tiburon	94920	Church MS Daphne C
Belvedere Tiburon	94920	Dorn DR & MRS Gregory H
Belvedere Tiburon	94920	Lawrence MR William C
Belvedere Tiburon	94920	Lowell MR & MRS Frederick K
Belvedere Tiburon	94920	McCormick MR & MRS Christopher R
Belvedere Tiburon	94920	Reich MR & MRS Marc La Fore
Berkeley	94703	Dewey MISS Frances W
Berkeley	94703	Huddleston MR John R
Berkeley	94704	Robbins MR & MRS William C 3D
Berkeley	94705	Edwards MS Daphne H
Berkeley	94705	McBride MR John G JR
Berkeley	94705	Nash MS Laurie Le N
Berkeley	94705	Peyton MR & MRS Bernard 3D
Berkeley	94705	Swan MR & MRS Stephen P
Berkeley	94706	Day MR Jeffrey F
Berkeley	94707	Ashbey MS Anne A
Berkeley	94707	Barth MRS Gunther P
Berkeley	94707	Cooper MRS William S 3D
Berkeley	94707	Lovell MRS Markle
Berkeley	94707	Taylor MR Samuel L & Fraser MS Maria C
Berkeley	94708	Foster DR Howard C
Berkeley	94708	Frantz MR & MRS Steven J
Berkeley	94709	Gordon DR & MRS Bertram M
Berkeley	94709	Vosburgh MR Peter G
Berkeley	94710	White MISS Mary B
Beverly Hills	90210	Blakely MR James E III
Beverly Hills	90210	Carrington COL (RET) & MRS George W
Beverly Hills	90210	Fentress MR Robert W
Beverly Hills	90210	Kersey MR James W JR
Beverly Hills	90210	Lapin MR & MRS David A
Beverly Hills	90211	Magee MR David B JR
Beverly Hills	90212	Christopher MS Lori A
Beverly Hills	90212	Murray MR & MRS Palmer N
Beverly Hills	90212	Nouri MR Michael D
Big Sur	93920	Cluett MR & MRS John S
Bishop	93515	Reid MR Alexander B
Bolinas	92924	Dibblee MR & MRS Thomas L
Bolinas	94924	Newcomb MRS J Stephen
Bonita	91902	Crossman MR & MRS John G
Borrego Springs	92004	Granbery MS Joya Weld
Boulder Creek	95006	Mangine MR & MRS Joseph C
Buellton	93427	Weed MR & MRS Arthur H
Burbank	91505	Solner HON & MRS Michael C
Burlingame	94010	Butterworth MR & MRS G Forrest 4TH
Burlingame	94010	Carey MR & MRS W Ward JR
Burlingame	94010	Dunne MR & MRS Peter F 3D
Burlingame	94010	Ferris MR & MRS Peter T
Burlingame	94010	Fick MR & MRS Bradley Borel
Burlingame	94010	Henderson MR & MRS Charles C
Burlingame	94010	Kromelow MR & MRS Justin M
Burlingame	94010	Lovell MR Jonathan H
Burlingame	94010	Lowdon MR & MRS Todd H
Burlingame	94010	Magowan MR & MRS Thomas C
Burlingame	94010	Maher MR & MRS J Sheppard
Burlingame	94010	Moore MR & MRS Mark A
Burlingame	94010	Reeth MR & MRS Timothy J P
Burlingame	94010	Robinette MR & MRS G Todd
Burlingame	94010	Wachhorst MR & MRS Brian G
Burlingame	94011	Caruso MR & MRS Jake A
Burlingame	94011	Roman MR Mafeo M
Calistoga	94515	Andriano-Moore CDR & MRS Richard
Calistoga	94515	Gansa MR & MRS Andrew N vonS
Calistoga	94515	Houghton MR & MRS James VanG
Calistoga	94515	Livermore MISS Caroline S
Calistoga	94515	McCoy MR Peter A
Calistoga	94515	Spencer MR Samuel 3D
Camarillo	93010	Baehr MR & MRS M R E Theodore
Camarillo	93010	Baehr MR & MRS Robert G
Camarillo	93012	Carroll MR & MRS Jeremy J
Cameron Park	95682	Carlson MR & MRS Ronald B
Cameron Park	95682	Coolidge MISS (DR) Jennifer W
Cardiff-by-the-Sea	92007	Armstrong MS Victoria S
Carlsbad	92008	Peabody MR & MRS Alexander B
Carlsbad	92009	Clarkson MR & MRS (DR) Jeffrey D
Carlsbad	92009	Dana MR David T 3D
Carlsbad	92009	De Young MR & MRS Peter D
Carlsbad	92009	Denton MRS (DR) Clarissa R
Carlsbad	92009	Lynch MR & MRS (DR) Francis P JR
Carlsbad	92011	Sherman MR & MRS Roger F JR
Carmel	93921	Buckminster MRS W Bradley
Carmel	93921	Moore MS Jaynie Thaler
Carmel	93921	Wells MR Peter Channing
Carmel	93922	Fish MRS Stuyvesant
Carmel	93923	Bates MR & MRS David T
Carmel	93923	Bates MRS S Wilson
Carmel	93923	Clancy MRS John A
Carmel	93923	Cook MR & MRS Arthur B 2D
Carmel	93923	Hanson MR & MRS Harry A JR
Carmel	93923	Lansdowne MRS F Mackinnon
Carmel	93923	McMahon MR & MRS Bernard J 3D
Carmel	93923	McWilliams MR John P
Carmel	93923	Politzer MRS Jerome F
Carmel	93923	Read MR & MRS Mark E
Carmel	93923	Ruth MRS Thomas N
Carmel	93923	Schneider MR & MRS Edward J III
Carmel	93923	Smith MS Deborah M
Carmel	93923	Thackara MRS James J
Carmel Valley	93924	Lansdowne MR & MRS Zachary F
Carmel Valley	93924	Mattmiller MS Suzanne Bowman
Carmel-by-the-Sea	93921	Sutherland MS Maria
Carmichael	95608	Davis MRS Duncan S
Carmichael	95608	Hayes MR & MRS Henry G IV
Carmichael	95608	Smith MR & MRS Courtney P
Carnelian Bay	96140	Davis MR & MRS Duncan C
Carnelian Bay	96140	de Bragança MISS Michele
Carpinteria	93013	Conrad MRS Barnaby
Carpinteria	93013	Crimmins MR & MRS James C
Carpinteria	93013	Farrell MR & MRS W Mason
Carpinteria	93013	Meeker MR William V
Carpinteria	93013	Preston MRS Robert S III
Carpinteria	93013	Ross MISS Elizabeth
Carpinteria	93013	Scott-Paine MR Mark H
Carpinteria	93013	Seaman MR & MRS Peter S
Carpinteria	93013	Watters MS Valeska A
Carpinteria	93014	Eagle MR & MRS J Frederick 3D
Castro Valley	94546	Mathews MISS Patricia A
Castro Valley	94552	Sprague MR & MRS Alexander T
Cayucos	93430	McNellie MR & MRS Rick A
Channel Islands Beach	93035	Ball MR & MRS H Carter II
Chico	95926	Akers MR & MRS Geoffrey L
Chico	95927	English MR Robert C
Chico	95928	Ellis DR & MRS Herman
Chula Vista	91911	Kendall DR Charles H JR
Chula Vista	91915	Levan MR & MRS Mark D
Citrus Heights	95610	Broyer MR & MRS Scott W

Claremont, CA—Hillsborough, CA

Claremont	91711	Davis MRS Nathaniel
Claremont	91711	Dodds DR & MRS Zachary B
Claremont	91711	Harpole MR & MRS John C
Claremont	91711	Lewis MR & MRS Joseph W JR
Clarksburg	95612	Armour MR & MRS Philip D III
Clarksburg	95612	Chew MR & MRS Stephen R
Clayton	94517	McCoun MR Peter T
Concord	94518	Bellenie MR Neil G & Browne MS Michele A
Concord	94518	Jerome MISS S E Jane
Concord	94520	McEachran MR & MRS James T
Corona del Mar	92625	Aujaghian MR & MRS Damir
Corona del Mar	92625	Easton MR & MRS Jake III
Corona Del Mar	92625	Kendall MRS Donna Lee
Corona Del Mar	92625	Shields MR & MRS Thomas J
Corona Del Mar	92625	Woolwine MR & MRS Woodrum E
Coronado	92118	Patterson MRS Henry D 2D
Corralitos	95076	Sutton MR M Joseph
Corte Madera	94925	Andrews MRS Perkins
Corte Madera	94925	Hinckley MR & MRS Samuel H
Corte Madera	94925	O'Keefe MR & MRS Peter G
Corte Madera	94925	O'Neil MR & MRS Rory B
Corte Madera	94925	Smallhorn MR & MRS Thomas A M
Corte Madera	94925	Spurzem MR & MRS Karl R
Corte Madera	94925	Whitridge MR & MRS David P
Corte Madera	94925	Wise MISS Catherine R
Costa Mesa	92626	Bradley MR & MRS Robert M
Costa Mesa	92626	Kolanoski MR Thomas E & Clemens DR Anji Dreger
Costa Mesa	92627	Boulos MR & MRS William M
Cottonwood	96022	Devine MR & MRS Kevin J
Culver City	90230	Warner MISS Nina E
Culver City	90232	Cousineau MR & MRS Ian
Culver City	90232	Simonds MR & MRS Robert B JR
Cupertino	95014	Bernet MISS Martha L
Cupertino	95014	McComas MR Oliver P JR
Cupertino	95014	Miller MR & MRS Robert H
Cupertino	95014	Russell MR & MRS Grant E JR
Daly City	94015	Moore MR Thomas G
Danville	94506	Fulweiler MR & MRS Spencer B JR
Danville	94506	Guastucci MR & MRS Robert R
Danville	94506	Henshaw MR & MRS Guy R
Danville	94506	Wood MR & MRS W Kip
Danville	94526	Dohrmann MR Eric B
Danville	94526	Livermore MRS Robert S
Davis	95618	Gede MR & MRS Thomas F
Del Mar	92014	Mitchell MR & MRS David W
Del Mar	92014	Riblet MR & MRS Roy J 3D
Desert Hot Springs	92240	Pike MR John J JR & Bochantin MR Julius F
Diablo	94528	Mehran MR & MRS Alexander R JR
Discovery Bay	94505	Leckrone MR & MRS Daniel
Dublin	94568	Fay MR & MRS William F JR
Dublin	94568	Jenkins MR & MRS Jason L
Duncans Mills	95430	Moore DR & MRS C Bradley
Durham	95938	Ramser MR & MRS Michael P
El Cerrito	94530	Donahue MR & MRS James A
El Cerrito	94530	Zavestoski DR & MRS Stephen M
El Dorado Hills	95762	Van De Water MR Joseph C 2D
El Macero	95618	Finley MRS Milbourne S & Mowery DR Thomas M
El Macero	95618	Scarlett MISS L Landon
Emerald Hills	94062	Eggli MR & MRS John R
Emerald Hills	94062	Wilkinson MR & MRS Edward P
Encinitas	92024	Carr MR & MRS Kevin E
Encinitas	92024	Knowles DR & MRS David S
Encinitas	92024	Leonard MR Anthony N
Encinitas	92024	McGinn MR & MRS Timothy J
Encinitas	92024	Newcomer MR & MRS John W
Encinitas	92024	Villasenor MRS Andrew J
Encino	91436	Reece MR & MRS David C
Escondido	92026	Coverley MRS Edwin D
Escondido	92026	Wicka MR & MRS Brian M
Escondido	92027	Penfold MR & MRS Paul E
Escondido	92029	Hellyer MRS Edith G
Fairfax	94930	Newton MISS Meredith M
Fairfield	94533	Hartnett MR & MRS Leonard J
Fairfield	94533	Lutz MRS Kenneth C
Fairfield	94534	Villmoare MR & MRS Edwin S III
Felicity	92283	Istel MR & MRS Jacques-Andre
Felton	95018	Fernow MISS Carola B
Foster City	94404	Barney MISS Frederica S
Foster City	94404	Fuller MR & MRS Walter G
Foster City	94404	McKeon MR Denis C
Fresno	93704	Hayhurst MR & MRS L Nelson
Fresno	93711	Adams DR & MRS Michael
Fresno	93720	Wells MR & MRS Francis D
Fresno	93755	Miles MRS James A
Fullerton	92835	Fox MRS Rector K 3D
Fullerton	92835	Menetrey MR & MRS Walter R
Fullerton	92835	O'Brien MR & MRS W Gardnar
Geyserville	95441	Bowles MR Chester B JR
Geyserville	95441	Luebkeman MR David J & Hanselman MS M J
Glen Ellen	95442	Williams MS Samantha
Glen Ellen	95442	Wilson MR & MRS John C
Glendale	91201	Dillard MS Anne C
Glendale	91203	Horner MR & MRS Robert C
Glendale	91206	Effinger MR & MRS Robert T IV
Glendale	91207	Merritt MR & MRS Bruce G
Goleta	93117	Glanville MR & MRS John H
Granite Bay	95746	Boring MR & MRS Douglas D
Greenbrae	94904	Dakin MR John H & Chase MRS Diana
Greenbrae	94904	du Pont MRS Jaime H
Greenbrae	94904	Frentzel MR Herman E
Greenbrae	94904	Frentzel MRS J Titzell
Greenbrae	94904	Jenkins MRS Louisa Bradbury
Greenbrae	94904	Moore MS Daphne d'A
Greenbrae	94904	Morshead MR & MRS Jeffory S
Greenbrae	94904	Rende MR & MRS Giandomenico
Greenbrae	94904	Shuey MRS Hayden
Greenbrae	94904	Van Voorhees MRS Mary B
Greenbrae	94904	Vance MRS C Albert
Greenbrae	94904	Walsh MRS Margaret F
Greenbrae	94904	Zingg MR & MRS Peter F
Hacienda Heights	91745	West MRS C David
Healdsburg	95448	de Peyster MR & MRS George L JR
Healdsburg	95448	Keller MR & MRS James G
Healdsburg	95448	Miller MR & MRS Clay Lowell
Healdsburg	95448	Mullen MR & MRS Robert W JR
Healdsburg	95448	Palmer MRS James K
Healdsburg	95448	Somers MR & MRS George W JR
Healdsburg	95448	Somers MR & MRS John W
Healdsburg	95448	Zellerbach MRS Stephen A
Hermosa Beach	90254	Chick MR & MRS Stephen C
Hillsborough	94010	Abrahamson MR & MRS Eric S
Hillsborough	94010	Bowman MR & MRS Richard P
Hillsborough	94010	Bryan MS Suzanne E
Hillsborough	94010	Cheston MR & MRS Morris III
Hillsborough	94010	Desrosiers MR & MRS Mark E
Hillsborough	94010	Fick MR & MRS Harold A JR
Hillsborough	94010	Field MR & MRS John E SR
Hillsborough	94010	Gotcher DR Robert E L
Hillsborough	94010	Gotcher MR & MRS Peter C
Hillsborough	94010	Grau MRS Fritz H
Hillsborough	94010	Greer MR & MRS John T
Hillsborough	94010	Hampton MR & MRS Gregory J

Hillsborough	94010	Haueter MR & MRS Eric S
Hillsborough	94010	Hooker MR & MRS Peter B
Hillsborough	94010	Jackson MR & MRS Cameron M
Hillsborough	94010	Jain MR & MRS Aalok N
Hillsborough	94010	Killea MR & MRS John W
Hillsborough	94010	Kovacevich MR & MRS Todd R
Hillsborough	94010	Love MR & MRS Howard McC JR
Hillsborough	94010	MacLean MR & MRS Angus Lloyd JR
Hillsborough	94010	Magowan MR Douglas R
Hillsborough	94010	Magowan MR Merrill L
Hillsborough	94010	McCall MRS Jennifer Jordan
Hillsborough	94010	McCormick MRS Ernest O III
Hillsborough	94010	Meyer MR & MRS G Christian 3D
Hillsborough	94010	Otter MR & MRS Richard C
Hillsborough	94010	Ream MR & MRS Miller JR
Hillsborough	94010	Renshaw MRS John P
Hillsborough	94010	Roberts MR & MRS Ralston P
Hillsborough	94010	Schmidt MR & MRS Alexis C
Hillsborough	94010	Schultz MR Jackson Le R
Hillsborough	94010	Taylor MR Richard S
Hillsborough	94010	Toms MR & MRS Joseph L
Hillsborough	94010	Turnbaugh MR Jeffrey & Duff MS Elizabeth G
Hollywood	90028	Herrlinger MR David H
Huntington Beach	92646	Morgan MR & MRS Ivan J
Huntington Beach	92646	Staller MR & MRS Christian B
Huntington Beach	92648	Conrad MRS Charles JR
Ignacio	94949	Morosi MR & MRS Donald J
Indian Wells	92210	Douglas MRS Lewis W JR
Indian Wells	92210	Hooker MRS Rodman L JR
Indian Wells	92210	McAllister MR Alexander B
Indian Wells	92210	McIntyre MRS Henry L
Indian Wells	92210	Ryland MRS Judith Dubben
Indian Wells	92210	Williams MR & MRS Kenneth C
Inverness	94937	Schwartz MR & MRS Edwin J
Inverness	94937	Tennyson MR Leonard B
Inverness	94937	Worsley MR & MRS Peter F
Irvine	92602	Mokhtari MRS Sara
Irvine	92604	Thompson MRS Laura E
Irvine	92604	Vodhanel MR & MRS Frank Joseph
Irvine	92614	Flannery MISS Jean M
Irvine	92614	Hateley MR & MRS James C III
Irvine	92618	Vail MR & MRS Gregory H
Irvine	92620	Eaton MR David W
Kelseyville	95451	Cooper MRS Vallen Widmer
Kensington	94707	Clark MR & MRS Thomas C 3D
Kensington	94708	McKown MRS Pamela B
Kentfield	94904	Bull MR & MRS Donald
Kentfield	94904	Cahill MR & MRS John E JR
Kentfield	94904	Campodonico MR & MRS A Anthony
Kentfield	94904	Colwell MR & MRS David H
Kentfield	94904	Evans DR & MRS Evan C 3D
Kentfield	94904	Evans MR & MRS Andrew W
Kentfield	94904	Goldsmith MR & MRS Robert H
Kentfield	94904	Gorham MR & MRS Sidney S IV
Kentfield	94904	Hooper MR & MRS Roger F
Kentfield	94904	LaHorgue MR & MRS Michael A
Kentfield	94904	Lewis MR & MRS Edison
Kentfield	94904	Palmer MR & MRS William F
Kentfield	94904	Roenisch MRS Clinton A
Kentfield	94904	Sutro JUDGE & MRS John A JR
Kentfield	94904	Sutro MR & MRS Stephen H
Kentfield	94904	Thomas MR & MRS David L
La Canada Flintridge	91011	Kassabian MR & MRS Mark M
La Jolla	92037	Armstrong MR John S III & Naegle MS Myrna T
La Jolla	92037	Beck von Peccoz MISS Martha Morse
La Jolla	92037	Browne MR & MRS Aldis J III
La Jolla	92037	Fetter MR & MRS Thompson
La Jolla	92037	Griffith MR & MRS William T
La Jolla	92037	Heaton MR & MRS James J
La Jolla	92037	Heenan MR & MRS Warren B
La Jolla	92037	James MRS Oliver B JR
La Jolla	92037	Kellogg MR & MRS Frederick C
La Jolla	92037	McCoy MR & MRS Charles W
La Jolla	92037	Simpkins DR & MRS (DR) Charles A JR
La Jolla	92037	Williams MR & MRS Albert N
La Quinta	92253	Hay MRS Stephen N
La Quinta	92253	Raffetto DR & MRS John
La Quinta	92253	Saltonstall MR & MRS David P
Ladera Ranch	92694	Larson MR & MRS Marc C
Lafayette	94549	Boone MR & MRS Jonathan O
Lafayette	94549	Browne MR & MRS Merrick JR
Lafayette	94549	Cooper MR & MRS John S
Lafayette	94549	Duff MR & MRS Alexander W
Lafayette	94549	Ely MRS George W
Lafayette	94549	Gregory MR & MRS William W
Lafayette	94549	Grove MR & MRS Henry S 3D
Lafayette	94549	Holt MR & MRS Richard W
Lafayette	94549	Miller MR & MRS William C
Lafayette	94549	Sayre MRS Richard W
Lafayette	94549	Strandberg MR & MRS Robert S
Lafayette	94549	Thom MR & MRS Peter R 3D
Laguna Beach	92651	Brooks MR & MRS Harvey S JR
Laguna Beach	92651	Colsman-Freyberger MR & MRS Ulrich
Laguna Beach	92651	Colsman-Freyberger MR Charles McKee
Laguna Beach	92651	McKechnie MR & MRS Christopher W
Laguna Beach	92651	McKenna MR & MRS Kevin L
Laguna Beach	92651	McKenna MR Michael R
Laguna Beach	92651	Newton MISS Priscilla A
Laguna Beach	92651	Sellers MRS William W
Laguna Beach	92651	Sommerfield MR Mark J
Laguna Hills	92653	Barrow MR & MRS R Austin 3D
Laguna Hills	92653	Mallinckrodt MRS Charles O
Laguna Hills	92653	von Grosse MRS Aristid V
Laguna Niguel	92677	Fowler MR Larned B
Laguna Niguel	92677	Vietor MRS Julia B
Laguna Woods	92637	Carr MR & MRS S Wyatt JR
Laguna Woods	92637	Farrington MRS William B
Lakeside	92040	Kenniston MR & MRS Salvador
Larkspur	94939	Burnham MR & MRS De Witt K JR
Larkspur	94939	Colwell MRS Kent L
Larkspur	94939	Ingraham MR & MRS David S
Larkspur	94939	James MISS Mary C
Larkspur	94939	Miller MR & MRS L Clarke
Larkspur	94939	Pillsbury MR & MRS Philip W III
Larkspur	94977	Forbes MRS Pamela
Lee Vining	93541	McQuilkin MR & MRS G J Geoffrey
Livermore	94550	Sauger MR & MRS James P
Livermore	94550	Thompson MR & MRS Steven L
Livermore	94551	Grandy MR Jeffrey McK
Lompoc	93436	Donohoe MRS Anita D
Long Beach	90802	Grew MR & MRS Frank J
Long Beach	90803	Vodhanel MS Wendi L
Long Beach	90806	Redfield MR & MRS LeGrand S
Loomis	95650	Paull MRS Heather B
Los Alamitos	90720	Lewis MR John R
Los Altos	94022	Hamilton MISS Ellen E
Los Altos	94022	Mungall MS Joanne D
Los Altos	94022	Peters MR & MRS J Girvin JR
Los Altos	94022	Redfield MR & MRS Christopher McK
Los Altos	94022	Twerdahl MR & MRS Timothy D
Los Altos	94022	Verkamp MISS Mary G
Los Altos	94024	Eastman MR & MRS Lee V 2D

To nominate a candidate for the Social Register Association, please email: SRCommittee@thesocialregister.org

Los Altos Hills, CA—Los Angeles, CA

Los Altos Hills	94022	Bilger MR & MRS Brent R
Los Altos Hills	94022	Gilmour MR & MRS (DR) David L
Los Altos Hills	94022	Gorham MR & MRS Nathaniel VIII
Los Altos Hills	94022	Melen DR & MRS Roger D
Los Angeles	90004	Ahmanson MR & MRS William H
Los Angeles	90004	Baker MR & MRS Robert C
Los Angeles	90004	Crimmins MR Martin Lalor 3D
Los Angeles	90004	Griffith MR & MRS Stephen E
Los Angeles	90004	Hawley MR & MRS John F
Los Angeles	90004	Hutchinson MR & MRS Charles H
Los Angeles	90004	Jenney MISS Lucinda K
Los Angeles	90004	Kuhns MR & MRS Matthew W
Los Angeles	90004	Salisbury MRS Robert E
Los Angeles	90004	Vodhanel MRS Frank J
Los Angeles	90004	Walton MR & MRS David B II
Los Angeles	90005	Medley MR H Anthony
Los Angeles	90006	Goethals REV Gregory M
Los Angeles	90013	Horner MR & MRS Edward W JR
Los Angeles	90013	Potthårst MR Russell C
Los Angeles	90014	Khan MR & MRS Ali Alexander
Los Angeles	90017	Newcomer MR & MRS Francis R
Los Angeles	90018	Munson MISS Mimi L
Los Angeles	90018	Munson MRS George R
Los Angeles	90020	Clyne MR & MRS V Shannon
Los Angeles	90020	Clyne MR A Taylor
Los Angeles	90020	Combs MRS P Craig
Los Angeles	90020	Doessant MR & MRS (DR) Emmanuel
Los Angeles	90020	Fain MR & MRS William Hart JR
Los Angeles	90020	McDonough MR & MRS David Lucas
Los Angeles	90020	Moser DR & MRS Franklin G
Los Angeles	90020	Reuben MR & MRS Jeffrey L
Los Angeles	90020	Welborne MR & MRS John Howard
Los Angeles	90024	Biondi MR & MRS Frank J JR
Los Angeles	90024	Brooks MR & MRS Preston W
Los Angeles	90024	Combs MR & MRS Christopher W
Los Angeles	90024	Dest MR & MRS Leonard R
Los Angeles	90024	Franklin MR Thomas S
Los Angeles	90024	Fuller MISS Kit
Los Angeles	90024	Hartwick MR & MRS Ronald S
Los Angeles	90024	Mogan MR & MRS Richard F 3D
Los Angeles	90024	Skouras MRS Charles P JR
Los Angeles	90024	Supple MS Ginny King
Los Angeles	90024	Wazzan MS Sabrina C
Los Angeles	90025	Bender MR & MRS D Farrell
Los Angeles	90025	Helme MR George W 4TH
Los Angeles	90025	Perkins MRS Wendy C
Los Angeles	90025	Starkey MISS Madeleine A E
Los Angeles	90025	Trump MR & MRS Michael
Los Angeles	90026	Huffman MR Gerald M JR
Los Angeles	90026	Kelly MR James H
Los Angeles	90026	Landreth MR & MRS Edward S JR
Los Angeles	90026	Macomber MR & MRS William B II
Los Angeles	90026	McHargue MR & MRS James C
Los Angeles	90026	Neubauer MR & MRS Robert A
Los Angeles	90026	Newbold MR Christopher H
Los Angeles	90026	Smith MR David B & Stockman MS Hope M
Los Angeles	90026	Totten MISS Juliet T
Los Angeles	90027	Angle MR & MRS Eliot P
Los Angeles	90027	Browne MR & MRS Mark A
Los Angeles	90027	Eckelberry MR & MRS Anthony E
Los Angeles	90027	Harold MR & MRS Joby A T
Los Angeles	90027	Hines MR & MRS Patrick K
Los Angeles	90027	Koppel MR & MRS Lucas G
Los Angeles	90027	Porter MISS Tess B
Los Angeles	90027	Reynolds MR & MRS Hal W
Los Angeles	90027	Rhodes MR Joseph B
Los Angeles	90027	Simonds MR Peter K & Colt MS Elizabeth S
Los Angeles	90027	Techentin MR & MRS Warren A
Los Angeles	90029	Harris MR & MRS Alexander J
Los Angeles	90034	Geer MR Charles L
Los Angeles	90035	Meehan MRS Mary
Los Angeles	90036	Bundy MRS Peter D
Los Angeles	90036	Mascheroni MISS Olivia F
Los Angeles	90036	Maybank MR & MRS John P F
Los Angeles	90036	McNabb MRS Diane
Los Angeles	90039	Chilcoat MR & MRS Thomas R
Los Angeles	90039	Plenys MR & MRS Thomas P M
Los Angeles	90041	Sherman MR & MRS Eric
Los Angeles	90042	Forster MR Duncan M
Los Angeles	90042	O'Malley MISS Sibyl H
Los Angeles	90045	Bassett MR & MRS Mitchell C
Los Angeles	90045	Paridon MR & MRS Scott J
Los Angeles	90045	Roosevelt MS Margot
Los Angeles	90046	Gardner MS Dorcas W
Los Angeles	90046	Godfrey MR Cyrus Vincent
Los Angeles	90046	Hastings DR & MRS Peter L
Los Angeles	90046	Kloman MR Peter J
Los Angeles	90046	Leone MR Christian D
Los Angeles	90046	Nelson MR & MRS Kelly E
Los Angeles	90046	Sallee MISS Samantha L
Los Angeles	90046	Steers MR Charles R C IV
Los Angeles	90046	Tener MISS Jenifer E
Los Angeles	90046	Van Rensselaer MR & MRS Kiliaen D
Los Angeles	90048	Magee MR John G 3D
Los Angeles	90049	Adair MR & MRS Scott L
Los Angeles	90049	Anderson MR & MRS Scot M
Los Angeles	90049	Andrulis MR Michael M
Los Angeles	90049	Cale MR & MRS Charles G
Los Angeles	90049	de Maigret CTSSE
Los Angeles	90049	Hoeksma MR & MRS Gerben F
Los Angeles	90049	Holberton MR & MRS Terry Hamilton 3D
Los Angeles	90049	Holbrook MR & MRS Robert K
Los Angeles	90049	Jones MR Ellis B
Los Angeles	90049	Link MRS (DR) George H
Los Angeles	90049	Loud MR & MRS Theodore E
Los Angeles	90049	Martin MR Daniel W & Myrin MS Arden V A
Los Angeles	90049	McLean MR & MRS Stuart L
Los Angeles	90049	McMahan MR & MRS James Albert
Los Angeles	90049	Pearce MR & MRS Richard I JR
Los Angeles	90049	Prince MISS Pamela
Los Angeles	90049	Soule MR & MRS Timothy W
Los Angeles	90049	Thompson MR & MRS Douglas Andrew
Los Angeles	90064	Hall MR & MRS Roger B
Los Angeles	90064	Jewett MR & MRS Lamon Harkness
Los Angeles	90064	Olney MR John C
Los Angeles	90065	Sholes MISS Natalie
Los Angeles	90066	Goodwin MR & MRS Thacher C
Los Angeles	90066	Scully MR & MRS John A JR
Los Angeles	90066	Severson MS Kirsten C McL
Los Angeles	90066	Stringfellow MR & MRS Matthew S
Los Angeles	90066	Torp MR & MRS Jonathan W
Los Angeles	90067	Econn MRS James W
Los Angeles	90067	Lumsden MR James G
Los Angeles	90067	Segerstrom MRS Yvonne de C
Los Angeles	90068	Biddle MR & MRS Jonathan W
Los Angeles	90068	Kroening MR & MRS Keith V
Los Angeles	90068	McCauley MR & MRS Christopher D
Los Angeles	90068	Morton MR Nicholas M & Schley MS Marie B
Los Angeles	90068	Newton MR & MRS Charles I
Los Angeles	90068	Raymond MR & MRS David F
Los Angeles	90069	Baxter MR & MRS John Hanley JR
Los Angeles	90069	Claflin MR & MRS John A

Los Angeles	90069	Farnam MR Henry W 4TH
Los Angeles	90069	Fay MR & MRS Sean M
Los Angeles	90069	Niven MR & MRS David JR
Los Angeles	90069	Villard MR & MRS Dimitri S
Los Angeles	90077	Corwin MR Jack B
Los Angeles	90077	Eddleman MR Roy T
Los Angeles	90077	Keller MR & MRS Paul N
Los Angeles	90077	Kranz MR & MRS Thomas F
Los Angeles	90077	Kresa MR Kent & Booth MS Lynn A
Los Angeles	90077	Luppen MR & MRS Luppe Ridgway
Los Angeles	90077	Thieriot MRS Charles H
Los Angeles	90077	Up de Graff MR James G
Los Angeles	90077	Widdoes MR & MRS James L
Los Gatos	95030	Wainwright MR & MRS Mark L
Los Gatos	95033	Fuller MR & MRS John M JR
Los Olivos	93441	Fleming MR Alexander M A
Los Osos	93402	Skinner MR & MRS James F 3D
Malibu	90265	Barrett MISS (DR) Cynthia T
Malibu	90265	Blake MR James E
Malibu	90265	Guarino MR & MRS Vincent J
Malibu	90265	Price MR & MRS William F JR
Malibu	90265	Reitter MISS Stefani A
Malibu	90265	Sebastian MR Bernard T II & Cooper MS Kimberly L
Malibu	90265	Vaill MR Edward E & Yang MS Joan C C
Mammoth Lakes	93546	Wiles MR & MRS Christopher C
Manhattan Beach	90266	Barbara MRS Tiffany
Manhattan Beach	90266	Bohan MRS Susan
Manhattan Beach	90266	Goodman MR & MRS William E V
Manhattan Beach	90266	Grady MR Michael del Valle
Manhattan Beach	90266	Majcher MR & MRS Stanley I
Manhattan Beach	90266	Raney MR & MRS Kristopher M
Manhattan Beach	90266	Rosen DR & MRS Charles D
Manhattan Beach	90266	van der Kieft MISS Daphne deG
Manhattan Beach	90266	Wilhelm MR & MRS Mark R
Manhattan Beach	90267	Kalin MISS Melinda A
Manteca	95337	Warner MR Rollin Miles JR
Marina	93933	Shapley MR & MRS Scott D
Marina Del Rey	90292	Hesse MR & MRS George E II
Mendocino	95460	Chapman MS Judith J
Menlo Park	94025	Conroy MR Curtis H
Menlo Park	94025	Cooper MR & MRS Tom R JR
Menlo Park	94025	Engelhardt MR & MRS Philip L
Menlo Park	94025	Gregory MR & MRS Quintard
Menlo Park	94025	Griffin DR & MRS John R
Menlo Park	94025	Hullar MR & MRS John P
Menlo Park	94025	Livermore MR Richard C
Menlo Park	94025	Madeira MR & MRS Stephen T
Menlo Park	94025	Morshead MRS Brandon
Menlo Park	94025	Morshead MS Marilynne M
Menlo Park	94025	Pribula MR & MRS Alexis J
Menlo Park	94025	Pringle MRS Robert C
Menlo Park	94025	Quist MR & MRS Robert L
Menlo Park	94025	Sakoda MR & MRS Jon M
Menlo Park	94025	Santana MR & MRS Mark C
Menlo Park	94025	Wagstaff MR & MRS David IV
Menlo Park	94025	Waldeck MR & MRS Gary C
Menlo Park	94025	Watson MR & MRS Lucas E
Menlo Park	94025	Wendell MR & MRS Harlan L P
Menlo Park	94026	Ramsay MISS Ann M
Mill Valley	94941	Armour MR & MRS D A Maximillian
Mill Valley	94941	Ball MR & MRS Harold A 3D
Mill Valley	94941	Becker DR & MRS Terrence C
Mill Valley	94941	Brady MISS Patricia J
Mill Valley	94941	Bucklin MR & MRS Nicholas K
Mill Valley	94941	Bucklin MRS William N 3D
Mill Valley	94941	Cornelius MR Craig R & Taylor MS Rennie M
Mill Valley	94941	Cressman MR & MRS Daniel M
Mill Valley	94941	Cruz MRS Elizabeth Parker
Mill Valley	94941	Dreyer MR Thomas A
Mill Valley	94941	Dreyer MRS L Lewis
Mill Valley	94941	du Pont MR David W
Mill Valley	94941	FitzGerald MR & MRS Gerald J
Mill Valley	94941	Forbes MS Suzannah P
Mill Valley	94941	Foster MR & MRS Paul S 3D
Mill Valley	94941	Gilmor MR & MRS Christopher C
Mill Valley	94941	Hulley MR & MRS Charles B
Mill Valley	94941	Jacobs MR & MRS Carl B III
Mill Valley	94941	Jacobs MR & MRS James A
Mill Valley	94941	Janetos MR & MRS Gregory M
Mill Valley	94941	Kollock MR & MRS George T
Mill Valley	94941	Lewis MRS M Davies
Mill Valley	94941	Logan MR Walton M
Mill Valley	94941	Maniha MRS Julie G
Mill Valley	94941	Mann MS Courtney P
Mill Valley	94941	McFerran MR & MRS Frederick P
Mill Valley	94941	McFerrin MR & MRS Matthew M
Mill Valley	94941	Mills MRS William N
Mill Valley	94941	Parker MR & MRS Samuel F
Mill Valley	94941	Parmenter MRS Marian N
Mill Valley	94941	Pickering MR & MRS Kendall A
Mill Valley	94941	Rosegard MR & MRS Erik J
Mill Valley	94941	Sadlier MR & MRS Kevin M
Mill Valley	94941	Sailer MR & MRS Samuel C
Mill Valley	94941	Schurz MR & MRS James M
Mill Valley	94941	Simon MR & MRS Ryan S
Mill Valley	94941	Symmes MRS Laurence M
Mill Valley	94941	Taylor MRS Richard Sward
Mill Valley	94941	Thomson MRS George G
Mill Valley	94941	Tribolet MR & MRS Perry A
Mill Valley	94941	Wang MR & MRS M Thomas
Mill Valley	94941	Wheelock MRS A Bassett
Millbrae	94030	Laidlaw MR & MRS Douglas A
Modesto	95354	Parker MISS Melanie S
Modesto	95355	Brereton MR & MRS Hugh E
Modesto	95356	Kokesh MR & MRS Michael O
Modesto	95356	Stockton MISS Nadine Y
Monarch Beach	92629	Sullivan MR & MRS Brian P SR
Monte Sereno	95030	Schurman MR Jacob G 4TH
Montecito	93108	Bianchi MR & MRS Adam 2D
Montecito	93108	Jackson MRS Lionel S
Montecito	93108	Kendall MR & MRS Robert E
Montecito	93108	Mullen MR & MRS Edward J
Montecito	93108	Pizzinat MR & MRS Arthur Franklin
Montecito	93108	Tenney MRS Patricia L
Montecito	93108	Walker MR David H JR
Montecito	93108	Walker MS Margo Geer
Montecito	93108	Walmsley MR & MRS Peter S
Montecito	93108	Wolf MR & MRS Richard A
Moraga	94556	Buckley MR & MRS Patrick C
Moraga	94556	Cooper MR & MRS William B
Moraga	94556	Fitzpatrick MR & MRS Kenneth F III
Moraga	94556	Gray MR & MRS Colby S
Moraga	94556	Livermore DR & MRS Norman B 3D
Moraga	94556	Moyer DR & MRS David B JR
Morgan Hill	95037	Espinosa de los Monteros MR Martin A
Morgan Hill	95037	Wood MR & MRS Leighton C JR
Morro Bay	93442	Symington REV Sidney S
Mount Shasta	96067	Kirkwood MR & MRS John H
Mountain View	94039	Withers MR & MRS John P JR
Mountain View	94040	McGuckin MISS Alice C
Mountain View	94040	Meigs MRS Patricia
Mountain View	94043	Donahue MISS Mary K

To nominate a candidate for the Social Register Association, please email: SRCommittee@thesocialregister.org

Napa, CA—Palm Desert, CA

Napa 94558 Bakker MR & MRS Peter A
Napa 94558 Gouveia MR & MRS Anthony B
Napa 94558 Hills MR & MRS Justin
Napa 94558 Lambert DR & MRS Scott C JR
Napa 94558 Miller MISS (DR) Amanda B
Napa 94558 Russell MR & MRS Brian C
Napa 94558 Williams MR & MRS Richard D
Napa 94558 Wilson MR & MRS Terrence G
Napa 94559 Donohoe MR & MRS Richard D
Napa 94559 Hyde MR & MRS Laurence W
Napa 94559 McComic MR & MRS R Barry
Napa 94559 Tirrell MISS Angela
Napa 94588 Wilson MR & MRS David H S
Nevada City 95959 Ely MRS Elizabeth M
Nevada City 95959 Lapham MISS Ellen V B
Newbury Park 91320 Lind MR & MRS H Robert
Newhall 91321 Jhaveri MR & MRS Ajay
Newport Beach 92660 Connolly DR & MRS John E
Newport Beach 92660 du Pont MR & MRS Edmond A R
Newport Beach 92660 Hughes MR & MRS William W JR
Newport Beach 92660 Lavington MS Camille Perkins
Newport Beach 92660 Loveland MR & MRS William A
Newport Beach 92660 Maxwell MISS Linda S
Newport Beach 92660 O'Riley MRS J Michael
Newport Beach 92660 Patton MR & MRS Scott B
Newport Beach 92660 Robbins MR & MRS Donald M
Newport Beach 92660 Schaffer MR & MRS Jeffrey P
Newport Beach 92660 Schoellerman MR & MRS Jack L
Newport Beach 92660 Stimpson MR & MRS Alexander F
Newport Beach 92660 Trester MR Irwin
Newport Beach 92662 Koll MRS Donald M
Newport Beach 92663 Connelly MR & MRS James M
Newport Beach 92663 Rogers MRS Edmund H JR
Newport Beach 92663 Shepherdson MR & MRS James A III
Nicasio 94946 Casey MR & MRS A Michael
Nicasio 94946 Leonard MISS Lindsay M
North Hollywood 91601 Choi MR & MRS Ronald
North Tustin 92705 Pence MR & MRS Eldon D III
Northridge 91324 Trent MR & MRS John B JR
Novato 94945 Abel MR & MRS Robert B JR
Novato 94945 Holden MISS Cynthia G
Novato 94945 Pressley MR & MRS David D
Novato 94947 Futcher MISS Jane P
Novato 94947 Haas MRS Josephine Baum
Novato 94947 Melone MR & MRS Robert Woodward
Novato 94948 Cooley MR & MRS A Crawford
Novato 94949 Hall MR & MRS Winslow Wyatt
Novato 94949 Winans MR Kenneth G & Wreyford MS Deborah A
Oak Park 91377 DeGraw MRS Austin R
Oakland 94502 Van Riper MR Ransom E & Wyndham MS Kristine A
Oakland 94602 Forney MR William McD
Oakland 94602 Miottel MR & MRS Ward John 3D
Oakland 94602 Wild MR & MRS Scott M
Oakland 94602 Williams MR & MRS Andrew T
Oakland 94603 Ely MR Sterling Barclay
Oakland 94605 Campbell MISS Priscilla L
Oakland 94605 Conolly MR & MRS Christopher J
Oakland 94605 Thys MS Danielle C
Oakland 94608 Righter MISS Amy L
Oakland 94609 Chipman MR & MRS Michael J
Oakland 94609 Dixon MR & MRS Andrew D
Oakland 94610 Hasley MR & MRS Michael S
Oakland 94610 Jones MR & MRS Benjamin R
Oakland 94610 Oldham MS Elaine D
Oakland 94610 Sasso MR Michael W
Oakland 94610 Sasso MRS Leonard P
Oakland 94611 Silbergh MR & MRS Alan C M
Oakland 94611 Williams MRS Robert W JR
Oakland 94612 Ames MRS Lawrence C JR
Oakland 94612 Richardson MRS Blanchard
Oakland 94618 Brenman MR & MRS (DR) Bob S II
Oakland 94618 Butler MRS Marianna M
Oakland 94618 Marble MRS Hillary H
Oakland 94618 Swartz MR & MRS Thomas B
Occidental 95465 Moore MR Charles R H
Occidental 95465 Wallis MR Charles M
Oceanside 92054 Borie MR & MRS J Stewart
Oceanside 92054 Penton MR Hugh V
Oceanside 92057 Fern MR & MRS George M
Ojai 93023 Di Capua MR & MRS Peter A
Ojai 93023 Grantham MR & MRS Jesse 3D
Olympic Valley 96146 Roach MRS Caryl L M
Olympic Valley 96146 Thys MR & MRS E Barry
Ontario 91761 Fujii MRS Jane Robin Rees
Orinda 94563 Curtis MR Ralston
Orinda 94563 Hall MR & MRS George G
Orinda 94563 Llewellyn MR Taylor M
Orinda 94563 Llewellyn MRS David S
Orinda 94563 Reardon MR & MRS Mark C
Orinda 94563 Rogers MR & MRS Glenn R
Pacific Grove 93950 Chomat MR & MRS Pierre A
Pacific Palisades 90272 Allnatt MR Matthew J
Pacific Palisades 90272 Allnatt MS Margaret Sculley
Pacific Palisades 90272 Brown MR & MRS David I JR
Pacific Palisades 90272 Brown MR & MRS Michael M
Pacific Palisades 90272 Burton MR & MRS Matthew N
Pacific Palisades 90272 Commons MR & MRS Richard B
Pacific Palisades 90272 Costin MRS W Gilmor 3D
Pacific Palisades 90272 Eamer MR & MRS Richard K
Pacific Palisades 90272 Ford MR & MRS B James
Pacific Palisades 90272 George MS Deborah M
Pacific Palisades 90272 Giovine MR & MRS Thomas A
Pacific Palisades 90272 Grose MR & MRS William F P
Pacific Palisades 90272 Heisel MR John Kurtland
Pacific Palisades 90272 Irvine MR & MRS Thomas A
Pacific Palisades 90272 Kreitler REV & MRS Peter G
Pacific Palisades 90272 Morrin MS Lisa Hay
Pacific Palisades 90272 O'Toole MR & MRS David D
Pacific Palisades 90272 Overland MR & MRS Mark Eric
Pacific Palisades 90272 Pecsok MS Marilyn S
Pacific Palisades 90272 Porter MR & MRS Clark Willard
Pacific Palisades 90272 Root MR & MRS Henry W
Pacific Palisades 90272 Simon MR & MRS Christopher
Pacific Palisades 90272 Sinnott MR & MRS Robert V
Pacific Palisades 90272 Slater MR & MRS Clifford E JR
Pacific Palisades 90272 Stuempfig MR & MRS Alexander C P
Pacific Palisades 90272 Tower MR & MRS Jonathan R
Pacific Palisades 90272 Vlietstra MR & MRS Klaas F
Pacific Palisades 90272 White MR & MRS Alexander W JR
Pacific Palisades 90272 Wickser MR & MRS Philip J II
Pacific Palisades 90272 Winn MR & MRS Charles M A
Palm Desert 92211 Huber MR & MRS Daniel
Palm Desert 92260 Anderson MR A William JR
Palm Desert 92260 Collins MR & MRS James S JR
Palm Desert 92260 Colville MS Kim
Palm Desert 92260 Haywood MR & MRS Edward Gregory
Palm Desert 92260 Haywood MR & MRS T Holt JR
Palm Desert 92260 Inch MR & MRS Robert W
Palm Desert 92260 McGovern MR & MRS Neil O JR
Palm Desert 92260 Phillips MR & MRS Peter M
Palm Desert 92260 Sura MRS Clarinda S
Palm Desert 92260 Waggaman MR & MRS John F II

Palm Springs	92262	Moore MR Franklin H
Palm Springs	92262	Noble MR Frederick W
Palm Springs	92262	Winsor MR R H Bancroft JR
Palm Springs	92264	Eckert MR Peter L & Cantrell PRCSS Karen
Palm Springs	92264	Frentzel MR H Christian
Palm Springs	92264	Hay MS Laura Stanhope
Palm Springs	92264	Laflin MRS Lloyd Alan
Palm Springs	92264	Lawton MR James R
Palo Alto	94301	Beckett MRS John C
Palo Alto	94301	Clewe DR Thomas H
Palo Alto	94301	Ericson MR & MRS (DR) Bruce A
Palo Alto	94301	Hinstorff MR & MRS Herbert L JR
Palo Alto	94301	Hoster MR & MRS Thomas C
Palo Alto	94301	MacMorris MR & MRS John W III
Palo Alto	94301	Mitchell MS Carol C
Palo Alto	94301	Vanderbilt MRS Katharine S
Palo Alto	94303	Prioleau MR & MRS Marc T R
Palo Alto	94303	Wilbur MR & MRS Colburn S
Palo Alto	94304	Armstrong MS Mary Helen
Palo Alto	94304	Ely MRS Leonard W
Palo Alto	94304	King MR Edmund T 2D
Palo Alto	94306	Beckett MR & MRS James W
Palo Alto	94306	Bischof MR George P
Palo Alto	94306	Grant-Valdez MR & MRS Iein
Palo Alto	94306	Moore MR & MRS Thomas G
Palo Alto	94306	Neumann DR Peter G
Palo Alto	94306	Supplee MR & MRS Edward A JR
Palo Alto	94306	Supplee MRS Edward A
Palos Verdes Estates	90274	Fountain MR & MRS Rex Edward JR
Palos Verdes Estates	90274	Gunson MR & MRS John C
Palos Verdes Estates	90274	Harman MR & MRS Reed L
Pasadena	91101	Heuer MRS Scott JR
Pasadena	91101	McAniff MR John Edward
Pasadena	91101	Watson MRS Walter J
Pasadena	91103	Adams MR & MRS Peter S
Pasadena	91103	Doughty MRS Elizabeth C
Pasadena	91103	Holbrook MR & MRS William Sumner 3D
Pasadena	91103	Palmer MR & MRS Everett A JR
Pasadena	91103	Richards MR & MRS William P JR
Pasadena	91103	Wheaton MRS Polly J
Pasadena	91104	Cady MR Colin L
Pasadena	91104	Dohrmann MR & MRS Robert L
Pasadena	91104	Huber MS Caroline B
Pasadena	91105	Barngrove MRS Sally Ann
Pasadena	91105	Belmont MS Martyn S
Pasadena	91105	Bianchi MR & MRS David W
Pasadena	91105	Clark MR & MRS Richard H
Pasadena	91105	Currier MISS Gwendolyn L
Pasadena	91105	Dickason MRS James Frank
Pasadena	91105	Edmiston DR W Allan & Harrigan MR P Simmons
Pasadena	91105	Engs MR & MRS Edward W III
Pasadena	91105	Hansen DR & MRS Robert E JR
Pasadena	91105	Hanson MR Bradley N
Pasadena	91105	Hoecker MR & MRS Gary Wayne
Pasadena	91105	Hollern MR Terrence L
Pasadena	91105	Johnson MR & MRS Frederick D
Pasadena	91105	Jones MR & MRS Richard Welton
Pasadena	91105	Kennedy MR & MRS William T
Pasadena	91105	Leonard MRS Nelson J
Pasadena	91105	LeRoy MR & MRS Michael D
Pasadena	91105	Link MR & MRS Christopher L
Pasadena	91105	Link MR & MRS Thomas H
Pasadena	91105	Livingstone MRS Victoria
Pasadena	91105	MacVaugh MR & MRS Horace IV
Pasadena	91105	Morton MRS Janelle H
Pasadena	91105	Oler REV & MRS Clarke K
Pasadena	91105	Pestana MR & MRS Gary P
Pasadena	91105	Rader MRS Frederic A
Pasadena	91105	Rose MR & MRS Walter B
Pasadena	91105	Sample MRS Stephen B
Pasadena	91105	Shoch MR & MRS James R III
Pasadena	91105	Stanford MR & MRS Alan G
Pasadena	91105	Stewart MR & MRS R Bruce
Pasadena	91105	Taylor MR & MRS Marshall M
Pasadena	91106	Burrows MRS William David
Pasadena	91106	Gilfillan MR & MRS Graeme A
Pasadena	91106	Harrison MR & MRS Berkeley G
Pasadena	91106	Ryan MRS James J
Pasadena	91106	Snyder MR & MRS David W
Pasadena	91106	Techentin MR & MRS Thomas A
Pasadena	91107	Halferty MR & MRS James F
Pasadena	91107	Lloyd MR & MRS Bruce M
Pasadena	91107	Montgomery MR Donnell Harry
Pasadena	91107	Suter DR & MRS Glen H
Pasadena	91108	Young MR & MRS Brinton O C
Paso Robles	93446	Ghan MRS Ronald W
Paso Robles	93446	Hanneken MR Christopher L
Paso Robles	93446	Perkins MR & MRS Elliott K
Paso Robles	93447	Wheaton MRS Margery J
Pauma Valley	92061	Huntington MR Charles G
Pebble Beach	93953	Cecconi MR & MRS Giuseppe Enzo
Pebble Beach	93953	Lansbury MR & MRS James E
Pebble Beach	93953	Shaw MRS William V
Penngrove	94951	Rodgers MS Diana L
Petaluma	94952	Cover MRS S Detert
Petaluma	94952	Winter MR & MRS Matthew F
Piedmont	94610	Edgerton MR & MRS Albert S
Piedmont	94610	Farrand MR & MRS A Brady
Piedmont	94610	Vosburg MR & MRS Bruce D JR
Piedmont	94611	Abel MR & MRS John A
Piedmont	94611	Bassett MR & MRS John W
Piedmont	94611	Bates MR & MRS Charles W
Piedmont	94611	Bleich MR & MRS Jeffrey L
Piedmont	94611	Bryan MRS John M
Piedmont	94611	Henshaw MRS William G III
Piedmont	94611	Inch MR & MRS Robert W JR
Piedmont	94611	Keville MR & MRS F Hollister
Piedmont	94611	MacBride MR & MRS Thomas J JR
Piedmont	94611	Moe MR & MRS John C JR
Piedmont	94611	Phillips MR & MRS Raborn S
Piedmont	94611	Prioleau MR & MRS Frost René R
Piedmont	94611	Prioleau MR & MRS Horry Frost
Piedmont	94611	Reese MR Charles W JR
Piedmont	94611	Seavey MR William A
Piedmont	94611	Staley MR & MRS David R
Piedmont	94611	Tunney MR & MRS Peter W
Placerville	95667	Smith MR & MRS Gregory B
Pleasanton	94588	Miller MR & MRS Ludlow
Pleasanton	94588	West MRS Harry I JR
Point Reyes Station	94956	Baxter MS Anne W
Port Hueneme	93041	de Mailly MISS Diane B
Portola Valley	94028	Anderson MR & MRS E Forrest
Portola Valley	94028	Bark MR & MRS Dennis L
Portola Valley	94028	Foster MR & MRS Hugh W
Portola Valley	94028	Giles MR & MRS Robert E
Portola Valley	94028	Knoop MR Frederick W
Portola Valley	94028	Millard MR & MRS Stephens F
Portola Valley	94028	Philbin MR Ewing R JR
Portola Valley	94028	Ross MRS Donald F
Portola Valley	94028	Westerfield MR & MRS Putney
Poway	92064	Grew MR Raymond E
Rancho Cucamonga	91730	Barry MR & MRS Robert B 4TH

To nominate a candidate for the Social Register Association, please email: SRCommittee@thesocialregister.org

Rancho Cucamonga, CA—San Francisco, CA

Rancho Cucamonga...... 91737......... Dunham MR & MRS Samuel G
Rancho Mirage............. 92270......... Goldsborough MR Nicholas Tilghman
Rancho Mirage............. 92270......... Legvold MR Paul A
Rancho Mirage............. 92270......... McKee MR & MRS A Kingston
Rancho Mirage............. 92270......... McKee MR & MRS Kingston
Rancho Mirage............. 92270......... Piano MRS Anastasia
Rancho Mirage............. 92270......... Talmage MR Kenneth K
Rancho Mission Viejo .. 92694......... Monge MRS Julia Burdick
Rancho Santa Fe........... 92067......... David DR & MRS Eric M
Rancho Santa Fe........... 92067......... Hand MR Edward S
Rancho Santa Fe........... 92067......... Harazim MR Stanley C
Rancho Santa Fe........... 92067......... Lewis MS Katharine A
Rancho Santa Fe........... 92067......... Queen MR & MRS John R
Rancho Santa Fe........... 92067......... Rikkers MR & MRS John W
Rancho Santa Fe........... 92067......... Tufaro DR & MRS (DR) Francis
Rancho Santa Fe........... 92091......... Hickox MRS James P
Rancho Santa Fe........... 92091......... Loftman MR & MRS Russell E
Rancho Santa Fe........... 92091......... Newsom MR & MRS Noble
Ranchp Palos Verdes.... 90275......... Fuller MISS Cary Randolph
Redding......................... 96001......... Blatchford MRS W Larned
Redding......................... 96001......... Franck MRS Peter T
Redding......................... 96001......... Hollins MR Michael J
Redlands........................ 92373......... Beall MRS Kathleen A
Redlands........................ 92373......... Covington MISS Emily I
Redlands........................ 92373......... Emerson MR & MRS Dan R
Redlands........................ 92373......... Williams MR John C
Redondo Beach............. 90277......... Brock MR & MRS Dallas D E
Redondo Beach............. 90277......... Jerome MR J Ramsay
Redwood City................ 94061......... Gunson MRS Leo J JR
Redwood City................ 94061......... Manning MRS Florence T H
Redwood City................ 94061......... Wall MR & MRS Nicholas J
Redwood City................ 94062......... Alfenito DR Mark R
Redwood City................ 94062......... MacWilliams MR P Huntington
Redwood City................ 94063 .... Madeira MRS Mary V
Redwood City................ 94063 .... Martine MR Christian A
Redwood City................ 94063 .... Van Fleet MR & MRS Alan C
Redwood City................ 94065......... Huffman MR Paul B III
Redwood City................ 94065......... Seymour MRS Charles W JR
Redwood City................ 94065......... Ware MR William JR
Reseda........................... 91335......... Brennan MISS Martha Ellen
Richmond...................... 94804......... Gunter MR & MRS Jason E
Richmond...................... 94805......... Mullally MR Kevin M
Rio Vista........................ 94571......... Pope MISS Patricia M
Riverside....................... 92507......... Kietzman MR B T
& Macdonald-Kietzman MRS A P
Rocklin.......................... 95765......... Moore MR & MRS James R
Rohnert Park................. 94928......... Thomson MR & MRS James W
Rolling Hills.................. 90274......... Higholt DR Howard W
Rolling Hills.................. 90274......... Schoettle MR & MRS Michael B
Rosamond...................... 93560......... Trapnell MR David S
Roseville........................ 95678......... Byrne MR & MRS Michael J
Ross............................... 94957......... Bakker MS Kimberly Q
Ross............................... 94957......... Barron MR & MRS Hugh D
Ross............................... 94957......... Brown MISS Elizabeth Taft
Ross............................... 94957......... Cahill MR & MRS William R
Ross............................... 94957......... Gamble MR & MRS Mark D
Ross............................... 94957......... Gammill MR & MRS Lee M JR
Ross............................... 94957......... Kern MR & MRS John C JR
Ross............................... 94957......... Laidlaw MR & MRS Peter C
Ross............................... 94957......... Livermore MR & MRS Samuel M
Ross............................... 94957......... Maurus MR & MRS E Zachary
Ross............................... 94957......... Reed MR & MRS John M
Ross............................... 94957......... Williams MR Sean O'C
Ross............................... 94957......... Wilson MR & MRS Milton 3D
Rough And Ready......... 95975......... Lakusta MR Boris H JR
Rumsey.......................... 95679......... McCloskey MR & MRS Paul N JR

Sacramento.................... 95816......... Silva-Sadder MR Alexander G
Sacramento.................... 95819......... Ferrera MR & MRS Neil J
Sacramento.................... 95819......... Mee MR John H 3D
Sacramento.................... 95821......... Phillips MR Steven P & Siegman MS Jessica L
Sacramento.................... 95825......... Ford MR & MRS A James
Sacramento.................... 95825......... Kleinsorge MR Edward R
Sacramento.................... 95827......... McCormick MISS Catherine E
Sacramento.................... 95828......... Hayes MR Stephen O
Sacramento.................... 95831......... Bradley MR & MRS David N
Sacramento.................... 95833......... Perrott MR & MRS Frank R
Sacramento.................... 95864......... de Witt MR & MRS Clinton J
Sacramento.................... 95864......... Shattuck MRS Peter H
Salinas........................... 93908......... Haller MR & MRS John F
Salinas........................... 93908......... Martin MRS John R
Salinas........................... 93908......... Politzer MR & MRS Jerome F JR
San Anselmo................. 94960......... Bradley MS Jennifer T
San Anselmo................. 94960......... Brunet MR & MRS Stuart R
San Anselmo................. 94960......... Cowley MRS Alexandra Barney
San Anselmo................. 94960......... Gerner MR & MRS Christopher R
San Anselmo................. 94960......... Hatch MR & MRS Duncan S
San Anselmo................. 94960......... Logan MS Aimee Green
San Anselmo................. 94960......... Martin REV & MRS Christopher H
San Anselmo................. 94960......... McGinn MR Michael E
San Anselmo................. 94960......... Morrison MR & MRS James A
San Anselmo................. 94960......... Noble MR & MRS Morris H JR
San Anselmo................. 94960......... Page MRS G Goss
San Anselmo................. 94960......... Peterson MR & MRS Frederick L
San Anselmo................. 94960......... Rosenberg MR & MRS Martin E
San Anselmo................. 94979......... Geisler REV CANON & MRS William F
San Carlos..................... 94070......... Selfridge MISS Cynthia B
San Clemente................ 92672......... Pickle MR & MRS Kenneth A
San Diego...................... 92103......... Clay MR & MRS George M
San Diego...................... 92103......... Rees MRS Malcolm C JR
San Diego...................... 92103......... Singer MRS Sandra Clothier
San Diego...................... 92106......... Derrick MRS Donna Chilton
San Diego...................... 92106......... Gildred MR & MRS George Lewis
San Diego...................... 92106......... Hope MR & MRS Frank L JR
San Diego...................... 92106......... Jones MR & MRS Evan Voorhees
San Diego...................... 92108......... Carne MRS Rew P
San Diego...................... 92109......... Jardine MR & MRS Theodore P JR
San Diego...................... 92109......... Simpkins DR C Alexander
San Diego...................... 92110......... Carey REV & MRS Brenton H
San Diego...................... 92115......... Brooks MR Andrew D
San Diego...................... 92116......... Snook MR & MRS James E
San Diego...................... 92122......... Ogelsby MR & MRS William P 3D
San Diego...................... 92124......... Kent DR & MRS Graham M
San Diego...................... 92126......... Benjamin MR Gregory P
San Diego...................... 92127......... Estes REV & MRS James G
San Diego...................... 92127......... Oyler MRS Thomas T
San Diego...................... 92128......... Ferrer MISS Florence C
San Diego...................... 92130......... Milton MR A Fenner
San Diego...................... 92130......... Ratchuk MR & MRS Gregory R
San Diego...................... 92131......... Hobson MR Christopher L
& Fuller Hobson MS M
San Diego...................... 92131......... Peterkin MR Christopher M
San Diego...................... 92131......... Rees MR Stuart M
San Francisco................ 91109......... Hayes MR & MRS Andrew R
San Francisco................ 94102......... Haas MR James W
San Francisco................ 94103......... Francis MISS Marie T C
San Francisco................ 94103......... Latham MR & MRS James T
San Francisco................ 94103......... Leefeldt MR Robert C
San Francisco................ 94104......... Low MR & MRS Christian C
San Francisco................ 94107......... Cochran MR & MRS Dwight M 3D
San Francisco................ 94107......... Fullerton MRS Mallan
San Francisco................ 94107......... Lortz MR Edward K
San Francisco................ 94107......... Schell REV & MRS Donald J

San Francisco........ 94107........ Taylor MR & MRS Michael J
San Francisco........ 94108........ Blake MR Igor Robert
San Francisco........ 94108........ Bowman MR Lindsey C
San Francisco........ 94108........ Campbell MR & MRS James A
San Francisco........ 94108........ Chace MS Diana
San Francisco........ 94108........ Clark MR Warren H
San Francisco........ 94108........ Cook MR & MRS Ransom S
San Francisco........ 94108........ Cope MRS Newton A
San Francisco........ 94108........ de Bretteville MISS Leslie
San Francisco........ 94108........ Hampson MRS Alfred A
San Francisco........ 94108........ Merrill MRS C McCormick
San Francisco........ 94108........ Ritchie MR & MRS Mark H
San Francisco........ 94109........ Atlas MR Jeffrey L
San Francisco........ 94109........ Biederbeck MR & MRS Douglas P
San Francisco........ 94109........ Black MS Alexandra C
San Francisco........ 94109........ Bowers MRS Dione T L
San Francisco........ 94109........ Bowes MRS John Garland
San Francisco........ 94109........ Carlisle MRS Henry C
San Francisco........ 94109........ Casey MRS Donna M
San Francisco........ 94109........ de Castro MR Peter R
San Francisco........ 94109........ DiCarlo DR & MRS Lorenzo A JR
San Francisco........ 94109........ Dunckel MR & MRS Peter B
San Francisco........ 94109........ Dunham MRS Lawrence D
San Francisco........ 94109........ Ede MR Jared C
San Francisco........ 94109........ Fitch MRS George Hopper
San Francisco........ 94109........ Fritz MRS Arthur Joseph JR
San Francisco........ 94109........ Fullerton MR George L
San Francisco........ 94109........ Gamble MR & MRS Launce E
San Francisco........ 94109........ Goldfarb MS Ronni
San Francisco........ 94109........ Griffin MR & MRS Andrew
San Francisco........ 94109........ Harris MRS Louise E
San Francisco........ 94109........ Hendrickson MS Alexandra K
San Francisco........ 94109........ Howard MR Duncan L
San Francisco........ 94109........ Johnson MR & MRS Dustin McC
San Francisco........ 94109........ Lilienthal MISS Brett A
San Francisco........ 94109........ Ludwig MR & MRS James J
San Francisco........ 94109........ McDaniel MRS David Jamison
San Francisco........ 94109........ McKeever MRS Chauncey
San Francisco........ 94109........ Milholland MR Thatcher L P
San Francisco........ 94109........ Moffitt MRS Herbert C
San Francisco........ 94109........ Moore MR & MRS Wesley D
San Francisco........ 94109........ Moore MRS Gail Bliss
San Francisco........ 94109........ Morrissey MR & MRS Peter G
San Francisco........ 94109........ Musto MR Peter Johnson
San Francisco........ 94109........ Osborne MR & MRS Christopher R-L
San Francisco........ 94109........ Parker MR Harrison H
San Francisco........ 94109........ Pfaff MR & MRS Richard A
San Francisco........ 94109........ Phleger MRS Atherton M
San Francisco........ 94109........ Postley MRS Clarence S
San Francisco........ 94109........ Prideaux-Brune MRS Rowland D C
San Francisco........ 94109........ Reque MR Peter A
San Francisco........ 94109........ Saunders MS Sally Love
San Francisco........ 94109........ Seddon MR & MRS R Carter
San Francisco........ 94109........ Seip MR & MRS Jared S
San Francisco........ 94109........ Strawbridge MR Robert E IV
San Francisco........ 94109........ Sullivan MR Charles T & Greene MS G McNealy
San Francisco........ 94109........ Tobin MR Joseph O II
San Francisco........ 94109........ Van Rensselaer MRS Nina M
San Francisco........ 94109........ Wagner MRS Barry G
San Francisco........ 94109........ Whisnand MR & MRS Tyler S
San Francisco........ 94109........ Woods MRS Leslie
San Francisco........ 94110........ Osborn MR & MRS (DR) John J JR
San Francisco........ 94110........ Sawyer MISS Rebecca
San Francisco........ 94110........ Schwartz MR & MRS Jonathan I
San Francisco........ 94111........ Inch MRS Arlene
San Francisco........ 94111........ Lapena MR Jaime & Han MS Lei
San Francisco........ 94111........ Quarré MS Simone Marie
San Francisco........ 94111........ Shen MR Jeff & Yu MS Sally
San Francisco........ 94112........ Callander MR & MRS Clark N
San Francisco........ 94112........ McCormick MR Michael T
San Francisco........ 94112........ Walk MR & MRS Hunter E
San Francisco........ 94112........ Wilson MR & MRS James B
San Francisco........ 94112........ Zanze MS Denise W
San Francisco........ 94114........ McDonough MR & MRS Michael L
San Francisco........ 94114........ McMillan MR & MRS S Sterling 4TH
San Francisco........ 94114........ Moran MR Thomas J JR
San Francisco........ 94114........ Pence MR John G
San Francisco........ 94114........ Rose MR & MRS Benjamin H 3D
San Francisco........ 94114........ Schwartz MISS Victoria B
San Francisco........ 94114........ Vermeule MISS Emily D Blakey
San Francisco........ 94115........ Andrews MR Kirk Austin
San Francisco........ 94115........ Atkinson MR & MRS Mark D
San Francisco........ 94115........ Bastick MR & MRS William F
San Francisco........ 94115........ Bogart MRS Johnson S
San Francisco........ 94115........ Bolton MR & MRS George B
San Francisco........ 94115........ Bowles MR Malcolm H
San Francisco........ 94115........ Brown MR & MRS Cabot
San Francisco........ 94115........ Burnham MRS De Witt K
San Francisco........ 94115........ Casey MR & MRS Charles Ranieri
San Francisco........ 94115........ Casey MR & MRS Lyman H
San Francisco........ 94115........ Damon MR & MRS Allen F
San Francisco........ 94115........ Davidson MR & MRS Stuart P
San Francisco........ 94115........ Donlon MRS David D
San Francisco........ 94115........ Drewes MR Stephen R
San Francisco........ 94115........ Dunham MS Eveline
San Francisco........ 94115........ Ede MRS Carol Duncan
San Francisco........ 94115........ Ehrlich MR & MRS Paul R
San Francisco........ 94115........ Ellinwood MRS George S
San Francisco........ 94115........ Fay MS Sally S
San Francisco........ 94115........ Fell MR Jeffrey L
San Francisco........ 94115........ Fergus MR & MRS Gary S
San Francisco........ 94115........ Fish MR & MRS Jason M
San Francisco........ 94115........ Gallagher MR & MRS Michael H
San Francisco........ 94115........ Getty MR & MRS Gordon P
San Francisco........ 94115........ Goss MR & MRS Richard W 2D
San Francisco........ 94115........ Grimes MR Spencer B
San Francisco........ 94115........ High MRS Kenneth G
San Francisco........ 94115........ Hills MR & MRS Austin E
San Francisco........ 94115........ Hodges MR Eliot I
San Francisco........ 94115........ Hutchinson MRS William N L JR
San Francisco........ 94115........ Jewett MRS George F JR
San Francisco........ 94115........ Kocks DR & MRS Peter F
San Francisco........ 94115........ Kunin DR & MRS Richard A
San Francisco........ 94115........ Lampen MR & MRS Stephen H
San Francisco........ 94115........ Lampen MRS Ambrose M D
San Francisco........ 94115........ Leo MR & MRS Austin J
San Francisco........ 94115........ Lewis MR & MRS Craig J
San Francisco........ 94115........ Ligamari MR & MRS Anthony B
San Francisco........ 94115........ Linke MR & MRS Gordon F JR
San Francisco........ 94115........ MacKay MRS Edward H
San Francisco........ 94115........ MacLean MISS Nancy L
San Francisco........ 94115........ Merrill MR Steven L
San Francisco........ 94115........ Mittendorf MR & MRS William F
San Francisco........ 94115........ Noble MRS Morris H
San Francisco........ 94115........ Paxton MR & MRS John C
San Francisco........ 94115........ Peterson MR & MRS Randolph J
San Francisco........ 94115........ Plouffe MR & MRS David A
San Francisco........ 94115........ Prien MRS Henry I
San Francisco........ 94115........ Reich MR & MRS Alexander Sommer
San Francisco........ 94115........ Richardson MR & MRS Weston B
San Francisco........ 94115........ Seidler MRS Francis F
San Francisco........ 94115........ Thieriot MR & MRS Richard T

To nominate a candidate for the Social Register Association, please email: SRCommittee@thesocialregister.org

San Francisco, CA—San Francisco, CA

San Francisco .... 94115 .... Thieriot MR Juan Pablo
San Francisco .... 94115 .... Traina MR & MRS Todd B
San Francisco .... 94115 .... Traina MR & MRS Trevor D
San Francisco .... 94115 .... Upton MR & MRS John R JR
San Francisco .... 94115 .... Vaughan MR Reginald Bethune
San Francisco .... 94115 .... Wheeler MR Halsted W JR
San Francisco .... 94115 .... Williamson MR & MRS D Stephen C
San Francisco .... 94115 .... Wilmans MS A Carlie
San Francisco .... 94115 .... Wilsey MRS Alfred S
San Francisco .... 94115 .... Withers MR & MRS Charles L
San Francisco .... 94115 .... Zanze MR & MRS James F
San Francisco .... 94117 .... Beale MR & MRS Karl M
San Francisco .... 94117 .... Donahoe MR & MRS Daniel J 4TH
San Francisco .... 94117 .... Garvin MR & MRS B Russell JR
San Francisco .... 94117 .... Griffith MR & MRS Millen VI
San Francisco .... 94117 .... Hartman MR & MRS Daniel J
San Francisco .... 94117 .... Hemphill MR Julian JR
San Francisco .... 94117 .... Hooper MR & MRS John C
San Francisco .... 94117 .... Jones MRS Magda R
San Francisco .... 94117 .... Karr MR & MRS Paul G
San Francisco .... 94117 .... Keats MR & MRS Matthew R
San Francisco .... 94117 .... Leonard MR & MRS Edward M
San Francisco .... 94117 .... Putzel MR Christof B & Taft MS Julia H
San Francisco .... 94117 .... Seligman MR & MRS Thomas K
San Francisco .... 94117 .... Vahle MR Peter B & Belt-Vahle MRS C Kilty
San Francisco .... 94117 .... Volberding DR & MRS (DR) Paul A
San Francisco .... 94118 .... Allen MR Jonathan B
San Francisco .... 94118 .... Barkan MRS Thomas A
San Francisco .... 94118 .... Bauer MR & MRS Ernst S
San Francisco .... 94118 .... Bethell MR Ralph A
San Francisco .... 94118 .... Bingham MRS (REV CANON) Sally Grover
San Francisco .... 94118 .... Bowles MR & MRS Philip E 3D
San Francisco .... 94118 .... Bryan MISS Amanda Atherton
San Francisco .... 94118 .... Bulkley MR & MRS Jonathan D
San Francisco .... 94118 .... Callander MR & MRS Bruce H
San Francisco .... 94118 .... Cobb MR & MRS Brodie L
San Francisco .... 94118 .... Congdon MR & MRS Jeffrey H
San Francisco .... 94118 .... Consagra MR & MRS George D
San Francisco .... 94118 .... Cooper MR & MRS William Betts
San Francisco .... 94118 .... Coulter MR & MRS James G
San Francisco .... 94118 .... Crawford DR & MRS J Brooks
San Francisco .... 94118 .... Dearie MR & MRS William D
San Francisco .... 94118 .... DeMicheli MRS Robert J
San Francisco .... 94118 .... Dierkhising MR & MRS Adam F
San Francisco .... 94118 .... Dohrmann MRS Elizabeth O
San Francisco .... 94118 .... Doubleday MR & MRS George II
San Francisco .... 94118 .... Everdell MR & MRS Coburn D
San Francisco .... 94118 .... Eyre MISS Janet V S
San Francisco .... 94118 .... Fay MR & MRS Paul B 3D
San Francisco .... 94118 .... Flood MR & MRS James C
San Francisco .... 94118 .... Folger MR & MRS Peter M
San Francisco .... 94118 .... Folger MS Elizabeth J
San Francisco .... 94118 .... Gable MR & MRS John S
San Francisco .... 94118 .... Gamble MR & MRS Launce L
San Francisco .... 94118 .... Gansa DR & MRS Alexander N
San Francisco .... 94118 .... Glen MR & MRS Robert M
San Francisco .... 94118 .... Gores MR Guido J JR
San Francisco .... 94118 .... Gregg MR & MRS James G
San Francisco .... 94118 .... Gregory MR & MRS Daniel P
San Francisco .... 94118 .... Hall MR & MRS Robert C
San Francisco .... 94118 .... Hallanan MR Paul K
San Francisco .... 94118 .... Hansen MR & MRS Lee C
San Francisco .... 94118 .... Hazeltine MR Jed D
San Francisco .... 94118 .... Henderson MR & MRS James A
San Francisco .... 94118 .... Holden MISS Catharine C
San Francisco .... 94118 .... Horner MR & MRS Douglas C JR
San Francisco .... 94118 .... Hume MR & MRS George H
San Francisco .... 94118 .... Hume MR & MRS William J
San Francisco .... 94118 .... Johnson MR & MRS William P
San Francisco .... 94118 .... Koukopoulos MR & MRS (DR) Nicholas
San Francisco .... 94118 .... LeFevre MR & MRS A Scott
San Francisco .... 94118 .... MacDermid MR & MRS Lindsay
San Francisco .... 94118 .... Madsen MR & MRS Todd L
San Francisco .... 94118 .... Malarkey MRS Thomas B JR
San Francisco .... 94118 .... McBaine MR & MRS J Patterson
San Francisco .... 94118 .... McGettigan MR & MRS Charles C JR
San Francisco .... 94118 .... McInerney MR & MRS Mark J
San Francisco .... 94118 .... McKleroy MR & MRS Bruce G
San Francisco .... 94118 .... McLellan MRS Douglas Buckingham
San Francisco .... 94118 .... Mehran MR Alexander R
San Francisco .... 94118 .... Moon MR Frederick F 3D
San Francisco .... 94118 .... Moore MR & MRS Douglas G
San Francisco .... 94118 .... Noble MR & MRS William L
San Francisco .... 94118 .... Notides MR & MRS Russell J
San Francisco .... 94118 .... Ogilvie MR & MRS Andrew J
San Francisco .... 94118 .... Orrick MRS William H
San Francisco .... 94118 .... Porpora MR & MRS Devon M
San Francisco .... 94118 .... Rende MR & MRS John W
San Francisco .... 94118 .... Robbins MR & MRS Thomas N
San Francisco .... 94118 .... Roberts MR & MRS John B
San Francisco .... 94118 .... Romaine MR & MRS Arthur C
San Francisco .... 94118 .... Sacerdoti MR & MRS Tod M
San Francisco .... 94118 .... Saroyan MR & MRS Jason D
San Francisco .... 94118 .... Sears MR & MRS Nathaniel R
San Francisco .... 94118 .... Sellman MR & MRS Charles R
San Francisco .... 94118 .... Stovell MR & MRS James B II
San Francisco .... 94118 .... Stovell MR & MRS Peter M
San Francisco .... 94118 .... Thieriot MS Leslie
San Francisco .... 94118 .... Tracy MR & MRS D Scott
San Francisco .... 94118 .... Tran MR & MRS Ly Kinh
San Francisco .... 94118 .... Ward MR & MRS Charles F L
San Francisco .... 94118 .... Weber DR & MRS Barrett H
San Francisco .... 94118 .... Weber DR & MRS Peter B
San Francisco .... 94118 .... Weber DR & MRS Robert W
San Francisco .... 94118 .... Weber MR Barrett F
San Francisco .... 94118 .... Wilkinson MR & MRS Bary S
San Francisco .... 94119 .... Littlefield MRS Edmund W
San Francisco .... 94121 .... Ball MR & MRS Christopher R
San Francisco .... 94121 .... Brigham MRS Charles A
San Francisco .... 94121 .... Callan MR & MRS John C JR
San Francisco .... 94121 .... Callan MRS John C
San Francisco .... 94121 .... Crawford MR & MRS Peter B
San Francisco .... 94121 .... Dean MR & MRS Christopher S
San Francisco .... 94121 .... Fleishhacker MR & MRS William M
San Francisco .... 94121 .... Gores MRS Adriana S
San Francisco .... 94121 .... Grayson MR & MRS William E
San Francisco .... 94121 .... Jones DR Henry W III & Turnbull MRS Margaret D
San Francisco .... 94121 .... Kennedy MR & MRS Duncan R
San Francisco .... 94121 .... King DR James Jung-Kan
San Francisco .... 94121 .... King MR & MRS Jeff T
San Francisco .... 94121 .... Lefferts MR & MRS Leffert JR
San Francisco .... 94121 .... MacDonald MR & MRS Edmund B JR
San Francisco .... 94121 .... Motlow MR & MRS (DR) John G
San Francisco .... 94121 .... Robinson MR & MRS Gardner J H
San Francisco .... 94121 .... Saviano MRS Diana Morris
San Francisco .... 94121 .... Smith MR & MRS Richard B
San Francisco .... 94121 .... Stephens MR & MRS Craig A
San Francisco .... 94121 .... Waste MR & MRS William H II
San Francisco .... 94121 .... Woods MR & MRS F Montgomery III
San Francisco .... 94121 .... Zachrisson MRS Carl U
San Francisco .... 94122 .... Barkan MR & MRS John R

San Francisco, CA—San Marino, CA

San Francisco	94122	Harvie-Watt MISS Jennifer
San Francisco	94122	Newlin MR & MRS William V P JR
San Francisco	94122	Reece MR & MRS J Brooks III
San Francisco	94122	Skinner MR & MRS E Lemoine III
San Francisco	94123	Andrews MRS Adolphus JR
San Francisco	94123	Barton MISS Zoë E
San Francisco	94123	Brettkelly MR & MRS Antony A
San Francisco	94123	Brown MISS L Lee
San Francisco	94123	Brown MR & MRS Edward M
San Francisco	94123	Callan MISS Leslie M
San Francisco	94123	Callander MRS John N
San Francisco	94123	Campodonico MR & MRS John R
San Francisco	94123	Colwell MISS Stacy A
San Francisco	94123	Conner MR & MRS Edward J
San Francisco	94123	Connolly MR & MRS Ryan P
San Francisco	94123	Cravens MISS Carol C
San Francisco	94123	Dohrmann MR & MRS Bruce P
San Francisco	94123	Ellsworth MR & MRS Robert A
San Francisco	94123	Engelhardt MR & MRS Paul D
San Francisco	94123	Escher MR & MRS Thomas C
San Francisco	94123	Fleishhacker MR & MRS David
San Francisco	94123	Foster MISS Cornelia A
San Francisco	94123	Gordon MR & MRS J Kingman
San Francisco	94123	Gorman MISS Frances P
San Francisco	94123	Gregory MR Donald M JR
San Francisco	94123	Hamilton MR & MRS Perrin C III
San Francisco	94123	Harris MR & MRS Joseph M JR
San Francisco	94123	Holbrook MR & MRS Peter Moffitt
San Francisco	94123	Holden MRS St George
San Francisco	94123	Hulting MRS Patricia L
San Francisco	94123	Hutchins MR Callum C
San Francisco	94123	Jensen MR Christian McLean
San Francisco	94123	Kales MR & MRS William R II
San Francisco	94123	Kelley MR John E T
San Francisco	94123	Kiernan MRS Thomas F
San Francisco	94123	Kirkham MR & MRS James F
San Francisco	94123	Lauricella MR & MRS Francis E JR
San Francisco	94123	Long MRS Syida H
San Francisco	94123	Miller MR Harry E 3D
San Francisco	94123	Mills MR & MRS Samuel W JR
San Francisco	94123	Montgomery MR & MRS George G JR
San Francisco	94123	Nebel MR & MRS Matthew J
San Francisco	94123	Oppedahl MR John F
San Francisco	94123	Parker MR Angus M & Martin MS Araceli
San Francisco	94123	Pfau MR & MRS George H JR
San Francisco	94123	Poole MR & MRS Edward G
San Francisco	94123	Robbins MR & MRS William LeB
San Francisco	94123	Robinson MR & MRS Richard H
San Francisco	94123	Russell MISS Mary E
San Francisco	94123	Saveri MR Guido
San Francisco	94123	Skewes-Cox MR & MRS Peter D
San Francisco	94123	Stent MRS Ferdinand R
San Francisco	94123	Tiedemann MR & MRS H Keith
San Francisco	94123	Weaver MR Andrew MacF
San Francisco	94123	Webster MR & MRS Charles W III
San Francisco	94123	Wernig MR & MRS Patrick L
San Francisco	94123	Will MR & MRS Tyler W
San Francisco	94123	Wilson MRS Milton JR
San Francisco	94123	Wise MR & MRS Richard H
San Francisco	94124	Jensen MR Rollin A
San Francisco	94126	Wolf MR & MRS Christopher R
San Francisco	94127	Davalos MR & MRS Gerald C
San Francisco	94127	Emby MR & MRS Christopher J S
San Francisco	94129	Jonas MISS Eloise A
San Francisco	94129	McMillan MR & MRS Peter H
San Francisco	94131	Bieler MR Louis H JR
San Francisco	94131	de Maigret MR Clarke J & Tiews MR Matthew E
San Francisco	94131	Dunham MRS Hustead D
San Francisco	94131	London DR & MRS Adam P
San Francisco	94131	Martinez MR & MRS Michael J
San Francisco	94131	Parker MR Richard Lee
San Francisco	94131	Potter MR & MRS David
San Francisco	94131	Rutter MR N Edward C 3d
San Francisco	94131	Taylor MISS Jennifer H
San Francisco	94131	Young MISS Margaret A Chisholm
San Francisco	94133	Baron DR & MRS Barry C
San Francisco	94133	Brady MR William J B III
San Francisco	94133	Casey MR & MRS Ryan W
San Francisco	94133	Crocker MR & MRS Charles
San Francisco	94133	Dibble MRS Kathleen M
San Francisco	94133	Follis MR James G
San Francisco	94133	Gantner MR Anthony F
San Francisco	94133	Gardiner MR John J 3D
San Francisco	94133	Griswold MS Sandra S
San Francisco	94133	Hale MRS Prentis Cobb
San Francisco	94133	Hume MR & MRS J George
San Francisco	94133	Hunt MR & MRS Harry S
San Francisco	94133	Janin MRS Blaine C
San Francisco	94133	Kendrick MR & MRS Stephen H
San Francisco	94133	Lane MR Christopher T
San Francisco	94133	Leonard MR & MRS Andrew W
San Francisco	94133	Livermore MR Thomas B
San Francisco	94133	Malloy MISS Elizabeth G
San Francisco	94133	Manace DR E David
San Francisco	94133	Nicolaus MR Edward A 3D
San Francisco	94133	Otto MS Marie Luise
San Francisco	94133	Patton MR & MRS Paul L
San Francisco	94133	Pogue MR & MRS Michael D
San Francisco	94133	Roe MISS Hilda L
San Francisco	94133	Rosborough MR Robert S
San Francisco	94133	Steremberg MR & MRS Alan J
San Francisco	94133	Tobin MISS Katherine O
San Francisco	94133	Wood MR & MRS Christopher W II
San Francisco	94133	Zacher MRS Nancy Nicolaus
San Francisco	94141	Mein MR G Logan
San Francisco	94158	Field MR & MRS Charles S
San Francisco	94158	Galbraith MR & MRS John H
San Francisco	94965	Bradley MR Brendan P
San Francisco	994116	Hunter MRS Robert E JR
San Franciscoo	94118	Pickering MR & MRS John A
San Jose	95124	Gavin MR & MRS James M
San Jose	95125	de Kay REV Eckford J
San Jose	95125	Gilmore MR & MRS William F
San Jose	95125	Irvine MR & MRS K Andrew JR
San Jose	95135	Thompson MRS Peggy K
San Jose	95138	Van Tassel DR & MRS John P
San Juan Capistrano	92675	Zeile MR Todd E & Beach MS Kristin Gamboa
San Luis Obispo	93401	Miller DR & MRS Don Robert
San Luis Obispo	93405	Simmons MRS Rebecca K
San Marcos	92078	Carr MISS Carolyn K
San Marcos	92078	Dees MRS Bowen C
San Marino	91108	Brown MRS Milton
San Marino	91108	Day MR & MRS William R
San Marino	91108	Galbraith MR & MRS James M
San Marino	91108	Holdsworth MR & MRS Mark K
San Marino	91108	Hotchkis MR Brian P
San Marino	91108	Jones MR & MRS Louis W JR
San Marino	91108	Medearis MRS Roger N
San Marino	91108	Newell MR & MRS Robert M JR
San Marino	91108	Reed MR & MRS Charles C
San Marino	91108	Talt MR & MRS Stephen S
San Marino	91108	Walsh MR & MRS David M

To nominate a candidate for the Social Register Association, please email: SRCommittee@thesocialregister.org

San Marino, CA—Santa Monica, CA

San Marino	91108	Watson MR & MRS Robert C
San Marino	91108	Williams MR & MRS John P
San Martin	95046	Lorenceau MRS Stacy V
San Mateo	94401	Barkan MRS Adolph William
San Mateo	94401	Brown MRS Stephen Cabot
San Mateo	94401	de Guigné MR Christian 4TH
San Mateo	94401	de Guigné MRS V Hills
San Mateo	94401	Grady MR Reginald del Valle JR
San Mateo	94401	Holt MISS Stannie S
San Mateo	94401	Montague MRS Andrew A
San Mateo	94401	Wilson MRS Charles F JR
San Mateo	94402	Ghiselli MR & MRS Stephen G
San Mateo	94402	Griffith MR & MRS Charles L III
San Mateo	94402	Judson MR & MRS Robert D JR
San Mateo	94402	Pettit MRS Lindsay F
San Mateo	94402	Richey MISS Rue Doyé
San Mateo	94402	Wilson MR & MRS Laurence P
San Mateo	94403	Meek MR & MRS Kenneth J
San Mateo	94403	Roias MR & MRS John
San Pedro	90731	Fahy MISS Christina C
San Rafael	94901	Fetcher MR Frederick S
San Rafael	94901	Johnson MR & MRS Sidney G 2D
San Rafael	94901	Martin MR & MRS William R JR
San Rafael	94901	Nyland MRS Katherine M
San Rafael	94901	Simenstad MRS Susan O
San Rafael	94901	Wundrow MR & MRS David T
San Rafael	94903	Andrews MR & MRS Adolphus 3D
San Rafael	94903	Arnold MRS Anthony
San Rafael	94903	Chase MR & MRS John H
San Rafael	94903	Cheston MR & MRS Eugene M JR
San Rafael	94903	Dal Porto MR & MRS Jeffrey J
San Rafael	94903	de Marcellus MR & MRS Henri V
San Rafael	94903	Garrison MRS Maynard
San Rafael	94903	Johnston MRS J Buckhout
San Rafael	94903	Kehl MR D Christian
San Rafael	94903	LeFeaver MRS James H JR
San Rafael	94903	McAndrew MRS W Peter
San Rafael	94903	McNealy MRS Dean B
San Rafael	94903	Tirrell MR David J & Scott MRS Patricia K
San Rafael	94903	Wooldridge MRS William P
San Rafael	94912	Herrick MR & MRS B Brooks JR
San Ramon	94583	Lee MR & MRS Jeffrey A
San Ramon	94583	Oestreich MR William A
San Ysidro	92173	Jernigan MR & MRS Stephen A
Santa Barbara	93018	Herman MR & MRS Christian M
Santa Barbara	93101	Andrews MR Brian W
Santa Barbara	93101	Aquino MISS Jeannette Cox
Santa Barbara	93103	Carlson MRS Robert F
Santa Barbara	93103	Collier MISS (DR) Mary B
Santa Barbara	93103	Mack MR & MRS Thomas H
Santa Barbara	93103	Makepeace MS Marilyn A
Santa Barbara	93103	Margolis MR John Prince
Santa Barbara	93103	Regan MR & MRS Robert J
Santa Barbara	93105	Black DR & MRS William M
Santa Barbara	93105	Burke MR & MRS William B
Santa Barbara	93105	Clark MISS Carnzu A
Santa Barbara	93105	Hintzen MR & MRS John A
Santa Barbara	93105	Loizeaux MS Christine
Santa Barbara	93105	Nash DR & MRS (DR) A E Keir
Santa Barbara	93105	Woodhouse THE REV DR Marjorie M
Santa Barbara	93108	Amory MRS Carolyn P
Santa Barbara	93108	Amory MRS Thomas Carhart
Santa Barbara	93108	Breeden MRS Greta T
Santa Barbara	93108	Brittingham MR & MRS Scott C
Santa Barbara	93108	Bryant MRS Gloria W
Santa Barbara	93108	Dillon MRS Herbert L JR
Santa Barbara	93108	Doubleday MR & MRS Edward B
Santa Barbara	93108	Farrell MR & MRS Bowen C
Santa Barbara	93108	Foster MRS Hugh K
Santa Barbara	93108	Gross MRS Shirley Davis
Santa Barbara	93108	Hagerman MR & MRS George W
Santa Barbara	93108	Huey MR & MRS G H Harris
Santa Barbara	93108	Ittner MR & MRS George D
Santa Barbara	93108	Kendrick DR & MRS Frank E JR
Santa Barbara	93108	Kusserow MR & MRS Paul B
Santa Barbara	93108	Miller MRS Robert N 3D
Santa Barbara	93108	Moore MRS Stanley W
Santa Barbara	93108	Morton-Smith DR William S
Santa Barbara	93108	Petersen MR & MRS Charles D
Santa Barbara	93108	Platt MRS Diana D
Santa Barbara	93108	Pulitzer MR & MRS Michael E
Santa Barbara	93108	Rake MISS Susannah E
Santa Barbara	93108	Reed MRS Frank Fremont II
Santa Barbara	93108	Renfrew MRS Susan G
Santa Barbara	93108	Supplee MRS Cochran B
Santa Barbara	93108	Valentine MRS Edward R
Santa Barbara	93108	von Raits MR Peter de P
Santa Barbara	93108	Wray MR & MRS Michael B
Santa Barbara	93109	Blass MR & MRS Stephen M
Santa Barbara	93109	Bryant MRS S Beard
Santa Barbara	93109	Dallett MR & MRS Richard S S
Santa Barbara	93109	Keshen DR & MRS (DR) Tamir H
Santa Barbara	93110	Econn MR & MRS Gregory W
Santa Barbara	93111	Taylor MR & MRS Kirk A
Santa Barbara	93111	Wilson MR & MRS (DR) Mark D
Santa Barbara	93121	Wilson MS Signe E
Santa Barbara	93150	Kirst MRS Lynn P
Santa Barbara	93190	Hoffman MS Lori & Ogden MR William
Santa Barbara	94117	Heatwole MR & MRS Mark M
Santa Clara	95050	Davis MR & MRS Gordon R
Santa Cruz	95060	Millard MISS Olivia P
Santa Cruz	95060	Schwab MR & MRS Matthew R
Santa Cruz	95062	Hooker MR & MRS Henry G
Santa Cruz	95062	Meynell MR Richard Balfour
Santa Cruz	95062	Smith MR & MRS James P III
Santa Monica	90402	Barrie MRS George 4TH
Santa Monica	90402	Kissinger MR & MRS David A
Santa Monica	90402	Register MR & MRS Peter E
Santa Monica	90402	Sanchez-Elia MR Diego
Santa Monica	90402	Schotz MR & MRS Jon P
Santa Monica	90402	Sobelle MR & MRS Richard E
Santa Monica	90402	Stern DR W Eugene
Santa Monica	90402	Tandy MR J Napper II & Firestone MS Mary C
Santa Monica	90402	Woods MR & MRS Donald F JR
Santa Monica	90403	Brown MR & MRS Mason B
Santa Monica	90403	de Wolf MS Ainslee Colt
Santa Monica	90403	Fuller MISS Susannah J
Santa Monica	90403	Gimelstob MR & MRS Justin J
Santa Monica	90403	Greenwood MR & MRS Wixon A
Santa Monica	90403	Lincoln MRS & DR Thomas L
Santa Monica	90403	MacWilliams MR & MRS W Brewster
Santa Monica	90403	Maher MR William J
Santa Monica	90403	Mullen MR & MRS (DR) Edward J JR
Santa Monica	90403	O'Shea MR Sean T
Santa Monica	90403	Pulling MS Victoria Sonne
Santa Monica	90403	Rust MR Edgar C III
Santa Monica	90403	Senter MS Alexis C
Santa Monica	90403	Williams MR & MRS Arnold F
Santa Monica	90404	Siebens MR & MRS Geoffrey A
Santa Monica	90405	Dewey MR Frederick R
Santa Monica	90405	Gallagher MR & MRS Rollin McC IV
Santa Monica	90405	Johnson MR & MRS Scott E

Santa Monica .... 90405 .... Vogel MR & MRS Ralph B 2D
Santa Monica .... 90406 .... Goodhue MR Nicholas B
Santa Rosa...................... 95401......... Good MR Matthew K & Cabral MS (DR) Emily C
Santa Rosa...................... 95403......... Morrison MR & MRS Andrew P
Santa Rosa...................... 95404 .... Garrett DR & MRS Thomas H
Santa Rosa...................... 95409 .... Desmond MRS Anne Hoge
Santa Rosa...................... 95409 .... Hill MR & MRS Jeffrey D
Santa Rosa...................... 95409 .... Kenney MR & MRS Charles C II
Santa Rosa...................... 95409 .... Taylor MR & MRS Benjamin R
Santa Ynez .... 93460 .... Duxbury MRS Pauline C
Santa Ynez .... 93460 .... Moran MRS (REV) Lansing S
Saratoga.......................... 95070......... Cousins MR & MRS Robert E
Saratoga.......................... 95070......... Cunningham MR & MRS Stephen S
Sausalito......................... 94965......... Anderson MISS Sara Jane
Sausalito......................... 94965......... Barker MR & MRS Morgan R
Sausalito......................... 94965......... Cavallero MR & MRS Robert C
Sausalito......................... 94965......... Crowley MR & MRS Amos H 3D
Sausalito......................... 94965......... Edwards MRS Ellen T
Sausalito......................... 94965......... Franks MR & MRS F Benjamin IV
Sausalito......................... 94965......... Hambleton MR Charles M
Sausalito......................... 94965......... Holbrook MRS Donald R
Sausalito......................... 94965......... James MR & MRS Geoffrey L
Sausalito......................... 94965......... Kuhn MR Dixon S
Sausalito......................... 94965......... Leonard MRS Jeanne P
Sausalito......................... 94965......... Major MR Robert A JR
Sausalito......................... 94965......... Munson MISS Marjorie S
Sausalito......................... 94965......... Newhall MR & MRS George A III
Sausalito......................... 94965......... Nilsson Levin MISS Lisa D
Sausalito......................... 94965......... Pomeroy MS Margaret C
Sausalito......................... 94965......... Reich MR & MRS Ronald E
Sausalito......................... 94965......... Rhinelander MISS Clare H
Sausalito......................... 94965......... Robinson MRS C David
Sausalito......................... 94965......... Roby MRS Cynthia H
Sausalito......................... 94965......... Smith MR Philip MacAulay
Sausalito......................... 94965......... Walsham DR & MRS John G
Sausalito......................... 94965......... Watson MS Lucinda B
Sausalito......................... 94965......... White MISS Sandra Macleod
Sausalito......................... 94966......... Leonard MISS Stephanie
Sausalito......................... 94966......... McMillen MRS Julie C
Sherman Oaks .... 91401 .... Richmond MS Janet V V M
Sherman Oaks .... 91403 .... Gould MRS Kira
Simi Valley...................... 93065......... Lakeman MRS David J
Simi Valley...................... 93065......... Lott MR & MRS Edward M 3D
Solana Beach .... 92075......... Fenton MR & MRS Martin JR
Solana Beach .... 92075......... Hatch MRS L Robertson
Solana Beach .... 92075......... Rogers CAPT (RET) & MRS Thomas W
Solana Beach .... 92075......... Schieffelin MR & MRS Nicholas W
Soledad........................... 93960......... Beckett MR & MRS Paul T
Solvang........................... 93463......... Firestone MR & MRS A Brooks
Solvang........................... 93463......... Firestone MR & MRS Adam B
Solvang........................... 93463......... Taliaferro MR & MRS Robin L
Sonoma........................... 95476......... Browning MISS Kim
Sonoma........................... 95476......... Crutchfield DR Susan
Sonoma........................... 95476......... Evans MRS John D
Sonoma........................... 95476......... Latini MRS Francesco B
Sonoma........................... 95476......... Leach MR & MRS Paul C
Sonoma........................... 95476......... Maushardt MR & MRS Peter W
Sonoma........................... 95476......... O'Hara MR & MRS Peter J
Sonoma........................... 95476......... Shoop MR & MRS Hugh K III
Sonoma........................... 95476......... Townsend MRS Stephen S JR
Sonoma........................... 95476......... Weeks MISS Ann S
Sonoma........................... 95476......... Woodward MISS P Lynn
Sonoma........................... 95476......... Woodward MR & MRS W Philip
South Lake Tahoe.......... 96150......... Langlois MR & MRS Ralph M
South Lake Tahoe.......... 96158......... Bates MR Lesley A
South Pasadena............. 91030......... Easterby MR Stewart D IV
South Pasadena............. 91030......... Howe MR & MRS Jonathan S
South Pasadena............. 91030......... Pile MR & MRS Sterling 3D
St Helena .... 94574......... Garrett MR & MRS Thomas H JR
St Helena .... 94574......... Gilpin MR & MRS Lawrence M
St Helena .... 94574......... Haslip MR & MRS James C
St Helena .... 94574......... Hayne MR & MRS William A 4TH
St Helena .... 94574......... Livermore MS Sara Sealy
St Helena .... 94574......... Norfleet MR & MRS Philip S
St Helena .... 94574......... Pohlers MRS Mary Judith B
St Helena .... 94574......... Smith MR & MRS W S Burges
St Helena .... 94574......... Stockton MRS Diana H
St Helena .... 94574......... Upton MR & MRS W Sloan
St Helena .... 94574......... Williamson MISS Charlotte M
Stanford.......................... 94305......... Gardner MRS John W
Stanford.......................... 94305......... Hanushek MR & MRS Eric A
Stanford.......................... 94305......... Siegman MRS Anthony E
Stinson Beach................ 94970......... Banta MR & MRS Philip L
Stinson Beach................ 94970......... Felch MR & MRS William C JR
Stinson Beach................ 94970......... Jones MR John Lowell
Stockton .... 95204......... Hachman MR & MRS Timothy J
Stockton .... 95207......... Melone MRS Jonathan
Stockton .... 95209......... Fox MS Lydia K
Stockton .... 95219......... Hilken MR & MRS Keith D
Studio City..................... 91604......... Carter MR & MRS Jeffrey C
Studio City..................... 91604......... Wallace MR Peter de L
Summerland .... 93067......... Blunt MRS Sara Conrad
Summerland .... 93067......... Bongaerts MR & MRS Joost J
Sunnyvale .... 94085......... Ziegler MR Frederick S
Sunnyvale .... 94086 .... Martin MR & MRS Dana B
Sunnyvale .... 94087......... Lee MS Antonia S
Sunol.............................. 94586......... Barnes MR & MRS Graham R
Tahoe City...................... 96145......... Douglas MR & MRS David H
Tahoma .... 96142......... Smith MR & MRS Jonathan T
Tarzana.......................... 91356......... Ehrlich MR & MRS Scott H
Temecula........................ 92591......... Biddle MR & MRS Nicholas JR
Temecula........................ 92593......... Wiley MRS Richard M
Templeton...................... 93465......... Coleman MRS R Jackson
Templeton...................... 93465......... Fowler MR Lindsay Anderson
The Sea Ranch............... 95497......... Kleeman MR Michael J
Thousand Oaks............. 91360......... Weld MRS Lothrop M JR
Tiburon .... 94920......... Ames MR & MRS Alden 3D
Tiburon .... 94920......... Callander DR & MRS Peter W
Tiburon .... 94920......... Carroll MR & MRS Brewster B
Tiburon .... 94920......... Erickson MRS Valerie
Tiburon .... 94920......... Ewald MR & MRS Charles R
Tiburon .... 94920......... Gale MRS Daniel B II
Tiburon .... 94920......... Harle MR & MRS Jonathan E
Tiburon .... 94920......... Jenkins MS Alexandra
Tiburon .... 94920......... Lovejoy MR Sherwood JR
Tiburon .... 94920......... Moorhouse MR & MRS William H JR
Tiburon .... 94920......... Pressley MR & MRS James F 4TH
Tiburon .... 94920......... Reynolds MRS Ralph E
Tiburon .... 94920......... Scheetz MR & MRS Edwin F III
Tiburon .... 94920......... Schneider MR & MRS Edward J IV
Tiburon .... 94920......... Wilhelm MR & MRS Brian T
Tiburon .... 94920......... Zanze MR Anthony O
Tiburon .... 94920......... Ziesing MR & MRS Hunter S
Toluca Lake.................... 91602......... Roski MS Patricia Reon
Topanga.......................... 90290......... Everett MISS Elizabeth E
Topanga.......................... 90290......... Nalle MR & MRS Edwin N B
Topanga.......................... 90290......... Shore MR & MRS Daniel B
Topanga.......................... 90290......... Tomerlin MR & MRS Monte Durham
Truckee........................... 96160......... Eaton DR & MRS John M
Truckee........................... 96160......... Watson MRS Katrine
Truckee........................... 96161 .... Bassett MR & MRS Todd C
Truckee........................... 96161 .... Jacopi MR & MRS Gordon J

Truckee, CA—Boulder, CO

Truckee 96161 Tornga MR & MRS Andrew J
Valencia 91355 Bigelow MR & MRS John I H
Vallejo 94590 Mein MR & MRS Gardner W
Valley View 91607 Wallace MS Helen W
Valley Village 91607 Allen MR Kevin S
Van Nuys 91406 Breithaupt MR Richard H JR
Venice 90291 Browne MR Junius H JR
Venice 90291 Cudney MR & MRS Luke A
Venice 90291 de Montebello MR & MRS Marc L
Venice 90291 Gaston MRS Lynch
Venice 90291 Parker MR Richard S JR
Venice 90291 Pohl MR & MRS Otto C
Venice 90291 Reilly MR & MRS Jamie S T
Venice 90291 Solomon MR & MRS John W
Venice 90291 Wadick MISS Miriam W
Venice 90291 Waggaman MR & MRS William M
Ventura 93001 Crew MR & MRS William W
Ventura 93001 Tudor MR Geoffrey W
Ventura 93003 Perry DR J Mitchell
Vista 92083 Wagstaff MR & MRS Richard B
Walnut Creek 94595 Hume MR & MRS R Stuart JR
Walnut Creek 94595 Lott MRS Edward M JR
Walnut Creek 94595 Moore MR J Bart
Walnut Creek 94595 Nutting MRS Raymond J
Walnut Creek 94595 Waram MRS J Thomas C
Walnut Creek 94595 Wright MR & MRS Carroll A
Walnut Creek 94596 Clopp MRS Mary P
Walnut Creek 94596 Mitchell MR & MRS David R
Walnut Creek 94596 Rogers MRS Robert V
Walnut Creek 94597 Watson MRS Douglas
Walnut Creek 94598 Davis MR & MRS Peter W
Walnut Creek 94598 Moore MR & MRS Alexander R
West Covina 91791 Seldon MRS M Robert
West Hills 91304 Worrell MS Sharyn D
West Hollywood 90046 Everett MR Morris 3D
West Hollywood 90046 Harrington MISS Lauren S
West Hollywood 90046 Sterling MR Ian W
West Hollywood 90046 Stoddart MS Nancy
West Hollywood 90046 Sudler MR Carroll H 4TH
West Hollywood 90069 Day MR & MRS Peter S
West Hollywood 90069 Lippincott MR William D'O 2D
West Los Angeles 90064 Holden MISS Ellen B
Williams 95987 LaGrande MR & MRS Kenneth M
Windsor 95492 Fritz MR & MRS Clayton B
Windsor 95492 Mooney MRS Alan P
Woodbridge 95258 Husting MR & MRS James C
Woodland 91364 Loeb MR Nicholas M
Woodland 95695 Loud MS Elizabeth A
Woodland Hills 91364 Pereira MR & MRS Gaston E
Woodland Hills 91367 Butler MS Diane L
Woodside 94062 Barry MS Ann Fay
Woodside 94062 Bulkeley MR & MRS John Z
Woodside 94062 Cahill MR J Peter
Woodside 94062 Caldwell MR & MRS James E JR
Woodside 94062 Cleary MR & MRS Michael J
Woodside 94062 Dickey MRS Frank B
Woodside 94062 Donohoe MRS Edward
Woodside 94062 Evans MR & MRS Oliver A
Woodside 94062 Gonzalez MRS Richard I
Woodside 94062 Harper MR & MRS Owen H
Woodside 94062 Hills MRS Reuben W 3D
Woodside 94062 Hunter MR & MRS Derek K
Woodside 94062 Jamplis MRS Robert W
Woodside 94062 Jones MR & MRS Robert Trent JR
Woodside 94062 Kerko MR & MRS David M
Woodside 94062 Knight MR & MRS Steven N
Woodside 94062 Patterson MR & MRS Victor E
Woodside 94062 Phipps MR & MRS George D
Woodside 94062 Poole MRS Gordon L
Woodside 94062 Quinby MR & MRS Jonathan S
Woodside 94062 Thompson MRS Morley P
Woodside 94062 Wallace MRS M Kelleher
Woodside 94062 Wickett MR & MRS James F
Yountville 94599 Cleveland MR & MRS Charles A JR
Yountville 94599 Moffitt MS (DR) Elizabeth

COLORADO

Arvada 80007 Sterrett MR & MRS William D 3D
Aspen 81611 Adam MR & MRS Karl W
Aspen 81611 Cleveland MR Clement 4TH
Aspen 81611 Cooley MR & MRS John B JR
Aspen 81611 DeRosa MR & MRS Thomas J
Aspen 81611 Fisher MISS Elsie M
Aspen 81611 Foster MR & MRS David W
Aspen 81611 Gaston MR & MRS John E
Aspen 81611 Godfrey MR & MRS Andrew H
Aspen 81611 Holton MR & MRS Robert H
Aspen 81611 Newton MS Barbara L
Aspen 81611 Rutgers MR & MRS Anthony L
Aspen 81611 Whipple MR & MRS George S
Aspen 81612 Augur MR & MRS Harrison H
Aspen 81612 Blodgett MR & MRS Mark W
Aspen 81612 Hritz MRS Tracy D
Aspen 81612 Hunt MR William O JR
Aspen 81612 Myrin MR Cuthbert L JR & Madden MR Walter R
Aspen 81612 Sadron MRS Alexandra
Aurora 80014 Conrad MR & MRS Thomas V
Avon 81620 Ayers MR & MRS David F P II
Avon 81620 Beavers MR & MRS Ryan E
Avon 81620 Day MRS Gail E
Avon 81620 Pope MR & MRS Frederick C B
Basalt 81621 Curry MR & MRS Patrick D
Basalt 81621 Hogen MR Timothy L
Boulder 80301 Cooper MR & MRS Charles W
Boulder 80301 Enos MR & MRS Alanson T V
Boulder 80301 Ford MR & MRS Peter B
Boulder 80301 McAllister MR Bruce R
Boulder 80301 Simpson MRS William C
Boulder 80301 Talmage MR & MRS E T Hunt 3D
Boulder 80301 Young MR Webster A
Boulder 80302 Grauer MR & MRS Frederick M JR
Boulder 80302 Long MR & MRS Thomas F
Boulder 80302 Merryman MR & MRS L James
Boulder 80302 Robinson MR & MRS Beverley
Boulder 80302 Simpson MR & MRS William J
Boulder 80302 Taylor MR & MRS John I JR
Boulder 80302 Thomas MR & MRS Kyle W
Boulder 80302 Thorne DR Oakleigh II
Boulder 80302 Wirth MR & MRS Christopher W
Boulder 80303 Bakewell MISS Claire McN
Boulder 80303 Barth MR & MRS Gilbert R
Boulder 80303 Wilder MR Charlton M
Boulder 80304 Allen MR & MRS Samuel W
Boulder 80304 Bennett MR Tyson & Conway MS Martine
Boulder 80304 Bonetti MR & MRS Paolo M
Boulder 80304 Dana MR & MRS John P
Boulder 80304 Davison MR & MRS Andrew B
Boulder 80304 Espinosa de los Monteros MS Rebecca M
Boulder 80304 Glass MR & MRS Peter J P
Boulder 80304 McKnight MRS Diana A

Boulder, CO—Englewood, CO

Boulder	80304	Van Ness MRS A Wulfing
Boulder	80304	Woodruff MR Robert A
Boulder	80305	Bautista-Biddle MS Martha M & Bautista-Biddle MS Candice J B
Boulder	80305	Lawrence MR & MRS Joseph C
Boulder	80305	Levandowski DR & MRS William B
Boulder	80305	Livingston MISS Eleanor M
Bow Mar	80123	Larkin MR & MRS Fred C
Breckenridge	80424	Krueger MR & MRS Myron W III
Breckenridge	80424	ReQua MS Katherine F
Brighton	80602	Stoddart MISS Anne E
Broomfield	80023	Stewart MR Christopher F
Broomfield	80023	van Orman MR & MRS Cameron W
Carbondale	81623	Eustis MRS George P
Carbondale	81623	Strang MR & MRS Michael L
Castle Rock	80104	Pritzlaff MR & MRS John C 3D
Castle Rock	80108	Pfeiffer MR & MRS John S
Centennial	80112	Bayne MRS Martha G
Centennial	80112	Lordi MR & MRS Alan A
Centennial	80112	Pierpont MR & MRS Douglas C
Cherry Hills	80111	Ripley MR Henry B H 3D
Cherry Hills Village	80113	White MR & MRS Thomas J SR
Collbran	81624	Coe MR Robert S
Collbran	81624	Coe MRS Diana D
Colorado Springs	80903	Dew MR T Roderick
Colorado Springs	80903	Smith MISS Jessica W
Colorado Springs	80904	Reynolds MR & MRS Wiley R III
Colorado Springs	80906	Fischer MR & MRS Lindsay E
Colorado Springs	80906	Moore MR & MRS Christian A
Colorado Springs	80906	Morrison MR & MRS James R
Colorado Springs	80906	Tutt MR & MRS R Thayer JR
Colorado Springs	80907	Bridgman MR & MRS Victor H 3D
Colorado Springs	80920	McConnell MR & MRS Scott K
Creede	81130	Augur MR & MRS Avery H
Crested Butte	81224	Wyckoff MR & MRS Ashton G
Del Norte	81132	McCammon MR David G
Denver	80202	Lawrence MR John U
Denver	80202	Rich MR & MRS Robert S
Denver	80205	Hodges MR Arthur C JR
Denver	80206	Alijani DR & MRS A Todd
Denver	80206	Berkey MR Charles Peter
Denver	80206	de Koning MR & MRS Kendrik J JR
Denver	80206	Hoversten MRS Alison H
Denver	80206	Kenney MR Horace S 3D
Denver	80206	Lee MRS W Ashton
Denver	80206	Reid DR & MRS Mark B
Denver	80206	Ripley MRS Dianne
Denver	80206	Ross MISS Gwen
Denver	80206	Valentine MRS Bruce
Denver	80209	Close MRS Edward B
Denver	80209	Durham MR B Grady & Payne Durham MS Lori
Denver	80209	Goddard MR Edward Q
Denver	80209	Grey MRS Schuyler E
Denver	80209	Hamilton MR & MRS Crawford M
Denver	80209	Hamilton MRS Frederic C
Denver	80209	Hansen MS Gillette K
Denver	80209	Kellen MR & MRS James M
Denver	80209	Kellogg MISS Consuelo M
Denver	80209	Kirkpatrick MRS E Tieken
Denver	80209	Stoddart MR John T 3D
Denver	80209	Weil MR & MRS Richard MacC
Denver	80210	Alexander MR & MRS Edward T
Denver	80210	Clay MR & MRS Fraser G
Denver	80210	Cobb MR & MRS Joshua S
Denver	80210	Driscoll MR & MRS Lee F 3D
Denver	80210	Kinney MR & MRS Jeremy F
Denver	80210	McKelvy MRS F Shepard
Denver	80210	Smithers MR & MRS P Christopher
Denver	80210	Wood MRS Benjamin S JR
Denver	80210	Wulsin MRS Pamela P
Denver	80211	Lee MR & MRS Thomas G
Denver	80212	Holiday MR & MRS Scott A
Denver	80212	Marsters MISS Amy V
Denver	80218	Anderson MRS Martin E JR
Denver	80218	Bain MR Donald K
Denver	80218	Bermingham MR John R
Denver	80218	Connors MR & MRS Edward P
Denver	80218	Cox MR & MRS Louis A JR
Denver	80218	Labrot MRS Elizabeth B
Denver	80218	Mathias MR & MRS David H
Denver	80218	Moore MR & MRS David A C
Denver	80218	Shannon MRS James R
Denver	80218	Sibley MR & MRS David P
Denver	80218	Stokes MISS Anne Kemble
Denver	80218	Tieken MISS Nancy B
Denver	80219	Russell MR & MRS M Cannon JR
Denver	80220	Blaustein MR & MRS Andrew L
Denver	80220	Creighton MR & MRS (DR) Thomas E JR
Denver	80220	Gallaway MR & MRS Steven M
Denver	80220	Grey MR & MRS Schuyler E III
Denver	80220	Hawkey MR & MRS Harold W JR
Denver	80220	Lupo MR & MRS Christopher M
Denver	80220	Ransom MR & MRS Donald L JR
Denver	80220	Shaw MS (DR) Deborah S
Denver	80220	Sidley MRS William F
Denver	80220	Valentine MR & MRS Bruce JR
Denver	80220	Woody MR & MRS Bernard L
Denver	80222	Connors MR Timothy P
Denver	80222	Connors MS Hope B
Denver	80232	Lukens MR David B & Newton MS Susan K
Denver	80237	Herrlinger MR & MRS Mark H
Denver	80237	Jolas MR & MRS Philip G
Denver	80238	Cobb MR & MRS John W
Denver	80246	Luppens MR & MRS Carl H
Denver	80246	White MR Thomas J JR
Denver	80247	Klenk MRS Eugene L
Denver	80247	Whiteman MR Daniel S III
Dillon	80435	Kraatz MR & MRS Erik C
Dillon	80435	Lloyd MR & MRS H Gates JR
Dillon	80435	Smith MR & MRS Nicholas O
Durango	81301	Keen MR & MRS George B
Durango	81301	Oldstone MR & MRS Michael B A JR
Durango	81301	Wharton MRS Charles W III
Eagle	81631	Foster MR & MRS H Crosby II
Eagle	81631	Landreth MR & MRS John T JR
Eagle	81631	Macy MR Josiah 3D
Eagle	81631	Spaeth MR & MRS E Alexander
Edwards	81632	Bergh MR & MRS R Throop
Elizabeth	80107	Duke MR & MRS H Benjamin 3D
Englewood	80110	Douglass MRS Louise J
Englewood	80110	Kurtz MR & MRS Charles H
Englewood	80110	Sidley MR Peter F
Englewood	80110	White MR & MRS E Laurence 3D
Englewood	80111	Gawthrop MR & MRS Alfred 3D
Englewood	80112	Hickey MRS Carolyn B
Englewood	80112	Lawrence MR Richard S
Englewood	80113	Bittman MR Chris & Noble MS Kenda
Englewood	80113	Clute MR & MRS Peter R
Englewood	80113	Ford MR & MRS Mills H
Englewood	80113	Hamilton MS Elsie C
Englewood	80113	MacKenzie MR & MRS Donald
Englewood	80113	Rand MR & MRS John F

To nominate a candidate for the Social Register Association, please email: SRCommittee@thesocialregister.org

Evergreen, CO—Cheshire, CT

Evergreen	80439	Connell MRS Elisabeth A
Evergreen	80439	Cunningham MR & MRS Michael J
Evergreen	80439	Humes MR & MRS William O
Evergreen	80439	McMahon MS Kelly Ann
Evergreen	80439	Wilson MR & MRS Michael S
Fort Collins	80526	Gagné MR & MRS Roderick B
Franktown	80016	Rockwell MR Thomas E
Franktown	80116	Ayers MR & MRS David W P
Frisco	80443	Briggs MR J Alden JR
Fruita	81521	Bigelow MS Bettina A
Ft Collins	80521	Edwards MR & MRS L Michael
Ft Collins	80521	Lawrence MR J Townsend JR
Ft Collins	80521	White MISS Hilary Bowen
Ft Collins	80524	Jeanes MR & MRS Henry T
Ft Collins	80524	Ostheimer MR & MRS John M
Ft Collins	80525	Currier MR & MRS E Gray
Ft Collins	80525	Moran MR & MRS John Patrick JR
Ft Collins	80525	Peterkin MISS Kate
Ft Collins	80525	Withers MR & MRS William Z
Ft Collins	80526	Birmingham MR & MRS John M
Georgetown	804444	Hale MRS Thomas H
Glenwood Springs	81602	Odén MISS Lisbeth N
Golden	80401	Dinegar MR & MRS Leonard A
Golden	80401	Keating MR & MRS Cletus 3D
Golden	80403	Emig REV & MRS James A
Granby	80446	Rienhoff MRS MacCallum
Grand Junction	81505	Davis MRS S Boyer
Grand Junction	81507	Maurer MR & MRS Donald E
Greeley	80634	Goehring MR & MRS Westlake L
Greenwood Village	80111	Kelley MR & MRS Douglas A
Greenwood Village	80111	Rutgers MRS Nicholas G JR
Highlands Ranch	80126	Billings MR & MRS Charles A JR
Highlands Ranch	80126	von Russow MR & MRS Wolfgang L
Highlands Ranch	80130	Hoversten MISS Barbara S
Jamestown	80455	Armour MS Hilda L
Lafayette	80026	de Labar MRS Margot
Lafayette	80026	Renchard MS Cynthia
Lafayette	80026	Wood MR David W III
Lakewood	80227	Cannon MS Sue
Lakewood	80228	Romano MR & MRS Mark S
Littleton	80120	Trask MR & MRS Frederick K 3D
Littleton	80121	Duke MRS H Benjamin JR
Littleton	80121	Hoffman MR & MRS Martin C JR
Littleton	80121	Loucks MR & MRS Thomas A
Littleton	80121	Talbot MR & MRS Bradford C
Littleton	80123	Heckscher MR & MRS Stevens II
Littleton	80123	Matthias MR & MRS William W
Littleton	80123	McGuinness MR & MRS Aims C JR
Littleton	80123	Peterson MR & MRS David S
Littleton	80123	Rollhaus MR & MRS Philip E III
Littleton	80127	Whiteman MR George M
Littleton	80128	Herzl MR & MRS Alfred
Littleton	80128	Vander Poel MR Halsted B 2D
Longmont	80503	Brown MRS Edward O
Longmont	80503	Doering MR & MRS Edmund J 4TH
Longmont	80503	Smith MR & MRS Robert T
Louisville	80027	McAleenan MRS Clifford C
Loveland	80538	Carty MR Steven M & Wright MS Hilary C
Lyons	80540	Jones MR & MRS (DR) Dayton L
Mesa	81643	Ames MS Nathalie E
Monument	80132	Ragusa MR & MRS Milton E JR
Niwot	80503	Beuf MRS Francesco G
Parker	80134	Alcott MR & MRS Leverett C
Pueblo	81001	Humes MR & MRS James C
Ridgway	81432	Dicus DR & MRS Paul E
Silverthorne	80498	Rutherfurd MR & MRS Hugo JR
Silverthorne	80498	Stetson MRS Griswold
Snowmass Village	81615	Hart MR & MRS George D JR
Snowmass Village	81615	Shallcross MR & MRS James E
South Fork	81154	Hayes MRS Patrick H JR
Steamboat Springs	80477	Lambart MR & MRS Harry S
Steamboat Springs	80477	Van Rensselaer MISS Kate M
Steamboat Springs	80488	Larson MR & MRS James W
Telluride	81435	Branscomb MR & MRS Lewis McA
Telluride	81435	Hanson MR & MRS Geoffrey S
Telluride	81435	Winter MR & MRS Frank C II
Vail	81657	Battin MR Peter S
Vail	81657	Cook MRS Laura A
Vail	81657	Dandy MR & MRS Walter E III
Vail	81657	Hollenbeck MR & MRS Drew H
Vail	81657	Hoversten MR & MRS Philip E
Vail	81657	Savin MR & MRS Adam Maxwell
Vail	81657	Stockmar MR J Brian
Vail	81658	Lyons MR & MRS John P

CONNECTICUT

Andover	06232	Bolton MR John B
Ansonia	06401	Longcore MR Matthew J
Ashford	06278	Pinkham MRS Arthur D JR
Avon	06001	Barzun MS H Kathleen
Avon	06001	Colket MR & MRS Meredith B 3D
Avon	06001	Guida MR & MRS James F
Avon	06001	Levin MR & MRS Michael B
Avon	06001	MacColl MRS N Alexander JR
Avon	06001	Ryan MRS Jennifer
Avon	06001	Tilney MR & MRS James W
Avon	06001	Timme MR & MRS W Frederick III
Bethany	06524	Enders MR Thomas O & Thoron MS Elise
Bethel	06801	Siddig MR & MRS Zaid
Black Rock	06605	Williams MR & MRS Davidson D
Bloomfield	06002	Blackwood MR & MRS Terence R
Bloomfield	06002	Fowler MR & MRS Gordon B
Bloomfield	06002	Furse MISS Elizabeth W
Bloomfield	06002	Grover MRS Robinson A
Bloomfield	06002	Hatch MR & MRS W Ross
Bloomfield	06002	Loomis MRS A Worthington
Bloomfield	06002	Morris MR Thomas
Bloomfield	06002	Sargent MRS Edward C
Bloomfield	06002	Wheat MR & MRS John H P
Bloomfield	06002	Wright MR & MRS Christopher Q
Branford	06405	Colyer MR Andrew J & Henry MS (DR) Marion C W
Branford	06405	Gottschalk DR & MRS (DR) P Christopher H
Branford	06405	Wierzel MR Robert M & Sugg MS P Michele
Branford	06405	Wise MR Parker S
Bridgeport	06604	Kerekes de Kelecsény MR Tibor
Bridgeport	06604	Shaw MR Robert G
Bridgeport	06605	Curran MR & MRS H Peter
Bridgeport	06605	O'Donnell MR & MRS Robert J JR
Bridgeport	06605	Symington MRS Nancy R
Bridgewater	06752	Pendergast MR & MRS Stephen W
Brookfield	06804	Ayvazian MR & MRS Ara K
Brookfield	06804	Scott MRS Henry C JR
Brooklyn	06234	Newell MR John O JR
Burlington	06013	Hanson MR & MRS John H JR
Canaan	06018	Morgan MR John S
Canton	06019	Adams MR Bryan G
Canton	06019	Brainard MR & MRS Peter Bulkeley
Canton	06019	Duncan MR & MRS William M
Canton	06019	Stanley MR & MRS Frank L
Cheshire	06410	Corcoran MR & MRS John F

Cheshire, CT—Easton, CT

Cheshire	06410	Ingerson MRS Sarah D
Cheshire	06410	McKee MISS M Jean
Chester	06412	Bradley MR & MRS George C JR
Chester	06412	Hoehnebart MR Victor
Chester	06412	Hoehnebart MRS C Hutchings
Chester	06412	Johnson MR & MRS Stuart C
Chester	06412	Whitmer MR & MRS Robert F IV
Collinsville	06019	Beir MR John A
Cornwall Bridge	06754	Purnell MISS Marguerite W
Cornwall Bridge	06754	Ule MR Guy Maxwell JR
Cos Cob	06807	Allardt MR & MRS Frederick E A III
Cos Cob	06807	Anderson MRS Susan L M Detchon
Cos Cob	06807	Appleman MR & MRS Craig C
Cos Cob	06807	Boutelle MR & MRS James G
Cos Cob	06807	Cabot MR & MRS James W
Cos Cob	06807	Chickering MR & MRS Philip D
Cos Cob	06807	Costantino MR & MRS Anthony P
Cos Cob	06807	Cragin MR & MRS Stuart W JR
Cos Cob	06807	Curran MR Donald E III
Cos Cob	06807	Elwell MR & MRS Scott P
Cos Cob	06807	Howell MRS Sarah T
Cos Cob	06807	Irvine MR Kenneth A
Cos Cob	06807	Jervis MR & MRS Wayne T III
Cos Cob	06807	Litchfield MR Christopher S
Cos Cob	06807	McKinley MRS (REV) Ellen B
Cos Cob	06807	Merrill MR & MRS George V
Cos Cob	06807	O'Brien MR & MRS Justus J
Cos Cob	06807	Ogilvy MS Jeannette M
Cos Cob	06807	Oliver MR & MRS Andrew II
Cos Cob	06807	O'Shaughnessy MR & MRS James P
Cos Cob	06807	Sill MR & MRS Louis F
Cos Cob	06807	Sterling MR & MRS Robert L
Cos Cob	06807	Welch MR Noble
Cromwell	06416	Coolidge REV & MRS Edward C
Danbury	06810	Patricola MR Steven L
Darien	06820	Arguimbau MR & MRS Vincent C 3D
Darien	06820	Bailey MRS Glenn W
Darien	06820	Baird MR Gordon A
Darien	06820	Baker MR & MRS Wilder Du Puy
Darien	06820	Baldwin MR & MRS Rosecrans 3D
Darien	06820	Barker MR & MRS James R
Darien	06820	Bartels MR & MRS Charles A
Darien	06820	Bass MR & MRS Shannon M
Darien	06820	Battey MR & MRS William R JR
Darien	06820	Baurmeister MR & MRS Eric J
Darien	06820	Bayne MR & MRS David F
Darien	06820	Boehm MR August W & Hubner MS Melissa B
Darien	06820	Bowditch MR & MRS Charles F
Darien	06820	Bradbury MR John Randolph JR
Darien	06820	Bronson MRS Van Rensselaer
Darien	06820	Bushing MR & MRS F William 3D
Darien	06820	Carter MR & MRS Warwick M JR
Darien	06820	Cooke MR & MRS H Emerson
Darien	06820	Cruice MR & MRS J Seth H JR
Darien	06820	Cutler MR & MRS Earle N 4TH
Darien	06820	Dale MR & MRS Thomas D
Darien	06820	de Carbonnel MR & MRS Charles E
Darien	06820	Dewey MR & MRS Chauncey F JR
Darien	06820	DeWitt MR & MRS Anthony P
Darien	06820	Doering MR & MRS Peter E
Darien	06820	du Pont MR & MRS George F
Darien	06820	Eglin MR & MRS T Wilson JR
Darien	06820	England MR & MRS Jonathan D
Darien	06820	FitzPatrick MR & MRS Mark H
Darien	06820	Ford MRS Quintin U
Darien	06820	Frank MR & MRS Stephen H
Darien	06820	Frelinghuysen MR & MRS Denis de V
Darien	06820	Galper MR & MRS David A
Darien	06820	Garnett MR & MRS Alexander Y P 3D
Darien	06820	Gould MR & MRS Howard B
Darien	06820	Guthrie MRS C Jones
Darien	06820	Hanau-Schaumburg PRC & MRS Christoph H
Darien	06820	Harvey MR & MRS H Darrell
Darien	06820	Harvey MR & MRS John B
Darien	06820	Haverstick MR & MRS Samuel A III
Darien	06820	Heekin MR & MRS Kenneth P
Darien	06820	Hole MR & MRS Brandon T
Darien	06820	Hord MR & MRS Jesse J
Darien	06820	Horn MRS Ann M
Darien	06820	Huebsch MR & MRS Michael C
Darien	06820	Jackson MR & MRS Thomas J
Darien	06820	Jacobs MR & MRS Philip M
Darien	06820	Jones MR & MRS Samuel Bancroft
Darien	06820	Jones MR & MRS William P JR
Darien	06820	Kilbourn MRS Samuel V D
Darien	06820	Kratovil MR & MRS Werner DeW
Darien	06820	Leach MR & MRS Alexander D
Darien	06820	Lefferts MR Gillet
Darien	06820	MacAusland MISS Robin
Darien	06820	MacLear MR & MRS Malcolm G
Darien	06820	McCallum MR & MRS Peter W
Darien	06820	Moss MR & MRS Philip A
Darien	06820	Nottebohm MR & MRS Johann D JR
Darien	06820	O'Donnell MR & MRS William T 3D
Darien	06820	Penrose MRS Charles JR
Darien	06820	Rankin MR & MRS Harley JR
Darien	06820	Riegel MR & MRS Guy R
Darien	06820	Robinson MR & MRS Blake W
Darien	06820	Robinson MR & MRS Patrick M
Darien	06820	Rosen MR & MRS Matthew L
Darien	06820	Shepard MR & MRS William B III
Darien	06820	Shuhy MR & MRS Robert P JR
Darien	06820	Slack MRS Henry Campbell
Darien	06820	Sparkman MR & MRS Palmer D JR
Darien	06820	Spurgeon MR & MRS Edward V R
Darien	06820	Taney MR & MRS Damon G
Darien	06820	Tattar MRS Joseph J
Darien	06820	Thayer MR & MRS Thomas R
Darien	06820	Thompson MR & MRS Christopher C
Darien	06820	Upson MS Carlyle N
Darien	06820	van der Kieft MR & MRS John W 3D
Darien	06820	van Nierop MR & MRS Jan H
Darien	06820	Vartanian MR & MRS Nishan P
Darien	06820	von Stade MR & MRS John T JR
Darien	06820	Watson MR & MRS Gavin W
Darien	06820	West MR & MRS Travis T
Darien	06820	Wetmore MR & MRS Charles D
Darien	06820	Whitney MR & MRS Christopher C
Darien	06820	Wiggin MR & MRS Rollin H JR
Darien	06820	Wilber MR & MRS Vance W
Darien	06820	Williams MR & MRS Charles R
Darien	06820	Williams MR & MRS Edward S
Darien	06820	Willis MR & MRS Gregory T
Deep River	06417	Hutchings MR William H
East Hampton	06424	Connor MR & MRS Herschel W JR
East Woodstock	06244	Benkhart MR Bruce S
East Woodstock	06244	Seybolt MRS Reva B
Easton	06612	Davenport MISS Carolyn W
Easton	06612	Dunsby MR & MRS Adam W
Easton	06612	Foster MR & MRS James R
Easton	06612	Niles MR Nicholas 3D
Easton	06612	Smith MR & MRS Peter L

To nominate a candidate for the Social Register Association, please email: SRCommittee@thesocialregister.org

Easton, CT—Greenwich, CT

Easton 06612 Twombly MR & MRS Kenneth L
Essex 06426 Bowditch MR & MRS Patrick F
Essex 06426 Brown MRS H Templeton JR
Essex 06426 Bundy MRS Frederick McG
Essex 06426 Cunningham MR & MRS Thomas D III
Essex 06426 Devine MR & MRS Rodney W
Essex 06426 Dole MR & MRS Charles Minot JR
Essex 06426 Fitton MRS Julia H
Essex 06426 Floyd MR & MRS J P Chadwick
Essex 06426 Guernsey MR & MRS David T JR
Essex 06426 Handy MR & MRS Parker D
Essex 06426 Leonard MRS James G
Essex 06426 Lewis MRS Henry 3D
Essex 06426 Makrianes MRS James K
Essex 06426 Millard MR & MRS Richard T
Essex 06426 O'Connor MR & MRS Anthony M
Essex 06426 Osborn MRS James E 2D
Essex 06426 Parsons MR & MRS Harris B
Essex 06426 Peake MRS J H Cameron
Essex 06426 Penniman MR & MRS George W
Essex 06426 Penniman MR Caleb J
Essex 06426 Perkins MRS John M C
Essex 06426 Pfeffer MR & MRS James L
Essex 06426 Pollard MR & MRS William A
Essex 06426 Reynolds MR & MRS Philip B
Essex 06426 Smithers MRS Ruth H
Essex 06426 Stubenbord DR & MRS William T
Essex 06426 Weber MRS John J
Essex 06426 West MRS Eric F
Essex 06426 Wetmore MRS Edward W
Essex 06426 Williams MR & MRS Sydney M 3D
Essex 06426 Williamson MRS Harold L JR
Essex 06426 Worm de Geldern MR & MRS Vagn
Fairfield 06430 Carter MR & MRS C Carroll JR
Fairfield 06430 Conzelman MR & MRS James G III
Fairfield 06430 du Pont MRS F George
Fairfield 06430 Hoffman MR & MRS Peter K
Fairfield 06430 Larsen MR & MRS Robert Roy
Fairfield 06430 Selden MR & MRS James K
Fairfield 06430 Smith MR & MRS Timothy H
Fairfield 06824 Bradley MR & MRS James P
Fairfield 06824 Bürki MR & MRS Peter G
Fairfield 06824 Clark MR & MRS Christopher P
Fairfield 06824 Collins MRS Phyllis D
Fairfield 06824 Curtis MRS Charles B
Fairfield 06824 De Long MRS Thomas A 2D
Fairfield 06824 Dean MR & MRS James H
Fairfield 06824 Duer MR & MRS John B
Fairfield 06824 Flink MR & MRS Peter H
Fairfield 06824 Fox MR & MRS Samuel M 4TH
Fairfield 06824 Gordon MR Steven & Moon MS Nancy
Fairfield 06824 Grayson MR & MRS Mark W
Fairfield 06824 Howe MR & MRS Henry W
Fairfield 06824 Hulme MISS Elizabeth R
Fairfield 06824 Kingston MR & MRS Samuel S R
Fairfield 06824 Low MR & MRS John M
Fairfield 06824 Malkin MR & MRS Andrew R
Fairfield 06824 Menéndez MS Lydia S
Fairfield 06824 Norton MR & MRS Lawrence A JR
Fairfield 06824 Patterson MR & MRS James W
Fairfield 06824 Perkins MR Gilman C & Millard MS Jayne N
Fairfield 06824 Piotrowska MS Magdalena P
Fairfield 06824 Rexford MR & MRS Stephen C JR
Fairfield 06824 Roessler MRS Carl C
Fairfield 06824 Shaw MRS Harry L
Fairfield 06824 Sinclair MR & MRS Ian R L
Fairfield 06824 Smalley MR & MRS Brian W
Fairfield 06824 Stovell DR & MRS Peter B
Fairfield 06824 Tunnell MR & MRS Bertram A III
Fairfield 06825 Cutter MR & MRS Arthur F III
Fairfield 06825 de Lara MS Angela D
Fairfield 06825 Hubbard MR & MRS Thomas R
Fairfield 06825 Mathews MR & MRS John B
Fairfield 06825 Roessler MR Carl C
Fairfield 06830 Mackenzie MR & MRS Guy David
Fairfield 06830 Mackenzie MS Madeleine G
Falls Village 06031 Boyse MR & MRS Matthew G
Falls Village 06031 Brown MR & MRS Charles C R
Falls Village 06031 Kuhn MISS Jacqueline H
Farmington 06032 Ashmead DR Duffield IV
Farmington 06032 Emerson MR & MRS Jonathan E
Farmington 06032 Godfrey MR & MRS Loren
Farmington 06032 Granger MR & MRS Harold C
Farmington 06032 Holden MR & MRS R Stuart JR
Farmington 06032 Lansing MR & MRS Joseph D JR
Farmington 06032 Nevius MRS Garrett W
Farmington 06034 de Rham MRS David P
Farmington 06085 Paquet MR & MRS Raymond M
Glastonbury 06033 Dellenbaugh MR & MRS Geoffrey G
Goshen 06756 Wright MR & MRS John S
Greens Farms 06436 Block MR & MRS Huntington M
Greens Farms 06838 Crawford MR & MRS Harden L 4TH
Greens Farms 06838 Gibbons MRS Anne T
Greenwich 06630 Swindell MR & MRS Robert H 3D
Greenwich 06830 Agnew MRS Cornelius R JR
Greenwich 06830 Anderson MR & MRS Carlton E II
Greenwich 06830 Antell DR & MRS (DR) Darrick E
Greenwich 06830 Antell MR Darrick E JR
Greenwich 06830 Bancroft MR & MRS Townsend W
Greenwich 06830 Barrett MR & MRS John D II
Greenwich 06830 Bernard MR Matthew L
Greenwich 06830 Borie MRS David B
Greenwich 06830 Boynton MR & MRS Perry S 3D
Greenwich 06830 Britton MRS Roy
Greenwich 06830 Burke MR & MRS Duncan G
Greenwich 06830 Burke MR & MRS Edwin M III
Greenwich 06830 Burrows MR & MRS David D
Greenwich 06830 Butler MR & MRS James
Greenwich 06830 Case MR & MRS George S
Greenwich 06830 Cassin MR & MRS J Matthew JR
Greenwich 06830 Caulfield MISS Alexandra R
Greenwich 06830 Caulfield MR & MRS Jerome J
Greenwich 06830 Caulfield MR Andrew McC
Greenwich 06830 Chickering MR & MRS Howard A
Greenwich 06830 Cobbs MR & MRS James W JR
Greenwich 06830 Coe MR & MRS John T J
Greenwich 06830 Cook MR & MRS Bruce Stewart
Greenwich 06830 Corbin MR & MRS Parker S
Greenwich 06830 Coudert MRS Victor R JR
Greenwich 06830 Cox MR & MRS John C
Greenwich 06830 Crawford MR & MRS Alexander I
Greenwich 06830 Cushman MR & MRS Andrew L
Greenwich 06830 Davies MR & MRS Peter E
Greenwich 06830 Delano MR & MRS Lyman
Greenwich 06830 di Galoma MR & MRS Thomas L
Greenwich 06830 Dixon MR Bruce De W
Greenwich 06830 Douthit MR & MRS Philip S
Greenwich 06830 Du Bois MISS Serena D
Greenwich 06830 Du Bois MRS Adrienne A
Greenwich 06830 Duff MRS Louis D
Greenwich 06830 Dush MR & MRS Michael W
Greenwich 06830 Eddy MR & MRS John R

Greenwich 06830 Edlin MRS Frank W
Greenwich 06830 Egbert MRS George Pennington JR
Greenwich 06830 Egbert MRS Richard Cook
Greenwich 06830 Elliman MRS Edward S
Greenwich 06830 Elsberry REV & MRS Terence L
Greenwich 06830 Erdman MR & MRS John H JR
Greenwich 06830 Ettinger MRS Barbara L
Greenwich 06830 Evans DR & MRS David D
Greenwich 06830 French MR & MRS John R
Greenwich 06830 Gagarin MR Peter S
Greenwich 06830 Gardiner MR & MRS A Denny
Greenwich 06830 Gardiner MR & MRS Alexander H
Greenwich 06830 Gibbons MRS Maxfield S
Greenwich 06830 Goodwin MR & MRS J Barton
Greenwich 06830 Gray MR & MRS Robert D
Greenwich 06830 Gray MR & MRS Taylor C
Greenwich 06830 Green MR & MRS Gregory H
Greenwich 06830 Gross MRS William A O
Greenwich 06830 Hall MRS John H
Greenwich 06830 Hanson MR & MRS Fridolf A
Greenwich 06830 Heidenreich MR & MRS Fritz
Greenwich 06830 Henderson MR & MRS James R
Greenwich 06830 Henze MR & MRS Raymond F 3D
Greenwich 06830 Hershey MR Edwin M II
Greenwich 06830 Hinrichs MRS Peter A
Greenwich 06830 Hoffman MR & MRS John H
Greenwich 06830 Holbrook MR & MRS Christopher C
Greenwich 06830 Host MRS Stig
Greenwich 06830 Hotchkiss MRS Joseph W
Greenwich 06830 Howe MR & MRS Nathaniel S JR
Greenwich 06830 Huffard MRS P Phillip 3D
Greenwich 06830 Huffman MR & MRS Jeffrey J
Greenwich 06830 Hughes MR & MRS William L
Greenwich 06830 Ireland MR & MRS Thomas E
Greenwich 06830 Juhas MR & MRS Peter L
Greenwich 06830 Kärst MR & MRS Jan F
Greenwich 06830 Kendall MR & MRS Donald McIntosh
Greenwich 06830 King MR & MRS Charles H 3D
Greenwich 06830 Knight MR & MRS James E
Greenwich 06830 Knight MRS Thomas S JR
Greenwich 06830 Kryzak REV & MRS Andrew A
Greenwich 06830 Lake MR & MRS Douglas T JR
Greenwich 06830 Lee MR & MRS Daniel G III
Greenwich 06830 Lewis MRS Mary Hope
Greenwich 06830 Lovell MR & MRS John E
Greenwich 06830 Maulsby MRS Allen F
Greenwich 06830 McDowell MR & MRS William W JR
Greenwich 06830 Meek MRS M Holgate
Greenwich 06830 Miranda MR César
Greenwich 06830 Moran MR & MRS Garrett M
Greenwich 06830 More MR & MRS Douglas McL
Greenwich 06830 Ness MR & MRS Peter S
Greenwich 06830 Ness MR & MRS Philip W JR
Greenwich 06830 Neuman MR & MRS Richard J
Greenwich 06830 Newington MRS John C
Greenwich 06830 Norfleet MR & MRS Charles C
Greenwich 06830 Norfleet MR John V R JR
Greenwich 06830 Oates MR & MRS Thomas N
Greenwich 06830 Ogilvy MR & MRS David F
Greenwich 06830 Palache MR & MRS John G JR
Greenwich 06830 Peale MRS Patricia
Greenwich 06830 Peterson MRS Robert L
Greenwich 06830 Petty MRS Elizabeth M B
Greenwich 06830 Philip MR & MRS Thomas W
Greenwich 06830 Potter MR & MRS Philip C JR
Greenwich 06830 Prouty MR & MRS Norman R JR
Greenwich 06830 Putnam MR & MRS Frederic P
Greenwich 06830 Raezer MR & MRS James T
Greenwich 06830 Raquet MR Walter F
Greenwich 06830 Reibel DR & MRS James S
Greenwich 06830 Reimers DR & MRS Carl D 3D
Greenwich 06830 Reynolds MR Russell S III
Greenwich 06830 Robinson MR Winthrop A
Greenwich 06830 Roome MISS Barbara S
Greenwich 06830 Royce MRS Karen F
Greenwich 06830 Rumbough MR & MRS Stanley Hutton
Greenwich 06830 Savage MRS Elizabeth O
Greenwich 06830 Schieffelin MR & MRS Timothy P
Greenwich 06830 Schulze MR Richard G
Greenwich 06830 Searle MR & MRS Robert S
Greenwich 06830 Shaw MR & MRS L Edward JR
Greenwich 06830 Shaw MR & MRS William D JR
Greenwich 06830 Skouras MR & MRS Spyros S JR
Greenwich 06830 Smith MR & MRS E J Noble
Greenwich 06830 Smith MR & MRS Patrick D
Greenwich 06830 Smith MRS Sheilah T
Greenwich 06830 Spencer MR & MRS Henry B 2D
Greenwich 06830 Sterling MR & MRS Cameron P
Greenwich 06830 Sterling MRS Deborah P
Greenwich 06830 Strickland MR & MRS Seth DeV
Greenwich 06830 Sturges MR & MRS (DR) Hollister 3D
Greenwich 06830 Thaxter MRS Anne
Greenwich 06830 Thorson MR & MRS Robert D JR
Greenwich 06830 Tillman MR & MRS Eric W
Greenwich 06830 Tingley MR & MRS C Nicholas
Greenwich 06830 Victor MRS Alice S
Greenwich 06830 Vitton MR & MRS Michael S
Greenwich 06830 Walker MR & MRS Alexander D III
Greenwich 06830 Wallace MR & MRS David W
Greenwich 06830 Walsh MR Frederick R JR & Mauran MS Hope I
Greenwich 06830 Wayt MR & MRS John A III
Greenwich 06830 Weir MRS Michael B
Greenwich 06830 Welch MR & MRS Samuel P
Greenwich 06830 Welles MR & MRS Arnold
Greenwich 06830 Whittall MRS Ian Q
Greenwich 06830 Whittemore MR & MRS Laurence F III
Greenwich 06830 Williams MR & MRS John S III
Greenwich 06830 Winthrop MR & MRS John JR
Greenwich 06830 Woolworth MR & MRS Richard G JR
Greenwich 06830 Yonce MRS Samuel McC
Greenwich 06831 Baccile MR & MRS Peter E
Greenwich 06831 Bartol MRS John Hone
Greenwich 06831 Bartow MR & MRS Philip K III
Greenwich 06831 Bell MR Theodore A III
Greenwich 06831 Bernann MR Bruce K
Greenwich 06831 Bingham MRS Hiram A
Greenwich 06831 Blackiston MR Henry C 3D
Greenwich 06831 Burgard MR Clark van K
Greenwich 06831 Chatfield MR Charlton H
Greenwich 06831 Clark MR Marshall
Greenwich 06831 Clarkson MR & MRS Geoffrey L
Greenwich 06831 Codraro MR & MRS Lawrence F JR
Greenwich 06831 Cook MR & MRS Langdon P
Greenwich 06831 Cook MRS Hobart A H
Greenwich 06831 Corroon MRS Robert F
Greenwich 06831 Critchell MR & MRS Bradley G
Greenwich 06831 Crooks MRS William C
Greenwich 06831 Cutting MISS Lucy
Greenwich 06831 Davol MR & MRS Ward M
Greenwich 06831 de Saint Phalle MR & MRS Jacques
Greenwich 06831 de Veer MR & MRS Robert Kipp III
Greenwich 06831 Dent MRS Richard H

Greenwich, CT—Lakeville, CT

Greenwich	06831	Fey DR & MRS Christopher P V
Greenwich	06831	Fisher MRS Bennett L
Greenwich	06831	Foley MR & MRS Thomas C
Greenwich	06831	Ford MR & MRS David B
Greenwich	06831	Ford MR & MRS F Richards 3D
Greenwich	06831	Ghazarossian MR & MRS Antreas E
Greenwich	06831	Ghriskey MR & MRS H Williamson JR
Greenwich	06831	Glanville MR & MRS (DR) Robert E
Greenwich	06831	Grant MRS J Barrett
Greenwich	06831	Griffin DR & MRS Raymond A
Greenwich	06831	Hamilton MR & MRS Thomas M
Greenwich	06831	Hammond MR & MRS Ogden H JR
Greenwich	06831	Harrington MRS Robert D JR
Greenwich	06831	Henderson MR & MRS Edward T
Greenwich	06831	Henriques MRS Claire W
Greenwich	06831	Hoffman MR & MRS Harrison B W
Greenwich	06831	Holden MR & MRS Michael H
Greenwich	06831	Holmyard MRS Harold R
Greenwich	06831	Jahncke MRS Cornelia D
Greenwich	06831	Jennings MR & MRS Jeffrey H
Greenwich	06831	Juge MR & MRS David A
Greenwich	06831	Keefe MRS Harry V JR
Greenwich	06831	Kelley MR & MRS David K
Greenwich	06831	Ketcham MR & MRS William P
Greenwich	06831	Kiernan MR & MRS Peter de L 3D
Greenwich	06831	Kingsley MRS John McC JR
Greenwich	06831	Kinnear MR James W 3D
Greenwich	06831	Kovner MR Michael A & Doyen de Montaillou MR Jean
Greenwich	06831	LeComte MR & MRS Jonathan B
Greenwich	06831	Lehrman MR & MRS Lewis E
Greenwich	06831	Lindstrom MR & MRS James M
Greenwich	06831	Lovejoy MR & MRS Thomas B
Greenwich	06831	Lynch MR & MRS William R
Greenwich	06831	Maher MRS John Francis
Greenwich	06831	Mallory MR & MRS Charles
Greenwich	06831	Marlas MR & MRS James C
Greenwich	06831	McDonnell MRS Hubert
Greenwich	06831	Meeker MR & MRS James B
Greenwich	06831	Moffat MISS Jane-Kerin
Greenwich	06831	Moore MR & MRS William H 3D
Greenwich	06831	Morris MR & MRS Roland JR
Greenwich	06831	Morris MR Seymour JR
Greenwich	06831	Mortimer MR & MRS E Paul
Greenwich	06831	Mountain MR & MRS Robert P JR
Greenwich	06831	Murkland MRS John C
Greenwich	06831	Nickerson MR & MRS William H
Greenwich	06831	O'Malley MR & MRS C Hooker
Greenwich	06831	Parker MR & MRS Michael R
Greenwich	06831	Peterson MR & MRS Jeffrey R F
Greenwich	06831	Piro DR & MRS Philip A JR
Greenwich	06831	Rees MR & MRS Homer McK
Greenwich	06831	Reynolds MR & MRS Russell S JR
Greenwich	06831	Robinson DR & MRS Rowland P
Greenwich	06831	Robinson MR & MRS John R
Greenwich	06831	Robinson MR & MRS Marc C
Greenwich	06831	Roe MR & MRS Ralph C
Greenwich	06831	Rose MR & MRS Charles T III
Greenwich	06831	Roth MR & MRS David S
Greenwich	06831	Salyer MR & MRS Stephen S
Greenwich	06831	Sammis MR & MRS Jesse F 3D
Greenwich	06831	Santry MR & MRS Peter T
Greenwich	06831	Scully MR Michael E
Greenwich	06831	Sheehan MR & MRS William Butler
Greenwich	06831	Soper MR Scott C & Blair MRS Laura V
Greenwich	06831	Stauffer MR & MRS John E
Greenwich	06831	Steel MR & MRS Robert K
Greenwich	06831	Stephenson MRS J Clayton
Greenwich	06831	Stiles MRS Ned B
Greenwich	06831	Stitzer MR & MRS Mark
Greenwich	06831	Stone MR & MRS Charles Lanier
Greenwich	06831	Streeter MS Ruth C
Greenwich	06831	Thébaud MRS Reynal de St M
Greenwich	06831	Thomas MR & MRS Douglas McM
Greenwich	06831	Tolles MR & MRS James F
Greenwich	06831	Van Norden MRS Langdon
Greenwich	06831	Vehslage MRS Stephen T
Greenwich	06831	von Gontard MR & MRS Adalbert JR
Greenwich	06831	Wall MR & MRS D Scott
Greenwich	06831	Weld MRS William G JR
Greenwich	06831	Wendell MR & MRS Jonathan P
Greenwich	06831	White MRS John H
Greenwich	06831	Willis MRS William H JR
Greenwich	06831	Wolf MRS Christine M
Greenwich	06831	Yonce MR & MRS Clifford M
Greenwich	06835	Motherwell MRS Robert
Greenwich	06836	Merrill MRS Joan
Groton	06340	Johnson MR & MRS Edward R
Groton	06340	Savage MR Michael D
Guilford	06437	Angle MR & MRS Richard W JR
Guilford	06437	Baugh MISS Carol A
Guilford	06437	Hansen MR & MRS Timothy E
Guilford	06437	Killiam MR Theodore R
Guilford	06437	Locke REV Bradford B JR
Guilford	06437	Noble MR & MRS Lawrence M JR
Guilford	06437	Peabody MRS Sarah B
Guilford	06437	Rae MR & MRS James M
Guilford	06437	Sands MR & MRS Theodore D
Guilford	06437	Seibert MR & MRS Edward P
Guilford	06437	Shahid DR & MRS Kameron R
Haddam	06438	Jones MRS Andrew B
Hadlyme	06439	Fiske MR & MRS William J
Hadlyme	06439	Paxton MRS Frank Roberts
Hamden	06514	Robbins MR Henry C
Hamden	06517	Bogardus DR & MRS Sidney T JR
Hamden	06517	Fox MRS Joseph Carrère
Hamden	06517	Gammon DR & MRS G Davis
Hamden	06517	Grebe MRS Frank
Hamden	06517	Hunt MR R Peter
Hamden	06517	Mallory MR & MRS Raburn M
Hamden	06517	McAllister MRS William B
Hamden	06517	Palumbo MR & MRS Jonathan B
Hamden	06517	Persse MR John W III
Hamden	06517	Swords MRS Gerard S
Hamden	06715	McKinney MR James E
Hartford	06105	Casey MR & MRS Coleman H
Hartford	06105	Eakins REV & MRS (REV) William J
Hartford	06105	Hennessy MR & MRS Matthew J
Hartford	06105	Smith MR & MRS Robert H JR
Hartford	06105	Wheeler MR Charles H 3D
Harwinton	06791	Robertson MS (DR) Sarah Wells
Ivoryton	06442	Tingue MR Howard B
Ivoryton	06442	Wyeth MR & MRS Leonard J VI
Kent	06757	Hinman MR John R JR & Dallett MS C Athenaide H
Kent	06757	Schell MR Richardson W
Kent	06757	Stearns MRS James P
Kent	06757	Todd MRS Anne P
Kent	06757	Zunino MR & MRS F Anthony 3D
Lakeville	06039	Gevalt MR & MRS Peter Young
Lakeville	06039	Koven MRS Stephanie H
Lakeville	06039	Light MR & MRS J Thomas

Lakeville	06039	Marvel MR & MRS H Jackson
Lakeville	06039	McKelvy MR & MRS William G
Lakeville	06039	Reilly MR & MRS Michael F
Litchfield	06759	Auchincloss MR & MRS Edgar S 5TH
Litchfield	06759	Boynton MR & MRS Oren K
Litchfield	06759	Coolidge MR & MRS Thomas R
Litchfield	06759	Devlin MR & MRS Raymond J JR
Litchfield	06759	Doty MRS Sharon H S
Litchfield	06759	Funnell MR & MRS E Stephen
Litchfield	06759	Furniss MR & MRS Richard A JR
Litchfield	06759	Griswold MRS Tracy H
Litchfield	06759	Grose MR William R 2D
Litchfield	06759	Kennedy MRS Pamela G
Litchfield	06759	Kleinhans MRS Lewis C 3D
Litchfield	06759	Magary MR & MRS Alan B
Litchfield	06759	McKinney MRS Ann M
Litchfield	06759	Morosani CAPT & MRS Daniel C
Litchfield	06759	Morosani MR & MRS John W
Litchfield	06759	Morosani MR & MRS Reto W
Litchfield	06759	O'Reilly MR & MRS Gerald A
Litchfield	06759	Outwater MR & MRS Thomas D
Litchfield	06759	Pollock MRS James H
Litchfield	06759	Rath MRS Nancy Prosser
Litchfield	06759	Schlumberger MR & MRS Wilfrid N
Litchfield	06759	Staub MR John H II
Litchfield	06759	Warner MISS Elizabeth T
Lyme	06371	Barney MR & MRS Robert W
Lyme	06371	Boyd MR & MRS Thomas M
Lyme	06371	Butler MR & MRS Jonathan P
Lyme	06371	Childs MR & MRS James McM
Lyme	06371	David MRS Barbara Osborn
Lyme	06371	Holth MR & MRS Fredrik T
Lyme	06371	Holth MRS Fredrik D
Lyme	06371	McCall MISS Alison G
Lyme	06371	McCawley DR & MRS (DR) Christopher L
Lyme	06371	Payne MRS David M
Lyme	06371	Roosevelt MR & MRS Christopher du P
Madison	06443	Armstrong MR & MRS John M
Madison	06443	Clement MR & MRS Peter Wickham
Madison	06443	Lester MR & MRS Anthony M
Madison	06443	Logan MRS Kevin M
Madison	06443	Parker MRS Frederick A JR
Madison	06443	Platt MR & MRS William R
Madison	06443	Reynolds DR & MRS Jeffrey T
Madison	06443	Rianhard MR & MRS Perry D
Madison	06443	Wetmore MRS Andrew C
Madison	06443	Wetmore MS Virginia L
Mansfield Center	06520	Wemple MR Francis H JR
Middletown	06457	Savard MR & MRS Edward L
Milford	06460	Bayne MR & MRS Michael C
Milford	06460	Fiore MR & MRS Daniel R
Milford	06460	Michaels MR & MRS Gregory J
Monroe	06468	Gale MRS Robert A
Monroe	06468	Hamilton MR & MRS Thomas W
Monroe	06468	Richardson MR & MRS Tolbert N 3D
Mystic	06355	Anderson MR Henry H JR
Mystic	06355	Burr MRS Francis H
Mystic	06355	Curry MRS Susanne M
Mystic	06355	Cutler MR & MRS William B
Mystic	06355	Manigault MRS Landine
Mystic	06355	O'Connor MR Robert J
Mystic	06355	Reid MR & MRS James G
Mystic	06355	Russell MRS Edwin F
Mystic	06355	Shaw MR & MRS George T
Mystic	06355	Trimble MRS Richard
Mystic	06355	Visscher DR & MRS Pieter T
Mystic	06355	Wharton MRS C William JR
Mystic	06355	Wick MR & MRS (DR) Christopher M
New Canaan	06840	Allen MRS M Bruns
New Canaan	06840	Beecher DR & MRS Henry G
New Canaan	06840	Belak MS C Pierce
New Canaan	06840	Benington MR & MRS George A
New Canaan	06840	Birmingham MR & MRS William J JR
New Canaan	06840	Bitting MR & MRS Jonathan K
New Canaan	06840	Boggess MR & MRS Spencer N
New Canaan	06840	Brennan MR & MRS Noel E McK
New Canaan	06840	Brown MRS George Edwin JR
New Canaan	06840	Buttrick MR & MRS Samuel C
New Canaan	06840	Carroll MRS J Otis
New Canaan	06840	Carter MRS Diana D
New Canaan	06840	Casey MR & MRS John E
New Canaan	06840	Celiberti MR & MRS Thomas A
New Canaan	06840	Chapin MR & MRS Aldus N
New Canaan	06840	Clark MISS Robin J
New Canaan	06840	Clarkson MRS Andrew M
New Canaan	06840	Clay MR & MRS Philip G
New Canaan	06840	Cluett MR & MRS W Scott JR
New Canaan	06840	Cole MR & MRS James E
New Canaan	06840	Corcoran MR & MRS Andrew P
New Canaan	06840	Corcoran MR & MRS John B
New Canaan	06840	Curry MR & MRS Robert V K
New Canaan	06840	de Menocal MR & MRS George W
New Canaan	06840	Dearborn MRS Angelica G
New Canaan	06840	Di Capua MR & MRS Lawrence H
New Canaan	06840	du Pont MR & MRS F George JR
New Canaan	06840	du Pont MR & MRS Reynolds III
New Canaan	06840	Emery MR & MRS William 3D
New Canaan	06840	English MR & MRS J Scott
New Canaan	06840	Erdmann MR & MRS John F 2D
New Canaan	06840	Evans MR & MRS Carter S JR
New Canaan	06840	Farrell MR & MRS J Michael
New Canaan	06840	Ferris MR & MRS Jeffrey B
New Canaan	06840	Fleming MR & MRS David W 2D
New Canaan	06840	Fog MR & MRS Stephen C
New Canaan	06840	Foley MR & MRS Paul
New Canaan	06840	Fowler MR & MRS Paul D
New Canaan	06840	Fox MR & MRS Matthew C
New Canaan	06840	Gardner MRS Shawn Dunn
New Canaan	06840	Gaumer MR & MRS Michael J
New Canaan	06840	Gidez MR & MRS Howard J
New Canaan	06840	Goodrich MR & MRS John Alden
New Canaan	06840	Goodyear MR & MRS Laurence H
New Canaan	06840	Gores MRS Landis
New Canaan	06840	Gray MRS Bowman 3D
New Canaan	06840	Greenwood MR & MRS Douglas C W
New Canaan	06840	Gulden MRS Charles F
New Canaan	06840	Guthrie MR & MRS Nicholas D
New Canaan	06840	Hamill MR & MRS Robert B
New Canaan	06840	Hart MRS William D JR
New Canaan	06840	Hetherington MR & MRS John W
New Canaan	06840	Hillman MR Howard B
New Canaan	06840	Holmes MISS C Collinson
New Canaan	06840	Hubbard MRS Michelle R
New Canaan	06840	Hutcheson MR & MRS Neale C
New Canaan	06840	Hutchins MR & MRS John S
New Canaan	06840	Jones MR & MRS Christopher S
New Canaan	06840	Kammerer MR David W & Lovejoy MS Kindra H
New Canaan	06840	Kerridge MR & MRS Douglas C
New Canaan	06840	King MRS Robert Morgan
New Canaan	06840	Knechtle MRS Emilio B
New Canaan	06840	Lane MR & MRS John L

New Canaan, CT—Norwalk, CT

New Canaan ... 06840 ... LeConey MR & MRS M Morgan JR
New Canaan ... 06840 ... Liebau MR & MRS F Jack JR
New Canaan ... 06840 ... MacEwan MR & MRS Nigel S
New Canaan ... 06840 ... MacLear MR & MRS Bruce A
New Canaan ... 06840 ... Maggard MR & MRS Robert H
New Canaan ... 06840 ... Matthews MS Kathryn
New Canaan ... 06840 ... Mattison MR & MRS Mark H
New Canaan ... 06840 ... Matviak MR & MRS Aleksandr P
New Canaan ... 06840 ... McCulloch MR & MRS Andrew H
New Canaan ... 06840 ... McKenna MR David M
New Canaan ... 06840 ... McLanahan MR Bruce
New Canaan ... 06840 ... McLane MR & MRS Thomas L
New Canaan ... 06840 ... Michels MR & MRS Mark R
New Canaan ... 06840 ... Miller MR & MRS Malcolm E
New Canaan ... 06840 ... Miller MRS L Garrison JR
New Canaan ... 06840 ... Moore MRS George B
New Canaan ... 06840 ... Mundy MR Nathaniel E
New Canaan ... 06840 ... Nemiroff MR & MRS Peter G C
New Canaan ... 06840 ... Nissley MR & MRS Thomas W
New Canaan ... 06840 ... Norton MR & MRS Christopher K
New Canaan ... 06840 ... Oak MR & MRS Matthew B
New Canaan ... 06840 ... Ogden MR & MRS Dayton JR
New Canaan ... 06840 ... Owen MR & MRS John E
New Canaan ... 06840 ... Pfeil MRS (REV) Susan M
New Canaan ... 06840 ... Post MR William S
New Canaan ... 06840 ... Proctor MR & MRS Schuyler J
New Canaan ... 06840 ... Pyne MS Alison W
New Canaan ... 06840 ... Ramseur MRS Thomas M
New Canaan ... 06840 ... Reid MR & MRS John M
New Canaan ... 06840 ... Reid MS Amy Weber
New Canaan ... 06840 ... Richards MR & MRS Eric P
New Canaan ... 06840 ... Risom MR & MRS C Nicholas
New Canaan ... 06840 ... Roberts MR & MRS Ralston P JR
New Canaan ... 06840 ... Robinson MR & MRS Michael W
New Canaan ... 06840 ... Saverin MR & MRS Kenneth A
New Canaan ... 06840 ... Scannell MR & MRS David G
New Canaan ... 06840 ... Schmidt MR & MRS Jeffrey D
New Canaan ... 06840 ... Scott MR & MRS Alexander L
New Canaan ... 06840 ... Scott MR & MRS M Simon
New Canaan ... 06840 ... Simonds MR Charles S
New Canaan ... 06840 ... Smith MRS Sidney S
New Canaan ... 06840 ... Steever DR Sanford B
New Canaan ... 06840 ... Stowe MR Henry B
New Canaan ... 06840 ... Sultan MRS Arthur P
New Canaan ... 06840 ... Thompson MRS Robert T
New Canaan ... 06840 ... Tilghman MR & MRS Richard A JR
New Canaan ... 06840 ... Toland MRS Lita
New Canaan ... 06840 ... Trotman MR & MRS Arthur E 2D
New Canaan ... 06840 ... Troy MR Richard H
New Canaan ... 06840 ... Turullols MR & MRS José L A
New Canaan ... 06840 ... Ulrich MR & MRS Ronald J
New Canaan ... 06840 ... Urbahn MR & MRS Maximilian O III
New Canaan ... 06840 ... Urstadt MR James Jeffrey
New Canaan ... 06840 ... Van Nest MR Dean G JR
New Canaan ... 06840 ... van Roden MR & MRS Peter W
New Canaan ... 06840 ... Walker MR & MRS Norman S JR
New Canaan ... 06840 ... Watson MR & MRS Charles E
New Canaan ... 06840 ... Welles MR & MRS Eric C
New Canaan ... 06840 ... Wiley MR & MRS Hugh C
New Canaan ... 06840 ... Williams MRS Roderick O
New Canaan ... 06840 ... Wittmann MR & MRS Christopher J
New Canaan ... 06840 ... Wyckoff MR & MRS Stephen S
New Canaan ... 06840 ... Young MR & MRS William B JR
New Canaan ... 06840 ... Youngman MR & MRS John G
New Canaan ... 06840 ... Zara MR & MRS Thomas D
New Haven ... 06510 ... Bell MR & MRS Scott S
New Haven ... 06510 ... Lord MR Henry
New Haven ... 06510 ... Nadai MISS Elizabeth G
New Haven ... 06511 ... Ambach MRS Gordon M
New Haven ... 06511 ... Cooke MR & MRS Edward S JR
New Haven ... 06511 ... DuBois DR & MRS Arthur B
New Haven ... 06511 ... Ford MR & MRS Brin R
New Haven ... 06511 ... Karl MISS Katherine L
New Haven ... 06511 ... Knight MR & MRS George C
New Haven ... 06511 ... Lamont MR & MRS Nicholas S
New Haven ... 06511 ... Mason MR & MRS Thomas J
New Haven ... 06511 ... Nelson MR Arvid R
New Haven ... 06511 ... Purves MR & MRS Alexander
New Haven ... 06511 ... Strebeigh MRS Waring C
New Haven ... 06511 ... Williamson DR & MRS Edwin D JR
New Haven ... 06512 ... Pendergast MISS Mary H
New Haven ... 06515 ... Thornton MR James S M & Russell MS Sara L
New London ... 06320 ... Day MR & MRS Patrick J
New London ... 06320 ... Griffis MR Hughes
New London ... 06320 ... Hayes DR David
New Milford ... 06776 ... Rush MISS Susan B
New Preston ... 06777 ... Benedict MR & MRS Williston R
New Preston ... 06777 ... Woodroofe REV & MRS Robert W 3D
Newtown ... 06470 ... Elkins MR & MRS George W 4TH
Niantic ... 06357 ... Foster MR & MRS Christopher P
Niantic ... 06357 ... Gleason MRS Aleta M
Niantic ... 06357 ... Lambert MR John T JR
Niantic ... 06357 ... Smithers MS Bonnie L
Noank ... 06340 ... Hatfield MR & MRS Thomas A
Noank ... 06340 ... Pratt REV & MRS James L
Noank ... 06340 ... Strong MRS Bonsall
Norfolk ... 06058 ... Childs MRS Timothy W
Norfolk ... 06058 ... Ducas MRS Robert I
Norfolk ... 06058 ... Garside MRS Grenville
Norfolk ... 06058 ... Potter MR & MRS H David
Norfolk ... 06058 ... Thomson MR & MRS Schuyler W
Norfolk ... 06058 ... Vanderlip MRS Christina
North Branford ... 06471 ... Platt MRS Thomas C
North Branford ... 06471 ... Riley MRS Cathleen D
North Branford ... 06471 ... van Marx MR & MRS Robert P E
North Branford ... 06471 ... Woolverton MRS Ethel M
North Haven ... 06473 ... Duble MRS Nancy S
North Haven ... 06473 ... Hungerford MISS Sally-Byrd
North Haven ... 06473 ... May MISS Jennie W
North Stamford ... 06903 ... Cutter MR & MRS Bruce A
Norwalk ... 06850 ... Danforth MR & MRS Michael S
Norwalk ... 06850 ... Escher-de Haas MRS Amy
Norwalk ... 06850 ... Goddard MR & MRS Preston L
Norwalk ... 06850 ... Nields MR & MRS Benjamin IV
Norwalk ... 06850 ... Pfeil MR & MRS Roy S
Norwalk ... 06850 ... Post MR George B
Norwalk ... 06850 ... Satterthwaite MR & MRS Henry B
Norwalk ... 06850 ... Schwab MRS D Johnson
Norwalk ... 06850 ... York MR & MRS Clifton Gaston
Norwalk ... 06851 ... Cholmeley-Jones MRS Richard G 2D
Norwalk ... 06851 ... Lane MR & MRS Jeffrey G
Norwalk ... 06851 ... White MR & MRS Stephen B 3D
Norwalk ... 06853 ... Collins MR & MRS Garry T
Norwalk ... 06853 ... Sellschop MR & MRS Richard M
Norwalk ... 06854 ... Burke MR & MRS Geoffrey K
Norwalk ... 06854 ... Clulow MISS Evelyn K
Norwalk ... 06854 ... Dimond MRS Pamela C
Norwalk ... 06854 ... Erdmann MR & MRS John F 3D
Norwalk ... 06854 ... Fisher MR & MRS James D
Norwalk ... 06854 ... Hewson MS Helshi L
Norwalk ... 06854 ... Mathiason MS Brianne N
Norwalk ... 06854 ... Miller MR & MRS Jeffrey C

Norwalk .... 06854 .... Redfield MR & MRS LeGrand S JR
Norwalk .... 06854 .... Silva-Sadder MR & MRS André R
Norwalk .... 06854 .... Stevens MISS (DR) Emily C
Norwalk .... 06854 .... Wallace MR & MRS Andrew F
Norwalk .... 06854 .... Williams MR & MRS Ralph B II
Norwalk .... 06855 .... Clarke MR & MRS Jeffrey B
Norwalk .... 06856 .... Benjamin MR & MRS Stephen D
Old Greenwich .... 06870 .... Adams MR & MRS Daniel N
Old Greenwich .... 06870 .... Bissell MR & MRS E Perot IV
Old Greenwich .... 06870 .... Byers MS Candace F
Old Greenwich .... 06870 .... Day DR & MRS Richard B
Old Greenwich .... 06870 .... Dempsey MRS William L JR
Old Greenwich .... 06870 .... Dimsey MR & MRS Christopher P M
Old Greenwich .... 06870 .... Fearey MR & MRS John L S
Old greenwich .... 06870 .... Halsey MISS Sally J
Old Greenwich .... 06870 .... Jacks MR & MRS Robert L
Old Greenwich .... 06870 .... Johnson MR & MRS Thomas E S
Old Greenwich .... 06870 .... Kriz MR Christopher J
Old Greenwich .... 06870 .... Perlis MR & MRS Michael S
Old Greenwich .... 06870 .... Rasmussen MR & MRS David J
Old Greenwich .... 06870 .... Sterling MR & MRS William Lee
Old Greenwich .... 06870 .... Thierry MR & MRS Charles A
Old Greenwich .... 06870 .... van Meel MR & MRS Cornelis H A
Old Greenwich .... 06870 .... Weed MR & MRS Joseph J 2D
Old Greenwich .... 06870 .... Young MISS Anne H
Old Greenwich .... 06870 .... Young MR John R
Old Lyme .... 06371 .... Alsop MRS John deK
Old Lyme .... 06371 .... Baxter MR & MRS John H
Old Lyme .... 06371 .... Brainerd MRS Stanford H
Old Lyme .... 06371 .... Breeding MR Edwin C JR
Old Lyme .... 06371 .... Brinley MR & MRS Charles E II
Old Lyme .... 06371 .... Cliffe MRS Frederic T JR
Old Lyme .... 06371 .... Danenhower MR & MRS Sloan M
Old Lyme .... 06371 .... Dangremond MR & MRS David W
Old Lyme .... 06371 .... Fowler MR & MRS Thomas G
Old Lyme .... 06371 .... Gerster MR & MRS Peter W
Old Lyme .... 06371 .... Greenho MR & MRS Brian D
Old Lyme .... 06371 .... Jones MR & MRS Edward E JR
Old Lyme .... 06371 .... Lyman MISS Charlotte P
Old Lyme .... 06371 .... Mallory MRS Diane Driggs
Old Lyme .... 06371 .... McAdams MR Kenneth G & Bingham MS Marian
Old Lyme .... 06371 .... Mundy MR & MRS Edward S
Old Lyme .... 06371 .... Pierson MRS (DR) Anne B
Old Lyme .... 06371 .... Renault MRS Robert
Old Lyme .... 06371 .... Sedgwick MR & MRS Henry D
Old Lyme .... 06371 .... Tracy MR & MRS Ernest B JR
Old Lyme .... 06371 .... Waldron MRS Mary S
Old Lyme .... 06371 .... Whelan MR & MRS Sidney S JR
Old Lyme .... 06371 .... White MR & MRS Robert K
Old Lyme .... 06371 .... Williams MR & MRS Sydney M 4TH
Old Saybrook .... 06475 .... Babcock MR & MRS Orville Elias 3D
Old Saybrook .... 06475 .... Bakewell MR Henry P JR
Old Saybrook .... 06475 .... Jones MR & MRS Samuel B 4TH
Old Saybrook .... 06475 .... Soper MR John W
Pomfret .... 06258 .... Jones MR & MRS Jeremiah W
Pomfret .... 06259 .... Leary MR Nicholas P & Hatfield MS Susan W
Pomfret Center .... 06259 .... Gaumond MR & MRS Robert L
Redding .... 06896 .... Berry MR & MRS Ronald A
Redding .... 06896 .... Bird MRS Howard JR
Redding .... 06896 .... Edmonston MR & MRS Charles H
Redding .... 06896 .... Kaskell MR & MRS Peter H
Redding .... 06896 .... McCreary MR & MRS Pierce N JR
Redding .... 06896 .... Minot MRS Henry D JR
Redding .... 06896 .... Pearson MR & MRS Lawrence D
Redding .... 06896 .... Rodiger MRS Walter G JR
Redding .... 06896 .... Salatto MR Christopher T & Doty MS Brownson S
Redding .... 06896 .... Wiedel MRS Philip D
Redding Center .... 06875 .... Meyers MR & MRS Peter
Ridgefield .... 06877 .... Blackwell MRS James M IV
Ridgefield .... 06877 .... Brewster MR Carroll W
Ridgefield .... 06877 .... Bricken MR & MRS Jonathan M
Ridgefield .... 06877 .... Champion MS Sara S
Ridgefield .... 06877 .... Clark MR & MRS Peter S I
Ridgefield .... 06877 .... Coleman MR Daniel T Le V
Ridgefield .... 06877 .... Connard MR & MRS Frank L III
Ridgefield .... 06877 .... Cooke MR Nelson K
Ridgefield .... 06877 .... de Noüe CTE Jehan-Sébastien & CTSSE
Ridgefield .... 06877 .... Donnelly MR Kenneth C
Ridgefield .... 06877 .... Eagle MR & MRS Jeremy C W
Ridgefield .... 06877 .... Elkman MRS Steven M
Ridgefield .... 06877 .... Fleuette MR & MRS Marc J
Ridgefield .... 06877 .... Foote MRS Richard L
Ridgefield .... 06877 .... Katzenbach MR & MRS E Thomas
Ridgefield .... 06877 .... Kinnear MR & MRS John K JR
Ridgefield .... 06877 .... Linke MR & MRS Scott B
Ridgefield .... 06877 .... Mueller MR & MRS Michael H H
Ridgefield .... 06877 .... Percival MR & MRS J Nicholas
Ridgefield .... 06877 .... Spofford MR & MRS C Nicholas
Ridgefield .... 06877 .... Vandervoorn MR & MRS Richard M
Riverside .... 06878 .... Bacon MR & MRS Stephen H JR
Riverside .... 06878 .... Bonsal MR & MRS Stephen
Riverside .... 06878 .... Coulson MRS Robert
Riverside .... 06878 .... de Milhau MR David L
Riverside .... 06878 .... Drake MR & MRS J William 3D
Riverside .... 06878 .... Franco MR & MRS Christopher P
Riverside .... 06878 .... Frantz MR & MRS L Scott
Riverside .... 06878 .... Gorin MR & MRS Thomas B
Riverside .... 06878 .... Harper MR & MRS James V
Riverside .... 06878 .... Humphrey MR & MRS Joseph J H
Riverside .... 06878 .... Huth MR & MRS Henry C JR
Riverside .... 06878 .... Jackson MR & MRS Alexander E
Riverside .... 06878 .... Kampmann MR & MRS Eric M
Riverside .... 06878 .... Koehler MRS Hugo G
Riverside .... 06878 .... Lea MS Hilary Martin
Riverside .... 06878 .... Lowther MR & MRS George 4TH
Riverside .... 06878 .... Lufkin MR & MRS Timothy B
Riverside .... 06878 .... Moffly MR & MRS John W IV
Riverside .... 06878 .... Parris MRS S Nye
Riverside .... 06878 .... Phillips MR & MRS Christopher L
Riverside .... 06878 .... Pray MS Natasha Justina
Riverside .... 06878 .... Reid MR & MRS Michael W
Riverside .... 06878 .... Royce MR & MRS Charles M
Riverside .... 06878 .... Sibley MR & MRS J Holden
Riverside .... 06878 .... Strong MISS Katerina M
Riverside .... 06878 .... Wardell MR & MRS Charles W B IV
Riverside .... 06878 .... Weicker MR & MRS Scot B
Riverside .... 06878 .... Weintz MR & MRS J Frederick JR
Rocky Hill .... 06067 .... Almy MR & MRS Thomas
Rocky Hill .... 06067 .... Van Alstyne MISS (DR) Gretchen A
Rocky Hill .... 06067 .... Ward MR & MRS Timothy D
Rowayton .... 06853 .... Buck MR & MRS N Harrison
Rowayton .... 06853 .... Burton MR & MRS Bruce R
Rowayton .... 06853 .... Farnum MR & MRS Peter R JR
Rowayton .... 06853 .... Gerster MR & MRS John A
Rowayton .... 06853 .... Hollyday MR & MRS Richard C 5TH
Rowayton .... 06853 .... Hubbard MR & MRS D Seeley
Rowayton .... 06853 .... Lowe MR & MRS David M
Rowayton .... 06853 .... Morphy MR & MRS Calvin P
Rowayton .... 06853 .... O'Neil MR & MRS J Pierce
Rowayton .... 06853 .... Reynolds MR & MRS John D JR
Rowayton .... 06853 .... Wheeler MR & MRS Halsted W
Rowayton .... 06853 .... Woods MR & MRS Richard M

Roxbury, CT—Stamford, CT

Roxbury	06783	Daly MRS T F Gilroy
Roxbury	06783	Kelsey MS Sterett-Gittings
Salem	06420	Bingham MR & MRS Robert K
Salisbury	06068	Armstrong MRS John K
Salisbury	06068	Balagueró MR & MRS Miguel
Salisbury	06068	Boyd MR & MRS Robert S
Salisbury	06068	Francke MR & MRS Albert
Salisbury	06068	Haines MRS Thomas D
Salisbury	06068	Harris MR & MRS William R JR
Salisbury	06068	Hathaway MR Phillips
Salisbury	06068	Lynch MR John D
Salisbury	06068	Matlock MR & MRS Scott W
Salisbury	06068	Niles MRS Barbara E
Salisbury	06068	Rees MR & MRS W Trevor
Salisbury	06068	Schoenly MR & MRS Newton C JR
Salisbury	06068	Scott MS Katherine B
Salisbury	06068	Shattuck MR George H 3D
Salisbury	06068	Smith MRS C Carter JR
Salisbury	06068	Thomas MRS Wilmer J JR
Sharon	06069	Bancroft MR Harding F JR
Sharon	06069	Coords MRS Deane M
Sharon	06069	DuVal MR Clive L III
Sharon	06069	Goldfrank MR & MRS Lionel III
Sharon	06069	Gordon MR & MRS Nicholas
Sharon	06069	Hart MR & MRS C Caldwell JR
Sharon	06069	Hunter MRS Madeline M
Sharon	06069	Letteron MR Edward H
Sharon	06069	Lindgren MR Robert K & Gibb MR Thomas W
Sharon	06069	Lynch MR & MRS Michael D
Sharon	06069	Martinez MR & MRS Oscar R
Sharon	06069	McColley MR Sutherland
Sharon	06069	Mesniaeff MR Gregory
Sharon	06069	Rand MR & MRS Laurance B 3D
Sharon	06069	Roberts MR & MRS Clarence L JR
Sharon	06069	Simonin MR & MRS L Taylor
Sharon	06069	Symmers MISS Deborah K
Sharon	06069	Trowbridge MR William W H
Sharon	06069	Turnure MISS Barbara F
Shelton	06484	Blake MR & MRS Brian P T
Shelton	06484	Hoffman MRS John N JR
Sherman	06784	Maginnis MR Duncan H & Starr MR Ogden P Jr
Simsbury	06070	Hadden MR & MRS J C David
Simsbury	06070	Howe MR & MRS Barclay G
Simsbury	06070	Merriman MR & MRS M Heminway 3D
Simsbury	06070	Philip MR & MRS William V N
Simsbury	06070	Proctor MR & MRS Robert W
South Glastonbury	06073	MacDonald MR & MRS Jeffrey S
South Kent	06785	Baker MR & MRS John Milnes
South Kent	06785	Humphreys MISS Inness
South Kent	06785	Mellen MRS Henry W
South Kent	06785	Myers MR R Graham
South Kent	06785	Symonds MR & MRS Toby E
South Lyme	06376	Judson MRS William David
South Norwalk	06854	de Spoelberch MR & MRS Jacques A
South Norwalk	06854	Garnett MR Alexander Y P 4TH
South Norwalk	06854	Miller MR & MRS William H JR
Southbury	06488	Cole MRS William K
Southbury	06488	Craigmyle MRS M Martin
Southbury	06488	Erickson MR & MRS Jon W
Southbury	06488	Hook MR Thomas W
Southbury	06488	Hutton MRS Caroline DuBois
Southbury	06488	Lucey MR & MRS Denis
Southbury	06488	Millett MRS Daniel C
Southbury	06488	Pennell MR & MRS Henry B 3D
Southbury	06488	Robeson-Miller MR S
Southbury	06488	Sutton MRS James P
Southbury	06488	Sweeney MRS Diana M
Southbury	06488	Tucker MRS Joseph W
Southbury	06488	Williams MR & MRS Edward H SR
Southington	06489	Moeller DR & MRS Paul D
Southport	06490	Hawley MRS Alexander
Southport	06490	Sheppard MR & MRS W Stevens
Southport	06490	Soper MR & MRS John M
Southport	06490	Wheeler MRS Wilmot F JR
Southport	06890	Anderson MR Derby F
Southport	06890	Baker MR & MRS Benjamin M III
Southport	06890	Bonner MR Henry M JR
Southport	06890	Burton MR & MRS Donald C
Southport	06890	Cargill MR Samuel W
Southport	06890	Crawford MR & MRS W Michael
Southport	06890	Crolius MR & MRS Thomas Potter
Southport	06890	De Vecchi MR Robert P
Southport	06890	Della Rocca MR & MRS Steven
Southport	06890	du Pont MRS Henry B 3D
Southport	06890	Dunn MRS Charles Wesley JR
Southport	06890	Frantz MS Ruth P
Southport	06890	Gates MR & MRS Christopher D
Southport	06890	Heyn MR & MRS Christopher H
Southport	06890	Ijams MR & MRS John H 2D
Southport	06890	Lewis MRS Julia B
Southport	06890	Montgomery MR Hugh
Southport	06890	Morehouse MR & MRS W Bradley
Southport	06890	Munroe MRS Henry W
Southport	06890	Parker MR David Scott
Southport	06890	Rogers MR & MRS H Elliott JR
Southport	06890	Ross MR & MRS James W O
Southport	06890	Schlachter DR Todd R & Dunn MS Anne Renwick McKinne
Southport	06890	Schoen DR & MRS (DR) Robert T
Southport	06890	Stetson MRS Charles P
Southport	06890	Stokes MRS John W 2D
Southport	06890	Storrs MR & MRS David K
Southport	06890	Wilbur MR & MRS E Packer 4TH
Stamford	06901	Christian MR Robert G JR
Stamford	06902	Baldwin MRS Alexander T JR
Stamford	06902	Cammann MISS Carola C
Stamford	06902	Crihfield MR & MRS Owen S
Stamford	06902	Cushman MRS Robin L
Stamford	06902	Dionne MR & MRS Dino
Stamford	06902	Fahnestock MRS Pamela R
Stamford	06902	Gould MISS Daisy M
Stamford	06902	Hume MRS Stephen N
Stamford	06902	King MR & MRS William A
Stamford	06902	Lannamann MR & MRS Thomas C
Stamford	06902	Manée MRS Monte Stewart
Stamford	06902	May MRS William F
Stamford	06902	Miller MRS Donald F
Stamford	06902	Morgan MR & MRS John A
Stamford	06902	Saypol MR & MRS Austin O
Stamford	06902	Shrady MISS Marina C
Stamford	06902	Steers MRS John C
Stamford	06902	Stewart MRS John M III
Stamford	06902	Straat MR & MRS Kent L
Stamford	06902	Thaxter MR Edward H
Stamford	06902	Van Deventer MRS Francis H
Stamford	06902	Vietor MR Edward M
Stamford	06902	Welles MR Arnold S & Erasmus MR Hendrik S
Stamford	06903	Abernethy MR & MRS Samuel F
Stamford	06903	Ball MR & MRS Stephen F W JR
Stamford	06903	Borman MRS Pamela S
Stamford	06903	Havens MR & MRS Paul M

Stamford, CT—Westport, CT

Stamford	06903	Lange MR & MRS Kenneth R
Stamford	06903	Lannamann MRS Margaret P
Stamford	06903	Larned MR & MRS Michael C
Stamford	06903	Osterhus MR & MRS Edward M E
Stamford	06903	Oswald MR & MRS David D C
Stamford	06903	Sartorius MR & MRS John M III
Stamford	06903	Wells MR & MRS Mason B II
Stamford	06903	Yudain MR & MRS David M
Stamford	06905	Campbell MR & MRS Douglas 3D
Stamford	06905	Carter MISS Alice S
Stamford	06905	Dunn MRS Paxton T
Stamford	06905	Etherington MISS A Lawrence
Stamford	06905	Gray MR William S
Stamford	06905	Wheat MR & MRS Clayton E
Stamford	06906	White MR & MRS John H JR
Stamford	06907	Budds MR & MRS Rory N
Stamford	06907	Evans MR & MRS Craig C
Stamford	06907	Harris MR David W
Stamford	06907	Lencyk MR & MRS George P
Stamford	06907	Poole MRS Peter R
Stonington	06378	Bell MR Bertrand F III
Stonington	06378	Brown MRS Meredith M
Stonington	06378	Brown MRS Peter Megargee
Stonington	06378	Bump MS Josephine R
Stonington	06378	Burchenal DR & MRS (DR) David H
Stonington	06378	Casey MRS E Geyelin
Stonington	06378	Davis MR & MRS Michael Hamilton
Stonington	06378	Griscom MRS Clement A
Stonington	06378	Harvey MR & MRS Peter A
Stonington	06378	Houston MRS James A
Stonington	06378	Johnstone MR & MRS Philip M
Stonington	06378	Knapp MRS Harry K
Stonington	06378	Knapp MRS Theodosia B
Stonington	06378	Lane MR Garrison Fairfield
Stonington	06378	Langmann MRS Robert D
Stonington	06378	Lynch MRS Frank C
Stonington	06378	MacFadyen MRS John A JR
Stonington	06378	Mitchell MRS John F B
Stonington	06378	Muller MR & MRS Scott W
Stonington	06378	Nicholas MR Frederick S JR
Stonington	06378	Noyes MR Joseph C 4TH
Stonington	06378	Pearson MR & MRS Daniel A
Stonington	06378	Peterkin MR George U
Stonington	06378	Schefers MR Michael E & Lynch MS Sylvia Leland
Stonington	06378	Smith MR & MRS Cornelius H
Stonington	06378	Stebbins MR & MRS Rowland III
Stonington	06378	Thacher MRS Peter S
Stony Creek	06405	Kernan MR & MRS John D JR
Stratford	06614	Lovejoy MS Aletta T
Stratford	06614	Taylor MR James B 4TH
Stratford	06614	Wales MR & MRS Gwynne H
Stratford	06615	Erenhouse MR & MRS Ryan S
Stratford	06615	Munson MRS John H G
Taconic	06079	Cabot MR & MRS G Blake
Tariffville	06081	Blount MISS Madeleine D
Trumbull	06611	Downes MR John
Trumbull	06611	Payson MR & MRS Blakeney D
Trumbull	06611	Steers MR & MRS Michael
Wallingford	06492	Foster MR & MRS Benjamin R
Wallingford	06492	Fuller MISS Faith B
Wallingford	06492	Senocak MS Beatrice S
Wallingford	06492	Senocak MS Natali R
Washington	06793	Bent MR & MRS Edward S
Washington	06793	Boyer MR & MRS John
Washington	06793	Caroe MR Michael R
Washington	06793	Dubow MR & MRS Charles S
Washington	06793	Eldridge MRS Deborah W
Washington	06793	Fowlkes MR & MRS J Winston 3D
Washington	06793	Gibson MR R Dana
Washington	06793	Horan MR & MRS John R
Washington	06793	Malkin MR & MRS Jonathan R
Washington	06793	Maxwell MR John C III
Washington	06793	Payson MR & MRS Phillips H
Washington	06793	Solley MR Nicholas N
Washington	06793	Walker MR C Carter JR
Washington	06794	Giese MR & MRS Gary C
Washington Depot	06794	Dyer MRS Elisha JR
Washington Depot	06794	Frantz MR & MRS Leroy JR
Washington Depot	06794	Kappler MR & MRS Christopher A
Waterbury	06708	Upson MR & MRS Thomas F
Waterbury	06710	Wild MR Henry S
Waterford	06385	Mattison MR & MRS Robert W
Watertown	06795	Kenerson MR & MRS John B 2D
Watertown	06795	Merriman MISS Natalie-Smith
Watertown	06795	Merriman MRS M Heminway 2D
Weatogue	06089	Trevor MR & MRS Bronson JR
West Granby	06090	Brown MR & MRS Daniel P JR
West Hartford	06105	Davis MS Ethel F
West Hartford	06105	Hyland MR & MRS Douglas K S
West Hartford	06105	Walker MRS James E C
West Hartford	06107	Adams MR & MRS Bruce H
West Hartford	06107	Almond DR & MRS Douglas V
West Hartford	06107	Compton MR & MRS Douglass M JR
West Hartford	06107	Harrison MR & MRS William R
West Hartford	06107	Little MR Lawrence S
West Hartford	06107	Steel MRS Alfred JR
West Hartford	06107	Walker MR & MRS Kenneth B
West Hartford	06117	Bainbridge MR & MRS Robert H
West Hartford	06117	Jackson MR & MRS Jay W
West Hartford	06117	Lyons MR & MRS George A II
West Hartford	06117	Montgelas MR & MRS Rudolph M A JR
West Hartford	06117	Nolan MR & MRS John B
West Hartford	06117	Seymour MR & MRS Allyn JR
West Hartford	06117	Whittemore MR & MRS Edward B
West Hartford	06119	Beers MR & MRS David B III
West Hartford	06119	Beers MS Margaret Horne Evans
West Hartford	06119	Robinson MS M Merritt
West Haven	06516	Bowman MISS Alexandra Kip
West Haven	06516	Darling MR F Corey JR
West Redding	06896	Honan MR & MRS William Holmes
West Redding	06896	Merritt MR & MRS (DR) Henry F
West Redding	06896	Reeve MR & MRS Stuart A
West Simsbury	06092	Dempsey MR & MRS Jeffrey A
West Simsbury	06092	Swain MR & MRS David S
Westbrook	06498	Comstock MR & MRS John B 2D
Weston	06883	Belak MR Edmund R JR
Weston	06883	Butt MR & MRS Clement van B
Weston	06883	Emberling MR & MRS David M
Weston	06883	Field MR & MRS R Gregory
Weston	06883	Glascott MR & MRS Jeffrey R
Weston	06883	Littlejohn MRS Jacqueline S
Weston	06883	Peterstam MR & MRS Niklas P H
Weston	06883	van Daalen MR & MRS M Anthony E
Westport	06880	Allen MR & MRS Charles E G
Westport	06880	Andrade MR & MRS Eduardo N T
Westport	06880	Califano MR & MRS Joseph A JR
Westport	06880	Dearth MISS Margaret D
Westport	06880	Dillon MR & MRS John S II
Westport	06880	Du Vivier MRS Lynne
Westport	06880	Eckert MR Tim M
Westport	06880	Frantz MR & MRS C Christopher

Westport, CT—Wilmington, DE

Westport	06880	Griggs MRS Northam Lee JR
Westport	06880	Hammond MR Randall A & Thomas MR Andrew J
Westport	06880	Harris MR & MRS Holton E
Westport	06880	Howard MR & MRS Livingston G
Westport	06880	Howell MR & MRS T T Anthony JR
Westport	06880	King MR Alfred F 3D
Westport	06880	Miller MR & MRS Robert J
Westport	06880	Moore MS Clarissa
Westport	06880	Robinson MR & MRS Steven L
Westport	06880	Tucker MR & MRS Peter J
Westport	06880	Webb MR & MRS Richard N
Westport	06880	Weber MR & MRS Douglas J
Westport	06880	Weddle LT & MRS Ryan B
Westport	06880	Whiting MR & MRS Brian C SR
Westport	06880	Widmann MR Anthony
Westport	06880	Wilcox MR & MRS G Jarvis G JR
Westport	06880	Williams MR & MRS Edward H JR
Westport	06880	Woodson MR & MRS A Hartswell 3D
Westport	06881	Gibson MR Christopher L
Wethersfield	06109	Cregeau MR & MRS (DR) Damien M
Willimantic	06226	Wilson MR Winn Cameron
Wilton	06897	Browning MRS Jordice G
Wilton	06897	Corper MR & MRS Douglas P
Wilton	06897	Cromie MR & MRS Daniel E
Wilton	06897	Cromwell MR & MRS Jarvis 2D
Wilton	06897	Filley MR & MRS Patrick O
Wilton	06897	Follett MR & MRS William R
Wilton	06897	Freeman MR & MRS Douglas P B
Wilton	06897	Gaston MR & MRS Frederick K III
Wilton	06897	Gaston MR & MRS Frederick K IV
Wilton	06897	Geary MS Daphne H
Wilton	06897	Gillespie MR & MRS Richard R
Wilton	06897	Gilmor MR & MRS Mark C
Wilton	06897	Helling MR Robert E
Wilton	06897	Higgins MR & MRS Kevin J
Wilton	06897	Jeanes MR & MRS Christopher B
Wilton	06897	Keating MR & MRS David B
Wilton	06897	Kineon MR & MRS James C JR
Wilton	06897	King MR & MRS Charles H JR
Wilton	06897	Lerch MR & MRS Robert B
Wilton	06897	Mitchell MR & MRS Richard B
Wilton	06897	Norfleet MR & MRS Christopher McC
Wilton	06897	Ottman MRS John B
Wilton	06897	Parisot MR & MRS Ricardo
Wilton	06897	Patterson MR & MRS Alexander E JR
Wilton	06897	Quigley MRS Amy Wing
Wilton	06897	Rodiger MR & MRS W Gregory III
Wilton	06897	Schneider MR & MRS Thomas P
Wilton	06897	Shields MR & MRS Day R
Wilton	06897	Stevenson MR & MRS G Barnes 3D
Wilton	06897	Sutherland MRS Beverley W
Wilton	06897	Swanson MR & MRS Russell M
Wilton	06897	Thors MR & MRS Tyler E
Wilton	06897	Vehslage MR & MRS Stephen T JR
Wilton	06897	Walker MR & MRS Brian D
Wilton	06897	White MR & MRS Stephen H
Wilton	06897	Wickersham MR & MRS William W
Winsted	06098	Stanley MISS (DR) Elizabeth K
Woodbridge	06525	Just MS Jennifer R
Woodbridge	06525	Luther MR & MRS Michael
Woodbury	06798	Caroe MR & MRS Timothy R
Woodbury	06798	Gersky MR & MRS Peter K
Woodbury	06798	Hildreth MR & MRS William C
Woodbury	06798	Nichols MRS Katharine M
Woodbury	06798	North MR & MRS Peter W
Woodbury	06798	Rianhard MR & MRS Thomas McM JR
Woodbury	06798	Thomson MISS Melissa Pell
Woodbury	06798	Weyburn MRS Reed A
Woodstock	06281	Harvey MRS Cyrus I JR
Woodstock	06281	Mark MR & MRS Christopher W

DELAWARE

Ardentown	19810	Dwyer MRS Page W
Bethany Beach	19930	Guernsey MR & MRS Kent C
Bethany Beach	19930	Palmer MR H Meredith
Centerville	19807	Scott MR & MRS Thomas S
Dover	19901	Peterkin MR DeWitt III
Greenville	19807	Allison MRS Peter
Greenville	19807	Bartolec MR & MRS Thomas A
Greenville	19807	Borda MR & MRS Luke H
Greenville	19807	Copeland MR & MRS Gerret van S
Greenville	19807	Denham MR & MRS Willard A S
Greenville	19807	Diedrick MS Samantha
Greenville	19807	du Pont MR Charles F
Greenville	19807	du Pont MRS Henry E I
Greenville	19807	Flint MR & MRS Peter H
Greenville	19807	Hoopes MR & MRS David
Greenville	19807	Jolles MR Martin & Pilling MRS Janet K
Greenville	19807	Layton MRS Greta Brown
Greenville	19807	Lovett MRS Robert S II
Greenville	19807	Lundgren MR & MRS (DR) Andrew A
Greenville	19807	Rose MR & MRS Andrew C
Greenville	19807	Sailer MR & MRS Christopher A
Greenville	19807	Scott MRS Sidney JR
Greenville	19807	Strawbridge MR George JR
Greenville	19807	Townsend MR & MRS P Coleman JR
Greenville	19807	Wilcox MRS F Samuel JR
Greenville	19870	Fleming MR Wilson B JR & Buell MS (DR) Martha J
Hockessin	19707	Frederick MR & MRS William H JR
Hockessin	19707	Newbold MR & MRS Michael JR
Hockessin	19707	Price MR & MRS Dwight L
Hockessin	19707	Tisdall MR Joseph C
Lewes	19958	Haskell MR & MRS Paul T
Middletown	19709	DeBergh DR & MRS John R
Middletown	19709	Speers MR William S
Milton	19968	Brown MR & MRS James C L
Montchanin	19710	Day MR & MRS Matthew T
Montchanin	19710	du Pont MR & MRS Irénée JR
Montchanin	19710	Elliman MR & MRS D Trowbridge 3D
Montchanin	19710	Greeley MISS Laura H
Montchanin	19710	Hutchinson MR & MRS James H
Montchanin	19710	Pearson MRS G Burton JR
Newark	19711	de Garbolewski MR & MRS Mark E
Newark	19711	Getze MR Frederick B
Newark	19713	Timmins DR & MRS Steven J
Rehoboth Beach	19971	Hastings MR Matthew T
Rehoboth Beach	19971	Hooper MRS Charles
Rehoboth Beach	19971	Sisson CAPT (RET) & MRS Thomas U JR
Rehoboth Beach	19971	Weir MS Ann H
Rockland	19732	Ashford MR & MRS Theodore H
Rockland	19732	du Pont MR & MRS Benjamin Franklin
Rockland	19732	du Pont MR & MRS Pierre S
Rockland	19732	Harrell MR & MRS Paul H JR
Rockland	19732	Jenney MR & MRS John L K
Rockland	19732	Jenney MR John L K JR
Rockland Mills	19732	Copeland MRS Ann Bellah
Wilmington	19801	Elliman MR William B
Wilmington	19803	Clemmer DR & MRS Richard I JR
Wilmington	19803	Morris MS Rebecca M

Wilmington.................. 19805......... Cashman MR W Timothy II
Wilmington.................. 19805......... Corroon MR & MRS Richard F II
Wilmington.................. 19805......... Jones MR & MRS Richard I G JR
Wilmington.................. 19805......... Newlin MR & MRS John E III
Wilmington.................. 19805......... Scott MR & MRS Harlan
Wilmington.................. 19805......... Scott MS Lindsay
Wilmington.................. 19806......... Elliott MRS Mary Jane
Wilmington.................. 19806......... Flinn MR & MRS C Barr
Wilmington.................. 19806......... Jenney MISS Caroline K
Wilmington.................. 19806......... Lindley MR & MRS Daniel F
Wilmington.................. 19806......... Manning MS Julia W
Wilmington.................. 19806......... Morris MR Owen III
Wilmington.................. 19806......... Murray MRS Francis Key
Wilmington.................. 19806......... Sailer MR & MRS John JR
Wilmington.................. 19806......... Shelnutt MRS Martha Budd
Wilmington.................. 19806......... Sheppard MRS Penelope L
Wilmington.................. 19806......... Speers REV & MRS Thomas G 3D
Wilmington.................. 19806......... Stryker MRS A Bartlett JR
Wilmington.................. 19806......... Vest MS Phebe Alexandra
Wilmington.................. 19806......... Weymouth MR Charles M
Wilmington.................. 19807......... Belger MR & MRS James M
Wilmington.................. 19807......... Biggs MRS John III
Wilmington.................. 19807......... Bolling MRS Robert H JR
Wilmington.................. 19807......... Bonmartini CTSS Charlotte
Wilmington.................. 19807......... Brokaw MR & MRS Roberts Wyckoff III
Wilmington.................. 19807......... Burchenal MRS John J
Wilmington.................. 19807......... Carpenter MRS Edmund N II
Wilmington.................. 19807......... Cist MS Mary Harding L
Wilmington.................. 19807......... Davis MR & MRS Michael J
Wilmington.................. 19807......... du Pont MR & MRS Henry E I II
Wilmington.................. 19807......... du Pont MRS Edward B
Wilmington.................. 19807......... Edinger MR & MRS John S JR
Wilmington.................. 19807......... Fenton MR & MRS Wendell
Wilmington.................. 19807......... Gahagan MR & MRS William G
Wilmington.................. 19807......... Helme MRS Karen R
Wilmington.................. 19807......... Hyland MR & MRS Samuel I du P
Wilmington.................. 19807......... Lassen MR & MRS John Kai
Wilmington.................. 19807......... Maroney MR & MRS Whitney M
Wilmington.................. 19807......... McConnel MR & MRS Ian Roberts
Wilmington.................. 19807......... Mellon MR & MRS Henry C S
Wilmington.................. 19807......... Middleton MR & MRS John J
Wilmington.................. 19807......... Miller MR & MRS Barton H
Wilmington.................. 19807......... Moore MRS Daniel W
Wilmington.................. 19807......... Nichols MR & MRS (DR) David P
Wilmington.................. 19807......... Sanger MR & MRS Christopher D
Wilmington.................. 19807......... Scott MR Edgar 3D
Wilmington.................. 19807......... Seiffert MR John E & Biggs MS Anna M
Wilmington.................. 19807......... Solacoff DR & MRS (DR) David K
Wilmington.................. 19807......... Worth MR William A JR
Wilmington.................. 19807......... Zug MR & MRS James W JR
Wilmington.................. 19808......... Bartram MR & MRS Brent E
Wilmington.................. 19808......... Hotchkiss MR Benjamin G
Wilmington.................. 19808......... Shellenberger MISS Elisabeth
Wilmington.................. 19810......... Coburn MR George M
Wilmington.................. 19810......... Fish MRS Peter S
Wilmington.................. 19810......... Hoscheit MRS Diana H
Wilmington.................. 19810......... Littleton MR & MRS Peter D
Wilmington.................. 19899......... Ward MR & MRS Rodman JR
Wimington.................... 19086......... Roben MR & MRS Adam W B
Yorklyn........................... 19736......... Ledyard MR & MRS Michael M
Yorklyn........................... 19736......... Quimby MR & MRS Steven H

DISTRICT OF COLUMBIA

Washington.................. 20001......... Aspero MR & MRS Benedict V JR
Washington.................. 20001......... Boomer MS Catherine R
Washington.................. 20001......... Boomer MS Ellen M
Washington.................. 20001......... Warren MR Stephen W R
& Garside MS Elizabeth R
Washington.................. 20002......... Bauer MISS E Sage H
Washington.................. 20002......... Behn MS Sharon M
Washington.................. 20002......... Bolton MR Charles H
Washington.................. 20002......... Huxley MR & MRS Samuel D
Washington.................. 20002......... Meers MR & MRS H Philip
Washington.................. 20002......... Mika MR & MRS Steven P JR
Washington.................. 20002......... Norton MR & MRS Randell H
Washington.................. 20002......... Pedersen MR & MRS William F
Washington.................. 20002......... Pyle MR & MRS Nicholas A
Washington.................. 20002......... Randall MR Ross G II
Washington.................. 20002......... Toulmin MR & MRS Charles N
Washington.................. 20002......... Wylie MRS (DR) Harold W JR
Washington.................. 20003......... Gold CDR Robert A & Ames MS Amelia E
Washington.................. 20003......... MacKenzie MR Scott Anderson
Washington.................. 20003......... Spencer MR & MRS Duncan C
Washington.................. 20005......... Beekman MR & MRS Izaak B
Washington.................. 20005......... Frelinghuysen MR & MRS Cyrus T
Washington.................. 20005......... Sidamon-Eristoff MISS Elizabeth
Washington.................. 20006......... Bolton MR John Wood JR
Washington.................. 20006......... Calkins MR John T
Washington.................. 20006......... de Wolf MR & MRS Francis C III
Washington.................. 20007......... Allen MRS George V JR
Washington.................. 20007......... Apple MRS Raymond Walter JR
Washington.................. 20007......... Arnold MR Robert Carter
Washington.................. 20007......... Aukamp MR & MRS Brooks M
Washington.................. 20007......... Baker MRS Caroline A A
Washington.................. 20007......... Bartlett MRS Charles L
Washington.................. 20007......... Battle MR & MRS T Westray III
Washington.................. 20007......... Billings MR & MRS Jonathan L
Washington.................. 20007......... Blake MRS Robert O
Washington.................. 20007......... Bonner MR & MRS Paul B
Washington.................. 20007......... Brooks MR & MRS A Oakley
Washington.................. 20007......... Bull MR & MRS Richard C
Washington.................. 20007......... Burden MR & MRS I Townsend 3D
Washington.................. 20007......... Burnham MR & MRS Richard I
Washington.................. 20007......... Cameron MRS Juan M
Washington.................. 20007......... Collins MR & MRS Terence Winslow
Washington.................. 20007......... Combes MISS M L deRaismes
Washington.................. 20007......... Coolidge MRS Eliska H
Washington.................. 20007......... Davidson MRS Stuart C
Washington.................. 20007......... Davis MRS Edward L JR
Washington.................. 20007......... Dodds MR & MRS Robert F
Washington.................. 20007......... Dreyer MR & MRS Scott E
Washington.................. 20007......... DuBois MR & MRS Raymond F JR
Washington.................. 20007......... Duff MR Daniel S R
Washington.................. 20007......... Dwinell MR John L
Washington.................. 20007......... Emes MR & MRS Edward L JR
Washington.................. 20007......... Emmet MS Anne Livingston
Washington.................. 20007......... Evans DR & MRS Martin D D
Washington.................. 20007......... Farnum MISS Melissa Lufkin
Washington.................. 20007......... Farr MR & MRS H Bartow 3D
Washington.................. 20007......... Farrington MR & MRS Henry M
Washington.................. 20007......... Fosburgh MR & MRS P Whitney JR
Washington.................. 20007......... Fox MS Yolande Dolly
Washington.................. 20007......... Frazier MR Seth & Thompson MS Gale E
Washington.................. 20007......... Gabriel MR & MRS Robert P
Washington.................. 20007......... Gibby MR & MRS Todd E
Washington.................. 20007......... Graham MR & MRS R Hilles
Washington.................. 20007......... Green DR & MRS Edward C

Washington, DC—Washington, DC

Washington.................... 20007 .... Grennan MR Anderson G & Haney MS Mae E
Washington.................... 20007 .... Gummey MR & MRS Michael F
Washington.................... 20007 .... Hawkins MR & MRS Val P JR
Washington.................... 20007 .... Henry MR C Wolcott 3D
Washington.................... 20007 .... Herrington MRS Alison S
Washington.................... 20007 .... Hodges MR & MRS John A
Washington.................... 20007 .... Hodges MR Sven C
Washington.................... 20007 .... Hornblower MR Luke R
Washington.................... 20007 .... Horsey MR & MRS Outerbridge
Washington.................... 20007 .... Houghton MR Amory JR
Washington.................... 20007 .... Huber MR & MRS Richard M JR
Washington.................... 20007 .... Hurd MRS James Douglas
Washington.................... 20007 .... Hurt MR & MRS Robert H
Washington.................... 20007 .... Husted MRS John G W
Washington.................... 20007 .... Isles MR & MRS Adam R
Washington.................... 20007 .... Jensen MISS Catherine S H
Washington.................... 20007 .... Jones MR & MRS Thomas VI
Washington.................... 20007 .... Kaempfer MRS Joseph W JR
Washington.................... 20007 .... Kaye MR & MRS William E
Washington.................... 20007 .... Kennedy MISS Patricia E
Washington.................... 20007 .... Kraft COL (RET) Kenneth A
Washington.................... 20007 .... Lapham MRS Anthony A
Washington.................... 20007 .... Lawrence MR Sidney S 3D & Birch MR Thomas L
Washington.................... 20007 .... Lewis MR & MRS Ronald B
Washington.................... 20007 .... Macomber MR John De W
Washington.................... 20007 .... Martin MR & MRS Christopher B
Washington.................... 20007 .... Marvin MRS Camilla
Washington.................... 20007 .... Mathias MR Charles B
Washington.................... 20007 .... McClelland MRS Donald R
Washington.................... 20007 .... McRae MR John Ashton
Washington.................... 20007 .... Mefford MR Thomas Fleetwood
Washington.................... 20007 .... Miller MR & MRS Edward Terhune
Washington.................... 20007 .... Mocek MR & MRS Gregory G
Washington.................... 20007 .... Moroney MR & MRS William R
Washington.................... 20007 .... Newell MR & MRS John P JR
Washington.................... 20007 .... Nichols MS Dane Anderson
Washington.................... 20007 .... Nicholson MR & MRS John B
Washington.................... 20007 .... Nitze MR & MRS William A
Washington.................... 20007 .... O'Brien MR & MRS Lawrence F 3D
Washington.................... 20007 .... Ohl MR Edwin
Washington.................... 20007 .... Oliphant MR Christopher H
Washington.................... 20007 .... Oliphant MR Cortright Wetherill
Washington.................... 20007 .... Parker MR & MRS Anthony W
Washington.................... 20007 .... Peabody MR & MRS Malcolm E
Washington.................... 20007 .... Peckham MR Rufus W JR
Washington.................... 20007 .... Pell MR & MRS Haven N B
Washington.................... 20007 .... Pessey MR & MRS Jean-Baptiste M
Washington.................... 20007 .... Pew MR James S
Washington.................... 20007 .... Porter MRS Elisabeth Scott
Washington.................... 20007 .... Prince MRS Frederick H
Washington.................... 20007 .... Quillen MRS Jacqueline L
Washington.................... 20007 .... Rankin MR & MRS Douglas W
Washington.................... 20007 .... Rasmussen MR & MRS Garret G
Washington.................... 20007 .... Richardson MR & MRS John D
Washington.................... 20007 .... Riginos MR & MRS Vasilis E
Washington.................... 20007 .... Robinson MS Page
Washington.................... 20007 .... Ross MR & MRS Robert S JR
Washington.................... 20007 .... Roth MRS William V JR
Washington.................... 20007 .... Rublee MR & MRS George
Washington.................... 20007 .... Saenger MR & MRS Christopher D
Washington.................... 20007 .... Satterthwaite MISS Ann
Washington.................... 20007 .... Schaefer MRS Henry W
Washington.................... 20007 .... Schafer MR & MRS John H
Washington.................... 20007 .... Sedgwick MR & MRS Theodore
Washington.................... 20007 .... Shepard MRS Addison
Washington.................... 20007 .... Sidamon-Eristoff MR & MRS Simon
Washington.................... 20007 .... Skallerup MRS Walter T JR
Washington.................... 20007 .... Smith MR & MRS W N Harrell 4TH
Washington.................... 20007 .... Smith MR George Patrick II
Washington.................... 20007 .... Song DR & MRS David H
Washington.................... 20007 .... Stanley MISS Florence C
Washington.................... 20007 .... Stone MR & MRS Roger D
Washington.................... 20007 .... Symington DR & MRS (DR) John S
Washington.................... 20007 .... Taylor MRS W Waverly
Washington.................... 20007 .... Thorpe MR & MRS Merle L III
Washington.................... 20007 .... Towell MISS Dane Billings
Washington.................... 20007 .... Towell MR Timothy Lathrop
Washington.................... 20007 .... Trimble MR & MRS William C 3D
Washington.................... 20007 .... Truslow MR & MRS Frederic J
Washington.................... 20007 .... Van Arsdall MR & MRS (DR) Michael G
Washington.................... 20007 .... van Roijen MR & MRS Peter P
Washington.................... 20007 .... van Roijen MR Christopher T
Washington.................... 20007 .... Walker MR & MRS W Alexander
Washington.................... 20007 .... Warner MRS William W
Washington.................... 20007 .... Watson MR & MRS George E 3D
Washington.................... 20007 .... Weimer MR Douglas Reid
Washington.................... 20007 .... Wendt MR E Allan
Washington.................... 20007 .... West MR & MRS J Robinson
Washington.................... 20007 .... Wilkins MR & MRS Fraser Bryan
Washington.................... 20007 .... Williamson MR & MRS Edwin D
Washington.................... 20007 .... Wilson MR Edward C
Washington.................... 20007 .... Wood MISS Nancy C
Washington.................... 20007 .... Young MR & MRS H Peyton
Washington.................... 20008 .... Acheson MR David C
Washington.................... 20008 .... Armstrong MAJ (RET) Anne C
Washington.................... 20008 .... Arnold DR & MRS Douglas McN
Washington.................... 20008 .... Athy MR Andrew JR
Washington.................... 20008 .... Barnum MRS John W
Washington.................... 20008 .... Beckner MR & MRS R Bruce
Washington.................... 20008 .... Bilodeau MR & MRS Harrison Otis C
Washington.................... 20008 .... Buchanan MR & MRS John G 3D
Washington.................... 20008 .... Carlisle MR Miles
Washington.................... 20008 .... Carr MRS Keith Armistead
Washington.................... 20008 .... Carter MR & MRS Charles Carroll
Washington.................... 20008 .... Chapin MR & MRS Christopher K
Washington.................... 20008 .... Clark MR & MRS Colin S
Washington.................... 20008 .... Clark MR & MRS Warren JR
Washington.................... 20008 .... Cleveland MRS Robert G
Washington.................... 20008 .... Conger MS Elizabeth B
Washington.................... 20008 .... Davis MR Henry A
Washington.................... 20008 .... Dick MS Diana H
Washington.................... 20008 .... Dominick MRS Theodore W
Washington.................... 20008 .... Ekimian MR Rafael A & Arrott MS Elizabeth
Washington.................... 20008 .... Florance MR Colden L'H R & Griscom MS Nancy E
Washington.................... 20008 .... Folger MR & MRS Lee M
Washington.................... 20008 .... Folger MR John D
Washington.................... 20008 .... Garrett MR & MRS Darryl N
Washington.................... 20008 .... Graeber MR George K
Washington.................... 20008 .... Grayson MR George
Washington.................... 20008 .... Grove MR Brandon Hambright JR
Washington.................... 20008 .... Gustafson MR & MRS (REV) Thomas
Washington.................... 20008 .... Hardy MR & MRS Randolph Willson
Washington.................... 20008 .... Henderson MISS Aline J
Washington.................... 20008 .... Herrick MRS Anita G
Washington.................... 20008 .... Higdon MR Robert M JR
Washington.................... 20008 .... Houser MRS William D
Washington.................... 20008 .... Howells MR & MRS Horace W
Washington.................... 20008 .... Howells MR & MRS William Dean
Washington.................... 20008 .... Ignatius MR & MRS Paul Robert

Washington........20008........Kaminer MR Stevenson S
Washington........20008........Keatley MR & MRS Robert L
Washington........20008........Kulski DR & MRS Julian
Washington........20008........La Farge MR & MRS Edward T
Washington........20008........Lawson MR W David IV
Washington........20008........Maloney MRS James P JR
Washington........20008........Marr MR & MRS William Corbin
Washington........20008........Martin MR & MRS Isaiah Guyman III
Washington........20008........Martinez MR & MRS Roman V
Washington........20008........Maruca MR & MRS Samuel M
Washington........20008........McLarty MR & MRS Thomas F III
Washington........20008........Milton MRS I Orwicz
Washington........20008........Mullan MRS Hugh
Washington........20008........Nalle MRS David
Washington........20008........Newlin MR & MRS William V P
Washington........20008........Oliver MR & MRS Daniel
Washington........20008........Peters MR F Whitten
Washington........20008........Pillsbury MR & MRS Philip W JR
Washington........20008........Price DR & MRS G Wesley
Washington........20008........Reppas DR & MRS (DR) John B
Washington........20008........Richardson MR & MRS (HON) John L
Washington........20008........Serfaty MR & MRS Alexis L
Washington........20008........Serfaty MR & MRS Simon H
Washington........20008........Sierck MR & MRS Alexander W
Washington........20008........Smith MR & MRS Stephen Grant
Washington........20008........Smith MR Timothy D
Washington........20008........Spencer MRS John M
Washington........20008........Steadman JUDGE & MRS John M
Washington........20008........Tilghman MR & MRS Christian D
Washington........20008........Tilghman MR & MRS William F
Washington........20008........Tobin MRS Maurice B
Washington........20008........Train MR C Bowdoin
& Sanger MS Georgina M C
Washington........20008........Warner MR John B
Washington........20008........Wheelock MR & MRS Arthur K JR
Washington........20008........Whitmore MR & MRS John R
Washington........20008........Wright MR & MRS Minturn T IV
Washington........20008........Wyman MR Franklin 3D
Washington........20009........Alford MR & MRS Michael R
Washington........20009........Cooper MR R Clarke
Washington........20009........Dixon MS Doris L
Washington........20009........Gantner MR Stephen E
Washington........20009........Hague MR & MRS James D
Washington........20009........Heitman MR & MRS Timothy J
Washington........20009........Houghton MRS Linda L
Washington........20009........Kellogg MR & MRS Frederic R
Washington........20009........Morgan MR Robert A
Washington........20009........Nitze MR & MRS Paul K
Washington........20009........Phillips MR D Colin
Washington........20009........Reid MR & MRS Alexander L
Washington........20009........Sumner MR & MRS Wilson W
Washington........20009........Wetmore MR & MRS David Harding
Washington........20009........Wickham MR John Channing 2D
Washington........20010........Alexander MRS William B V
Washington........20010........Brown MR & MRS Malcolm A
Washington........20010........Longstreth MR & MRS Richard W
Washington........20010........Seligman MR Edward S
Washington........20010........Thompson MISS Felicity B
Washington........20010........Waters MR & MRS Edward A
Washington........20011........Baker MR & MRS John P
Washington........20011........Bishop MR & MRS James D Pell III
Washington........20011........Jewett MR Charles W JR
Washington........20011........Jewett MRS Martha S
Washington........20011........Lewis MR & MRS John Van Dusen
Washington........20011........Moss MR Hunter V
Washington........20011........Muller MR Daryl A & Reynolds MR William J
Washington........20012........Bell MR & MRS John C 4TH
Washington........20012........Jones MR Bryan D & Packard MS Elise B
Washington........20015........Anderson MR & MRS Daniel G
Washington........20015........Cross MR & MRS Daniel C
Washington........20015........Dallett MS Estelina L
Washington........20015........Dorsey MRS Joshua W 3D
Washington........20015........Emery MR & MRS James J
Washington........20015........Engert MR Roderick M
Washington........20015........Fleck MRS Francis E
Washington........20015........Fuller MISS Marilynn J
Washington........20015........Greig MRS Pickett M
Washington........20015........Hart MR & MRS Jeffrey P
Washington........20015........Howard CAPT (RET) Macauley
Washington........20015........Hughes MR & MRS Gerard B
Washington........20015........Hunsiker MS Marguerite B
Washington........20015........Kiker MR & MRS Douglas C
Washington........20015........Kingsley MR & MRS Robert L
Washington........20015........Kirk MR & MRS Roger
Washington........20015........Kreimer MISS Mary S
Washington........20015........Kuhl MR & MRS Nevin E
Washington........20015........Kuser MISS Suzanne D
Washington........20015........Lang MR & MRS (DR) François-Michel
Washington........20015........Luke MISS Lindsay H
Washington........20015........Malloy DR Bernard M
Washington........20015........McCabe MRS Walter C
Washington........20015........Palmer MRS Charles D
Washington........20015........Pearson MR Richard E
Washington........20015........Pike MRS Colette P
Washington........20015........Purdy MR & MRS Christopher H
Washington........20015........Roberts MRS Thomas M
Washington........20015........Sanders MR Cameron H JR
Washington........20015........Slidell MRS John R
Washington........20015........Stewart MR & MRS William H
Washington........20015........Struse MR & MRS Charles R
Washington........20015........Willard MR & MRS Daniel 3D
Washington........20015........Worsley MR & MRS James R JR
Washington........20015........Wyrough COL & MRS Richard R
Washington........20015........Young MRS Roslyn D JR
Washington........20016........Abeles MR & MRS Nathaniel C
Washington........20016........Allen MR & MRS Bradley Theodore
Washington........20016........Anderson DR & MRS Frank H
Washington........20016........Ayres MRS Merribel S
Washington........20016........Beach MR Samuel F JR
Washington........20016........Beatty MR & MRS Richard S
Washington........20016........Belman MR & MRS Murray J
Washington........20016........Bennett MRS W Tapley JR
Washington........20016........Bird MRS Collins
Washington........20016........Birney MR & MRS Arthur A
Washington........20016........Blue MRS E Stuart
Washington........20016........Breckinridge MRS Isabella G
Washington........20016........Browning MR Hays R JR
Washington........20016........Buchanan MR & MRS Wiley T III
Washington........20016........Buchanan MRS Wiley T JR
Washington........20016........Buckley MR & MRS Christopher T
Washington........20016........Burke MRS Nicholas R
Washington........20016........Carlson MR & MRS Buckley S P
Washington........20016........Carlson MR & MRS Tucker S McNear
Washington........20016........Carpenter MR & MRS Michael H JR
Washington........20016........Carter MR & MRS Adam Augustine
Washington........20016........Caskin MRS Francis H
Washington........20016........Constable MR & MRS Richard D J
Washington........20016........Corrigan MR & MRS James N
Washington........20016........Corrigan MR & MRS James N JR
Washington........20016........Dale MR Gordon T & Carter MS Constance T
Washington........20016........Darlington MISS Rebecca P
Washington........20016........Doughty MR & MRS Jeffrey C

To nominate a candidate for the Social Register Association, please email: SRCommittee@thesocialregister.org

Washington, DC—Washington, DC

Washington.................... 20016.......... Dove MS Hilary Pell
Washington.................... 20016.......... Dwight MR & MRS Griz Kingston
Washington.................... 20016.......... Eaton MR & MRS William F
Washington.................... 20016.......... Eberstadt MR & MRS Nicholas N
Washington.................... 20016.......... Ecton MR & MRS Stephen M
Washington.................... 20016.......... Edgeworth MRS Arthur B JR
Washington.................... 20016.......... Ellis MISS Isobel L
Washington.................... 20016.......... Elmore MR & MRS Stancliff C JR
Washington.................... 20016.......... English MRS Joseph G
Washington.................... 20016.......... Feinstein MRS Martin
Washington.................... 20016.......... Fenwick MR & MRS John A B
Washington.................... 20016.......... Florance MR & MRS Andrew C
Washington.................... 20016.......... Gasch MRS (DR) Alice T
Washington.................... 20016.......... Gould MR & MRS Jonathan V
Washington.................... 20016.......... Graham MRS Claire W
Washington.................... 20016.......... Gregory MR & MRS Richard S II
Washington.................... 20016.......... Gross MR Jason J
& Pendleton MS Constance M
Washington.................... 20016.......... Hall MR & MRS Ridgway M JR
Washington.................... 20016.......... Harper MRS John C
Washington.................... 20016.......... Hawkings MR & MRS David M JR
Washington.................... 20016.......... Hellmuth MR & MRS William K
Washington.................... 20016.......... Hemingway MISS Margaret
Washington.................... 20016.......... Herter MRS Christian A JR
Washington.................... 20016.......... Hilyard MR & MRS Benjamin A
Washington.................... 20016.......... Houghton MR Arthur A 3D
Washington.................... 20016.......... Houghton MRS Sherrill M
Washington.................... 20016.......... Howe MR & MRS Barclay G JR
Washington.................... 20016.......... Isham MR & MRS Christopher E
Washington.................... 20016.......... Jackson MRS Wayne G
Washington.................... 20016.......... Kopper MRS Juliette Starr
Washington.................... 20016.......... Kozumbo MR James Lukasz
Washington.................... 20016.......... Lattu RR ADM (RET) & MRS Onnie P
Washington.................... 20016.......... Leclerc MRS Ivor
Washington.................... 20016.......... Leigh MR Catesby M
Washington.................... 20016.......... Lewis MR & MRS Burton O JR
Washington.................... 20016.......... Lilley MR & MRS William 3D
Washington.................... 20016.......... Lowe MR James Rowland JR
Washington.................... 20016.......... Marsteller MR & MRS Robert W
Washington.................... 20016.......... Martin MRS W Swift III
Washington.................... 20016.......... Matheson MRS Bonnie B
Washington.................... 20016.......... Mause MR & MRS Philip J
Washington.................... 20016.......... Maxwell MR & MRS Thomas F III
Washington.................... 20016.......... McConihe MRS Julie M
Washington.................... 20016.......... McGuigan MR & MRS E Gayle JR
Washington.................... 20016.......... McLean MR & MRS Renwick L
Washington.................... 20016.......... McManaman MR Patrick V & Peters MS Mary I
Washington.................... 20016.......... Mermoud MR J Frank
Washington.................... 20016.......... Metz MR & MRS Craig H
Washington.................... 20016.......... Muir MR & MRS J Dapray
Washington.................... 20016.......... Myer MR & MRS Theodore H
Washington.................... 20016.......... Norden MRS Carl F
Washington.................... 20016.......... Nottingham MRS R Kendall
Washington.................... 20016.......... Oliphant MRS S Parker
Washington.................... 20016.......... Onnen MR & MRS Ferdinand H III
Washington.................... 20016.......... Orr MR & MRS P Welles
Washington.................... 20016.......... Patlovich MR & MRS Eric J
Washington.................... 20016.......... Patterson MRS John McC
Washington.................... 20016.......... Peabody MR & MRS Payson R
Washington.................... 20016.......... Pendleton MS Elisabeth
Washington.................... 20016.......... Pingree MRS Sally E
Washington.................... 20016.......... Portner MR John A D JR
Washington.................... 20016.......... Quinn REV DR E Frederick & Irish MRS
Washington.................... 20016.......... Richards MR & MRS Frederick III
Washington.................... 20016.......... Riepe MR & MRS James S JR
Washington.................... 20016.......... Ritchie MRS Charles J JR
Washington.................... 20016.......... Rockwell MRS Stuart W
Washington.................... 20016.......... Ryder MR & MRS James Bradford
Washington.................... 20016.......... Sachs MR & MRS Stephen F
Washington.................... 20016.......... Sanders MR Henry C C B
Washington.................... 20016.......... Sargent MR Christopher S
Washington.................... 20016.......... Saunders MISS Patricia G
Washington.................... 20016.......... Schneider MS Laura T
Washington.................... 20016.......... Sears MR & MRS Stephen Truxtun
Washington.................... 20016.......... Seidlitz MR & MRS Charles N 3D
Washington.................... 20016.......... Sheldon MR & MRS George W III
Washington.................... 20016.......... Sills MISS Hilary H
Washington.................... 20016.......... Smith MR & MRS Howard W 3D
Washington.................... 20016.......... Smith MR & MRS William J
Washington.................... 20016.......... Stancioff MR Andrew
& Chanler MS F Randall
Washington.................... 20016.......... Stewart MS A Leigh
Washington.................... 20016.......... Sturtevant MR & MRS Albert D
Washington.................... 20016.......... Swift MRS Patricia W
Washington.................... 20016.......... Symington MR & MRS James W
Washington.................... 20016.......... Taylor MRS E Drayton
Washington.................... 20016.......... Terry MISS Elizabeth
Washington.................... 20016.......... Thompson MR & MRS Henry L
Washington.................... 20016.......... Thurston MRS Elliott Ladd JR
Washington.................... 20016.......... Trebing MR David M
Washington.................... 20016.......... Trotter MR & MRS Andrew F
Washington.................... 20016.......... Truitt MR William S & Vaughn MR Philip M
Washington.................... 20016.......... Underwood MR & MRS Frederic G W
Washington.................... 20016.......... Waldrop MR Andrew C
Washington.................... 20016.......... Walker MR & MRS Mallory
Washington.................... 20016.......... Walker MR & MRS William M
Washington.................... 20016.......... Webb MISS Dorothy Parker
Washington.................... 20016.......... Whalen MRS Nan Shaver
Washington.................... 20016.......... Wheeler MR & MRS Alexander B JR
Washington.................... 20016.......... Wheelock MR & MRS George F
Washington.................... 20016.......... Winans MRS Thomas J
Washington.................... 20017.......... Madsen MR & MRS Deane A
Washington.................... 20018.......... Coleman MR Joseph E III
Washington.................... 20024.......... Herndon MR Edward T JR
Washington.................... 20024.......... Maxwell MR R Bruce
Washington.................... 20036.......... Beall MR John P
Washington.................... 20036.......... Brown MISS Christina M
Washington.................... 20036.......... Carew MR Lawrence R
Washington.................... 20036.......... Hoskinson MR & MRS John K
Washington.................... 20036.......... Wheeler MR & MRS George Y III
Washington.................... 20037.......... Brewer MR & MRS Michael F
Washington.................... 20037.......... Clarke MRS Thomas C
Washington.................... 20037.......... Eatman MR George Hackney
Washington.................... 20037.......... Gabriel MRS K Georg
Washington.................... 20037.......... Irelan MR John Peters
Washington.................... 20037.......... Jepson MS Tisha E
Washington.................... 20037.......... Kingsland MRS Mary E
Washington.................... 20037.......... Krech MR Shepard III & ffolliott MS Sheila
Washington.................... 20037.......... McCormick MR Matthew B
Washington.................... 20037.......... McKee MR Paul W
Washington.................... 20037.......... Moore MR & MRS Arthur Cotton
Washington.................... 20037.......... Moss MR & MRS Robert E
Washington.................... 20037.......... Platt MR & MRS Roger
Washington.................... 20037.......... Schepers MISS Jean
Washington.................... 20037.......... Webster MR Christopher White
Washington.................... 20521.......... Wilberding MR & MRS Augustus Van C

FLORIDA

Amelia Island........ 32034........ Fowle MRS Wilson F
Amelia Island........ 32034........ van Amerongen MR & MRS Jan A T
Anna Maria........ 34216........ Talbot DR & MRS (DR) George H
Atlantic Beach........ 32233........ Coleman MISS Martha J
Atlantic Beach........ 32233........ Dennis MR & MRS Robert W
Atlantic Beach........ 32233........ Holt MR & MRS William J JR
Atlantic Beach........ 32233........ Hutton MR & MRS Robert C
Atlantic Beach........ 32233........ Medina MR & MRS Harold R 3D
Atlantic Beach........ 32233........ Parrish MRS Anthony R
Atlantic Beach........ 32233........ Schlaff MR Richard J
Atlantis........ 33462........ Ullmann MR & MRS Henry J
Bal Harbour........ 33154........ Bandler MRS Richard
Belleair........ 33756........ Haydon MR & MRS R Winston
Boca Grande........ 33921........ Armour MRS T Stanton
Boca Grande........ 33921........ Bender MRS Michael A
Boca Grande........ 33921........ Branin MR & MRS Francis S JR
Boca Grande........ 33921........ Charman MRS Walter M JR
Boca Grande........ 33921........ Clarke MR & MRS Eliot C
Boca Grande........ 33921........ Cocroft MR & MRS Duncan H
Boca Grande........ 33921........ Conklin MRS Theodore B JR
Boca Grande........ 33921........ Eddy MR & MRS Paul C
Boca Grande........ 33921........ Eddy MR & MRS Randolph Post JR
Boca Grande........ 33921........ Ellis MR & MRS G Corson 3D
Boca Grande........ 33921........ Ferguson MISS Jane S
Boca Grande........ 33921........ Gardner MRS Stephen V
Boca Grande........ 33921........ Gorman MRS K Aubrey
Boca Grande........ 33921........ Howard MRS Reese Evans
Boca Grande........ 33921........ Ives MRS Kenneth A JR
Boca Grande........ 33921........ Johnson MR & MRS L Oakley
Boca Grande........ 33921........ Junkin MR & MRS Joseph S
Boca Grande........ 33921........ Large MR & MRS W Mifflin JR
Boca Grande........ 33921........ Marvel MR & MRS Robert
Boca Grande........ 33921........ Mauran MRS Louise
Boca Grande........ 33921........ McBean MRS Peter
Boca Grande........ 33921........ Miller MR & MRS Gerald A
Boca Grande........ 33921........ Milne DR & MRS George McL JR
Boca Grande........ 33921........ Niles MR John A
Boca Grande........ 33921........ Richardson MR & MRS Thomas F
Boca Grande........ 33921........ Russell MR & MRS Harold S
Boca Grande........ 33921........ Samuel MR & MRS Aderton P
Boca Grande........ 33921........ Sanderson MR & MRS James A
Boca Grande........ 33921........ Schwartz MRS Philip W
Boca Grande........ 33921........ Scudder MR & MRS Barrett
Boca Grande........ 33921........ Stanley MR & MRS Harlan F
Boca Grande........ 33921........ Stout MR & MRS Merrell L JR
Boca Grande........ 33921........ Talbot MR & MRS Richmond deP JR
Boca Grande........ 33921........ Verney MR & MRS E Geoffrey
Boca Grande........ 33921........ Vestner MR & MRS Eliot N
Boca Grande........ 33921........ Wallace MRS Constance H
Boca Grande........ 33921........ Waud MR & MRS Cornelius Byron
Boca Grande........ 33921........ Wolcott MRS Frank E III
Boca Raton........ 33428........ Land MR Ian S
Boca Raton........ 33431........ Catáo MR & MRS Alvaro L B
Boca Raton........ 33432........ Eberts MR & MRS Dustin W
Boca Raton........ 33432........ Graham DR & MRS Peter M
Boca Raton........ 33432........ Kaiser MR Stephen Hyatt JR
Boca Raton........ 33432........ Moore DR & MRS Matthew R
Boca Raton........ 33433........ Biays MR & MRS W Tuckerman
Boca Raton........ 33434........ Gubelmann MRS Susan McC
Boca Raton........ 33434........ Land MR & MRS Andre Paul
Boca Raton........ 33486........ Lavin MRS Katherine S
Boca Raton........ 33487........ Harris MRS (DR) Alexandra M
Bonita Springs........ 34133........ Kean MRS Patricia P
Bonita Springs........ 34134........ Adams MR & MRS Weston W JR
Bonita Springs........ 34134........ Coburn MR & MRS John JR
Bonita Springs........ 34134........ Foltz MR & MRS C Robert
Bonita Springs........ 34134........ Hanson MR & MRS Michael F 2D
Bonita Springs........ 34135........ Backerman MRS Millard M
Bonita Springs........ 34135........ Crawford MR & MRS (DR) Rollin H
Bonita Springs........ 34135........ Vauclain MISS Edwina F
Boynton Beach........ 33426........ Ward MRS Forbes
Boynton Beach........ 33435........ Maxwell MR F Rollins 3D
Boynton Beach........ 33435........ Shore MISS Barbara G
Boynton Beach........ 33435........ Smith MR & MRS Edward J JR
Boynton Beach........ 33435........ Smith MR George V 3D
Boynton Beach........ 33436........ Breakwell MR & MRS Phillip J
Boynton Beach........ 33436........ Casella MR & MRS Robert C
Boynton Beach........ 33436........ Coyle MR & MRS Norton Van V JR
Boynton Beach........ 33436........ Devens MR & MRS Charles JR
Boynton Beach........ 33436........ Elliman MR & MRS D Trowbridge
Boynton Beach........ 33436........ Emmet MR & MRS Grenville T 3D
Boynton Beach........ 33436........ Garner MR & MRS James A
Boynton Beach........ 33436........ Geib MR & MRS Joshua B
Boynton Beach........ 33436........ Harris MR Gregory S
Boynton Beach........ 33436........ Rowley MR & MRS E Davis JR
Boynton Beach........ 33436........ Whittemore MR & MRS Allen W
Boynton Beach........ 33437........ Wade DR George R
Boynton Beach........ 33472........ Hamilton MISS Jessica D
Bradenton........ 34205........ Durham MISS Mignon
Bradenton........ 34205........ Pederson MR Robert H
& Righter MRS Elizabeth C
Bradenton........ 34206........ Rowe MR Peter J
Bradenton........ 34209........ Bettle MR & MRS Griscom IV
Bradenton........ 34209........ Cashen DR & MRS David V
Bradenton........ 34210........ Alsop MR & MRS Robert C
Bradenton........ 34210........ McLean MR & MRS Stafford 3D
Bradenton........ 34212........ Fay MRS Nomina Twining
Cape Coral........ 33914........ Helme MR & MRS Jay E
Cape Coral........ 33991........ Bockemuehl MRS Robert R
Cape Coral........ 33991........ Bockemuehl MRS Robert R
Captiva Island........ 33924........ Loomis MR Thomas H
Captiva Island........ 33924........ Odén MRS Robert R
Celebration........ 34747........ Morocco MR & MRS John W JR
Clearwater........ 33756........ Eckelberry MRS Renée D
Clearwater........ 33767........ Dunne MR Maurice F JR
Cocoa Beach........ 32931........ Smyth MR Constantine J 3D
Cocoa Beach........ 32932........ Bush MISS Cornelia W
Coconut Grove........ 33133........ Amato BRN Carlo C B & BRNSS
Coconut Grove........ 33133........ Caplow MR & MRS Theodore JR
Coconut Grove........ 33133........ Carey MR & MRS Philip N
Coconut Grove........ 33133........ Djerejian MR & MRS Gregory P
Coconut Grove........ 33133........ Smyth MR David R
Coconut Grove........ 33133........ Sullivan MR & MRS A Gary
Coral Gables........ 33133........ Hilton MR & MRS John A JR
Coral Gables........ 33134........ Burke MR & MRS James Van V
Coral Gables........ 33134........ Fanjul MR & MRS Harry M JR
Coral Gables........ 33134........ Kilborne MR & MRS William Skinner
Coral Gables........ 33134........ Kobusch MR & MRS Richard B JR
Coral Gables........ 33134........ Markham MRS Sanford
Coral Gables........ 33134........ Montoro MQSE Rafael de
Coral Gables........ 33143........ Glascock MR & MRS Miles B
Coral Gables........ 33146........ Behn MR William C
Coral Gables........ 33146........ Hucks MR & MRS Herbert deM IV
Coral Gables........ 33146........ Moss MR & MRS Ambler H JR
Coral Gables........ 33146........ Murphy MR & MRS Serre L
Coral Gables........ 33146........ Ross MRS Leroy W
Coral Gables........ 33156........ von Peterffy MR & MRS Conrad
Coral Gables........ 33158........ Ross MR & MRS Blaik P
Coral Springs........ 33065........ Bickley MR Johnathan E
Crawfordville........ 32327........ Benjamin MR Douglas S

Crystal River, FL—Gulf Stream, FL

Crystal River	34429	Smith MR & MRS Kennedy JR
Dania Beach	33004	Cassius MR & MRS Jack
De Land	32724	Devaney MR & MRS Richard T
Deerfield Beach	33442	Blonshine MR & MRS Kevin L
Deland	32724	McMeel DR & MRS J Wallace
Delray Beach	33444	Graebner MR & MRS Clark E JR
Delray Beach	33444	Laird MR & MRS Walter J IV
Delray Beach	33444	Wilmer MR & MRS John Whittingham
Delray Beach	33445	Hamilton MR & MRS Lewis T
Delray Beach	33445	Jones MR Alfred H JR
Delray Beach	33445	Peirce MRS William H
Delray Beach	33445	Potter MRS Sheldon III
Delray Beach	33445	Schaub MRS James Carter
Delray Beach	33483	Bissell MRS George P JR
Delray Beach	33483	Borger MRS Nancy
Delray Beach	33483	Bostwick MR & MRS George H JR
Delray Beach	33483	Bright MR & MRS J Reeve
Delray Beach	33483	Bromley MRS Richard N
Delray Beach	33483	Callaway MISS Leslie A
Delray Beach	33483	Cartier MR & MRS John G
Delray Beach	33483	Corey MR & MRS W Russell G
Delray Beach	33483	Costa MR & MRS William J
Delray Beach	33483	Cross MS Rosalind M
Delray Beach	33483	Cummings MR & MRS Francis P
Delray Beach	33483	Deming MR & MRS David H
Delray Beach	33483	Flinn MR & MRS Michael de V
Delray Beach	33483	Graziano MR & MRS Anthony W JR
Delray Beach	33483	Ijams MRS Porter
Delray Beach	33483	Johnson MR & MRS N Platt
Delray Beach	33483	Kopp MR & MRS Bradford B
Delray Beach	33483	Kraft MR & MRS F Gordon
Delray Beach	33483	Lloyd MR & MRS David
Delray Beach	33483	Love MS Marsha L
Delray Beach	33483	Martin MR & MRS Peter B
Delray Beach	33483	McCarrens MISS Constance
Delray Beach	33483	Mustin MR Henry C III
Delray Beach	33483	Page MR & MRS Chips C
Delray Beach	33483	Powell MR & MRS Robert H JR
Delray Beach	33483	Powers MRS Charles R
Delray Beach	33483	Pyne MR & MRS Robert W
Delray Beach	33483	Robertson MRS Edward L JR
Delray Beach	33483	Romaine MRS Henry S
Delray Beach	33483	Smith MRS Marcus W
Delray Beach	33483	Stimpson MR & MRS John W
Delray Beach	33483	Tilt MR & MRS Alexander C
Delray Beach	33483	Timpson MR & MRS Carl W JR
Delray Beach	33483	Tobin MR Joshua
Delray Beach	33483	Townsend MRS Wisner H
Delray Beach	33483	Vanderlip MR & MRS Henrik N
Delray Beach	33483	Walcott MR & MRS Eustis
Delray Beach	33483	Walker MR & MRS Robert G JR
Delray Beach	33483	Watkins MR Lowry Rush JR
Destin	32541	Maclin MR & MRS Henry W JR
Dunedin	34698	Schniewind MR Nelson R
Eastlake Weir	32133	Yoskin MR & MRS Jon W II
Englewood	34223	Buffum MRS Robert C
Englewood	34223	Cook MRS Arthur F JR
Englewood	34223	Earle MR & MRS Ralph 2D
Englewood	34223	Lockwood MR John M 2D
Englewood	34224	Seed MRS Barbara B
Estero	33928	Boomer MRS George du P
Eustis	32726	Baker MRS N Rogers
Eustis	32726	Perry MRS Barbara M
Flagler Beach	32136	Angelo MS Marjorie G
Flagler Beach	32136	Lenssen MR & MRS William
Frostproof	33843	Webster MRS Geoffrey Randolph
Ft Lauderdale	33301	O'Neil MR John H
Ft Lauderdale	33301	Smith MRS Philip C F
Ft Lauderdale	33304	Erickson MR Paul M
Ft Lauderdale	33304	Jenkins MR Thomas S
Ft Lauderdale	33304	Klapp MR Edward M K JR
Ft Lauderdale	33306	Halpin MR William C
Ft Lauderdale	33306	Leary MR & MRS Brian F
Ft Lauderdale	33308	Dearborn MR Philip N
Ft Lauderdale	33308	Green MR & MRS Jon A
Ft Lauderdale	33308	Hopkins MR Peyton S
Ft Lauderdale	33308	Morgan MR & MRS Henry
Ft Lauderdale	33308	Norfleet MR John V R
Ft Lauderdale	33308	Shannon MR James J JR
Ft Lauderdale	33308	Ziegler MR & MRS Robert E 3D
Ft Lauderdale	33312	Smith MRS June D
Ft Lauderdale	33315	Bartram MRS J Burr JR
Ft Lauderdale	33316	Cadwalader MR & MRS Craig JR
Ft Lauderdale	33316	Halle MRS Chisholm
Ft Lauderdale	33316	Larson MRS E Carruthers
Ft Lauderdale	33316	Lederer MRS Henry A 3D
Ft Lauderdale	33316	O'Shaughnessy MR & MRS Phillips P
Ft Lauderdale	33316	Sprague MRS George R
Ft Lauderdale	33316	Stevens MRS Charles J
Ft Lauderdale	33324	Murphy MS Stephanie Chouteau
Ft Myers	33907	Eaton DR Alexander Mellon
Ft Myers	33908	Bonistall MR & MRS Ernest R
Ft Myers	33908	Clegg MRS Charles B
Ft Myers	33908	Cooper MRS Virginia F
Ft Myers	33908	Deming MRS Donald L
Ft Myers	33908	King MR & MRS Timothy W
Ft Myers	33908	Kniskern MRS Philip N
Ft Myers	33908	Kruesi MRS Oscar R
Ft Myers	33908	Sprague MR Charles G JR
Ft Myers	33908	Thorndike MR & MRS William A
Ft Myers	33908	Wells MR & MRS Lloyd P
Ft Myers	33908	Winchell MR Albert B
Ft Myers	33908	Withington MR & MRS Lothrop JR
Ft Myers	33912	Evans MR & MRS Andrew M
Ft Myers	33901	Moorhouse MR & MRS Leslie C
Ft Myers	33913	Clark MR & MRS Grenville 3D
Ft Myers Beach	33931	Morgan MISS Margaret Eiluned
Ft Pierce	34951	Chapman MR & MRS John D 2D
Ft Pierce	34982	Brewster MR David K
Ft Walton Beach	32547	Lettiere MR & MRS Christopher A
Gainesville	32604	Weber MRS Mary-Evan
Gainesville	32605	Van Alstyne MR & MRS W Scott JR
Gainesville	32605	Wyatt-Brown MRS Bertram
Gainesville	32605	Yerkes MS Elizabeth T
Gainesville	32606	Hallowell MRS John G
Gainesville	32607	Emmet MRS H Dunscombe
Gainesville	32608	Murphy MR Justin G
Gainesville	32627	Hendrickson MR Robert A 3D
Gilf Stream	33483	Fay MISS Katherine F
Groveland	34736	de Mello MR & MRS Michael E S S
Gulf Breeze	32563	Alcott COL & MRS Henry S
Gulf Breeze	32563	Watson MR & MRS Walter 3D
Gulf Stream	33483	Beardsley MRS Henry W
Gulf Stream	33483	Brown MR & MRS W L Lyons JR
Gulf Stream	33483	Bundy MR & MRS Thomas F JR
Gulf Stream	33483	Burns MR & MRS Robert G
Gulf Stream	33483	Du Bois MRS Allen C
Gulf Stream	33483	Hardiman MR & MRS Joseph R
Gulf Stream	33483	Kent MRS S Ladove
Gulf Stream	33483	Losee MRS Thomas P JR
Gulf Stream	33483	Matthews MR & MRS L Churchill JR
Gulf Stream	33483	Merrill MR & MRS Barrant V

Gulf Stream	33483	O'Neil MRS Kenneth S
Gulf Stream	33483	Orthwein MR & MRS James B JR
Gulf Stream	33483	Ruth MR & MRS Christopher H
Gulf Stream	33483	Sloan MRS William Lytle 2D
Gulf Stream	33483	Spilman MRS Edward D
Gulf Stream	33483	Stokes MRS Alexander C
Gulf Stream	33483	Thomas MR & MRS Patrick J
Gulf Stream	33483	von Stade MR Frederick H
Gulf Stream	33483	Walton MR & MRS James M
Gulf Stream	33483	Wibbelsman MR & MRS Robert J
Hallandale	33009	Michaelsen MR & MRS Alwin C
Hallandale	33009	O'Reilly MRS Maurice F
Hernando	34442	Brumley MRS Charlotte H
Highland Beach	33487	Boiselle DR & MRS Phillip M
Highland Beach	33487	Fiorilla di Santa Croce MRS Giovanni
Hilliard	32046	Robertson MRS James Y
Hillsboro Beach	33062	Cook MRS John Ransom
Hillsboro Beach	33062	Secor MR & MRS James Jay III
Hillsboro Beach	33062	Snodgrass MR & MRS Francis R
Hillsboro Beach	33062	Wilson MR & MRS Gordon
Hobe Sound	33455	Ammidon MR & MRS Hoyt JR
Hobe Sound	33455	Anderson MR & MRS John B
Hobe Sound	33455	Annibali MR & MRS Philip A
Hobe Sound	33455	Barlow MRS Mary Lloyd
Hobe Sound	33455	Bell MR & MRS Stuart M
Hobe Sound	33455	Bell MRS James E
Hobe Sound	33455	Boothby MR & MRS Willard S III
Hobe Sound	33455	Brown MR & MRS William G
Hobe Sound	33455	Browne MRS (REV) Bliss W
Hobe Sound	33455	Bullen MRS George H
Hobe Sound	33455	Coleman MRS George L
Hobe Sound	33455	Collier MR & MRS Richard T
Hobe Sound	33455	Conze MR & MRS Peter Horst JR
Hobe Sound	33455	Cox MISS Heidi
Hobe Sound	33455	Cox MRS William C JR
Hobe Sound	33455	Crisp MR & MRS Peter O
Hobe Sound	33455	Day MR & MRS Rodney D 3D
Hobe Sound	33455	de Gunzburg BRN & BRNSS Dimitri
Hobe Sound	33455	Doubleday MRS Nelson
Hobe Sound	33455	Durling MR & MRS C Correll
Hobe Sound	33455	Fairman MR Joel M
Hobe Sound	33455	Field MR & MRS Marshall 5TH
Hobe Sound	33455	Field MR & MRS Richard D
Hobe Sound	33455	Fisher MR & MRS William A III
Hobe Sound	33455	Flinn MR & MRS Lawrence JR
Hobe Sound	33455	Fowlkes MRS George A
Hobe Sound	33455	French MRS Raymond A
Hobe Sound	33455	Geupel MRS John C
Hobe Sound	33455	Hall MR & MRS C Barrows
Hobe Sound	33455	Hanser MR & MRS Frederick O
Hobe Sound	33455	Hemmes MR & MRS Robert A JR
Hobe Sound	33455	Hotchkiss MR Winchester F
Hobe Sound	33455	Jansing MRS John C
Hobe Sound	33455	Kissel MR & MRS Frank A
Hobe Sound	33455	Lamont MRS Donald B
Hobe Sound	33455	Lamphere MR & MRS Gilbert H
Hobe Sound	33455	Laumont MRS Anne Adams
Hobe Sound	33455	Lawson-Johnston MR Peter O
Hobe Sound	33455	Lord MRS Charles E
Hobe Sound	33455	Lynch MRS Edmund C JR
Hobe Sound	33455	Mahoney MRS Jean W Bronson
Hobe Sound	33455	McGraw MR & MRS Theodore A JR
Hobe Sound	33455	Mead MRS Nelson S
Hobe Sound	33455	Montgomery MRS J Pauley
Hobe Sound	33455	Murray MR & MRS Francis W 3D
Hobe Sound	33455	Newell MISS Frances T
Hobe Sound	33455	Nutting MR & MRS William C
Hobe Sound	33455	Parsons MR & MRS Robert White
Hobe Sound	33455	Pidot MR & MRS Whitney D
Hobe Sound	33455	Plum MR & MRS Roy R
Hobe Sound	33455	Polk MR & MRS Samuel S
Hobe Sound	33455	Pool MR & MRS Philip B JR
Hobe Sound	33455	Reed MR & MRS Adrian W
Hobe Sound	33455	Reed MRS Nathaniel P
Hobe Sound	33455	Ridder MR & MRS Daniel H
Hobe Sound	33455	Riegel MRS & MR Richard E JR
Hobe Sound	33455	Robbins MRS James O
Hobe Sound	33455	Rogers MRS Howland P
Hobe Sound	33455	Roosevelt MS Sara Delano
Hobe Sound	33455	Rutherfurd MR & MRS John JR
Hobe Sound	33455	Seaman MRS Douglas
Hobe Sound	33455	Shattuck MR & MRS George H JR
Hobe Sound	33455	Sodi MRS Mario
Hobe Sound	33455	Spoehel HON & MRS Ronald R
Hobe Sound	33455	Strawbridge MR & MRS John III
Hobe Sound	33455	Stroh MRS Peter W
Hobe Sound	33455	Thorsen MR J Gwynne
Hobe Sound	33455	Tilghman MR & MRS Richard A
Hobe Sound	33455	Tilghman MRS George H
Hobe Sound	33455	Trotman MR & MRS Stanley S JR
Hobe Sound	33455	Van Rensselaer MR & MRS Alexander T
Hobe Sound	33455	Vogel MRS Ralph B
Hobe Sound	33455	Wall MRS Anne F
Hobe Sound	33455	Warner MR & MRS John W IV
Hobe Sound	33455	Warner MRS Rawleigh JR
Hobe Sound	33455	Welsh MR & MRS John E 3D
Hobe Sound	33455	Wheeler MRS George Y II
Hobe Sound	33455	Wilmerding MR & MRS Henry A JR
Hobe Sound	33455	Wilson MR Kendrick R 3D
Hobe Sound	33455	Witsell MR Frederick C JR
Hobe Sound	33475	Blair MRS Watson K
Hobe Sound	33475	Buhrman MR & MRS Christopher D
Hobe Sound	33475	Heckman MRS Margaret J
Hobe Sound	33475	Mettler MR John W III
Hobe Sound	33475	Ottley MR & MRS Philip G
Hobe Sound	33475	Steele MR & MRS Edward C
Hobe Sound	33475	Wellin MRS Ariane Y
Hobe Sound	33475	White MR & MRS Ogden JR
Homestead	33031	Morris MR & MRS Martin Van B
Homosassa	34448	Perry MR & MRS Winston C
Howey-in-the-Hills	34737	Clark DR & MRS (DR) Lowell F
Hypoluxo	33462	Leas MR & MRS Rodman W
Hypoluxo	33462	May MR James G G
Hypoluxo	33462	Moss MR & MRS Daniel K
Indialantic	32903	Miller DR & MRS Stuart P
Indian River Shores	32963	Curtis MS Caroline Page
Indian River Shores	32963	Davis MR & MRS Walter B JR
Indian River Shores	32963	Kelly MR Edward J JR
Islamorada	33036	Gagarin MR & MRS Andrew S
Jacksonville	32202	Wight MR Roger F & Cho MS Jane C E
Jacksonville	32205	Guthrie MR & MRS Michael P
Jacksonville	32205	Reichold MR & MRS Geoff
Jacksonville	32210	Brooke MS Beverley Cassidy
Jacksonville	32210	Cassidy MRS Arch Wilson
Jacksonville	32210	Emmet MR & MRS Patrick M
Jacksonville	32210	Haskell MR & MRS Preston H 3D
Jacksonville	32210	Hemphill MR & MRS David W
Jacksonville	32210	Irving COL (RET) & MRS Frederick F
Jacksonville	32210	Lee DR & MRS Harry G
Jacksonville	32210	Loomis MRS Henry
Jacksonville	32210	Pierpont MR & MRS Richard H
Jacksonville	32210	Smithwick DR & MRS Walter III

To nominate a candidate for the Social Register Association, please email: SRCommittee@thesocialregister.org

Jacksonville, FL—Miromar Lakes, FL

Jacksonville........ 32224........ Benedict MR John T
Jacksonville........ 32224........ Johnston DR & MRS Thomas S
Jacksonville........ 32225........ Gibson MR & MRS Henry C JR
Jacksonville........ 32244........ Mackroth MRS John R
Jacksonville........ 32256........ Crompton MRS Robert H III
Jacksonville........ 32256........ Gardner MR & MRS Robert H 3D
Jacksonville........ 32256........ Johnston MR & MRS Thomas S JR
Jacksonville........ 32256........ Kissel MR & MRS Peter F F JR
Jacksonville........ 33210........ May MR & MRS Edward L JR
Jacksonville Beach........ 32250........ McGauley MRS Lawrence P
Jacksonville Beach........ 32250........ Sander MRS Cintra Carter
Jacksonville Beach........ 32250........ Seaton DR & MRS Hugh Van
Jensen Beach........ 34957........ Buff MR & MRS William J 3D
Jensen Beach........ 34957........ Mulliken MR & MRS Alfred D
Juno Beach........ 33408........ Finch MR & MRS Rufus C JR
Juno Beach........ 33408........ Sloan MRS Julian R
Juno Beach........ 33408........ White MR & MRS Rollin H 3D
Jupiter........ 33458........ Curry MR James Prescott
Jupiter........ 33458........ Holder MR & MRS Albin Howard
Jupiter........ 33458........ Putnam MR Stuart G
Jupiter........ 33458........ Whiteley MR & MRS George C III
Jupiter........ 33469........ Maynard MISS Wendy G
Jupiter........ 33469........ Wullschleger MR & MRS A Jacques JR
Jupiter........ 33477........ Childs MR & MRS Walton
Jupiter........ 33477........ Doering DR & MRS Edmund J 3D
Jupiter........ 33477........ Finkenstaedt MRS Frederick B
Jupiter........ 33477........ Herrick MRS Peter
Jupiter........ 33478........ Carew MR G Stephen JR
Jupiter Island........ 33455........ Kallop MR & MRS Brooks M
Key Biscayne........ 33149........ Adams MS Katharine H
Key Biscayne........ 33149........ Ambrose MRS C Clarke
Key Biscayne........ 33149........ Kimball MR & MRS William F
Key Biscayne........ 33149........ Lindsay MR & MRS Alvin F III
Key Biscayne........ 33149........ Noyes MR & MRS William M
Key Largo........ 33037........ Christensen MR Paul W JR
Key Largo........ 33037........ Dicke MR & MRS James F II
Key Largo........ 33037........ Hayward MR & MRS Wallace M
Key Largo........ 33037........ Mitchell MRS Matthew J
Key Largo........ 33037........ Paige MR & MRS Francis U
Key Largo........ 33037........ Patton MR & MRS Rodman D
Key Largo........ 33037........ Ross MRS John G
Key Largo........ 33037........ Watson MR & MRS Thomas J III
Key Largo........ 33037........ Zug MR & MRS Graham F
Key West........ 33040........ Day MR & MRS Stanley R JR
Key West........ 33040........ Eberstadt MR Frederick
Key West........ 33040........ Monroe MR Daniel G
Key West........ 33040........ Verge MR William G
Key West........ 33040........ Wetmore MR Terry & Grannis MS Jane G
Kissimmee........ 34747........ Kraft MR & MRS John F 3D
Kissimmee........ 34747........ Schwarz DR & MRS Fred
Lady Lake........ 32159........ Fleming MRS William T
Lake Mary........ 32746........ Buckles MR Mark A
Lake Wales........ 33853........ McCance MR Thomas JR
Lake Wales........ 33859........ de Saint Phalle MR & MRS François
Lake Wales........ 33859........ Freeman MRS William G JR
Lake Wales........ 33859........ Littleton MR Richard S
Lake Wales........ 33859........ Miller DR Murray J & Hoyt MS Nancy Hale
Lake Wales........ 33859........ Newbold MISS Pamela deWindt
Lake Wales........ 33859........ Newbold MR & MRS Clement B JR
Lake Wales........ 33859........ Rogers MR Arthur M JR
Lake Wales........ 33859........ Trumbull MR & MRS Walter H
Lake Wales........ 33859........ Young MR & MRS Richard N JR
Lake Wales........ 33898........ Barrows MR & MRS Mercer B
Lake Wales........ 33898........ Phillips MR & MRS Peter L
Lake Wales........ 33898........ Smith MR & MRS James S
Lake Worth........ 33460........ Pickett MR & MRS John O III
Lake Worth........ 33461........ Carew MR Timothy L
Lakeland........ 33813........ Hull MRS John B
Lakewood Ranch........ 34202........ Hagar MR & MRS George L
Lakewood Ranch........ 34202........ Nourie MR & MRS Bruce L
Lantana........ 33462........ Carey MR Francis J III
Lantana........ 33462........ Marsh MISS Adrienne A
Lauderdale-by-the-Sea........ 33308........ Nield MR Ogden
Lecanto........ 34461........ McKim MISS Charlotte W
Leesburg........ 34748........ Gregg MR & MRS James R
Leesburg........ 34748........ Yoskin DR Maurice P
Lighthouse Point........ 33064........ Lavin MR Robert C
Lithia........ 33547........ Dawson MR & MRS David A
Longboat Key........ 34228........ Armitage MR & MRS Arthur L
Longboat Key........ 34228........ Monroe MR & MRS Andrew P
Longboat Key........ 34228........ Stern MR & MRS Todd R
Longboat Key........ 34228........ Uihlein MISS Lucia L
Longboat Key........ 34228........ Winder MRS Elizabeth W
Longwood........ 32750........ Hoffman MR & MRS Richard C
Longwood........ 32779........ Sabet MR & MRS Ashkon R
Longwood........ 32779........ Walker MR & MRS David A
Lower Sugarloaf Key........ 33042........ Bigelow MR & MRS Prescott III
Lutz........ 33549........ Timchak MRS Louis J JR
Lutz........ 33559........ Sands LT COL & MRS William D JR
Maitland........ 32751........ Irish MR Thomas Weddell
Maitland........ 32751........ Langdon MRS Deborah Taylor
Manalapan........ 33462........ Evans MR & MRS Robert Beverley JR
Marathon........ 33050........ Gilbert MR John
Marathon........ 33050........ Siemon MR & MRS Charles L
Marco Island........ 34145........ Barzun DR & MRS (DR) James L
Marco Island........ 34145........ Mutart MR & MRS Steven Lewis
Melbourne Beach........ 32951........ Bragdon MR & MRS Clifford R
Melbourne Beach........ 32951........ Brinckerhoff MR & MRS Starr E
Miami........ 33102........ Taylor MR & MRS Robert C JR
Miami........ 33130........ Shea MR Brooks C
Miami........ 33131........ Cappello MR Juan Pablo & Getty MS Christina
Miami........ 33131........ Dennis MR & MRS Phillip S
Miami........ 33131........ Mora MR & MRS Andres
Miami........ 33131........ Peniston MR E Winchester
Miami........ 33133........ Arnett MR & MRS George W III
Miami........ 33133........ Goodman MR & MRS David P
Miami........ 33133........ Hutton MRS William E 3D
Miami........ 33133........ Murray MR & MRS Robert A JR
Miami........ 33133........ Willits MR & MRS Christopher N
Miami........ 33133........ Wyrough MR & MRS Alexander Penn H
Miami........ 33139........ King MR & MRS John Andrews JR
Miami........ 33143........ Beeman MRS Ingrid Grace
Miami........ 33143........ Matheson MR Finlay L
Miami........ 33143........ Stengel MR & MRS Geoffrey III
Miami........ 33156........ Morgan MR & MRS George O JR
Miami........ 33156........ Ware MR Andrew C
Miami........ 33166........ Laffey MR Edwin W JR
Miami........ 33166........ Viault MR & MRS John Bartlett
Miami........ 33173........ Fontana MR & MRS (DR) Jason G
Miami........ 33173........ Nott MRS Thomas E 4TH
Miami........ 33186........ Beeman MR Charles R
Miami........ 33186........ Nuñez-Lawton MR Miguel
Miami Beach........ 33139........ Guest MR & MRS Frederick E II
Miami Beach........ 33139........ Heisler MR Stanley D
Miami Beach........ 33139........ Smith MR Lindsay Byron
Miami Beach........ 33139........ Stokes MR & MRS Walter H
Miami Beach........ 33139........ Thomas MRS Jeffrey F
Miami Beach........ 33139........ Williams MS Christine R
Miami Beach........ 33140........ Barish MR & MRS Keith
Miami Shore........ 33138........ Ronan MS Monica V
Middleburg........ 32068........ White MRS William B
Miromar Lakes........ 33913........ Davis MISS Diane

Monticello........ 32344........ Perkins MR & MRS Leigh H
Mt Dora........ 32757........ Webb MR H St John 3D
Mt. Dora........ 32757........ Hammer MISS Judith A
Myakka City........ 34251........ McKeithen MR & MRS Edward L
Naples........ 34101........ Smithers MR Charles F III
Naples........ 34101........ Swetland MR & MRS Eli B
Naples........ 34102........ Brown MR Harry C
Naples........ 34102........ Donham MRS Valerie Lawrence
Naples........ 34102........ Dudley MRS Robert W
Naples........ 34102........ Edmonds MR Dean Stockett JR
Naples........ 34102........ Egerton MR & MRS Stuart 2D
Naples........ 34102........ Fogg MR & MRS Joseph G III
Naples........ 34102........ Hamill MR & MRS Jonathan Corwith
Naples........ 34102........ Hayward MR & MRS Thomas Z JR
Naples........ 34102........ Mullaj MR & MRS Alban
Naples........ 34102........ Pettengill MRS Kroger
Naples........ 34102........ Rabbe MR George W
Naples........ 34102........ Rorer MR & MRS Edward C
Naples........ 34102........ Schoonmaker MR & MRS James M 2D
Naples........ 34102........ Smith MR & MRS Stephen B
Naples........ 34102........ Sonne DR Jonathan E
& Lambert MS (DR) Rebecca W
Naples........ 34102........ Warner MR John C
Naples........ 34102........ Weaver MRS Elizabeth L
Naples........ 34102........ Webb MRS Sarah C
Naples........ 34102........ Weyand MR William J
Naples........ 34102........ Wheeler MR & MRS A Jackson
Naples........ 34102........ Wheeler MR & MRS Thomas B
Naples........ 34102........ Whisnand MR & MRS R Van Arsdel JR
Naples........ 34102........ Wood MR & MRS Keith S
Naples........ 34103........ Dayton MRS Lee A
Naples........ 34103........ Hill MS Vianda Hale
Naples........ 34103........ Keeter DR & MRS Edward H
Naples........ 34103........ Leigh MR & MRS Anthony M
Naples........ 34103........ Linville MR & MRS David G
Naples........ 34103........ McInnes MRS Betsy V
Naples........ 34103........ Shepard MR & MRS William B JR
Naples........ 34103........ Shiverick MS M Brown
Naples........ 34105........ Augsbury MRS Frank A JR
Naples........ 34105........ Buchanan MR & MRS William H JR
Naples........ 34105........ Cabot MR & MRS Thomas D JR
Naples........ 34105........ Chamberlin MR & MRS Larry L
Naples........ 34105........ de Saint Phalle MRS Thibaut
Naples........ 34105........ Detweiler MR & MRS John C
Naples........ 34105........ Dunn MR & MRS M Douglas
Naples........ 34105........ Frank MR & MRS Charles A 3D
Naples........ 34105........ Jonas MR & MRS Robert P JR
Naples........ 34105........ Jones MRS Kaye Harding
Naples........ 34105........ Kelly MR & MRS John A JR
Naples........ 34105........ Lauck MRS Gerold McK JR
Naples........ 34105........ Lyons MR & MRS Dudley E
Naples........ 34105........ McGennis MR & MRS William J
Naples........ 34105........ McKean MR & MRS Paul F JR
Naples........ 34105........ McNally MR & MRS Edward C
Naples........ 34105........ Perkins MR & MRS James H JR
Naples........ 34105........ Van Nest MR & MRS Dean G
Naples........ 34106........ Jensen MR Jonathan
Naples........ 34106........ Niles MRS Nicholas JR
Naples........ 34108........ Baird MR & MRS Richard L
Naples........ 34108........ Gogolak MR & MRS Charles P
Naples........ 34108........ Herrlinger MR & MRS Roth F JR
Naples........ 34108........ Layng MR & MRS John G
Naples........ 34108........ Marsh MRS Theron L
Naples........ 34108........ Springs MISS Clare H
Naples........ 34108........ Tilney MR & MRS David W
Naples........ 34108........ Trivas MR Sam & White-Trivas MRS Stephanie
Naples........ 34108........ Wiley MR & MRS George S
Naples........ 34109........ Blau MR Andrew McD
Naples........ 34109........ Borman MR & MRS Earle K 3D
Naples........ 34109........ Bradley MRS Charles D
Naples........ 34109........ Hunt VERY REV DR & MRS Ernest E III
Naples........ 34109........ MacMahon MR & MRS J Thomas
Naples........ 34109........ McLaughlin MRS Marcellus H JR
Naples........ 34109........ Newhall MR & MRS Paul K
Naples........ 34109........ Page DR James A
Naples........ 34109........ Teare MR Rollin H
Naples........ 34109........ Wardell MR Charles W B III
Naples........ 34110........ Blackburn MR & MRS William L
Naples........ 34110........ Garesché MR & MRS Edmond A B III
Naples........ 34110........ Mattis MR & MRS Stephen van S
Naples........ 34110........ Richardson MR Ralph S JR
Naples........ 34110........ Stauffer MR & MRS Charles R JR
Naples........ 34112........ Harris MR & MRS David P
Naples........ 34112........ Mellon MRS Marian Carroll
Naples........ 34112........ Nichols MS Daphne Weld
Naples........ 34112........ Stephens MRS Joanna D
Naples........ 34113........ Jewell MR & MRS Raymond B
Naples........ 34113........ Newcomer MRS Waldo
Naples........ 34113........ Washburn MR & MRS Charles G III
Naples........ 34114........ Currie MR & MRS Frederick M H JR
Naples........ 34114........ Latos MR & MRS Eric B
Naples........ 34119........ Connors MRS Leslie M
Naples........ 34119........ Davis MR & MRS Orlin
Naples........ 34119........ Donan MR & MRS Holland R
Naples........ 60093........ Ellwood MR & MRS John H
New Smyrna Beach........ 32168........ Krueger MRS Sarah Hudson
New Smyrna Beach........ 32168........ Truslow MR & MRS Peter C
New Smyrna Beach........ 32168........ Truslow MRS Godfrey G
New Smyrna Beach........ 32168........ Wilhelm MR & MRS Frederick C S JR
Newberry........ 32669........ Infante MRS T Gillette
Nokomis........ 34275........ Argenti MR Tristan J M
Nokomis........ 34275........ Hansen MS Teri
Nokomis........ 34275........ Thayer MRS Seth A
Nokomis........ 34275........ Treat MRS Lucinda S
North Bay Village........ 33141........ Kirkbride MR Chalmer G JR
North Ft Myers........ 33917........ Zimmerman MR & MRS Paul M
North Key Largo........ 33037........ Pratt MRS Albert
North Palm Beach........ 33408........ Bartram MISS Elizabeth M
North Palm Beach........ 33408........ Curry MR & MRS (DR) John M
North Palm Beach........ 33408........ Frazier DR & MRS Thomas G
North Palm Beach........ 33408........ Gaudieri MR & MRS Alexander V J
North Palm Beach........ 33408........ Gilbert MR & MRS Steven J
North Palm Beach........ 33408........ Grist MR & MRS Walter W
North Palm Beach........ 33408........ Harris MR & MRS W Gibson II
North Palm Beach........ 33408........ Hopkins MRS Ben F JR
North Palm Beach........ 33408........ Lovejoy MRS Walter R
North Palm Beach........ 33408........ O'Hearn MRS Walter D
North Palm Beach........ 33408........ Quick MR & MRS Christopher C
North Palm Beach........ 33408........ Smyth MR & MRS John E
North Palm Beach........ 33408........ Stott MRS Joan Johnson
North Palm Beach........ 33408........ Van Deuren MRS Richard A
North Port........ 34287........ Howland MR John R
Oakland Park........ 33334........ Embler MR John W
Ocala........ 34471........ Cox MR Archibald 3D
Ocala........ 34477........ Weber MRS Charlotte C
Ocala........ 34481........ Boyd MR & MRS A Shapleigh 3D
Ocala........ 34481........ Weber MR Chester C
Ocala........ 34482........ Lowry MR & MRS William C 3D
Ocala........ 34482........ Reynolds MRS Nourse
Ocean Ridge........ 33435........ Bingham MRS Elisabeth P B
Ocean Ridge........ 33435........ Bridges MR & MRS Digby C
Ocean Ridge........ 33435........ DiPietro MR & MRS Richard Lee

Ocean Ridge, FL—Palm Beach, FL

Ocean Ridge	33435	Rollow MRS J Douglas JR
Ocean Ridge	33435	Toogood MR & MRS Granville N
Ocklawaha	32179	Kadey MRS Frederic L JR
Old St Augustine	32084	Brown MRS Katharine C
Orange Park	32073	Howard MRS Barnaby J
Orlando	32801	Steinmeyer MR & MRS Keith L
Orlando	32804	Gibbs MISS Emilie M
Orlando	32804	Owen MISS Frances T
Orlando	32804	van Roijen MR & MRS Robert D JR
Orlando	32806	Kelley MR Marc W
Orlando	32819	Palmer MRS Arnold D
Orlando	32821	Bickley MR & MRS Reed S
Orlando	32822	Doyle MR & MRS J Carol
Orlando	32827	Sidhu MR & MRS Rupinder S
Orlando	32835	Hurst MR John E 5TH
Ormond Beach	32174	Ford MR & MRS Anthony F W
Ormond Beach	32176	Deshler MRS C Franklin
Osprey	34229	Borthwick MR Antony T
Osprey	34229	Henderson MR & MRS Ronald H
Osprey	34229	Lannamann MR & MRS Richard S
Osprey	34229	Thomas MR & MRS Robert L
Oviedo	32765	Davis MR & MRS Mark B
Oviedo	32765	Drachlis MR & MRS Timothy C
Ozona	34660	Crawford MRS George L
Palm Beach	33480	Ainslie MR & MRS Michael L
Palm Beach	33480	Alger MR & MRS Frederick M III
Palm Beach	33480	Allan MR & MRS Robb A
Palm Beach	33480	Amling MR & MRS Jeffrey S
Palm Beach	33480	Anglejan-Chatillon BRNSS
Palm Beach	33480	Annan MR & MRS John W
Palm Beach	33480	Atterbury MR William W 3D & Redfield MS Elizabeth C
Palm Beach	33480	Auersperg PRC Alexander & PRCSS
Palm Beach	33480	Aylward MR & MRS E William
Palm Beach	33480	Bagley MRS Henry W
Palm Beach	33480	Baker MR & MRS Kane K
Palm Beach	33480	Barton MR & MRS David W JR
Palm Beach	33480	Bay MR & MRS James N
Palm Beach	33480	Bitting MR George Capen
Palm Beach	33480	Bivins MR & MRS Julian L
Palm Beach	33480	Boren MR & MRS Reid J
Palm Beach	33480	Bossidy MR & MRS Bruce H
Palm Beach	33480	Bossidy MRS B Haig
Palm Beach	33480	Bowers MR & MRS James R
Palm Beach	33480	Boykin MR & MRS Samuel M
Palm Beach	33480	Breyer MR & MRS Henry W III
Palm Beach	33480	Buchan MR & MRS R Duke III
Palm Beach	33480	Burke MRS Edwin Marston
Palm Beach	33480	Burt MR & MRS James M III
Palm Beach	33480	Butler MISS Reute
Palm Beach	33480	Butler MRS Michael J
Palm Beach	33480	Cabot MISS Melanie H
Palm Beach	33480	Callahan MR & MRS Edward W
Palm Beach	33480	Callaway MR & MRS L David 3D
Palm Beach	33480	Carden DR & MRS G Alexander
Palm Beach	33480	Carroll MR & MRS Charles P
Palm Beach	33480	Castle MR & MRS John Krob
Palm Beach	33480	Chase MRS Paul J
Palm Beach	33480	Claggett MR & MRS William M
Palm Beach	33480	Clark MS Karen
Palm Beach	33480	Clifford MR & MRS Stewart B
Palm Beach	33480	Codman MISS Laura D
Palm Beach	33480	Codman MRS Russell S JR
Palm Beach	33480	Coleman MR & MRS C Payson JR
Palm Beach	33480	Collins MRS Bradley I
Palm Beach	33480	Cook MR & MRS Kevit R
Palm Beach	33480	Cooke MRS James N III
Palm Beach	33480	Corbin MRS Justine M
Palm Beach	33480	Coudert MRS Dale
Palm Beach	33480	Cowell MR & MRS Richard C
Palm Beach	33480	Crichton MS Bunnie Anne
Palm Beach	33480	Damgard MR & MRS John M 2D
Palm Beach	33480	Darlington MR & MRS Henry JR
Palm Beach	33480	Darlington MR & MRS Stephen G
Palm Beach	33480	de Marcellus MISS Juliette
Palm Beach	33480	de Narvaez MRS Felix
Palm Beach	33480	de San Damián MQSA VIUDA
Palm Beach	33480	Dean MRS J Simpson JR
Palm Beach	33480	Deflin MRS Ashley
Palm Beach	33480	Dejoux MRS Jacques H L
Palm Beach	33480	Dennis DR & MRS Michael T B
Palm Beach	33480	Dickey MR Paul B JR
Palm Beach	33480	Doelger MR & MRS Peter W
Palm Beach	33480	Donaldson MRS Victoria B
Palm Beach	33480	Donnelley MR & MRS Robert G
Palm Beach	33480	Donnelley MRS Margaret C
Palm Beach	33480	Duncan MRS J Russell
Palm Beach	33480	Dunnington MRS Walter G JR
Palm Beach	33480	Eglin MRS Thomas W
Palm Beach	33480	Fanjul MR & MRS Alexander L
Palm Beach	33480	Fanjul MR & MRS J Pepe JR
Palm Beach	33480	Fanjul MR Alexander N
Palm Beach	33480	Firestone MR John D
Palm Beach	33480	Flanagan MR Joseph P
Palm Beach	33480	Fleitas MRS Allison F
Palm Beach	33480	Fletcher MR Dugald A
Palm Beach	33480	Fogg MR & MRS Nathaniel T G
Palm Beach	33480	Forbes MR & MRS Robert L
Palm Beach	33480	Forbes MR Miguel R
Palm Beach	33480	Forsythe MRS Sabrina P
Palm Beach	33480	Foster MR & MRS Ridgely M
Palm Beach	33480	Freeman MR & MRS James L
Palm Beach	33480	Freney MR & MRS James R
Palm Beach	33480	Frisbie MR & MRS Robert N
Palm Beach	33480	Fuller MS Gillian Spreckels
Palm Beach	33480	Furlaud MR & MRS Richard M
Palm Beach	33480	Gates MRS John M JR
Palm Beach	33480	Gay MR & MRS John JR
Palm Beach	33480	Geddes MR & MRS Gerald K
Palm Beach	33480	Geist MR & MRS Bradley B
Palm Beach	33480	Gillet MRS F Warrington JR
Palm Beach	33480	Glickman MR & MRS Donald
Palm Beach	33480	Gonzalez MR & MRS Peter W
Palm Beach	33480	Gould MR & MRS George D
Palm Beach	33480	Grace MR & MRS John R
Palm Beach	33480	Grace MR & MRS Morgan H JR
Palm Beach	33480	Grace MR & MRS Oliver R JR
Palm Beach	33480	Grant MRS William R
Palm Beach	33480	Greeff MRS Ernest T
Palm Beach	33480	Gruss MR & MRS Martin D
Palm Beach	33480	Gubelmann MR & MRS James B
Palm Beach	33480	Gubelmann MR & MRS William S
Palm Beach	33480	Gulden MRS Michael I
Palm Beach	33480	Guthrie DR & MRS Randolph H
Palm Beach	33480	Gwynne MR & MRS Jay M
Palm Beach	33480	Hamill MR & MRS Sterling Morton
Palm Beach	33480	Hamm MRS William H 3D
Palm Beach	33480	Hanley MRS William Lee JR
Palm Beach	33480	Harrison MRS James S 3D
Palm Beach	33480	Harrison MRS Ridgely W JR
Palm Beach	33480	Heathwood MR & MRS Desmond
Palm Beach	33480	Hill MR & MRS Peter H

Palm Beach........................ 33480.......... Hoffman MR & MRS Lindley M F
Palm Beach........................ 33480.......... Holton MR & MRS Richard
Palm Beach........................ 33480.......... Hoyt MR & MRS Barry G
Palm Beach........................ 33480.......... Hubbard MR & MRS Ezra N
Palm Beach........................ 33480.......... Hufty MS Page Lee
Palm Beach........................ 33480.......... Hulse MR & MRS R Douglas
Palm Beach........................ 33480.......... Hurley MR & MRS Geoffrey K
Palm Beach........................ 33480.......... Hurley MR & MRS John L
Palm Beach........................ 33480.......... Irons MR & MRS G Chester
Palm Beach........................ 33480.......... Irons MR & MRS Henry C
Palm Beach........................ 33480.......... Ives MR & MRS Philip A
Palm Beach........................ 33480.......... Ives MR Alexander C
Palm Beach........................ 33480.......... Johnson MR & MRS (DR) Charles B
Palm Beach........................ 33480.......... Johnson MR Stephen S II
Palm Beach........................ 33480.......... Jones MR & MRS Charles H JR
Palm Beach........................ 33480.......... Jones MRS Hildegard
Palm Beach........................ 33480.......... Kay MRS William G JR
Palm Beach........................ 33480.......... Kelley MR & MRS Russell P 3D
Palm Beach........................ 33480.......... Kellogg MR & MRS Christopher G
Palm Beach........................ 33480.......... Kemble MR & MRS William T JR
Palm Beach........................ 33480.......... Kent MR E Hewlett
Palm Beach........................ 33480.......... Kent MRS Jorie Butler
Palm Beach........................ 33480.......... Kielland MRS Belinda
Palm Beach........................ 33480.......... Kinsella MR & MRS Eugene Benoist
Palm Beach........................ 33480.......... Kirk MR Leo Harvey
Palm Beach........................ 33480.......... Kirkland MR & MRS David S
Palm Beach........................ 33480.......... Knollenberg MR & MRS Peter S
Palm Beach........................ 33480.......... Knowles MR & MRS Peter I C II
Palm Beach........................ 33480.......... Kramer DR Eric D & Skillern MS Sara R
Palm Beach........................ 33480.......... Lee DR & MRS Robert Earl
Palm Beach........................ 33480.......... Leidy MR & MRS Carter R III
Palm Beach........................ 33480.......... Lickle MR & MRS William C
Palm Beach........................ 33480.......... Lickle MR Garrison duP
Palm Beach........................ 33480.......... Limbocker MR & MRS Derek L
Palm Beach........................ 33480.......... Lind MR & MRS Gerard G
Palm Beach........................ 33480.......... Lloyd George HON & MRS Robert J D
Palm Beach........................ 33480.......... Low MR & MRS K Prescott
Palm Beach........................ 33480.......... Maddock MR & MRS Paul L JR
Palm Beach........................ 33480.......... Mahoney MRS David J
Palm Beach........................ 33480.......... Major MRS Howard B JR
Palm Beach........................ 33480.......... Marks MRS Randolph A
Palm Beach........................ 33480.......... Martin MRS Edward J
Palm Beach........................ 33480.......... Martin MRS Robin B
Palm Beach........................ 33480.......... Martinez MR & MRS Roman IV
Palm Beach........................ 33480.......... Mashek MRS Chandler C
Palm Beach........................ 33480.......... Mason MR Randolph D
Palm Beach........................ 33480.......... Matheson MR Robert R
Palm Beach........................ 33480.......... Matthews MR & MRS William Morrison
Palm Beach........................ 33480.......... McCarter MR Thomas N 3D
Palm Beach........................ 33480.......... McCarty MR Michael R
Palm Beach........................ 33480.......... McConnell MRS Julia C
Palm Beach........................ 33480.......... McDonough MR & MRS Michael P
Palm Beach........................ 33480.......... McGowan MR & MRS John B JR
Palm Beach........................ 33480.......... McIntosh MR & MRS Henry P 4TH
Palm Beach........................ 33480.......... McMakin MR & MRS Leigh A
Palm Beach........................ 33480.......... McSweeney MRS Edward F
Palm Beach........................ 33480.......... Mejia-Hernandez MR & MRS Alberto
Palm Beach........................ 33480.......... Melhado MRS Frederick A
Palm Beach........................ 33480.......... Merck MR & MRS George Frederick
Palm Beach........................ 33480.......... Merrill MR Arthur C JR
Palm Beach........................ 33480.......... Metzger MR & MRS J William JR
Palm Beach........................ 33480.......... Meyer MR & MRS Joseph P
Palm Beach........................ 33480.......... Miller MR & MRS Courtlandt G
Palm Beach........................ 33480.......... Miller MR & MRS Donald K
Palm Beach........................ 33480.......... Miller MR & MRS Leverett S
Palm Beach........................ 33480.......... Miller MR & MRS William R
Palm Beach........................ 33480.......... Miller MRS Dwight A
Palm Beach........................ 33480.......... Milliken MRS Christopher C
Palm Beach........................ 33480.......... Mills MR & MRS D Quinn
Palm Beach........................ 33480.......... Moffett MR & MRS George M 2D
Palm Beach........................ 33480.......... Monell MR & MRS Ambrose K
Palm Beach........................ 33480.......... Moore MR & MRS Charles J
Palm Beach........................ 33480.......... Morgan MR & MRS Alfred Y 3D
Palm Beach........................ 33480.......... Morrison MR & MRS Carlos G
Palm Beach........................ 33480.......... Moses MR Scott Bryan
Palm Beach........................ 33480.......... Murray MR & MRS W Stephen
Palm Beach........................ 33480.......... Myers MS Pamela Acheson
Palm Beach........................ 33480.......... Nix MRS Patricia
Palm Beach........................ 33480.......... Nype MR Russell L
Palm Beach........................ 33480.......... Ober MR David G
Palm Beach........................ 33480.......... Ober MRS David G
Palm Beach........................ 33480.......... Oelsner MS D Alexandra
Palm Beach........................ 33480.......... Orthwein MR & MRS Christopher DaCamara
Palm Beach........................ 33480.......... Page MR Jay J
Palm Beach........................ 33480.......... Papanicolaou MR Nicholas F
& Baker MRS Victoria O
Palm Beach........................ 33480.......... Paterniti MR Jason E & Watson MRS Nicole V
Palm Beach........................ 33480.......... Pepper MR & MRS Charles W
Palm Beach........................ 33480.......... Pickett MR & MRS John O JR
Palm Beach........................ 33480.......... Pitt MRS William H
Palm Beach........................ 33480.......... Pohanka MR & MRS John J
Palm Beach........................ 33480.......... Price MRS Sidney L
Palm Beach........................ 33480.......... Quick MR Thomas C
Palm Beach........................ 33480.......... Ramos MR & MRS Michael J
Palm Beach........................ 33480.......... Reed MRS G Peter Q
Palm Beach........................ 33480.......... Regalbuto MR & MRS Jason R
Palm Beach........................ 33480.......... Remington MRS George C T
Palm Beach........................ 33480.......... Rentschler MISS Farley M
Palm Beach........................ 33480.......... Reventlow CT Richard Haugwitz
Palm Beach........................ 33480.......... Richards MR William R II
& Cayzer MRS Beatrice Fairbanks
Palm Beach........................ 33480.......... Richardsson MR Richard K
Palm Beach........................ 33480.......... Ridgdill DR Charles M
Palm Beach........................ 33480.......... Roberts MR A Sydney JR
Palm Beach........................ 33480.......... Roberts MRS Christine G
Palm Beach........................ 33480.......... Rogers MR & MRS Douglas E
Palm Beach........................ 33480.......... Rogers MR & MRS M Weldon IV
Palm Beach........................ 33480.......... Rollhaus MRS Philip E JR
Palm Beach........................ 33480.......... Rose MR & MRS C Tanner JR
Palm Beach........................ 33480.......... Ross MR & MRS E Burke JR
Palm Beach........................ 33480.......... Ross MR & MRS Wilbur L JR
Palm Beach........................ 33480.......... Rumbough MRS Margaretha W
Palm Beach........................ 33480.......... Russell MS Alice F
Palm Beach........................ 33480.......... Rutherfurd MR & MRS Edward C
Palm Beach........................ 33480.......... Rutherfurd MR John M L II
Palm Beach........................ 33480.......... Ryan MISS Honoré A
Palm Beach........................ 33480.......... Ryan MR & MRS Allan A IV
Palm Beach........................ 33480.......... Sage MR Henry W
Palm Beach........................ 33480.......... Saunders MR & MRS Thomas A III
Palm Beach........................ 33480.......... Schoeller MR & MRS K Christian
Palm Beach........................ 33480.......... Schofield MR & MRS Robert H
Palm Beach........................ 33480.......... Schwartz MRS Alexander C JR
Palm Beach........................ 33480.......... Sculley MR & MRS John 3D
Palm Beach........................ 33480.......... Sculley MRS Leezy
Palm Beach........................ 33480.......... Shields MRS Francis A
Palm Beach........................ 33480.......... Shober MR Edward Wharton
Palm Beach........................ 33480.......... Smith MR & MRS Robert B JR
Palm Beach........................ 33480.......... Smith MRS Page W
Palm Beach........................ 33480.......... Sprague MRS Julie H
Palm Beach........................ 33480.......... Steinhart MR Percy P III
Palm Beach........................ 33480.......... Stephaich MRS Louise H
Palm Beach........................ 33480.......... Stevenson MR Borden W

Palm Beach, FL—Sarasota, FL

Palm Beach	33480	Story MR & MRS Howard C JR
Palm Beach	33480	Strawbridge MRS Christine P
Palm Beach	33480	Stuebe MRS William H
Palm Beach	33480	Sullivan MR A Michael JR
Palm Beach	33480	Summers MRS M Elizabeth M
Palm Beach	33480	Tapp MR & MRS Felix C
Palm Beach	33480	Thompson MR & MRS Gerard M
Palm Beach	33480	Thorndike MR & MRS John
Palm Beach	33480	Told MR & MRS William H JR
Palm Beach	33480	Townsend MRS Meredith A
Palm Beach	33480	Turner MR & MRS Wallace R
Palm Beach	33480	Van der Grift MR & MRS Paul J
Palm Beach	33480	Van Husan MRS Harold Mitchell
Palm Beach	33480	Van Pelt MRS Charles B P
Palm Beach	33480	Vanderpoel MRS Wynant D 3D
Palm Beach	33480	Victor MR & MRS Royall III
Palm Beach	33480	Vris-Johns DR Thomas W
Palm Beach	33480	Waldin MR & MRS Erik T
Palm Beach	33480	Walker DR Mark C
Palm Beach	33480	Watson MR Ralph E
Palm Beach	33480	Whitlock MS Penny
Palm Beach	33480	Whitman MR & MRS Charles S 3D
Palm Beach	33480	Wolbach MRS William W
Palm Beach	33480	Wyckoff MRS Clinton R III
Palm Beach	44380	Johnston MR & MRS William C
Palm Beach	334480	Straus MRS Kenneth H
Palm Beach Gardens	33410	Anathan MR & MRS Thomas J
Palm Beach Gardens	33410	Marshall MS Katherine Payson
Palm Beach Gardens	33410	McGrath MR & MRS Gordon R JR
Palm Beach Gardens	33410	McIntosh MS Constance H
Palm Beach Gardens	33410	Ostroff MR & MRS Noah S
Palm Beach Gardens	33418	Barnwell MR & MRS Robert W III
Palm Beach Gardens	33418	Blanchard MR & MRS Hartman E
Palm Beach Gardens	33418	Castroviejo MR Christopher R
Palm Beach Gardens	33418	Clay MISS Tiffany Alexandra
Palm Beach Gardens	33418	Davies MRS Lynn Covington
Palm Beach Gardens	33418	Knoll MR & MRS Christopher G
Palm Beach Gardens	33418	Lobo-Buhl MS Jennifer
Palm Beach Gardens	33418	Marshall MR & MRS Leonard L
Palm Beach Gardens	33418	Milne MRS Walgren
Palm Beach Gardens	33418	Reece DR & MRS Glen A
Palm Beach Gardens	33418	Roach MR & MRS John H JR
Palm Beach Gardens	33418	Scott MR Hugh III
Palm Beach Gardens	33418	Sheets MRS M Brennig
Palm Beach Gardens	33418	Smith MR Baldwin JR
Palm Beach Gardens	33418	Van Alen MR & MRS Lucas P
Palm Beach Gardens	33418	Walker MS Pamela Buchanan
Palm Beach Gardens	33418	Woods MR & MRS James A
Palm City	34990	Apostol MR Michael Mouravieff
Palm City	34990	Atterbury MRS William Wallace JR
Palm City	34990	Brett MR & MRS Philip M 3D
Palm City	34990	Cole MRS L Fletcher
Palm City	34990	Denton MR & MRS Stuart P
Palm City	34990	Eggleston MR & MRS Richard H JR
Palm City	34990	Lamb MR & MRS Gordon E
Palm City	34990	Norris MR & MRS John S
Palm City	34990	Pratt MR John T
Palm Coast	32137	Baruch MRS Earle E JR
Palm Coast	32137	Belknap MRS Robert E 3D
Palm Harbor	34683	Grayshaw MR & MRS James R
Palm Harbor	34683	Lee MR James H
Palm Harbor	34683	Steiger MR & MRS Frederick M
Palm Harbor	34684	Steiger MR Alexander M
Palm Island	33946	Aulenti MR & MRS Richard C
Palmetto Bay	31568	Baddour MR & MRS Frederick R
Palmetto Bay	33157	Grady MR & MRS (DR) Tyler del Valle
Palmetto Bay	33157	Reisinger MR & MRS Christopher B
Parkland	33067	Reksten MRS Astrid J
Pensacola	32506	Adamson MISS Helen Millicent
Pinecrest	33156	Baddour MRS Raymond F
Pinellas Park	33782	Lyman MR Joseph JR
Pinellas Park	33782	Reisinger MR & MRS Ronald B
Plantation	33324	Stouch MR & MRS Bruce C
Pompano Beach	33060	Lawrence MRS Stuart N
Pompano Beach	33062	Groesbeck MISS Gretchen A
Pompano Beach	33062	Vaughan MR & MRS Alan C
Pompano Beach	33064	Miller MRS Louisa H
Ponte Vedra	32082	Berg MR & MRS Davis C
Ponte Vedra	32082	Disston MR & MRS Geoffrey W JR
Ponte Vedra	32082	Ryan MR Cornelius T & Thorne MRS Phebe E
Ponte Vedra Beach	32004	Rowley MRS Charles F
Ponte Vedra Beach	32082	Baruch MR & MRS Earle E III
Ponte Vedra Beach	32082	Blaxter MRS Henry Vaughan JR
Ponte Vedra Beach	32082	Boland MR & MRS Jerry M
Ponte Vedra Beach	32082	Carroll MRS James B Mabon
Ponte Vedra Beach	32082	Cole MRS Daniel
Ponte Vedra Beach	32082	Dague MR Arthur D
Ponte Vedra Beach	32082	Davis MR & MRS Wendell JR
Ponte Vedra Beach	32082	Ducey MRS John F JR
Ponte Vedra Beach	32082	Duff MR & MRS Steven W
Ponte Vedra Beach	32082	Elledge MR & MRS Edman L
Ponte Vedra Beach	32082	Fernley MR & MRS Thomas A 3D
Ponte Vedra Beach	32082	Funke MR & MRS William P
Ponte Vedra Beach	32082	Giddens MR & MRS James W
Ponte Vedra Beach	32082	Goodall MR Herbert W III
Ponte Vedra Beach	32082	Greeff MRS Theodore
Ponte Vedra Beach	32082	Haskell MR & MRS Macdonald T
Ponte Vedra Beach	32082	Henry MR & MRS J Norman
Ponte Vedra Beach	32082	Johnson MRS Alexander B
Ponte Vedra Beach	32082	Patch MR & MRS Benjamin T
Ponte Vedra Beach	32082	Paul MRS Robert H 3D
Ponte Vedra Beach	32082	Phelps MRS Irene S
Ponte Vedra Beach	32082	Reece REV Nathaniel Treat
Ponte Vedra Beach	32082	Smith MR & MRS James P JR
Ponte Vedra Beach	32082	Snyder MR Paul H H
Ponte Vedra Beach	32082	Tissue MR & MRS John W
Ponte Vedra Beach	32082	Weekes MR & MRS James T
Ponte Vedra Beach	32082	Willim MR John S III
Ponte Vedra Beach	32082	Willim MRS John S
Port Orange	32127	Thomson MR John C
Port St Lucie	34953	Ott MR & MRS John Nash III
Port St Lucie	34983	Heath MS Pamela D
Punta Gorda	33950	Yacubian MRS Lawrence M
Rockledge	32955	Kaiser MR & MRS Franck Hyatt JR
Royal Palm Beach	33411	Mandelbaum MR Leonardo A
Sanibel	33957	Boyd MR & MRS Crosby N
Sanibel	33957	Dillon MRS John S
Sanibel	33957	Hart MR & MRS Charles C
Sanibel	33957	Osgood MR & MRS Edward H JR
Sanibel	33957	Sturtevant MR & MRS Peter A
Sanibel	33957	Trevor MR & MRS Alexander B
Sanibel	33957	Vollmer MR & MRS William L
Santa Rosa Beach	32459	Polakoff MR & MRS Keen J
Sarasota	34230	Everett MRS Virginia S
Sarasota	34231	Friend MRS Charles W
Sarasota	34231	Gourlay MR & MRS Lawrence
Sarasota	34231	Harris MR & MRS Christopher H
Sarasota	34231	Jones MR & MRS Cameron J
Sarasota	34231	Leeming MR & MRS John B
Sarasota	34231	Mahoney MR & MRS Jerome J
Sarasota	34231	Mannion MR William F JR & Bauer MS Gretchen K

Sarasota	34231	Moffitt MRS Anne Price
Sarasota	34231	Roome MR & MRS Reginald JR
Sarasota	34231	Sutton MRS Howard D
Sarasota	34231	Taylor MRS Robert G
Sarasota	34232	Bettle MR & MRS Griscom III
Sarasota	34232	Chapin MR Neil JR
Sarasota	34235	Boyd MRS Allen R
Sarasota	34235	Dame MR & MRS W Page III
Sarasota	34235	Purser MR & MRS Carr R JR
Sarasota	34236	Berne MR & MRS Chester H
Sarasota	34236	Burger MR & MRS F Gregg
Sarasota	34236	Daly MRS Rodney O
Sarasota	34236	Kerr REV DR & MRS Donald C
Sarasota	34236	Roebling MR Wainwright R
Sarasota	34236	Salsbury MR & MRS William B
Sarasota	34236	Van der Mije MR & MRS (DR) Albert W J
Sarasota	34236	Walker MRS W Wyatt JR
Sarasota	34238	Davenport MRS David W
Sarasota	34238	Harness MR & MRS Charles R
Sarasota	34238	Humphreys MRS Robert F
Sarasota	34238	Parsons MR & MRS John B
Sarasota	34238	Riker MRS Grace F
Sarasota	34238	Smylie MRS Charles A
Sarasota	34238	White MRS Harvey
Sarasota	34238	White MS Lyndsay Pond
Sarasota	34238	Wurts MRS John S
Sarasota	34239	Rose MR & MRS George H
Sarasota	34242	Andrus MR & MRS Vincent D
Sarasota	34242	Carter MRS Mai Garesché
Sarasota	34242	Drake MRS Clifford JR
Sarasota	34242	Garrett MR & MRS Thomas C JR
Sarasota	34243	Coorssen MRS Eugenia B
Sarasota	34243	Larsen REV & MRS Lawrence B JR
Sarasota	34243	Page MR C Donald
Sarasota	34277	Lombard MR & MRS James M
Sebastian	32958	Simpson DR & MRS Laurence S
Seminole	33776	Trigg MRS R C Ballard 3D
Sewall's Point	34996	Ryan MR & MRS Roderick N
Spring Hill	34610	Harding MRS Nancy J
St Augustine	32080	Bowman MR J Hunt 3D
		& Ginn MRS Judith A
St Augustine	32080	Man MRS Christine
St Augustine	32080	Rountree MR John G R
St Augustine	32084	Charles MR Michael H
St Augustine	32084	Coleman MR & MRS Wilfrid W
St Augustine	32084	Gushue MR & MRS Joseph T
St Augustine	32084	Hart MRS John A
St Augustine	32092	May MR Edward L
St Johns	32259	Porteous MR Louis D
St Petersburg	33701	Gallaway MRS John M
St Petersburg	33701	Rathborne MS Nancy Winship
St Petersburg	33702	Aspinwall MR Samuel
St Petersburg	33704	Leedy MRS Larry L
St Petersburg	33704	Neary MR & MRS Victor J
St Petersburg	33707	Worthington MISS Ann R
St Petersburg	33708	Ellis MRS D Rowland
St Petersburg	33710	Johnson MRS Evelyn M
Stuart	33497	Palmer MR Lansing R
Stuart	34994	Neale MRS Sterling L
Stuart	34995	Mattlage MISS L Valerie
Stuart	34996	Bauman MR Robert P
Stuart	34996	Boyce MS Jocelyn E
Stuart	34996	Downing MRS Patricia Del Piano
Stuart	34996	Irvine MRS John O
Stuart	34996	Ledyard MR Jason S
Stuart	34996	Lizars MRS Rawson G JR
Stuart	34996	Longmaid MR & MRS Ashley J S
Stuart	34997	Brown MR & MRS James P
Stuart	34997	Burton MR & MRS Robert L
Stuart	34997	de Mouchy DCHSS
Stuart	34997	Guthrie MR & MRS Alexander D
Stuart	34997	Hunt MRS George P
Stuart	34997	Irving MRS Christopher C
Stuart	34997	Madden MRS Robert L
Stuart	34997	Murray MR & MRS M Timothy
Stuart	34997	Ritter MRS William B
Stuart	34997	Wright MRS George I 3D
Sugarloaf Shores	33042	Maschal MR & MRS John R
Tallahassee	32309	Alexander MRS John S
Tallahassee	32309	Barloga MR & MRS Fred R
Tallahassee	32309	Putnam MISS Nancy W
Tallahassee	32312	Peipers MRS David H
Tallevast	34270	Feeley MR & MRS William L
Tampa	33602	Boatner MR B Herbert JR
Tampa	33606	Abel MR & MRS Taylor D
Tampa	33606	Davenport MR David N
Tampa	33609	Tucker MR & MRS Marshall O
Tampa	33609	Tucker MRS William R
Tampa	33610	Lyman MR & MRS Charles P JR
Tampa	33611	Harrell MR & MRS Cecil Stanford
Tampa	33611	Liggett MR & MRS Alexander P
Tampa	33611	Yerkes MRS J Nicholas
Tampa	33615	Thompson MR Peter H III
Tampa	33618	Pendleton MR & MRS Nathan S IV
Tampa	33626	Staniford MR & MRS Foye F JR
Tampa	33629	Harvey MR & MRS John W
Tampa	33629	Hupper MR Roger W
Tampa	33629	Liggett MR Ambler W
Tampa	33629	Reiss MR & MRS Michael B
Tampa	33629	Winter MRS John W
Tampa	33647	Sinkler MRS Richard K
Tavernier	33070	Stringham MR Elliott L
Tequesta	33469	Boeger MRS William A JR
Tequesta	33469	Cowell MR & MRS Richard C JR
Tequesta	33469	Findlay MRS Donald R
Tequesta	33469	Johnston MRS J Clement
Tequesta	33469	Kreimer MRS Ralph C
Tequesta	33469	Stinchcomb MR Carl J
Tequesta	33469	Whitlock MISS Veronica P
Tequesta	33469	York MR B Hamlin 3D
Tequesta	33469	York MRS Pamela D
Thonotosassa	33592	Thayer MRS A Bronson
Thonotosassa	33592	Tucker MS Elinor D W
Treasure Island	33706	Koons MR Garner M
Treasure Island	33706	Strebeigh MR Thomas T
Venice	34285	Cornell MR & MRS Duane F
Venice	34285	Coyle DR & MRS William R III
Venice	34285	Moore MR & MRS C Atwell JR
Venice	34292	Pratt MRS William C JR
Venice	34292	Weil MR & MRS Andrew L
Venice	34292	Wilson MR William H
Vero Beach	32960	Colket MR & MRS Tristram C 4TH
Vero Beach	32960	Krulak REV & MRS William M
Vero Beach	32961	Morgan MR & MRS Howard R
Vero Beach	32962	Kennedy MISS Ellen D
Vero Beach	32962	McKown MR & MRS David R
Vero Beach	32962	Pierpont MR Thomas H
Vero Beach	32962	Rianhard MR & MRS Lockwood
Vero Beach	32963	Adams MRS Stirling S
Vero Beach	32963	Alford MR & MRS Bryant K
Vero Beach	32963	Allen MS Rosamond Warren
Vero Beach	32963	Bailey MR & MRS Samuel JR

To nominate a candidate for the Social Register Association, please email: SRCommittee@thesocialregister.org

Vero Beach, FL—Vero Beach, FL

Vero Beach........................ 32963.......... Barnes MR & MRS T Ellis III
Vero Beach........................ 32963.......... Bass MRS Jane L
Vero Beach........................ 32963.......... Beeman MR Richard E
Vero Beach........................ 32963.......... Bellis MRS James L
Vero Beach........................ 32963.......... Benedict MR & MRS Peter B
Vero Beach........................ 32963.......... Boom MRS Willem E
Vero Beach........................ 32963.......... Borie MR & MRS David B JR
Vero Beach........................ 32963.......... Brandt MRS Frederick A
Vero Beach........................ 32963.......... Bray MR Michael D
Vero Beach........................ 32963.......... Brown MR & MRS James W L
Vero Beach........................ 32963.......... Buford MR & MRS Anthony A JR
Vero Beach........................ 32963.......... Cameron MR & MRS Nicholas A
Vero Beach........................ 32963.......... Carney MR & MRS James H 2D
Vero Beach........................ 32963.......... Casner MR & MRS Truman S
Vero Beach........................ 32963.......... Chadwick MRS Rosamond A
Vero Beach........................ 32963.......... Chewning MRS E Taylor JR
Vero Beach........................ 32963.......... Childs MR & MRS Thomas S JR
Vero Beach........................ 32963.......... Coe MRS George V III
Vero Beach........................ 32963.......... Cole MR & MRS Wallace H 3D
Vero Beach........................ 32963.......... Cole MRS Wallace H JR
Vero Beach........................ 32963.......... Coolidge MR & MRS E David III
Vero Beach........................ 32963.......... Coxhead MR Peter C
Vero Beach........................ 32963.......... Craigmyle MR & MRS Robert de R
Vero Beach........................ 32963.......... Cruice MR & MRS Charles S
Vero Beach........................ 32963.......... Delafield MISS Cecily
Vero Beach........................ 32963.......... Derby MRS Roger A JR
Vero Beach........................ 32963.......... Dolan MRS H Hoffman JR
Vero Beach........................ 32963.......... Dunn MR & MRS Stewart A JR
Vero Beach........................ 32963.......... Earle MR & MRS Hubert P JR
Vero Beach........................ 32963.......... Eiman MRS John W
Vero Beach........................ 32963.......... Feagin MR & MRS Douglas L
Vero Beach........................ 32963.......... Field MR & MRS H James JR
Vero Beach........................ 32963.......... Fischer MR & MRS George W
Vero Beach........................ 32963.......... Foley MRS Gifford P
Vero Beach........................ 32963.......... Fritts MR & MRS Guy A
Vero Beach........................ 32963.......... Gerstell MRS Marguerite F
Vero Beach........................ 32963.......... Gill MRS Kathryn M
Vero Beach........................ 32963.......... Gillespie MR & MRS Bruce A
Vero Beach........................ 32963.......... Goodman MRS William E IV
Vero Beach........................ 32963.......... Goss MRS Edward C
Vero Beach........................ 32963.......... Griswold MR & MRS H Bridgman
Vero Beach........................ 32963.......... Hall MRS Eben C
Vero Beach........................ 32963.......... Howard MR & MRS George H 3D
Vero Beach........................ 32963.......... Hubner MRS Robert W
Vero Beach........................ 32963.......... Hurley MR & MRS Richard S
Vero Beach........................ 32963.......... Hyde MRS George H
Vero Beach........................ 32963.......... Illick MRS Christopher D
Vero Beach........................ 32963.......... Ingraham MR & MRS Christopher C
Vero Beach........................ 32963.......... Jewett MR & MRS Jonathan
Vero Beach........................ 32963.......... Justi MR & MRS Henry K
Vero Beach........................ 32963.......... Kean MR & MRS John
Vero Beach........................ 32963.......... Keevil MR & MRS Philip C
Vero Beach........................ 32963.......... Kinsella MR & MRS William A 3D
Vero Beach........................ 32963.......... Kleinschmidt MR & MRS Robert W
Vero Beach........................ 32963.......... Lee MRS Burton J 3D
Vero Beach........................ 32963.......... Leighton MRS Charles M
Vero Beach........................ 32963.......... Lurie MR & MRS David V
Vero Beach........................ 32963.......... Marran MR & MRS Jack F
Vero Beach........................ 32963.......... McCluney MR & MRS Henry N
Vero Beach........................ 32963.......... McCuaig MR & MRS Victor C JR
Vero Beach........................ 32963.......... McFerran MR & MRS Alexander Y
Vero Beach........................ 32963.......... McLean MR & MRS Locke
Vero Beach........................ 32963.......... McLean MR & MRS Robert 2D
Vero Beach........................ 32963.......... McMullin MRS Gale T
Vero Beach........................ 32963.......... McShane MR & MRS Creighton
Vero Beach........................ 32963.......... Merrell MRS Stanley W 2D
Vero Beach........................ 32963.......... Miller MRS Polly S
Vero Beach........................ 32963.......... Moloney MRS Philip J
Vero Beach........................ 32963.......... Morphy MR & MRS James C
Vero Beach........................ 32963.......... Morris MRS George F
Vero Beach........................ 32963.......... Mortimer MR & MRS Henry T JR
Vero Beach........................ 32963.......... Murray MRS Arthur M JR
Vero Beach........................ 32963.......... Naess MRS Michael R
Vero Beach........................ 32963.......... Nicholson MR George S
Vero Beach........................ 32963.......... O'Brien MRS Patrick C JR
Vero Beach........................ 32963.......... Orrick MR & MRS Peter M
Vero Beach........................ 32963.......... Page MR & MRS David N
Vero Beach........................ 32963.......... Parks MR & MRS Nicholas R
Vero Beach........................ 32963.......... Peniston MR & MRS Eric W JR
Vero Beach........................ 32963.......... Penrose MR & MRS James C
Vero Beach........................ 32963.......... Pierpont MRS Harlan T JR
Vero Beach........................ 32963.......... Porter MR & MRS Christopher T
Vero Beach........................ 32963.......... Pottle MR & MRS Willard M JR
Vero Beach........................ 32963.......... Poutiatine MRS Michael
Vero Beach........................ 32963.......... Prentice MR William C H JR
Vero Beach........................ 32963.......... Prosser MR & MRS Robert L
Vero Beach........................ 32963.......... Pyle MR Robert M JR
Vero Beach........................ 32963.......... Richey MRS John M
Vero Beach........................ 32963.......... Riefler MR & MRS Donald B
Vero Beach........................ 32963.......... Riefler MR & MRS Duncan W
Vero Beach........................ 32963.......... Royster MRS Thomas S JR
Vero Beach........................ 32963.......... Rumbough MR & MRS Joseph Wright 3D
Vero Beach........................ 32963.......... Schmidt MR & MRS L Henry 3D
Vero Beach........................ 32963.......... Seed MRS William T
Vero Beach........................ 32963.......... Shedd MRS Patricia T
Vero Beach........................ 32963.......... Singer MR & MRS James W 3D
Vero Beach........................ 32963.......... Smith MR & MRS Crosby Rogers
Vero Beach........................ 32963.......... Smithers MR & MRS Francis C
Vero Beach........................ 32963.......... Stebbins MR & MRS John B
Vero Beach........................ 32963.......... Stickney MR & MRS Albert III
Vero Beach........................ 32963.......... Sullivan MR & MRS Barry R
Vero Beach........................ 32963.......... Sutro MRS Katharine B
Vero Beach........................ 32963.......... Tankoos MR & MRS Bradley J
Vero Beach........................ 32963.......... Tattersall MR & MRS Stowe H
Vero Beach........................ 32963.......... Taylor MR & MRS Carter S D
Vero Beach........................ 32963.......... Tifft MRS Henry N
Vero Beach........................ 32963.......... Tilney MR & MRS Farrar 3D
Vero Beach........................ 32963.......... Tingue MR & MRS William J
Vero Beach........................ 32963.......... Trippe MR & MRS Charles W
Vero Beach........................ 32963.......... Twiss MR & MRS Russell W
Vero Beach........................ 32963.......... Twiss MR Donald L
Vero Beach........................ 32963.......... Underwood MRS Agnes C
Vero Beach........................ 32963.......... Van Zonneveld MR & MRS Hans
Vero Beach........................ 32963.......... Velde MR & MRS Karl H JR
Vero Beach........................ 32963.......... Watson MR & MRS Charles G
Vero Beach........................ 32963.......... Weary MR & MRS Rollin D 3D
Vero Beach........................ 32963.......... Weary MR Rollin D JR
Vero Beach........................ 32963.......... Webster MR & MRS Richard G
Vero Beach........................ 32963.......... Weil DR & MRS Richard 3D
Vero Beach........................ 32963.......... Wonham MR & MRS Frederick S
Vero Beach........................ 32963.......... Woodhouse MR & MRS Henry Macauley
Vero Beach........................ 32963.......... Wright MRS Peter
Vero Beach........................ 32963.......... Young MRS Charles T 3D
Vero Beach........................ 32963.......... Young MRS Patricia P
Vero Beach........................ 32964.......... Beadle MR & MRS J Grant 3D
Vero Beach........................ 32964.......... Fotterall MR & MRS W W Law III
Vero Beach........................ 32964.......... Gwinn MRS Richard H
Vero Beach........................ 32964.......... McLean MR James H 3D
Vero Beach........................ 32964.......... Mulholland MR & MRS James S III
Vero Beach........................ 32964.......... Westerfield MR & MRS F Bradford
Vero Beach........................ 32966.......... Lawrence MRS William Van D
Vero Beach........................ 32966.......... Pryor MR & MRS Edward R

Vero Beach...... 32967...... Ballman MR & MRS B George
Vero Beach...... 32967...... Bubendey MR Paul F JR
Vero Beach...... 32967...... Busk MRS Joseph R JR
Vero Beach...... 32967...... Callen MRS John H JR
Vero Beach...... 32967...... Cochrane MRS William H
Vero Beach...... 32967...... Coffin MR & MRS Ralston H JR
Vero Beach...... 32967...... Dickson MRS Avery H
Vero Beach...... 32967...... Estey MRS John S
Vero Beach...... 32967...... Frankenthal MR & MRS Charles P A
Vero Beach...... 32967...... Johnston MR & MRS Waldo C M JR
Vero Beach...... 32967...... Lamborn MR George D F
Vero Beach...... 32967...... Maresi MR & MRS Henry J
Vero Beach...... 32967...... McIver MR Renwick S JR
Vero Beach...... 32967...... Owen MRS Frederick H JR
Vero Beach...... 32967...... Pennington MRS James S JR
Vero Beach...... 32967...... Perrott MR & MRS Robert S JR
Vero Beach...... 32967...... Schenkel MR & MRS John L H
Vero Beach...... 32967...... Van Vranken MR J Frederick JR
Vero Beach...... 32967...... Wall MR Wayne W
Vero Beach...... 32968...... Kellogg MR & MRS John M JR
Village of Golf...... 33436...... Lynch MR & MRS Thomas E
Village of Golf...... 33436...... McCulloch MRS Paul L
Village of Golf...... 33436...... Nadherny MRS Ferdinand
Village of Golf...... 33436...... Roberts MR & MRS Alan Y
Village of Golf...... 33436...... Sutter MRS William P
Wellington...... 33414...... Bane MRS David M
Wellington...... 33414...... Bright MRS Nicholas
Wellington...... 33414...... Celine MS Olexa
Wellington...... 33414...... Chisholm MRS Hugh J
Wellington...... 33414...... Cummin MR Arch W
Wellington...... 33414...... Highley MRS Anne Bobst
Wellington...... 33414...... Humes MRS Susan S
Wellington...... 33414...... Kiesewetter MR & MRS William B JR
Wellington...... 33414...... Long MISS Karen
Wellington...... 33414...... Mallinckrodt MISS Jane A
Wellington...... 33414...... Mills MR & MRS Ross D
Wellington...... 33414...... Montross MR & MRS Franklin IV
Wellington...... 33414...... Morris MR George H
Wellington...... 33414...... Murdoch-Muirhead MR Thomas
Wellington...... 33414...... Phelps MR Mason JR
Wellington...... 33414...... Pozzo MR & MRS Robert M
Wellington...... 33414...... Reid MR & MRS Samuel S
Wellington...... 33414...... Rockwell MR Thorson
Wellington...... 33414...... Rockwell MRS Melinda Highley
Wellington...... 33414...... Rumbough MRS Stanley M JR
Wellington...... 33414...... Rupp MRS Albert G
Wellington...... 33414...... Simpson MR & MRS Michael
Wellington...... 33414...... Sperling MRS Peter R
Wellington...... 33414...... Ylvisaker MRS Betsy M
Wellington...... 33449...... Garrett MRS Annabelle K
West Palm Beach...... 33401...... Abel MR & MRS William T
West Palm Beach...... 33401...... Alleman MRS H Edward JR
West Palm Beach...... 33401...... Azqueta MR & MRS Norberto JR
West Palm Beach...... 33401...... Barbey MISS Florence F
West Palm Beach...... 33401...... Bennett MRS Joseph B JR
West Palm Beach...... 33401...... Brickley MR & MRS Richard L JR
West Palm Beach...... 33401...... Cogan REV DR & MRS Timothy B
West Palm Beach...... 33401...... Cudahy MRS William B
West Palm Beach...... 33401...... de Peyster MR F Ashton 3D
West Palm Beach...... 33401...... Dillard MR & MRS Rodney J
West Palm Beach...... 33401...... Duryea MR & MRS William M JR
West Palm Beach...... 33401...... Eaton MR & MRS Frederick A
West Palm Beach...... 33401...... Foster MRS Jane de M
West Palm Beach...... 33401...... Foster MS India R
& Diaz MS (DR) Veronica
West Palm Beach...... 33401...... Gates MS Sarah E
West Palm Beach...... 33401...... Gauntt MS Samantha Leas
West Palm Beach...... 33401...... Giard MR & MRS George P JR
West Palm Beach...... 33401...... Goodhue MRS Albert
West Palm Beach...... 33401...... Hamilton MRS John T II
West Palm Beach...... 33401...... Hartz MR John C JR
West Palm Beach...... 33401...... Herrlinger MRS Edward F II
West Palm Beach...... 33401...... Johnston MR John W
West Palm Beach...... 33401...... Kendall MRS Messmore
West Palm Beach...... 33401...... Little MR & MRS David J
West Palm Beach...... 33401...... Livens MR & MRS John H
West Palm Beach...... 33401...... Lloyd MRS Tangley C
West Palm Beach...... 33401...... Loring MR John Robbins
West Palm Beach...... 33401...... Maddock MRS Victoria N
West Palm Beach...... 33401...... McKay MRS William C
West Palm Beach...... 33401...... Milne MR David IV
West Palm Beach...... 33401...... Ney MR & MRS Edward N
West Palm Beach...... 33401...... Norris MR Charles H
West Palm Beach...... 33401...... Nype MR Russell H
West Palm Beach...... 33401...... Oyer MR Harvey E III
West Palm Beach...... 33401...... Paolella MR & MRS John S
West Palm Beach...... 33401...... Papanicolaou MRS A Gardner
West Palm Beach...... 33401...... Peck MRS Lee Wallace
West Palm Beach...... 33401...... Phelps MR & MRS Richard J
West Palm Beach...... 33401...... Reed MR Stanley F
West Palm Beach...... 33401...... Reynolds MRS George I
West Palm Beach...... 33401...... Roberts MR Nathaniel T
& Zung MS Laura W-Y
West Palm Beach...... 33401...... Rockwell MISS Stephanie O
West Palm Beach...... 33401...... Rockwell MR & MRS Robin Markle
West Palm Beach...... 33401...... Schmidt MISS Joeanne Foskett
West Palm Beach...... 33401...... Smith MRS David Shiverick
West Palm Beach...... 33401...... Stautberg MRS Aubrey Theodore JR
West Palm Beach...... 33401...... Stillman MR J Whitney
West Palm Beach...... 33401...... Tailer MRS T Suffern
West Palm Beach...... 33401...... Trevor MR Ellis F
West Palm Beach...... 33401...... Vaughan Williams MR & MRS Rupert
West Palm Beach...... 33401...... Welsh MR Charles N JR
West Palm Beach...... 33401...... Wheelock MRS Morgan Dix JR
West Palm Beach...... 33401...... Whitman MR Robert Sturgis
West Palm Beach...... 33401...... Wick MR Walter D
West Palm Beach...... 33401...... Wood MRS Walter Abbott
West Palm Beach...... 33401...... Woodcock MRS Betty S B
West Palm Beach...... 33401...... Young DR Charles C
West Palm Beach...... 33401...... Zacharias MR & MRS Thomas E
West Palm Beach...... 33405...... Aspegren MS Theodora V
West Palm Beach...... 33405...... Baer MRS Theodore C JR
West Palm Beach...... 33405...... Bauer MRS Lucy Harrison
West Palm Beach...... 33405...... Benjamin MR & MRS William E III
West Palm Beach...... 33405...... Benjamin MR & MRS William E IV
West Palm Beach...... 33405...... Bingham MS Katharine K
West Palm Beach...... 33405...... Blackhurst MR & MRS W Robin
West Palm Beach...... 33405...... Breckenridge MR & MRS Mordelo V JR
West Palm Beach...... 33405...... Chaddock MR Jeffery D
West Palm Beach...... 33405...... Cole MRS Todd G
West Palm Beach...... 33405...... Coons MRS Richard F
West Palm Beach...... 33405...... Cumming MS Diane C
West Palm Beach...... 33405...... Curran MR & MRS Mortimer F
West Palm Beach...... 33405...... Darlington Safrin MRS Silvana L
West Palm Beach...... 33405...... Debbs MR & MRS Robert J
West Palm Beach...... 33405...... D'Elia MR Gregory W
West Palm Beach...... 33405...... Donnelly MISS Shannon K
West Palm Beach...... 33405...... Douglass MRS Whitney Miller
West Palm Beach...... 33405...... Draper MR J Sumner 2D
West Palm Beach...... 33405...... Dwinell MS Susanna D
West Palm Beach...... 33405...... Flynn MRS Allan A A
West Palm Beach...... 33405...... Howard-Smith MR & MRS John G

West Palm Beach, FL—Atlanta, GA

West Palm Beach.......... 33405......... Howard-Smith MR Stuart S
West Palm Beach.......... 33405......... Humes MR Christopher L
West Palm Beach.......... 33405......... Johnston MR & MRS Philip C
West Palm Beach.......... 33405......... Leidy MR & MRS Page R
West Palm Beach.......... 33405......... Lorber MR D Martin H B
West Palm Beach.......... 33405......... McGurk MRS John J III
West Palm Beach.......... 33405......... Morrish MR & MRS David H
West Palm Beach.......... 33405......... Morrow MR Mark A
West Palm Beach.......... 33405......... Neville MR & MRS Warwick F
West Palm Beach.......... 33405......... Pressly MRS James G
West Palm Beach.......... 33405......... Reed MR & MRS G Peter Q JR
West Palm Beach.......... 33405......... Rooks MRS Valerie
West Palm Beach.......... 33405......... Sallee MR & MRS John C
West Palm Beach.......... 33405......... Savage MR & MRS Edmund T
West Palm Beach.......... 33405......... Schneider MR & MRS James C
West Palm Beach.......... 33405......... Seymour MRS Caroline C
West Palm Beach.......... 33405......... Soper MR & MRS Jared E
West Palm Beach.......... 33405......... Straton MRS Marion H
West Palm Beach.......... 33405......... Van der Grift MR & MRS Frederic R
West Palm Beach.......... 33405......... Waller MRS Alexis
West Palm Beach.......... 33405......... Webster MRS Lucy Anthony
West Palm Beach.......... 33407......... Badman MR John III
West Palm Beach.......... 33407......... Bitting MR & MRS Kenneth H III
West Palm Beach.......... 33407......... Boykin MRS Sandra R
West Palm Beach.......... 33407......... Farkas MR & MRS Jonathan
West Palm Beach.......... 33407......... Frost MS Dorothy W
West Palm Beach.......... 33407......... Grattan MR & MRS Stephen
West Palm Beach.......... 33407......... McNally MR Brian J
West Palm Beach.......... 33407......... Quigley MR Frank K
West Palm Beach.......... 33407......... Skelly MR & MRS T McFarland
West Palm Beach.......... 33407......... von Arnim CTSS Camille
West Palm Beach.......... 33409......... Barrett MR & MRS Robert J III
West Palm Beach.......... 33409......... Elebash MR & MRS Peter H
West Palm Beach.......... 33409......... Sabo MRS Barbara H
West Palm Beach.......... 33411......... Harrison MRS William Henry 3D
West Palm Beach.......... 33411......... Kaiser MR Stephen Hyatt
West Palm Beach.......... 33411......... Ross MR Walter L III
West Palm Beach.......... 33411......... Van Winkle MR Edgar Beach III
West Palm Beach.......... 33412......... Lenahan MR & MRS Sheldon T
West Palm Beach.......... 33412......... Page MR & MRS Richard K JR
West Palm Beach.......... 33412......... Taylor MR & MRS Henry W JR
West Palm Beach.......... 33413......... Shearer MISS Joy B
West Palm Beach.......... 33415......... Hollister MR Gerald A B
Wilton Manors .... 33305......... Spalding MR & MRS Mark F
Wilton Manors .... 33311......... Maclaurin MR Peter J
Windermere.................. 34786......... Basque MR & MRS James F
Winter Garden.............. 34787......... Hutto MR & MRS Richard Jay
Winter Haven................ 33880......... Grew MR James H JR
Winter Park.................. 32789......... Allport MR & MRS Walter F P
Winter Park.................. 32789......... Davis MR & MRS DeForest P
Winter Park.................. 32789......... du Pont MR Scott T
Winter Park.................. 32789......... Emmet MR & MRS Herman Le Roy III
Winter Park.................. 32789......... Hanson MR & MRS Craig W
Winter Park.................. 32789......... Hardy MRS Leslie W
Winter Park.................. 32789......... Hosbein MR & MRS Peter C
Winter Park.................. 32789......... Morse MR Breton B
Winter Park.................. 32789......... Owen MRS David J SR
Winter Park.................. 32790......... Conlan DR & MRS Walter A 3D
Winter Park.................. 32792......... Creasman MR & MRS Carl E JR
Winter Park.................. 32792......... Goggin MR & MRS David B
Winter Park.................. 32792......... Graves MR William M JR
& Jackson MS Ruth R

GEORGIA

Alpharetta..................... 30004......... Gray MR Austen T III
Alpharetta..................... 30004......... Lindsay MR & MRS Alan H
Alpharetta..................... 30009......... Buck MR & MRS Jeffrey Paul
Alpharetta..................... 30022......... Horne MR & MRS William C
Alpharetta..................... 30022......... Moore MR & MRS William C
Appling.......................... 30802......... Speese MRS John JR
Athens .... 30605......... Lowrance MR & MRS Hughes W
Athens .... 30606......... Covert MRS Roger A
Athens .... 30606......... Taylor MR & MRS P Randolph
Athens .... 30606......... Winthrop MR & MRS Robert 2D
Atlanta.......................... 30305......... Bradford MR & MRS Bryan R
Atlanta.......................... 30305......... Brading MR & MRS Stanley G JR
Atlanta.......................... 30305......... Brooks MR & MRS William H
Atlanta.......................... 30305......... Brown REV J Robert
Atlanta.......................... 30305......... Christman MR & MRS Raymond R
Atlanta.......................... 30305......... Cogan MR & MRS Milo S
Atlanta.......................... 30305......... Colgin MR Robert Boston
Atlanta.......................... 30305......... Cushman MRS Gloria R
Atlanta.......................... 30305......... Denny MR & MRS James McC JR
Atlanta.......................... 30305......... Finnerty MR & MRS Peter F JR
Atlanta.......................... 30305......... Goodwin MISS Jane-Fenwick
Atlanta.......................... 30305......... Hale MR & MRS F Sheffield
Atlanta.......................... 30305......... Hall MISS Page E
Atlanta.......................... 30305......... Henagan MR & MRS William F
Atlanta.......................... 30305......... Jones MR & MRS Henry M T
Atlanta.......................... 30305......... Kirkpatrick MR & MRS David F
Atlanta.......................... 30305......... Leone MR & MRS Charles D II
Atlanta.......................... 30305......... Lindon MR & MRS Christopher A
Atlanta.......................... 30305......... Long DR Barbara
Atlanta.......................... 30305......... Macauley MR & MRS James E
Atlanta.......................... 30305......... McMullan MR & MRS John Edward
Atlanta.......................... 30305......... Miller MR & MRS F Keene
Atlanta.......................... 30305......... Nowland MR & MRS David T
Atlanta.......................... 30305......... Pirrung MR & MRS C Mark
Atlanta.......................... 30305......... Polk MR & MRS Thomas S
Atlanta.......................... 30305......... Reid MR & MRS Bruce Stanton JR
Atlanta.......................... 30305......... Schaefer MR & MRS Garrurd K
Atlanta.......................... 30305......... Schoettle MISS Catharine N
Atlanta.......................... 30305......... Seydel MR & MRS J Rutherford
Atlanta.......................... 30305......... Sterling MRS Joyce
Atlanta.......................... 30305......... Stone MR & MRS Wilson G
Atlanta.......................... 30305......... Swann MR & MRS Christopher D
Atlanta.......................... 30305......... Vreeland MR & MRS Jeffrey C
Atlanta.......................... 30305......... Wilmer MS Catherine G
Atlanta.......................... 30306......... Chance MR & MRS Benjamin P
Atlanta.......................... 30306......... Clarke MR & MRS George M 3D
Atlanta.......................... 30306......... Joseph MISS Courtney Valk
Atlanta.......................... 30306......... Rowland MR & MRS Walter S JR
Atlanta.......................... 30307......... Draper MR & MRS Alexander Y
Atlanta.......................... 30307......... Pierson MR & MRS R Hunter III
Atlanta.......................... 30307......... Selke MR Edward D
Atlanta.......................... 30308......... deKay MR Nicholas A D
Atlanta.......................... 30308......... Miller MR & MRS Charles J JR
Atlanta.......................... 30309......... Baker MS Lucy
Atlanta.......................... 30309......... Carr MR & MRS Thomas R T
Atlanta.......................... 30309......... Dimmick MR & MRS Paul H
Atlanta.......................... 30309......... Hewitt MR William Davis
Atlanta.......................... 30309......... Lum MR & MRS Jack Brady
Atlanta.......................... 30309......... Maurice MISS Michelle
Atlanta.......................... 30309......... Welch MR & MRS Douglas Reed
Atlanta.......................... 30309......... Whitney MRS Christina W
Atlanta.......................... 30312......... Galucki MR & MRS Jon T
Atlanta.......................... 30318......... Crawford MR & MRS W Blake
Atlanta.......................... 30318......... Shuford MR & MRS Robert A

Atlanta, GA—Savannah, GA

Atlanta	30318	Summers MR & MRS R Steven JR
Atlanta	30318	Wolf MR & MRS David D
Atlanta	30319	Mallory MR & MRS Thomas D JR
Atlanta	30319	Smethurst MRS Lucy C
Atlanta	30319	Sutton MR & MRS David A
Atlanta	30327	Ball MR & MRS P Butler
Atlanta	30327	Barney MR & MRS William R III
Atlanta	30327	Frazer MR & MRS John R
Atlanta	30327	Jenkins MR & MRS Walter D III
Atlanta	30327	LeBow MRS Laurel M
Atlanta	30327	Lutz MR & MRS Thomas B II
Atlanta	30327	McDonald MR & MRS John E JR
Atlanta	30327	Miller MR & MRS Prescott C
Atlanta	30327	Nalle MR & MRS Horace D JR
Atlanta	30327	Quintana MR & MRS Nicolas I
Atlanta	30327	Smith MR & MRS Todd J
Atlanta	30327	Spiegel MS Elizabeth D Morgan
Atlanta	30327	Tucker MR & MRS Jeffrey P
Atlanta	30327	Vetterlein MR & MRS J Rodney
Atlanta	30327	Wray HON & MRS Christopher A
Atlanta	30327	Young MR Hillyer McD
Atlanta	30327	Young MR Jonathan C
Atlanta	30328	Black MRS E Newbold IV
Atlanta	30339	Ford MR Bruce G
Atlanta	30339	Orthwein MR & MRS Adolphus B JR
Atlanta	30339	Rodgers MISS Jennifer E DeWitt
Atlanta	30339	Wilkinson MR & MRS Gordon C
Atlanta	30340	Koman MR Alan J
Atlanta	30340	McGuinness MR & MRS Alexander W
Atlanta	30342	Astrop MRS William Bowen
Atlanta	30342	Gardiner MR & MRS A Warren
Atlanta	30342	Ogilvie MR & MRS Charles P
Atlanta	30350	Moore MRS Matteo P
Atlanta	30350	Wulfing MR & MRS Frederick W
Augusta	30904	Watson MR Ross
Augusta	30909	O'Connor MR Francis F
Augusta	30909	Robinson MR & MRS (DR) E Champlin
Big Canoe	30143	Coffin MRS Lewis A 3D
Braselton	30517	Schulte MR & MRS Stephen A
Canton	30115	Hornor MR & MRS (DR) Gurdon W
Chamblee	30341	Hoag MR & MRS Andrew D
Columbus	31904	Andrews CAPT & MRS Charles W H JR
Columbus	31904	Woodbridge MRS M Brooks
Columbus	31906	Salter MRS Margaret S
Columbus	31906	Schley DR W Shain
Cumming	30028	Carlisle MR & MRS F Lewis
Cumming	30040	Beard MR Alexander R
Cumming	30040	Konecny MR & MRS Leonard K
Cumming	30040	Raphael MR & MRS Kenneth G
Cumming	30040	Sibley MRS John B
Cumming	30040	Szvetecz MR & MRS Charles F
Cumming	30131	Marrack MRS Richard M
Dacula	30019	Sanger MS A Rockage
Danielsville	30633	Gee MR Charles MacQ JR
Duluth	30097	Bonistall MR & MRS Ernest C
Duluth	30097	French MR & MRS G Remick
Dunwoody	30338	Armstrong MR & MRS James M
Dunwoody	30338	Christian MS Charlotte J
Dunwoody	30338	McLean DR & MRS Ephraim R 3D
East Cobb	30062	Kleinsorge MR & MRS William Peter
Evans	30809	Hurd LT CDR (RET) & MRS Michael F
Evans	30809	O'Connor MRS Joan D
Fairburn	30213	Polley MR & MRS Michael W
Fayetteville	30214	Scarff DR & MRS Timothy B
Greensboro	30642	Duncanson MRS Thomas JR
Griffin	30223	Barrell MR & MRS Thomas F
Hahira	31632	Odom MR John G
Holly Springs	30142	Bruce MR Thomas Allen
Kennesaw	30144	Coxe MR & MRS Robert W
Kennesaw	30144	Kole MR & MRS Michael U
Lawrenceville	30043	Hutchinson MR & MRS George F 3D
Lawrenceville	30043	Norton MR & MRS Scott B
Lula	30554	Livingston MR & MRS Deryck Van V
Macon	31201	Pickard MR Carey Owen 3D & Howard MR Christopher A D
Macon	31210	Van De Water DR Joseph M
Madison	30650	Morehouse MR & MRS M Dutton JR
Mansfield	30055	Morehouse MR & MRS Alexander G
Marietta	30060	Johnson MISS Carolyn N
Marietta	30064	Elliott MR & MRS Linton A
Marietta	30064	Elliott MR & MRS Thomas A JR
Marietta	30064	Gray MR & MRS John V
Marietta	30066	Callard MR & MRS George D
Marietta	30068	Hankey MR & MRS Charles W
Marietta	30068	Martin MR & MRS Andrew W
Millen	30442	Gleason MRS Frederick B III
Milton	30004	Barber MR & MRS Andrew T
Milton	30004	Burell MR & MRS Robert L
Milton	30004	Cottick MR & MRS Bret G
Norcross	30092	Whipple MR & MRS Jack V H 2D
Norman Park	31771	Davison MR Daniel P JR
Richmond Hill	31324	Davies MR & MRS Dwight R
Roswell	30075	Cogswell MRS James Kelsey IV
Roswell	30075	Hallowell MR & MRS Frederick H
Roswell	30075	McGee MR Shawn M & Fuller MS Jennifer L
Roswell	30076	Poole MR & MRS Lenwood H
Savannah	31401	Davis MR & MRS Asa B 3D
Savannah	31401	Labrot MRS Andrew G
Savannah	31401	Lientz MR & MRS James R II
Savannah	31401	Littlejohn MR & MRS Angus C JR
Savannah	31401	Menges MRS Devon S
Savannah	31401	Stevens MR & MRS Dana C
Savannah	31401	Steves MISS Gale C
Savannah	31404	Brenard MR & MRS Kris Thomas
Savannah	31404	Glenn MR & MRS Cooper L
Savannah	31404	Sayler MRS John M
Savannah	31404	Youles MR & MRS Charles R
Savannah	31404	Zipser MR & MRS John P
Savannah	31405	Barroll MR & MRS Lawrence L
Savannah	31405	Raibourn MRS Gerald R
Savannah	31405	Ryan MR & MRS W Hurley JR
Savannah	31405	Summers DR & MRS Roland S
Savannah	31405	Zemurray MR & MRS Samuel 3D
Savannah	31406	Divine MR & MRS Edward F
Savannah	31406	Dorroh MR William G 3D
Savannah	31406	Farr MR James Wells JR
Savannah	31406	Morrison MR & MRS Mills L JR
Savannah	31410	Bergen MR & MRS Frederick S
Savannah	31410	Deméré MR & MRS John B
Savannah	31410	Harrison MR & MRS Joseph H JR
Savannah	31410	Sayler MR & MRS John M JR
Savannah	31411	Beckman MR & MRS Charles E
Savannah	31411	Bell MR & MRS Jeffrey Graham
Savannah	31411	Cassard MRS Karen D
Savannah	31411	Cayer DR & MRS Roger P
Savannah	31411	Cluett MR & MRS Mark S
Savannah	31411	Coy MR & MRS Timothy E
Savannah	31411	Fawcett MR & MRS Michael S
Savannah	31411	French MR & MRS Clark M
Savannah	31411	Hairston MR & MRS Thomas F
Savannah	31411	Hearne MR & MRS Darrell L
Savannah	31411	Humphrey MR & MRS Peter B

To nominate a candidate for the Social Register Association, please email: SRCommittee@thesocialregister.org

Savannah, GA—Chicago, IL

Savannah	31411	Irwin MR & MRS Fred A
Savannah	31411	McCormack MR & MRS Brian P
Savannah	31411	Moncure DR & MRS Ashby C
Savannah	31411	Powelson MR & MRS Douglas V N
Savannah	31411	White MR & MRS Pendleton P
Savannah	31411	Wilkens MR & MRS Robert G JR
Savannah	31411	Withers MR & MRS Paul M
Savannah	31412	Meyer MR & MRS Richard III
Sea Island	31561	Laird MRS Antonia Bissell
Sea Island	31561	Stires MRS Ernest Van R
Smyrna	30080	Ottley MR & MRS James M
Smyrna	30080	Scherberger MR & MRS Joseph M JR
Smyrna	30080	Shannon MR & MRS Richard H
St Marys	31558	Stilson MR Colby JR
St Simons Island	31522	Flight MR & MRS Robert E
St Simons Island	31522	Hucks MR & MRS Herbert deM III
St Simons Island	31522	Rives MRS George L
Stone Mountain	30087	Stent MR & MRS Ferdinand T
Suwanee	30024	Poppleton MR & MRS Steven M
Thomasville	31792	Crozer MRS Robert P
Thomasville	31792	Jonklaas MR Anthony
Thomasville	31792	Middleton MR & MRS David J
Thomasville	31792	Oliva MR George JR
Thomasville	31792	Young MR & MRS Geoffrey P
Thomasville	31799	Bicknell MR & MRS Warren 3D
Tucker	30084	Hanson MISS Adelaide Berry
Tucker	30084	Wagner MR & MRS Stephen B
Valdosta	31602	Eager MRS William G 3D
Watkinsville	30677	Kleiner DR & MRS Scott A

HAWAII

Aiea, Oahu	96701	Fernley MR & MRS J Randolph
Haiku	96708	Gates MR & MRS Courtlandt D
Haleiwa	96712	Spencer MISS Shayla
Honokaa	96727	Massey MRS Calvin R
Honolulu	96813	Castle MR Alfred L 2D
Honolulu	96815	Bakewell MISS Sarah
Honolulu	96815	Brown MRS Zadoc W
Honolulu	96815	Cross MR & MRS Peter R
Honolulu	96815	Wood MRS David E
Honolulu	96816	Ogburn MRS Hugh B
Honolulu	96821	Brown MR & MRS James M 4TH
Honolulu	96821	Damon MRS Cyril F JR
Honolulu	96821	Dickey MR Paul B 3D
Honolulu	96822	Becker MR Robert L 3D
Honolulu	96822	de Neufville MR Robert E
Honolulu	96836	Chalker MR Dwight E
Honolulu	96839	Lorenz MR Keith JR
Kailua Kona	96739	Worsham MR & MRS David D
Kailua Kona	96740	Cochran MR & MRS Philip L III
Kailua, Oahu	96734	Drayton CAPT (RET) & MRS Henry E JR
Kaneohe	96744	Parmley MR & MRS John R
Kaneohe	96744	Taylor MR & MRS Carroll S
Kihei	96753	Bleck MR & MRS Paul M
Lahaina	96761	Teixeira MR & MRS Lucas C
Laupahoehoe	96764	Leonard DR & MRS Seton R
Makawao	96768	Dole MR Charles H JR
Makawao	96768	Killhour MR & MRS Gilson E
Pahoa	96778	Gilbert MR Francis B JR
Papaikou	96781	Sharkey MR Thomas 6TH & Ross MS Katherine C
Pukalani, Maui	96768	James DR & MRS William C

IDAHO

Boise	83702	Bergmann MR & MRS Michael R
Boise	83702	Dingman MR Robert J
Boise	83702	Pereira MR & MRS William C
Boise	83702	Soran MR & MRS Daniel P
Boise	83702	Wells MRS L Dana
Boise	83706	Holt MRS Jane Wells
Boise	83712	Dingman MRS Martha T
Coeur D'Alene	83815	Sedgwick MR & MRS Jonathan de Forest
Driggs	83422	Harrison MR & MRS R Brandon JR
Driggs	83422	Romaine MRS Allison N
Hailey	83333	Caron MRS Peter E
Hailey	83333	McKenna MR & MRS Michael W
Hailey	83333	Parkhill MR & MRS Clayton IV
Hailey	83333	Walker MR & MRS Taylor S
Hailey	83333	Ward MR & MRS Jeffrey C
Hailey	83333	Webel MRS Sandra L
Hailey	83333	Weekes MR & MRS Henry deF
Idaho Falls	83404	Hume MR & MRS Parker H
Ketchum	83340	Cannell MR & MRS William A E
Ketchum	83340	Cannell MR & MRS William B
Ketchum	83340	Colhoun MR & MRS Michael Deere
Ketchum	83340	Duff MR & MRS Richard P
Ketchum	83340	Fremont-Smith MR & MRS Paul JR
Ketchum	83340	Gardiner MR & MRS Woodward C III
Ketchum	83340	Hagenbuch MR & MRS John J
Ketchum	83340	Hovey MR & MRS William C
Ketchum	83340	Knott MRS Carolan
Ketchum	83340	McCain MISS Claudia V
Ketchum	83340	Noyes MR Robert M
Ketchum	83340	Ottley MISS Heidi H
Ketchum	83340	Swift MR & MRS Thomas B
Ketchum	83340	Weekes MR & MRS John M JR
Meridian	83642	Hayes DR & MRS David P
Moscow	83843	Fiske MRS John C
Moscow	83843	Rourke DR & MRS Arthur W
Post Falls	83854	Billingslea DR & MRS Christopher M
Sun Valley	83353	Colgate MR & MRS John K III
Sun Valley	83353	Cullen MR & MRS Craig W JR
Sun Valley	83353	Knight MR & MRS James Atwood
Sun Valley	83353	Ottley MR Philip G JR
Sun Valley	83353	Whiton MR Herman F JR
Sun Valley	83353	Whittelsey MRS Frank C III
Victor	83455	Brune MR & MRS Timothy H C
Victor	83455	Stilson MISS Hilary P W

ILLINOIS

Arlington Heights	60005	McKinney MR & MRS Christopher R
Barrington	60010	Bateman MR Peter L
Barrington	60010	Bischof MR & MRS Harrington
Barrington	60010	Graham MR & MRS Bruce D
Barrington	60010	Hamman MR & MRS James T
Barrington	60010	Hill MR & MRS Melville C III
Barrington	60010	Moore MR & MRS John C 3D
Barrington	60010	Rutter MR & MRS David M
Barrington Hills	60010	Ekstrom MR & MRS Loren E
Barrington Hills	60010	Golitz MR & MRS John T
Barrington Hills	60010	Stoettner MR & MRS Robert E JR
Barrington Hills	60010	Wirtz MR & MRS John W
Bloomington	61705	Ives MRS Timothy R
Burr Ridge	60527	Melby MRS Charles B
Burr Ridge	60527	Pfisterer MR & MRS Scott McKenna
Burr Ridge	60527	Thompson MR & MRS Wirt L III
Chicago	60018	Stocker MR & MRS Keith K JR

Chicago............................ 60601.......... Alberts MRS Lee Winfield
Chicago............................ 60601.......... Farrell MR & MRS Matthew R
Chicago............................ 60601.......... Jeffers MR & MRS Richard B
Chicago............................ 60601.......... Rauner MR & MRS Bruce V
Chicago............................ 60602.......... Sargent MRS Robert
Chicago............................ 60603.......... Bowers MRS Lloyd W
Chicago............................ 60603.......... Galt MR William C
Chicago............................ 60603.......... Kelly MR & MRS Arthur L
Chicago............................ 60605.......... Lamonia MR Anthony J & Berardocco MS Laura F
Chicago............................ 60607.......... Kruesi MR Jonathan E & Beattie MR Andrew
Chicago............................ 60610.......... Adams MR & MRS William IV
Chicago............................ 60610.......... Angevin MR Robert P B
Chicago............................ 60610.......... Archer MS Cyd L
Chicago............................ 60610.......... Blair MR & MRS Edward McC JR
Chicago............................ 60610.......... Borland MR & MRS John J JR
Chicago............................ 60610.......... Bross MR & MRS Jonathan M
Chicago............................ 60610.......... Bulley MR & MRS Allan E III
Chicago............................ 60610.......... Chaudruc MS Jeannene Nixon
Chicago............................ 60610.......... Cleveland MR & MRS Dwight M
Chicago............................ 60610.......... Collins MR Arthur D JR & Shaw MS Sophia
Chicago............................ 60610.......... Cooney MR Thomas J
Chicago............................ 60610.......... Cox MR William D JR
Chicago............................ 60610.......... Cremin MS Susan E
Chicago............................ 60610.......... Curtis MISS Diane
Chicago............................ 60610.......... Defty MR & MRS Matthew R F B
Chicago............................ 60610.......... Donnelley MRS James R
Chicago............................ 60610.......... Earle MR & MRS David P 3D
Chicago............................ 60610.......... Fetridge MR & MRS Clark W
Chicago............................ 60610.......... Florian MR Paul G A
Chicago............................ 60610.......... Front MR & MRS Marshall B
Chicago............................ 60610.......... Galt MISS Inez A
Chicago............................ 60610.......... Goodspeed MRS Norwick B H
Chicago............................ 60610.......... Gromacki MR Joseph P
Chicago............................ 60610.......... Gross MISS Merle A
Chicago............................ 60610.......... Hamilton MR & MRS David R
Chicago............................ 60610.......... Harvey MR & MRS Julian W
Chicago............................ 60610.......... Heestand MR & MRS Olin J JR
Chicago............................ 60610.......... Higinbotham MR & MRS Harlow N
Chicago............................ 60610.......... Hummer MR & MRS Philip W
Chicago............................ 60610.......... Jacobs MR & MRS Alexander B
Chicago............................ 60610.......... Johnson MR Steven E
Chicago............................ 60610.......... Krehbiel MR & MRS Jay F
Chicago............................ 60610.......... Landreth MR & MRS John Colt
Chicago............................ 60610.......... Lang MR & MRS Gordon JR
Chicago............................ 60610.......... Lennox MR & MRS Scott
Chicago............................ 60610.......... Lillie MR & MRS Richard H JR
Chicago............................ 60610.......... Mark MR Gordon Griffith
Chicago............................ 60610.......... Mark MR Peter C
Chicago............................ 60610.......... McGuigan MR Philip Palmer
Chicago............................ 60610.......... O'Connor MRS William F
Chicago............................ 60610.......... Olson MRS Charles W III
Chicago............................ 60610.......... Potter MS Barbara F
Chicago............................ 60610.......... Reilly MR & MRS Paul C
Chicago............................ 60610.......... Rogers MR Peter W & Chronister MS Wendy
Chicago............................ 60610.......... Scazzero MISS Sophia B
Chicago............................ 60610.......... Schell MR & MRS Frank C III
Chicago............................ 60610.......... Schink MR & MRS James H
Chicago............................ 60610.......... Senior MR & MRS Richard J L
Chicago............................ 60610.......... Sheffield MR & MRS Thomas C JR
Chicago............................ 60610.......... Snorf MS Margaret
Chicago............................ 60610.......... Spain MR & MRS Richard C
Chicago............................ 60610.......... Swift MR & MRS Edward F 3D
Chicago............................ 60610.......... Swift MR & MRS Nathan B
Chicago............................ 60610.......... Tausché MRS Thomas J
Chicago............................ 60610.......... Traylor MR & MRS Glen R
Chicago............................ 60610.......... Van Nice MR & MRS P Errett JR
Chicago............................ 60610.......... Van Nice MR & MRS Peter E
Chicago............................ 60610.......... Waller MRS Thatcher
Chicago............................ 60610.......... Wellford MR & MRS R Carter 5TH
Chicago............................ 60610.......... White MR Brian D & Kinney MR James M
Chicago............................ 60610.......... White MRS R Quincy JR
Chicago............................ 60610.......... Wood MR & MRS Robert E 2D
Chicago............................ 60611.......... Ahearne MRS John J
Chicago............................ 60611.......... Almeida MR & MRS Richard J
Chicago............................ 60611.......... Alsdorf MRS James W
Chicago............................ 60611.......... Bacon MRS Robert H JR
Chicago............................ 60611.......... Bartholomay MR William C
Chicago............................ 60611.......... Bingham MISS Penelope I
Chicago............................ 60611.......... Breyer MS Laura Louise
Chicago............................ 60611.......... Brodie MR & MRS R Kirkwood 3D
Chicago............................ 60611.......... Carr MR & MRS Walter S
Chicago............................ 60611.......... Crane MISS Sarah Q
Chicago............................ 60611.......... Drymalski MR Raymond
Chicago............................ 60611.......... Dunn MR & MRS E Bruce
Chicago............................ 60611.......... Gardner MISS Elizabeth F
Chicago............................ 60611.......... Gardner MR & MRS John R
Chicago............................ 60611.......... Garvey MR & MRS Robert V
Chicago............................ 60611.......... Gowenlock MRS Fisher
Chicago............................ 60611.......... Harron MR & MRS Michael F
Chicago............................ 60611.......... Hendrick MR George K III
& Hendrick MRS Kipper Lance
Chicago............................ 60611.......... Hermann MR Donald H J & Janott MR Jonathan
Chicago............................ 60611.......... Kealy MS Anna L Forstmann
Chicago............................ 60611.......... Kern MRS John C
Chicago............................ 60611.......... Mack MS Linda C
Chicago............................ 60611.......... Malkin MR & MRS Cary J
Chicago............................ 60611.......... McIlvaine MR & MRS William B
Chicago............................ 60611.......... McLucas MR & MRS Don H JR
Chicago............................ 60611.......... Moore MR & MRS William H 4TH
Chicago............................ 60611.......... Newman MRS Leslie H
Chicago............................ 60611.......... Palmer MR Potter
Chicago............................ 60611.......... Patterson MR & MRS Thomas G
Chicago............................ 60611.......... Pierpont MR & MRS James W
Chicago............................ 60611.......... Piette MS Lyssa
Chicago............................ 60611.......... Rau MR & MRS John
Chicago............................ 60611.......... Roberts MR & MRS John A
Chicago............................ 60611.......... Shaw MR & MRS Patrick
Chicago............................ 60611.......... Stoetzel MR & MRS John L
Chicago............................ 60611.......... Stout MR & MRS (DR) William S
Chicago............................ 60611.......... Theiss MR & MRS Steven M
Chicago............................ 60611.......... Tunney MR & MRS Jay R
Chicago............................ 60611.......... Vincent MR & MRS George A III
Chicago............................ 60613.......... Arnold MR & MRS Joseph Coleman JR
Chicago............................ 60613.......... Cortes MR & MRS Steven C
Chicago............................ 60613.......... Euston MR & MRS Geoffrey M
Chicago............................ 60613.......... Fox MR William M
Chicago............................ 60613.......... Hoos MR & MRS Kenneth C
Chicago............................ 60613.......... Kelly MISS Elizabeth J
Chicago............................ 60613.......... Lipford MR & MRS Rocque E JR
Chicago............................ 60613.......... Madden MS Carlyle K
Chicago............................ 60613.......... Meers MR & MRS Henry W III
Chicago............................ 60613.......... Rugo MR Steven A & de Frise MS Laura S
Chicago............................ 60613.......... Ruskin MR Ryan S & Andrews MR Michael C
Chicago............................ 60613.......... Thomure MR A Ryan & Morton MR Alex J
Chicago............................ 60614.......... Allen MR & MRS Ronald J
Chicago............................ 60614.......... Babcock MR & MRS Brian W SR
Chicago............................ 60614.......... Bodine MR & MRS Paul A
Chicago............................ 60614.......... Bross MR & MRS John A
Chicago............................ 60614.......... Burgdorfer MR Rex J & Stanley MS Melinda C
Chicago............................ 60614.......... Carter MR & MRS Allen G JR
Chicago............................ 60614.......... Cochran MR & MRS Andrew C
Chicago............................ 60614.......... Cook DR & MRS John Q

Chicago, IL—Evanston, IL

Chicago	60614	Donnelley MR & MRS Thomas E II
Chicago	60614	Douglas MR & MRS Justin S
Chicago	60614	Fairbank MR & MRS Joshua P
Chicago	60614	Fairbank MR Kellogg 3D
Chicago	60614	Farb MR Benson S & Wilkinson MS Anne M
Chicago	60614	Gaudieri MR Alexandre B E
Chicago	60614	Gauntt MR Jonathan K
Chicago	60614	Glaze MR Robert H
Chicago	60614	Haffner MR & MRS Edward C
Chicago	60614	Haffner MR William C
Chicago	60614	Hutchinson MR & MRS Leland E
Chicago	60614	Lagrange MS Jessica
Chicago	60614	Lewis MR & MRS Jonathan B SR
Chicago	60614	Lovett MR & MRS Patrick H
Chicago	60614	Mahoney MISS Abigail L
Chicago	60614	Mesrobian MR & MRS Peter M
Chicago	60614	Miller MR & MRS Samuel S
Chicago	60614	Mumford MRS Manly W
Chicago	60614	Murphy MISS Margaret J
Chicago	60614	Notz MR & MRS John K JR
Chicago	60614	Owen MR & MRS Rodger A
Chicago	60614	Richter MR & MRS Tobin M
Chicago	60614	Rutledge MR & MRS John W
Chicago	60614	Ryan MR & MRS John B
Chicago	60614	Schwalm MR & MRS Matson F
Chicago	60614	Senior MS Amanda T
Chicago	60614	Shields MR & MRS Stratford
Chicago	60614	Souder MR & MRS Edward H
Chicago	60614	Sudler MR & MRS Louis C JR
Chicago	60614	Thomas MR & MRS Robert W
Chicago	60614	Thomure MR & MRS Randall O
Chicago	60614	Unetich MR & MRS Michael E
Chicago	60614	Ungaretti MR & MRS Richard A
Chicago	60614	Wood-Prince MR & MRS Patrick B
Chicago	60615	Karafiol MR Paul J & Clark MS Allison B
Chicago	60615	Stonor Saunders MR & MRS Alexander W J
Chicago	60615	Watson MR & MRS Ian H
Chicago	60616	Bransfield MR & MRS Michael W
Chicago	60616	Tatosian MR Oscar S
Chicago	60618	Applegate MR & MRS Ralph W JR
Chicago	60618	Arnold MR & MRS Michael B
Chicago	60618	Cunneen MR William E JR
Chicago	60618	Jacobson MRS Lydia
Chicago	60618	Quinn MR & MRS Christopher E V
Chicago	60618	Wolff MR & MRS Scott E
Chicago	60622	Balanoff MR & MRS Paul J
Chicago	60622	Boles MR Edgar H III & Terrien MR Michael S
Chicago	60622	Booz MISS Michelle Storrs
Chicago	60622	Picard MISS Caroline J
Chicago	60622	Ruzicka MISS Christina F
Chicago	60625	Migely MR & MRS Peter B
Chicago	60625	Ranney MR & MRS G Benjamin
Chicago	60625	Sudler MR & MRS S Zachariah
Chicago	60626	McCammond MR & MRS James A
Chicago	60631	Gordon MR & MRS Matthew R
Chicago	60637	Cohen MRS Ted
Chicago	60637	Schmidt MR & MRS William R JR
Chicago	60637	Schwebel MR Todd D H & Beggs MR William IV
Chicago	60637	Straus DR Christopher M
Chicago	60637	Straus MRS Francis H 2D
Chicago	60640	Bayston MR & MRS Daniel D
Chicago	60640	Browne MR Howell E
Chicago	60640	Currie MS Carol W
Chicago	60640	Knapp MR & MRS Gregory W
Chicago	60640	Moore MRS Henrietta Ayres
Chicago	60640	Pollock MISS Katherine G
Chicago	60640	Sacco MR & MRS Steven J
Chicago	60641	Coleman MR & MRS William T
Chicago	60641	McNally DR & MRS Thomas A
Chicago	60642	Kenney MS Amber
Chicago	60642	Trevor MR Bronson III
Chicago	60646	Smith DR Frederick F A
Chicago	60647	Matteson MR & MRS Oren P
Chicago	60647	Shober MR & MRS Pemberton H JR
Chicago	60654	Field MRS Mary Jo
Chicago	60654	Shelleman MR Ross & Rooney MS Tricia A
Chicago	60654	Yeoman MR & MRS John W
Chicago	60657	Bailey MR & MRS Curt R
Chicago	60657	Boyce MR & MRS Sandford C
Chicago	60657	Cairo MR & MRS Richard J
Chicago	60657	Conrad MR & MRS Robert L
Chicago	60657	Davis MR & MRS Anthony B
Chicago	60657	Friedewald DR & MRS (DR) John J
Chicago	60657	Gates MR & MRS John S JR
Chicago	60657	Hall MR & MRS Chandler W
Chicago	60657	Lazarre MR & MRS Paul E
Chicago	60657	Lester MR Edmund H
Chicago	60657	Martin MISS Faith Hamilton
Chicago	60657	Mesires MR & MRS George R
Chicago	60657	Mower MR & MRS Grove N
Chicago	60657	Needham MR & MRS Joseph J
Chicago	60657	Newburn MR & MRS Jade E
Chicago	60657	Park MR Thomas J
Chicago	60657	Pearce MR & MRS Gregory B
Chicago	60657	Roberts MISS Anne C
Chicago	60657	Senior-Saywell MR & MRS Philip N
Chicago	60657	Stultz MR Elliot A
Chicago	60657	Ziv MS Julia
Chicago	60659	Cummings MR Mark F
Chicago	60660	Field MS Mary B
Chicago	60661	Cochrane MR & MRS Alexander L III
Chicago	60661	Wilbur MR Peter D
Chicago	60680	Goes MR & MRS Walter J
Clarendon Hills	60514	Evans MR & MRS C Anthony
Darien	60561	Livingood MR Charles A
Deerfield	60015	Heiser MR & MRS Gregory A
Deerfield	60015	Leckie MR Gregor W
Deerfield	60015	Meadows MR & MRS Bryan G
Des Plaines	60016	Hartman MR & MRS W George
Downers Grove	60515	McCormick MR Brooks JR
Downers Grove	60516	Brackett MR & MRS S Bismarck
Downers Grove	60516	Warden MR & MRS Eric
Dunlap	61525	Atterbury MR R Rennie III
Elburn	60119	Maranville MR & MRS Paul C
Elkhart	62634	McCutcheon MR & MRS Benjamin K
Elmhurst	60126	McKiernan MR & MRS Brian E
Evanston	60201	Atkinson MISS Susan S
Evanston	60201	Buchanan DR J Robert
Evanston	60201	Buchanan MR & MRS Ross T
Evanston	60201	Dorr MR & MRS James P
Evanston	60201	Gaud MR & MRS Henry T JR
Evanston	60201	Horne MR & MRS Peter D
Evanston	60201	King MRS H Barnard 3D
Evanston	60201	Livermore MISS Edith P
Evanston	60201	McClure MR & MRS Archibald
Evanston	60201	McInnis MRS John W
Evanston	60201	Robinson MR & MRS John B
Evanston	60201	Shiras MR & MRS Winfield 3D
Evanston	60201	Van Deusen MISS Kathleen E
Evanston	60201	Westerfield MRS Robert H
Evanston	60201	Whipple DR & MRS Jacob D
Evanston	60202	Lele DR & MRS Milind M

Evanston	60202	Page MR Christopher K
Evanston	60202	Roosevelt MISS (DR) Anna C
Evanston	60202	Stamell MR & MRS Neal A
Flossmoor	60422	Pumphrey MRS Edward A 3D
Frankfort	60423	Dana MRS Jacob
Frankfort	60423	Meers MR & MRS Henry W JR
Geneva	60134	Culley MRS Natalie C
Geneva	60134	McDonnell MR Lawrence B
Glen Ellyn	60137	Ambler MR & MRS Christian D
Glen Ellyn	60137	Conklin MRS Charles C
Glen Ellyn	60137	Detmer MR Martin J JR
Glen Ellyn	60137	Detmer MRS Martin J
Glen Ellyn	60137	Koch MR & MRS Robert S
Glen Ellyn	60137	Miekina MR & MRS Daniel B
Glen Ellyn	60137	Rom MR Paul R
Glencoe	60022	Cabanne MR & MRS Xavier
Glencoe	60022	Kapsimalis MR & MRS Dion T
Glencoe	60022	McOmber MR & MRS Frederick N III
Glencoe	60022	Schellenbach MR & MRS Peter W
Glencoe	60022	Scott MR & MRS Sean T
Glenview	60025	Littlefield MRS Arthur S JR
Glenview	60025	Mackie MR & MRS Charles L
Glenview	60025	Martin MR & MRS James F
Glenview	60025	Nemerovski MR & MRS Scott C
Glenview	60025	Sweet MISS Sandra H
Glenview	60026	Berek MR & MRS David A
Glenview	60026	Nichols MRS J Jay
Glenview	60026	Reighard MRS Clyde W
Golf	60029	Rieger MR & MRS Brian L
Highland Park	60035	Mackey MR & MRS Scott L
Hinsdale	60521	Auerbach MRS Darlene
Hinsdale	60521	Howson MR & MRS E Alexander JR
Hinsdale	60521	Moriarty MR & MRS Philip S J
Hinsdale	60521	Peluso MR & MRS David M
Ingleside	60041	Schoenfeld MR & MRS Benjamin F
Inverness	60010	DiMaio MR & MRS Richard H
Island Lake	60042	Schuyler MR & MRS David B
Kenilworth	60043	Barlow MR & MRS Aaron A
Kenilworth	60043	Barriger MR John W 4TH
Kenilworth	60043	Barriger MR John W 5TH
Kenilworth	60043	Buehler MR & MRS John H
Kenilworth	60043	Bulley MR & MRS Allan E JR
Kenilworth	60043	Dugan MR & MRS Timothy A
Kenilworth	60043	Klingenstein MR & MRS Christopher S
Kenilworth	60043	Patterson MR & MRS Michael C
Kenilworth	60043	Weiss MR & MRS John R
Lake Bluff	60044	Borland MR & MRS Edward S
Lake Bluff	60044	Coppins MR & MRS Cray J III
Lake Bluff	60044	Duplissis MR & MRS Jason M
Lake Bluff	60044	Gary MS Laura B
Lake Bluff	60044	Gummere MR & MRS Francis B JR
Lake Bluff	60044	Hartman MRS Hilary C
Lake Bluff	60044	Harvey MRS Bennet B JR
Lake Bluff	60044	Hill MRS Susannah
Lake Bluff	60044	Hooker MR & MRS Brady S
Lake Bluff	60044	Isham MR & MRS Robert T JR
Lake Bluff	60044	McCormick MR & MRS Christopher L
Lake Bluff	60044	Michael MR & MRS Leslie W
Lake Bluff	60044	Pawlick MRS Albert
Lake Bluff	60044	ReQua MRS Charles H
Lake Bluff	60044	Romanoff MRS S Cook
Lake Bluff	60044	Schiewe MR & MRS Ryan R
Lake Bluff	60044	Sheffield MR & MRS Thomas C 3D
Lake Bluff	60044	Spencer MR & MRS George H III
Lake Bluff	60044	Twichell MR & MRS Jonathan E
Lake Bluff	60044	Welles MR & MRS Donald P
Lake Bluff	60044	Wilbur DR & MRS Andrew C
Lake Bluff	60044	Winter MR & MRS Munroe A
Lake Bluff	60044	Wood MR & MRS Thomas W
Lake Forest	60045	Alley MR & MRS Brayton B
Lake Forest	60045	Bartram MR & MRS Stephen M
Lake Forest	60045	Basedow MR & MRS C Michael JR
Lake Forest	60045	Beidler MR & MRS Francis III
Lake Forest	60045	Bell MR & MRS Stephen G
Lake Forest	60045	Bennett MR & MRS Edward H 3D
Lake Forest	60045	Bensinger MR & MRS (DR) Peter B
Lake Forest	60045	Bent MRS Gordon
Lake Forest	60045	Bermingham MR David C & Searle MS Marion S
Lake Forest	60045	Bickford MR & MRS William T
Lake Forest	60045	Blair MRS Bowen
Lake Forest	60045	Blodgett MR & MRS Samuel T
Lake Forest	60045	Boggess MRS William P II
Lake Forest	60045	Borland MR & MRS Bruce D
Lake Forest	60045	Bowen MR & MRS Charles C
Lake Forest	60045	Brown MR Georges P
Lake Forest	60045	Brown MRS Cameron
Lake Forest	60045	Buchanan MR Kenneth H
Lake Forest	60045	Carroll MR & MRS Sean P
Lake Forest	60045	Carroll MRS Barry J
Lake Forest	60045	Chandler MR & MRS Henry T
Lake Forest	60045	Clarke MR & MRS Charles F JR
Lake Forest	60045	Clay MRS William D
Lake Forest	60045	Coffin MR & MRS Robert Parker
Lake Forest	60045	Coleman MR & MRS Timothy C
Lake Forest	60045	Crane MR & MRS William A
Lake Forest	60045	Crawford MR & MRS (REV) James E III
Lake Forest	60045	Davis MRS Dorothy Monek
Lake Forest	60045	DePree MR & MRS Julian F JR
Lake Forest	60045	DePree MR & MRS Spencer P
Lake Forest	60045	Dick MR & MRS John H SR
Lake Forest	60045	Dixon MR & MRS John W
Lake Forest	60045	Dixon MR Stewart S JR
Lake Forest	60045	Drake MS Charenton Z
Lake Forest	60045	Dugan MRS Madeleine B
Lake Forest	60045	Eldridge MRS Huntington
Lake Forest	60045	Elting MRS Josephine F
Lake Forest	60045	Erulkar DR & MRS Jonathan S
Lake Forest	60045	Farwell MRS Cameron W
Lake Forest	60045	Fritz MRS Annelia
Lake Forest	60045	Glasser MR & MRS James J
Lake Forest	60045	Goltra MR & MRS O Renard
Lake Forest	60045	Hart MRS Augustin S
Lake Forest	60045	Hayes MR & MRS C Kirtland JR
Lake Forest	60045	Huber MR & MRS Joseph F
Lake Forest	60045	Hughes MRS John W
Lake Forest	60045	Hull MR & MRS Roger Bradford
Lake Forest	60045	Jones MR & MRS Gregory K
Lake Forest	60045	Kane MR & MRS Michael J
Lake Forest	60045	Keil MR & MRS Bryant L
Lake Forest	60045	Keller MR & MRS David McD
Lake Forest	60045	Kinney MR & MRS Douglas M
Lake Forest	60045	Kinney MR & MRS Douglas M JR
Lake Forest	60045	Knight MR Robert P
Lake Forest	60045	Kujawa MRS Victoria Shore
Lake Forest	60045	Lansing MR & MRS Stuart D
Lake Forest	60045	Lekberg MR & MRS Erik J
Lake Forest	60045	Lillard MR & MRS John S
Lake Forest	60045	Marra MR & MRS Richard JR
Lake Forest	60045	Marshall MR & MRS Thomas C
Lake Forest	60045	Masterson MR & MRS Martin B
Lake Forest	60045	McGovern MRS John E III
Lake Forest	60045	McGovern MRS John E JR

To nominate a candidate for the Social Register Association, please email: SRCommittee@thesocialregister.org

Lake Forest, IL—Winnetka, IL

Lake Forest .... 60045 .... McLallen CAPT (RET) & MRS Walter F
Lake Forest .... 60045 .... McLaughlin MR Ian M W
Lake Forest .... 60045 .... McLucas MRS Don H
Lake Forest .... 60045 .... McTier MR & MRS Samuel E
Lake Forest .... 60045 .... Merlin MR & MRS Philip S
Lake Forest .... 60045 .... Morgan MRS Laurence W
Lake Forest .... 60045 .... Mower MR & MRS Chapin N
Lake Forest .... 60045 .... Murphy MR & MRS Stephen Chouteau
Lake Forest .... 60045 .... Notz MR & MRS Edward U
Lake Forest .... 60045 .... Notz MR & MRS Edward U JR
Lake Forest .... 60045 .... Preschlack MR & MRS James
Lake Forest .... 60045 .... Prochnow MR & MRS Herbert V JR
Lake Forest .... 60045 .... Pruett MR & MRS Shelby E L
Lake Forest .... 60045 .... Rich MRS B McNabb
Lake Forest .... 60045 .... Seaman MR & MRS Douglas JR
Lake Forest .... 60045 .... Seaman MRS Irving JR
Lake Forest .... 60045 .... Searle MRS William L
Lake Forest .... 60045 .... Smith MR & MRS Edward Byron JR
Lake Forest .... 60045 .... Smyth MISS Elizabeth Emery
Lake Forest .... 60045 .... Spiel MR & MRS Robert E JR
Lake Forest .... 60045 .... Stirling MR & MRS James P
Lake Forest .... 60045 .... Stuart MR & MRS Alexander D
Lake Forest .... 60045 .... Sweet MR & MRS David A F
Lake Forest .... 60045 .... Sweet MR & MRS P W Kirkland III
Lake Forest .... 60045 .... Sweet MR Philip W K JR
Lake Forest .... 60045 .... Swift MR & MRS Stewart G
Lake Forest .... 60045 .... Taylor MISS Marett A
Lake Forest .... 60045 .... Taylor MRS Robert C
Lake Forest .... 60045 .... TenBroek MR & MRS James P
Lake Forest .... 60045 .... Thompson MR & MRS Timothy Sands
Lake Forest .... 60045 .... Timbers MR & MRS Stephen B
Lake Forest .... 60045 .... Twede MRS Elizabeth K
Lake Forest .... 60045 .... Van Dusen MR & MRS Edwin R
Lake Forest .... 60045 .... Van Ness MR & MRS Gardiner B 3D
Lake Forest .... 60045 .... Waud MR & MRS Reeve B
Lake Forest .... 60045 .... Wheeler MRS Henry P
Lake Forest .... 60045 .... Whelan MR & MRS (DR) Robert F
Lake Forest .... 60045 .... White MR & MRS John P
Lake Forest .... 60045 .... Wilbur DR & MRS Richard S
Lake Forest .... 60045 .... Wilson MR & MRS L Raycroft
Lake Forest .... 60045 .... Winterbotham MRS John R JR
Lake Forest .... 60611 .... Buhler MR & MRS Robert A
Lake Zurich .... 60047 .... Sands MR & MRS R Blake
Lemont .... 60439 .... Rutledge MR & MRS Edward K
Libertyville .... 60048 .... Foltz MR & MRS Robert D
Lincolnshire .... 60069 .... Seely-Brown MR & MRS Horace 3D
Long Grove .... 60047 .... Bowers MRS Frances C
Long Grove .... 60047 .... Swift MR & MRS Shepard C
Loves Park .... 61111 .... Dent MR & MRS Ted H
Mattoon .... 61938 .... Lumpkin MR & MRS Richard A
Mettawa .... 60048 .... Brennan MR & MRS Charles M 3D
Mettawa .... 60048 .... Phillips MR & MRS Frederick F
Morton Grove .... 60053 .... Sutherland MR Malcolm R 3D
Mount Pulaski .... 62548 .... Buckles MR & MRS Stanley D
Mt Prospect .... 60056 .... Roome MRS Howard R
Mt Vernon .... 62864 .... Nixon MRS Emily Ward
Naperville .... 60540 .... Jensen MR & MRS (DR) Robert O JR
Naperville .... 60564 .... Clough MR Peter A
Naperville .... 60564 .... Henderlite MR & MRS Hunter F
Naperville .... 60565 .... Hall MR & MRS Peter D
Naperville .... 60565 .... Lansing MR & MRS John T
North Field .... 60093 .... Yntema MS Elizabeth B
Northbrook .... 60062 .... Anderson MR Albert M & Fields MRS Mary H
Northbrook .... 60062 .... Badger MRS Edwin Hunt JR
Northbrook .... 60062 .... Davies MRS Mary M
Northbrook .... 60062 .... Fabbioli MR & MRS Joseph M
Northbrook .... 60062 .... Meyers MR Philip G
Northbrook .... 60062 .... Otis MR & MRS Elliott N
Northbrook .... 60062 .... Whipple MRS Truxal
Northbrook .... 60062 .... Witt MR & MRS William J
Northfield .... 60093 .... Jaicks MR Wilson A JR
Oak Brook .... 60523 .... Beatty DR & MRS Robert A
Oak Park .... 60302 .... Patterson MRS Oliver M
Palatine .... 60067 .... Hinken MISS (DR) Joan M
Park Ridge .... 60068 .... Mills MRS Ralph J JR
Peoria .... 61606 .... Matuszak MR & MRS Mark E
Peoria .... 61614 .... Gibbs MISS Ramona H
Peoria .... 61615 .... Leiter MR & MRS Thomas E
Peoria Heights .... 61616 .... Khazzam MR & MRS Alexis N
Peoria Heights .... 61616 .... Temple MR & MRS Robert J II
Plainfield .... 60586 .... Mathews MRS Walter M
River Forest .... 60305 .... Hughes MR & MRS Robert David
Rockford .... 61107 .... Lambert MR & MRS J Laird
Rolling Meadows .... 60008 .... Priestley MR & MRS William Turk 3D
Spring Grove .... 60081 .... Hoyt MRS N Landon 3D
St Charles .... 60174 .... Hare MR & MRS Eugene T
Sycamore .... 60178 .... Castle MR & MRS John W
Urbana .... 61801 .... Johnson MR Timothy C
Urbana .... 61801 .... Taylor MS Susan
Wayne .... 60184 .... Cleavenger MR & MRS Timothy Q
West Chicago .... 60185 .... Feurich MISS Kathryn J
Western Springs .... 60558 .... Doyle MR & MRS Mark J
Western Springs .... 60558 .... Garvy MRS A Harrington
Wheaton .... 60187 .... Beard MR Gregory S & Higgins-Beard MRS Elizabeth F
Wheaton .... 60187 .... Hermann MR & MRS Scott R
Wheaton .... 60187 .... Margaglione MR & MRS Louis A
Wheaton .... 60187 .... Moore MR & MRS John A
Wheaton .... 60187 .... Perrin REV DR & MRS Nicholas
Wheaton .... 60189 .... Shafer MR J Bradley
Wilmette .... 60091 .... Adams CDR & MRS Christopher W D
Wilmette .... 60091 .... Baccich MR & MRS John A
Wilmette .... 60091 .... Berdell MRS Charles P 3D
Wilmette .... 60091 .... Borders MR William A JR
Wilmette .... 60091 .... Cornell MRS Pamela K
Wilmette .... 60091 .... Cue MR & MRS Bradley F
Wilmette .... 60091 .... Drake MRS William W
Wilmette .... 60091 .... Flanagin MR & MRS John M
Wilmette .... 60091 .... Grant MR & MRS William R
Wilmette .... 60091 .... Harris MR & MRS John A
Wilmette .... 60091 .... Hinchman MRS Denise H
Wilmette .... 60091 .... Parke MR & MRS William H
Wilmette .... 60091 .... Pigott MR & MRS Richard
Wilmette .... 60091 .... Sample MR & MRS Charles W
Wilmette .... 60091 .... Sawyer MR & MRS Charles R
Wilmette .... 60091 .... Smith MR & MRS Peter Byron
Wilmette .... 60091 .... Waller MR & MRS Thatcher JR
Wilmette .... 60091 .... Wright MRS Kenneth T
Wilmette .... 60201 .... Weiss MR & MRS John R
Winnetka .... 60093 .... Albertson MR & MRS Robert C
Winnetka .... 60093 .... Allport MR & MRS Peter B
Winnetka .... 60093 .... Baker MR & MRS R Cass
Winnetka .... 60093 .... Bodeen MR & MRS George H
Winnetka .... 60093 .... Boschen MR & MRS Dallas S
Winnetka .... 60093 .... Bovaird MRS James A 3D
Winnetka .... 60093 .... Braham MR & MRS Robert B
Winnetka .... 60093 .... Busch MR & MRS Michael J
Winnetka .... 60093 .... Canmann MR & MRS Michael S
Winnetka .... 60093 .... De Young MR & MRS James W
Winnetka .... 60093 .... Doyle MR & MRS William C
Winnetka .... 60093 .... Fiore MR & MRS John H
Winnetka .... 60093 .... Flickinger MR & MRS (DR) Thomas R

Winnetka .... 60093 .... Grannis MR Jonathan G
Winnetka .... 60093 .... Hambleton MR & MRS Chalkley Jay
Winnetka .... 60093 .... Hill MRS Melville C JR
Winnetka .... 60093 .... Hoban MR & MRS Anthony T
Winnetka .... 60093 .... Horne MR & MRS Robert D
Winnetka .... 60093 .... Hull MRS Gordon F 3D
Winnetka .... 60093 .... Jannotta MR & MRS Edgar D
Winnetka .... 60093 .... Kedzior MR & MRS Brett E
Winnetka .... 60093 .... Keller MR & MRS John P
Winnetka .... 60093 .... Larkin MR & MRS Richard W
Winnetka .... 60093 .... Lind MR & MRS Jon R
Winnetka .... 60093 .... Love MRS Norris
Winnetka .... 60093 .... Mack MRS Walter M
Winnetka .... 60093 .... Madigan MR & MRS John W
Winnetka .... 60093 .... Mathias MR & MRS Richard L
Winnetka .... 60093 .... McCullagh MR & MRS Grant G
Winnetka .... 60093 .... McDermott MR & MRS John H
Winnetka .... 60093 .... Nielsen MR & MRS J Christopher
Winnetka .... 60093 .... Norton MR Charles G & Barthel MS Carole A
Winnetka .... 60093 .... Pacelli MR & MRS Peter J
Winnetka .... 60093 .... Perlitz MR & MRS William C
Winnetka .... 60093 .... Puth MR & MRS John W
Winnetka .... 60093 .... Pyott MR & MRS Albert E
Winnetka .... 60093 .... Rider MR & MRS Hugh G
Winnetka .... 60093 .... Ristic MR & MRS Blasko C
Winnetka .... 60093 .... Rolighed MR & MRS Ronald A
Winnetka .... 60093 .... Senior MR & MRS (DR) Alden L
Winnetka .... 60093 .... Smart MRS Jackson W JR
Winnetka .... 60093 .... Smith MR & MRS Donald A
Winnetka .... 60093 .... Smith MR & MRS Scott C
Winnetka .... 60093 .... Tomazos MR Anastasios
& Thompson MS Samantha J
Winnetka .... 60093 .... Waddell MR & MRS Frederick H
Winnetka .... 60093 .... Whitesides MR & MRS Lawson E JR
Winnetka .... 60093 .... Wilkinson MR & MRS Leland
Winnetka .... 60093 .... Wirtz MR & MRS W Rockwell
Winnetka .... 60093 .... Wirtz MRS William W
Winnetka .... 60093 .... Yavitt MR & MRS Keith E

INDIANA

Bloomington .... 47401 .... Keppel MR David
Carmel .... 46033 .... Clyne MR & MRS Andrew McC
Ft Wayne .... 46818 .... Lavin MR & MRS Peter C
Hartsville .... 47244 .... Rentschler MR & MRS Charles E M
Hebron .... 46341 .... Hamilton MR Phillips H & Schneider MS Beatrice S
Indianapolis .... 46201 .... Gann MR & MRS Rick
Indianapolis .... 46205 .... Kirk MR & MRS Charles A
Indianapolis .... 46208 .... Henderson MRS Emily Smith
Indianapolis .... 46240 .... Kirk MRS Clarence L JR
Indianapolis .... 46260 .... Cronin MR & MRS Casey M
Indianapolis .... 46260 .... Henderson MR E Carlisle A
Indianapolis .... 46268 .... Hecking MR Dirck J II
Schererville .... 46375 .... Soohey MR Richard J & Cameron MRS Elizabeth F
South Bend .... 46617 .... Bulot MR Charles C & Chappell MRS Tobey J
Valparaiso .... 46385 .... Moore MS Cynthia H
Zionsville .... 46077 .... Brant MRS John R JR

IOWA

Cedar Falls .... 50613 .... Kirk MR & MRS Carey H
Cedar Rapids .... 52402 .... Stevens MRS Borden B
Davenport .... 52801 .... Beer MR R Carey
Des Moines .... 50312 .... Fitzgerald MR & MRS Jeffrey L
Des Moines .... 50312 .... Fletcher MR & MRS Jonathan R
Des Moines .... 50312 .... Reynal MR & MRS Michael L
Fairfield .... 52556 .... Sims MR Richard K
Fairfield .... 52556 .... Tracy MR & MRS Daniel W
Iowa City .... 52246 .... Roberts DR & MRS Dale M
Macedonia .... 51549 .... Clark MRS Frederick W
West Des Moines .... 50266 .... Prosser MRS Camilla S

KANSAS

Auburn .... 66402 .... Collier MR Inglis U
Fairway .... 66205 .... Hodge DR & MRS Charles 5TH
Lawrence .... 66044 .... Clark DR & MRS Jonathan C D
Leawood .... 62209 .... Nixon MR & MRS F Ward
Leawood .... 66206 .... Gibson MR Christopher C
Mission Hills .... 66208 .... Sutherland MR & MRS Dwight D JR
Olathe .... 66062 .... Hitchcock MR & MRS William L
Prairie Village .... 66208 .... Becker MR & MRS Michael T
Shawnee .... 66226 .... Sawyer MRS Dana A
Wichita .... 67206 .... Reals MRS William J
Wichita .... 67218 .... Morrison MISS (DR) Barbara

KENTUCKY

Cold Spring .... 41076 .... Hoskin MR & MRS Richard J C
Covington .... 41011 .... Baxter MS Barbara L
Covington .... 41011 .... Padgett MR Ronald E
Covington .... 41011 .... Sampson MRS Susan J
Covington .... 41011 .... Smith MR Timothy A & Newell MS Valerie L
Crestwood .... 40014 .... Houston MR & MRS Selby C T V
Cynthiana .... 41031 .... Dumaine MR & MRS Dudley B
Danville .... 40422 .... Porter MR & MRS Barkley N
Fort Wright .... 41011 .... Jones MR & MRS James Gregory
Frankfort .... 40601 .... Gable MR Robert E
Franklin .... 42134 .... Gillock MR & MRS John T II
Ft Mitchell .... 41011 .... Melville MR & MRS John A
Ft Mitchell .... 41011 .... Melville MRS John W
Glenview .... 40025 .... Lurding MR & MRS D Scott
Harrods Creek .... 40027 .... Hickox MRS Louise F
Harrodsburg .... 40330 .... Thomas MR & MRS James C
Lexington .... 40502 .... Bograd MR & MRS Louis M
Lexington .... 40502 .... Bullard MR & MRS Edward D
Lexington .... 40502 .... Cushny MISS Lillian B
Lexington .... 40502 .... De Camp MR & MRS Richard S
Lexington .... 40502 .... Kaiser MR & MRS David P
Lexington .... 40502 .... McCready MRS Jane Houston
Lexington .... 40502 .... Parker MR & MRS Francis Hill
Lexington .... 40502 .... Stuart MRS Mildred D
Lexington .... 40502 .... Thompson MR & MRS O David
Lexington .... 40503 .... Arndt MR & MRS John F JR
Lexington .... 40503 .... Fischer MR James B
Lexington .... 40511 .... Jewett MRS Margaret N
Lexington .... 40515 .... Breckinridge MRS Scott D JR
Lexington .... 40515 .... Hamilton MRS William
Lexington .... 40516 .... Thornberry MR & MRS James K
Lexington .... 40574 .... Petter MR Stanley DuB JR
Louisville .... 40202 .... Barzun MR & MRS Matthew W
Louisville .... 40203 .... Schrader MR William C III
Louisville .... 40204 .... Cunningham MR & MRS William W II
Louisville .... 40206 .... Arensberg MRS Charles S
Louisville .... 40206 .... Carrell MR William Pfingst II
Louisville .... 40206 .... Nation MR John H
Louisville .... 40206 .... Thomas MRS Samuel W
Louisville .... 40207 .... Brown MRS Morgan Scott
Louisville .... 40207 .... Herrington MR & MRS Kenneth F III
Louisville .... 40207 .... McLeod DR & MRS (DR) John E
Louisville .... 40207 .... Quasha MR & MRS Grant S
Louisville .... 40207 .... Robbins MR & MRS Keith W

Louisville, KY—Arrowsic, ME

Louisville	40207	Rummler MR David C
Louisville	40207	Smith MR & MRS Eugene C
Louisville	40222	Brown MRS Owsley II
Louisville	40222	Few MR Benjamin F JR
Louisville	40222	Wilson MR & MRS Orme 3D
Paducah	42001	Baldridge REV & MRS Kempton D
Paris	40361	Clay MS Mary McClinton
Prospect	40059	Bonnie MRS Edward S
Prospect	40059	Welch MR & MRS James S JR
Shelbyville	40065	Bennett MISS Julester J

LOUISIANA

Abita Springs	70420	Dossett MR & MRS William K
Abita Springs	70420	Goodyear MRS David L
Alexandria	71301	Merryman LT COL & MRS Pitt McL
Avery Island	70513	Moseley MR & MRS Madison C
Baton Rouge	70802	McAlpin MR & MRS Charles N JR
Baton Rouge	70808	Casey MRS Ashley
Baton Rouge	70815	Leiper MR & MRS Edwards F 3D
Covington	70433	Barnes DR & MRS Robert H
Covington	70433	Burke MR & MRS M G Ashmead
Covington	70433	LeBourgeois MRS Mary W S
Covington	70433	Loomis MR & MRS N Barton
Covington	70433	Maginnis MR & MRS Malcolm G JR
Covington	70433	Miltenberger MR & MRS Henry J JR
Folsom	70437	Massey MR & MRS (DR) Jon G
Hammond	70401	Shrock MR Peter J
Lafayette	70503	Shaw MISS Amidie E
Lafayette	70503	Shaw MR Alan West IV
Lake Charles	70605	Bonsack MR Michael L
Mandeville	70471	Fenton MR & MRS Nicholas W
Metairie	70003	Walgamotte MR Shannon R & Moreau MS Lynda P A
Metairie	70005	Freeman MR & MRS Louis M JR
Metairie	70005	Shea MR & MRS Daniel J
Metairie	70005	Swartwood MR & MRS Slater W JR
Metairie	70005	White MR & MRS Michael B
Natchitoches	71457	Harling MR Robert M III
New Iberia	70563	Dupuy MR & MRS David Davis
New Oleans	70125	McKinnon MR & MRS Ryan T
New Orleans	70113	Haspel MR & MRS Peter
New Orleans	70114	Pleasants MRS W Shepard JR
New Orleans	70115	Baldwin MR & MRS James McCall JR
New Orleans	70115	Bush MR & MRS Edward C
New Orleans	70115	Dupuy MR & MRS Peter H
New Orleans	70115	Engelhardt MR & MRS Miller B JR
New Orleans	70115	Ferguson MISS Caroline P
New Orleans	70115	Ferguson MR & MRS Charles A JR
New Orleans	70115	Frater MR & MRS M Ellis JR
New Orleans	70115	Goodyear MISS Ella C
New Orleans	70115	Haygood MR & MRS Paul M
New Orleans	70115	Hobson MR & MRS J Kendall
New Orleans	70115	Hunter MR & MRS David M
New Orleans	70115	Huppman MISS Olivia T
New Orleans	70115	Jahncke MR & MRS Davis Lee JR
New Orleans	70115	Lamar MR & MRS Albert L
New Orleans	70115	McCall MR & MRS Jonathan C JR
New Orleans	70115	McCall MR Jonathan C
New Orleans	70115	Peeper DR E Quinn & Harold MR Michael D
New Orleans	70115	Posey MR & MRS Marshall Lyne JR
New Orleans	70115	Rooth MR & MRS Robert S
New Orleans	70115	Rowan MR & MRS John F JR
New Orleans	70115	Schieffelin DR & MRS John S
New Orleans	70115	Selman MR J Larkin 3D
New Orleans	70115	Soniat MRS Robert U
New Orleans	70115	Swartwood MR & MRS Slater W
New Orleans	70115	Villeré MR & MRS St Denis J
New Orleans	70115	Wagstaff MR & MRS David III
New Orleans	70115	Wall MR & MRS Michael A P
New Orleans	70115	Werlein MR & MRS J Parham
New Orleans	70116	Jones MR & MRS Russell B 3D
New Orleans	70117	Blow MR John M
New Orleans	70118	Andrews MR & MRS E Wyllys V
New Orleans	70118	Benjamin MR & MRS Edward W
New Orleans	70118	Benjamin MRS Edward B JR
New Orleans	70118	Burke MISS Mary Lee
New Orleans	70118	Capomazza di Campolattaro MCHSE & MCHSA Carlo
New Orleans	70118	Emery MS Lin
New Orleans	70118	Freeman MR & MRS Peter Lawrence
New Orleans	70118	Gomila MR & MRS M Feild JR
New Orleans	70118	Gorham MRS Ann
New Orleans	70118	Kean MS Mary-Margaret
New Orleans	70118	Kock MR & MRS E James JR
New Orleans	70118	Legier MR & MRS David A JR
New Orleans	70118	Lemann MR & MRS Thomas B
New Orleans	70118	Mallory MR Charles King 4TH
New Orleans	70118	Maxwell MR & MRS Max E
New Orleans	70118	Ochsner DR & MRS John L
New Orleans	70118	Phelps MR & MRS Ashton JR
New Orleans	70118	Pierson MR & MRS R Hunter JR
New Orleans	70118	Preaus MR & MRS Eugene R
New Orleans	70118	Sarpy MS Courtney-Anne
New Orleans	70118	See MR & MRS Alva B 3D
New Orleans	70118	Strachan MR & MRS Minor S P
New Orleans	70118	Walmsley MR & MRS Robert M JR
New Orleans	70118	Woollam MR & MRS Philip M
New Orleans	70118	Wynn MR & MRS Charles B JR
New Orleans	70119	Lieder MR & MRS William K
New Orleans	70124	Dean MR & MRS Bruce C
New Orleans	70125	Bailey MR & MRS David Gunn
New Orleans	70125	Blum MR & MRS Richard K
New Orleans	70125	O'Reilly MR & MRS Brian J JR
New Orleans	70130	Beard MR & MRS Alexander S
New Orleans	70130	Fitzpatrick MR V Vaughan O
New Orleans	70130	Fox MR & MRS Barry M B
New Orleans	70130	Freeman MR & MRS Louis McDaniel
New Orleans	70130	Friedrichs MRS J M Gore
New Orleans	70130	Haack MR & MRS Frederick L
New Orleans	70130	Kelly DR John J III
New Orleans	70130	Labouisse MRS John Peter III
New Orleans	70130	Le Breton MRS Edward Francis JR
New Orleans	70130	Maginnis MR & MRS Donald A 3D
New Orleans	70130	McCall MRS Harry JR
New Orleans	70130	Porter DR & MRS George H 3D
New Orleans	70130	Rathborne MRS J Cornelius III
New Orleans	70130	Redd MR & MRS Edmund E
New Orleans	70130	Westfeldt MR & MRS Thomas D II
New Orleans	70131	Willcox MR & MRS Wayne C
New Orleans	70176	Flower MR & MRS Walter C 3D
New Orleans	70420	Whann MR & MRS Richard A
New Roads	70760	Parlange MRS Walter C JR
Prairieville	70769	Labouisse MR & MRS Charles J
Ruston	71270	Hindman MR & MRS Brian W
Thibodaux	70301	Blair MR & MRS Alfred F JR

MAINE

Alna	04535	Kelly MR A Preston JR
Alna	04535	Sage DR & MRS Louis E
Arrowsic	04530	Neilson MR & MRS William L

Auburn	04210	Low MR & MRS William H
Bangor	04401	O'Connor MR Roderic S & Méndez-Brady MS Marisa L
Bar Harbor	04609	Andrews MRS Stockton A
Bar Harbor	04609	Blanchard MR James A 3D
Bar Harbor	04609	Garrett MR Edwin A IV
Bar Harbor	04609	Lewis MRS R Warner
Bar Harbor	04609	Milbury MR & MRS K David
Bar Mills	04004	Thorndike MRS A Frye
Bath	04530	Ambler REV & MRS Michael Nash JR
Bath	04530	Gregg MR & MRS Walter H
Bath	04530	Limpert MR John H JR
Beals	04611	Anderson MR & MRS Gerald A
Belfast	04915	Campbell MR & MRS Christopher S
Belfast	04915	Homans MRS Robert
Biddeford Pool	04006	Blake MRS Richard R
Blue Hill	04614	Austin MRS William Mason
Blue Hill	04614	Blair MR & MRS Farnham D
Blue Hill	04614	Clews MRS Henrietta T
Blue Hill	04614	Guinness LADY Jane
Blue Hill	04614	Guinness SIR & LADY Kenelm E L
Blue Hill	04614	Gurin MR & MRS Richard S
Blue Hill	04614	Heller MR Anthony K
Blue Hill	04614	Thomas MR & MRS Lowell S JR
Boothbay	04537	Bonner MISS Jennifer
Boothbay Harbor	04538	Gillespie MRS John L
Boothbay Harbor	04538	Hastings MRS Ellison
Bradley	04411	Blakeley MR Bogart
Bremen	04551	Cotton MR & MRS Jefferson C
Bremen	04551	Emmet DR & MRS William Le R 2D
Bremen	04551	Kinney MS Eleanor H
Bridgton	04009	Duigan MR & MRS Shane P
Brooklin	04616	Gregg MR & MRS Arthur W
Brooklin	04616	Parson MR & MRS Timothy P
Brooksville	04617	Cassatt MRS Anne G
Brunswick	04011	Cherna MR Andrew R JR
Brunswick	04011	Cowenhoven MR & MRS Nicholas R
Brunswick	04011	Cutter MR & MRS Louis A
Brunswick	04011	Fenwick MR & MRS John G
Brunswick	04011	Goodyear MR & MRS Frank H III
Brunswick	04011	McIlvaine MRS Leighton H JR
Brunswick	04011	Nichols MR & MRS H Gilman
Brunswick	04011	Scully MISS Elizabeth A
Calais	04619	Remer MR John H JR
Camden	04843	Bowditch MR & MRS James L
Camden	04843	Chanler MR Bayard S
Camden	04843	Contento MR & MRS Vincent J JR
Camden	04843	Denckla MR & MRS C Paul JR
Camden	04843	Goldman MRS Rachel Bok
Camden	04843	Gruener MR & MRS Edward L
Camden	04843	Jones MR & MRS Patrick S JR
Camden	04843	Losee MR & MRS David B
Camden	04843	Mudge MR L Taylor
Camden	04843	Parker MRS Henry S JR
Camden	04843	Wheelwright MRS Henry J
Camden	04843	Williams DR & MRS John G JR
Canaan	04924	Haberstock MR & MRS Alan E
Cape Elizabeth	04107	Brewer MR & MRS Robert C
Cape Elizabeth	04107	Gordon MR & MRS Philip J
Cape Elizabeth	04107	Lynch MR & MRS Christopher C
Cape Elizabeth	04107	Newhall MR & MRS Thomas B
Cape Elizabeth	04107	Sprague MR & MRS Phineas
Cape Elizabeth	04107	Stickney MRS Charles E JR
Cape Neddick	03902	Remington MR & MRS David F
Castine	04421	Miller MRS Edward O
Castine	04421	Pedersen MR & MRS (DR) Matthew H
Castine	04421	Rogers MR James H 3D
Castine	04421	Wiswall MR & MRS Frank L JR
Chebeague Island	04017	Jordan MR & MRS Philip H JR
Chebeague Island	04017	Traina MRS Albert S
Corea	04624	Berkey MR & MRS J Addison 3D
Cornville	04976	Burdet MR & MRS René A
Cumberland	04021	Allen MR & MRS Brett S
Cumberland	04021	Curran MR & MRS Coalter Cabell
Cumberland	04021	Meyers MR & MRS John P O
Cumberland	04021	Morse MISS Judith B
Cumberland Center	04021	Bonechi MR & MRS Roberto
Cumberland Center	04021	Eldredge MR & MRS John McC
Cumberland Center	04021	Geoffroy MR & MRS Mark L
Cumberland Foreside	04110	Hilliard MRS Henry R JR
Cumberland Foreside	04110	Knight MR & MRS G Morgan
Cumberland Foreside	04110	Pomeroy MR & MRS Robert W 3D
Cushing	04563	Brewster MR & MRS Donald R
Cushing	04563	Cardon MR & MRS Patrick D
Cushing	04563	Fuller MR & MRS Benjamin A G JR
Damariscotta	04543	Gillespie MR & MRS Stuart P SR
Damariscotta	04543	Marsh MRS Helen H
Damariscotta	04543	Poor MISS Deborah
Deer Isle	04627	de Vries MR & MRS Peter J M
East Blue Hill	04629	Hatfield MR & MRS Charles J II
Edgecomb	04556	Abbott MRS Alice Reid
Ellsworth	04605	McGeorge MS Judith F
Falmouth	04105	Carpenter DR & MRS Charles C J JR
Falmouth	04105	Cartier MR & MRS George T
Falmouth	04105	Collins MR & MRS James Carstairs
Falmouth	04105	Evarts MR & MRS James M
Falmouth	04105	Fallon MR & MRS John T JR
Falmouth	04105	Herring MR David M JR & Leland MS London C
Falmouth	04105	Irving MR & MRS Alan M M
Falmouth	04105	Kipp MR & MRS John P JR
Falmouth	04105	McKee MR & MRS Todd C
Falmouth	04105	Miles MR & MRS Charles R
Falmouth	04105	Noble DR & MRS (DR) Cyrus B
Falmouth	04105	Parrish MRS Hugh M
Falmouth	04105	Scully MR & MRS John A
Falmouth	04105	Tilney MRS Robert W JR
Falmouth	04105	Wallis MR & MRS George R
Falmouth	04105	Wharton MR Lawrence R III
Falmouth Foreside	04105	Klebe MR & MRS Kurt E
Freeport	04032	Field MR & MRS Joseph H
Freeport	04032	Fremont-Smith MR & MRS Thomas P
Freeport	04032	Gribbel MR & MRS Theodore G
Freeport	04032	Hamlen MR & MRS William T
Freeport	04032	Hancock MR & MRS (REV) Morris C
Freeport	04032	Kise MRS James Nelson
Freeport	04032	Kyle MR & MRS G Clayton JR
Friendship	04547	Barlow MISS Eleanor Poe
Friendship	04547	von Hemert MR & MRS C A Philippe
Gardiner	04345	Crane MISS Carol E
Georgetown	04548	Browning MR & MRS George W
Georgetown	04548	Brune MR & MRS William H N II
Gouldsboro	04607	Howard MR J Bentley & Baldwin MS Letitia S
Hallowell	04347	Gibson MR George W
Hampden	04444	Fischer MR & MRS Jonathan B
Hancock	04640	Haskins MRS George Lee
Harpswell	04079	Pulsifer MR & MRS Stephen Mackintosh
Hiram	04041	deKay DR & MRS Joseph R D
Holden	04429	Thompson MR & MRS Christopher
Hollis	04042	Johnson MRS Hamilton S
Hulls Cove	04644	Cochran MR John
Islesboro	04848	Bartlett MRS May P
Islesboro	04848	Kelly MR & MRS John Whitney
Islesboro	04848	Love MRS Suzanna P

To nominate a candidate for the Social Register Association, please email: SRCommittee@thesocialregister.org

Kennebunk, ME—Topsham, ME

Kennebunk 04043 Hoffman MRS Theodore F
Kennebunk 04043 Larrabee MR & MRS Stephen F
Kennebunk 04043 Mirkil MR & MRS Jay R
Kennebunkport 04046 Forbes MR & MRS Edward K
Kennebunkport 04046 Groman MISS Elizabeth L
Kennebunkport 04046 Notman MRS Donald D
Kennebunkport 04046 Robinson MR & MRS Davis R
Kennebunkport 04046 Tilney MR & MRS Philip V R
Kennebunkport 04046 Wyckoff MR & MRS Ferdinand L JR
Kittery 03904 Bradford MS M Heun
Kittery 03904 Potter MR & MRS Bancroft S
Kittery Point 03905 Austin MR & MRS James P
Kittery Point 03905 Chapman MR David W & Kaledaite-Chapman MRS Jurgita
Kittery Point 03905 Howells MR John M
Kittery Point 03905 Howells MS Rose-Marie
Liberty 04949 Rotch MR & MRS A Lawrence
Lincolnville 04849 Goodale MR & MRS Nathaniel B E
Lincolnville 04849 Oppersdorff MR & MRS Anthony T
Lincolnville 04849 Watson MRS Margaret P
Lubec 04652 Pike MR C Davis
Lyman 04002 Nunan MRS Neil M
Manchester 04351 Weiss MAJ (DR) & MRS (DR) William B
Mt Desert 04660 Davis MR J Hornor 4TH
Mt Desert 04660 Dunleavy MR Erik N
Mt Desert 04660 Fox DR & MRS (DR) Samuel M 3D
Mt Desert 04660 Hague REV DR William
Mt Desert 04660 Johnson MRS Mildred T
Mt Desert 04660 Kennedy MR Moorhead
Mt Desert 04660 Randolph-Foster MR & MRS Douglas E
Mt Desert 04660 Richardson MR Charles S JR
Mt Desert 04660 Timpson MR & MRS Lawrence L
New Gloucester 04260 Gauvin MR & MRS Charles F
New Harbor 04554 Suydam MR Peter van C
Newcastle 04553 Corscaden MS Patricia
Newcastle 04553 Jenne MR & MRS Kirk Q
Newcastle 04553 Phillips MISS Caroline A
Norridgewock 04957 Norling MS Abigail Chandler
North Yarmouth 04097 Boardman MR & MRS Michael B
North Yarmouth 04097 Mote MR & MRS Peter D
Northeast Harbor 04662 Andrews MR & MRS Schofield 3D
Northeast Harbor 04662 Baltzell MR Francis D
Northeast Harbor 04662 Blair MR Francis I
Northeast Harbor 04662 Falt MR & MRS Robert L
Northeast Harbor 04662 Madeira MRS C Bradley
Northeast Harbor 04662 Rogers MR & MRS Peter M
Northeast Harbor 04662 van Heerden MR & MRS Christiaan I
Northeast Harbor 04662 Wilmerding MR & MRS James W W
Orono 04473 Harrington MR Dennis L
Orr's Island 04066 McFarland MR & MRS Malcolm JR
Owls Head 04854 Thomas MR & MRS Norman M III
Peaks Island 04108 Mott MR & MRS Lawrence H
Peaks Island 04108 Rynning MR & MRS Eivind P
Pemaquid 04558 Williams MR & MRS Guy G
Penobscot 04476 Connard MR & MRS Carroll S
Phillips 04966 Appell MR & MRS George N
Phippsburg 04562 Henderson MR Curtis B
Port Clyde 04855 Fischer MR & MRS Julian D
Portland 04101 Cabot MR & MRS James E
Portland 04101 Elliman MR & MRS Thomas T
Portland 04101 Graulty MS Sarah LeVaun
Portland 04101 Griswold MR & MRS John A 2D
Portland 04101 Higgins MR & MRS James H B
Portland 04101 Kinkade MRS Charles E
Portland 04101 Knake MR & MRS Robert K
Portland 04101 Nelson MRS Norman F 2D
Portland 04101 Pedersen MISS Emma T
Portland 04101 Smith MR & MRS Kaighn JR
Portland 04101 Spaulding MR & MRS Alexander H
Portland 04101 Thomas MISS Olivia Tucker
Portland 04102 Ames MR & MRS Charlton H
Portland 04102 Beal MR Alexander M
Portland 04102 Briggs MRS Taylor R
Portland 04102 de Rham MR & MRS William JR
Portland 04102 Emery MR & MRS J Josiah
Portland 04102 Hamlen MR & MRS Devens MacM
Portland 04102 Howells MR & MRS Edward S
Portland 04102 O'Rourke MR & MRS Charles G
Portland 04102 Robertson MR & MRS John O
Portland 04102 Robinson MR & MRS Thomas R
Portland 04102 Rogers MRS Richard M
Portland 04102 Williams MR & MRS Christopher Sewall
Portland 04102 Zilkha MR & MRS Daniel A
Portland 04103 Chase MRS Elisabeth Osborn
Portland 04103 Look MISS Ellen D
Portland 04103 More MR & MRS Henry Brooks
Portland 04103 Smith MR & MRS Gerard W
Portland 04103 Smith MR Justin Q
Portland 04103 Wheelock MISS Cynthia A
Rockland 04841 Bodine MR William W III
Rockland 04841 Richardson REV & MRS Peter T
Rockland 04841 Witherby MR & MRS Frederick R H JR
Rockport 04856 Armentrout MR & MRS Alexander VanDyke
Rockport 04856 Chatfield MR & MRS Frederick H JR
Rockport 04856 Goodale MR & MRS M Wing
Rockport 04856 Lawrence MR & MRS James IV
Rockport 04856 Rockefeller MR O Stillman
Rockport 04856 Smith MR & MRS Stephen G
Saco 04072 Schermerhorn MRS John E
Saco 04072 Stockwell MRS John F
Scarborough 04074 Buckley MRS John S
Scarborough 04074 Crawford MRS Seth T
Scarborough 04074 Dickey MRS Charles D JR
Scarborough 04074 Doermann MR Humphrey
Scarborough 04074 Fairburn MRS Gordon R
Scarborough 04074 Frothingham MR & MRS William B JR
Scarborough 04074 Gillies MR & MRS E Dillon
Scarborough 04074 James CAPT (RET) & MRS Nathaniel W 3D
Scarborough 04074 James DR Nathaniel W 4TH
Scarborough 04074 LaCasse MR & MRS William O
Scarborough 04074 Laverack MRS William
Scarborough 04074 Lennig MR Frederick III
Scarborough 04074 Lloyd MR Gulden G
Scarborough 04074 Maurer DR & MRS Richard K
Scarborough 04074 Pratt MRS Alexander
Scarborough 04074 Rogers DR & MRS Malcolm P
Scarborough 04074 Rose MR & MRS James McK JR
Scarborough 04074 Rossiter MR & MRS (DR) A Wickes
Scarborough 04074 Smith MR & MRS Christopher R
Scarborough 04074 Timpson MR & MRS Alexander
Scarborough 04074 Wise MRS John H JR
Seal Harbor 04675 Rockefeller MS Sydney Roberts
Sedgwick 04676 Everdell MR & MRS Preston
South Freeport 04032 Gribbel MR & MRS James L 2D
South Freeport 04078 Ring MR & MRS Thornton D
South Freeport 04078 Scott MR Winton F JR & McDill MRS Laura
South Harpswell 04079 Yancey MISS Sherod A
South Portland 04106 Savory MS Caroline D
Southport 04576 Mace MR & MRS Myles L JR
Southwest Harbor 04679 Fogarty MR & MRS Edward T
Tenants Harbor 04860 Cowperthwaite MR & MRS John K JR
Topsham 04086 Barron MR & MRS William A 3D

Topsham .... 04086 .... Bowditch MRS E Francis
Topsham .... 04086 .... Johnson MR & MRS Robert A
Topsham .... 04086 .... Neilson REV Albert P
Topsham .... 04086 .... Pulsifer MR Leonard H
Topsham .... 04086 .... Pulsifer MR Richard T S
Veazie .... 04401 .... Hudson MR & MRS Thomas B JR
Waldoboro .... 04572 .... Crane MR & MRS Sanford L
Waldoboro .... 04572 .... Morris MR & MRS John D 2D
Washington .... 04574 .... Rotch MR Edward C
Wellesley Hills .... 02481 .... Notman MR & MRS Donald D JR
Westbrook .... 04092 .... Hall MR Winthrop T
Wiscasset .... 04578 .... Clapp MR & MRS David D
Wiscasset .... 04578 .... Curran MR & MRS Maurice J III
Wiscasset .... 04578 .... Leslie MR & MRS Seaver W
Wiscasset .... 04578 .... Sortwell MR & MRS Daniel R JR
Woolwich .... 04579 .... Jackson MR & MRS Patrick T 3D
Yarmouth .... 04096 .... Barnes MS Sarah C
Yarmouth .... 04096 .... Brady MR & MRS James H
Yarmouth .... 04096 .... Carter MR & MRS William G
Yarmouth .... 04096 .... Ingraham MS Alice Wheatland
Yarmouth .... 04096 .... Jackson MR & MRS Patrick T JR
Yarmouth .... 04096 .... Johnson MR & MRS Jeffrey S
Yarmouth .... 04096 .... Kurtz MR & MRS Robert F JR
Yarmouth .... 04096 .... Whittaker MR & MRS Laurence H
Yarmouth .... 04096 .... Woodworth MRS J Gordon
York .... 03909 .... Burns MR & MRS Edward E JR
York .... 03909 .... Campbell MRS John P
York .... 03909 .... Harding MR & MRS Edward P
York .... 03909 .... Mirick MR & MRS Richard
York Harbor .... 03911 .... Driscoll MR & MRS Peter E
York Harbor .... 03911 .... Fox MRS Caleb F 4TH
York Harbor .... 03911 .... Hollingsworth MRS Mark
York Harbor .... 03911 .... Reid MR & MRS William S
York Harbor .... 03911 .... Richard MRS Peter L

MARYLAND

Adamstown .... 21710 .... Strand MR & MRS John G
Annapolis .... 20419 .... Vickery MR & MRS Howard L 2D
Annapolis .... 21401 .... Bergen MR & MRS William B JR
Annapolis .... 21401 .... Fagan MR & MRS Charles K
Annapolis .... 21401 .... Foster MR & MRS Malcolm C
Annapolis .... 21401 .... Fritz MR & MRS William F B
Annapolis .... 21401 .... Goldsborough MR & MRS Nicholas
Annapolis .... 21401 .... Knox MRS Nelson R JR
Annapolis .... 21401 .... Lyon MR & MRS Robert B JR
Annapolis .... 21401 .... Mahan MR & MRS Jeffrey S
Annapolis .... 21401 .... Morgan MRS Henry S
Annapolis .... 21401 .... Packard MR George R 2D
Annapolis .... 21401 .... Poe MRS L Harvey JR
Annapolis .... 21401 .... Sause HON & MRS John W JR
Annapolis .... 21401 .... Sherwood MR & MRS John R 3D
Annapolis .... 21401 .... Struse MR & MRS C Richard
Annapolis .... 21401 .... Wilmer MR & MRS William Holland 3D
Annapolis .... 21401 .... Wood MR & MRS Joseph L 3D
Annapolis .... 21403 .... Aiken MR & MRS R Kenneth
Annapolis .... 21403 .... Collins MRS Edward R
Annapolis .... 21403 .... Froeb MRS Cornelius F
Annapolis .... 21403 .... Hoyer-Ellefsen MR & MRS Richard M
Annapolis .... 21403 .... McCloy MR & MRS Rush M
Annapolis .... 21403 .... Melvin MRS Mary M
Annapolis .... 21403 .... Park MR & MRS Philip J
Annapolis .... 21403 .... Parker MR & MRS Brainard W 2D
Annapolis .... 21403 .... Petty MR & MRS Robert de S
Annapolis .... 21403 .... Ruegg MRS Michelle D
Annapolis .... 21403 .... Sandberg MR & MRS William L
Annapolis .... 21403 .... Schaller MR & MRS Charles R JR
Annapolis .... 21403 .... Smythe MR & MRS T H Butler 2D
Annapolis .... 21403 .... van Beuren MR Michael M
Annapolis .... 21403 .... Whitney MR & MRS (DR) Richard P
Annapolis .... 21404 .... McKenrick MR S Eyre JR
Annapolis .... 21409 .... Baker MR & MRS James Morrison
Annapolis .... 21409 .... Belson JUDGE James A
Annapolis .... 21409 .... Buchet MR Michael M X
Annapolis .... 21409 .... Carter MR & MRS Michael R E
Annapolis .... 21409 .... Ruegg MR & MRS Edward L JR
Annapolis .... 21409 .... Westcott MR & MRS Paul W
Arnold .... 21012 .... Kille MR & MRS John E
Arnold .... 21012 .... Rich MR & MRS Edward L III
Arnold .... 21012 .... Swift MR & MRS Peter W
Avenue .... 20609 .... Hughes MRS Gordon B
Baldwin .... 21013 .... Green MR & MRS Douglas J
Baltimore .... 21204 .... Arnot MR & MRS Nathaniel du B JR
Baltimore .... 21204 .... Banks MRS Andrew
Baltimore .... 21204 .... Blue MR & MRS Robert Garnett
Baltimore .... 21204 .... Cromwell DR & MRS David McE
Baltimore .... 21204 .... DeGroff MRS Ralph L JR
Baltimore .... 21204 .... Gatchell MR Richard Emory
Baltimore .... 21204 .... Horine MR & MRS John H
Baltimore .... 21204 .... Hundley MRS James W JR
Baltimore .... 21204 .... Johnson MR & MRS Thomas W
Baltimore .... 21204 .... Lewis MR & MRS Craig
Baltimore .... 21204 .... Merwin MR & MRS Jay G JR
Baltimore .... 21204 .... Morgan MISS Eugenia B
Baltimore .... 21204 .... O'Donovan DR & MRS Charles 3D
Baltimore .... 21204 .... O'Donovan MR & MRS Charles 5TH
Baltimore .... 21204 .... Parriott MR & MRS Jackson C JR
Baltimore .... 21204 .... Roulette MRS Carter B
Baltimore .... 21204 .... Swindell MR & MRS Robert H JR
Baltimore .... 21204 .... Weatherley MR & MRS Kent W
Baltimore .... 21204 .... Wilbanks MRS Sandra M
Baltimore .... 21209 .... Lord MR & MRS Henry Robbins
Baltimore .... 21209 .... Peyton REV & MRS F Bradley 4TH
Baltimore .... 21209 .... Shafer MR & MRS Graham M
Baltimore .... 21209 .... Weeks MR & MRS Louis S 3D
Baltimore .... 21210 .... Ashton MISS Ann Russell
Baltimore .... 21210 .... Baillière MRS Thomas H G JR
Baltimore .... 21210 .... Bergland MS M Christy & Morgan MS Mary Ann
Baltimore .... 21210 .... Berkeley MR & MRS Alfred R 3D
Baltimore .... 21210 .... Cadwalader MRS Thomas F JR
Baltimore .... 21210 .... Carroll MRS Charles 3D
Baltimore .... 21210 .... Courtemanche MR & MRS Edwin W
Baltimore .... 21210 .... Crawford MR & MRS Reagan M
Baltimore .... 21210 .... Deering MR & MRS Mark M
Baltimore .... 21210 .... DeLoskey DR & MRS Albert F
Baltimore .... 21210 .... Dietrich MR E Alexander JR
Baltimore .... 21210 .... Foster DR & MRS Giraud Vernam
Baltimore .... 21210 .... Foster MISS Sally L
Baltimore .... 21210 .... Franke MRS Edward P JR
Baltimore .... 21210 .... Goldsborough MR & MRS Leslie E JR
Baltimore .... 21210 .... Goldsborough MR Leslie E III
Baltimore .... 21210 .... Griffith MRS William L
Baltimore .... 21210 .... Harrison MRS (DR) Robert B 3D
Baltimore .... 21210 .... Hart MR Thornley A
Baltimore .... 21210 .... Herrmann MR & MRS R Leith
Baltimore .... 21210 .... Hopkins MR & MRS Samuel B
Baltimore .... 21210 .... Hopkins MRS Samuel
Baltimore .... 21210 .... Hynson MR & MRS Richard
Baltimore .... 21210 .... Hynson MR Peter D
Baltimore .... 21210 .... Iglehart DR & MRS Iredell W III
Baltimore .... 21210 .... Kouwenhoven MR & MRS Nicholas W
Baltimore .... 21210 .... Kouwenhoven MRS William G

Baltimore, MD—Bethesda, MD

Baltimore .... 21210 .... Kozumbo DR & MRS Walter J
Baltimore .... 21210 .... Lewin MR & MRS John H JR
Baltimore .... 21210 .... Maclay MR & MRS John B JR
Baltimore .... 21210 .... McKeldin MR & MRS Theodore R JR
Baltimore .... 21210 .... Millspaugh MR & MRS Thomas E D
Baltimore .... 21210 .... Pearre MR Aubrey 4TH
Baltimore .... 21210 .... Peter MS Martha Custis
Baltimore .... 21210 .... Podles DR & MRS Leon J
Baltimore .... 21210 .... Powell MR & MRS John B JR
Baltimore .... 21210 .... Rich MR & MRS Russell P
Baltimore .... 21210 .... Riggs MR & MRS Richard C JR
Baltimore .... 21210 .... Robertson MRS Barbara B
Baltimore .... 21210 .... Rome MR & MRS Robert P
Baltimore .... 21210 .... Rulon-Miller MR Berkeley T
Baltimore .... 21210 .... Savage MR & MRS Peter V
Baltimore .... 21210 .... Slingluff MR & MRS John K JR
Baltimore .... 21210 .... Springs MR & MRS Orlando W
Baltimore .... 21210 .... Stein MR Julian S JR
Baltimore .... 21210 .... van Wagenberg MR & MRS Hannes F
Baltimore .... 21210 .... Waterbury MRS Bayard H
Baltimore .... 21210 .... Waxter MR & MRS Thomas J S 3D
Baltimore .... 21210 .... Wheeler DR & MRS Paul S
Baltimore .... 21210 .... Whiting MRS J Marshall T
Baltimore .... 21210 .... Wieler MR & MRS Scott A
Baltimore .... 21210 .... Wise MRS Peyton R 2D
Baltimore .... 21210 .... Woodward MR & MRS Hiram W JR
Baltimore .... 21211 .... Chisolm MRS J Julian JR
Baltimore .... 21211 .... Dunn MISS Anneen
Baltimore .... 21211 .... Egerton MRS Stuart W
Baltimore .... 21211 .... Fielding MISS Margaret Fairfax
Baltimore .... 21211 .... Hardie MR & MRS Thomas G 2D
Baltimore .... 21211 .... Lambert MRS Barron P
Baltimore .... 21211 .... Lewis MRS H H Walker
Baltimore .... 21211 .... McBee MRS Keith W
Baltimore .... 21211 .... McDaniel MR John S 3D
Baltimore .... 21211 .... White MR Galen J III
Baltimore .... 21212 .... Ayers MR & MRS Allan W
Baltimore .... 21212 .... Baker MR & MRS William C
Baltimore .... 21212 .... Barnes MR Wilson K JR
Baltimore .... 21212 .... Bogue MR & MRS (DR) Robert W JR
Baltimore .... 21212 .... Brooke MR & MRS D William
Baltimore .... 21212 .... Brown MR & MRS William F L
Baltimore .... 21212 .... Bruch MR & MRS John L III
Baltimore .... 21212 .... Buchanan MRS Charles M
Baltimore .... 21212 .... Buhlman MR & MRS Carl O
Baltimore .... 21212 .... Burnett DR & MRS Joseph W
Baltimore .... 21212 .... Butler MR & MRS Edwin F A
Baltimore .... 21212 .... Byrholdt MRS Alfred J
Baltimore .... 21212 .... Clark MR & MRS Jonathan E JR
Baltimore .... 21212 .... Classen DR & MRS John N
Baltimore .... 21212 .... Dent MR & MRS Daniel F
Baltimore .... 21212 .... Duke MRS John F JR
Baltimore .... 21212 .... Dunn MR & MRS Edward K JR
Baltimore .... 21212 .... Ellis MR John C
Baltimore .... 21212 .... Fielding MRS Geoffrey W
Baltimore .... 21212 .... Fluharty MR & MRS Charles R
Baltimore .... 21212 .... Gatchell MR & MRS Richard Emory JR
Baltimore .... 21212 .... Giese MR & MRS Scott K
Baltimore .... 21212 .... Graeber MR & MRS Conrad R 3D
Baltimore .... 21212 .... Grieves MR & MRS James R JR
Baltimore .... 21212 .... Hale MR & MRS Richard T JR
Baltimore .... 21212 .... Hammann MRS Mary C
Baltimore .... 21212 .... Hoffberger MR & MRS Michael S
Baltimore .... 21212 .... Horton MRS William P
Baltimore .... 21212 .... Hurd MR & MRS Robert M
Baltimore .... 21212 .... Kernan MR Charles P H
Baltimore .... 21212 .... Klinefelter MR & MRS Stanard T
Baltimore .... 21212 .... Krulak MR & MRS William M JR
Baltimore .... 21212 .... Luetkemeyer MR & MRS John A JR
Baltimore .... 21212 .... Marburg MISS Barbara I
Baltimore .... 21212 .... Miller MR & MRS Christopher T
Baltimore .... 21212 .... Miller MR & MRS Cleaveland D
Baltimore .... 21212 .... Morgan MRS John M
Baltimore .... 21212 .... Murphy MR & MRS Kevin J
Baltimore .... 21212 .... O'Malley MR & MRS Niall H
Baltimore .... 21212 .... Park DR & MRS Lee Crandall
Baltimore .... 21212 .... Parvis MRS Mary L
Baltimore .... 21212 .... Paternotte MR & MRS William L
Baltimore .... 21212 .... Pendleton MR Philip R JR
Baltimore .... 21212 .... Perry MR & MRS Alexander T
Baltimore .... 21212 .... Reith MR John C
Baltimore .... 21212 .... Roulette MR & MRS Randolph B D
Baltimore .... 21212 .... Roulette MRS Philip Burwell
Baltimore .... 21212 .... Shehan MR John T
Baltimore .... 21212 .... Stichel MR H Mark
Baltimore .... 21212 .... Talbott MR & MRS Richard F
Baltimore .... 21212 .... Townsend MS Edith H
Baltimore .... 21212 .... Watson MR & MRS George E IV
Baltimore .... 21212 .... Willard MR & MRS Thomson C
Baltimore .... 21217 .... Maulsby MR & MRS David L JR
Baltimore .... 21218 .... Clapp MR & MRS Harvey R 3D
Baltimore .... 21218 .... Davis MR W Bowdoin JR
Baltimore .... 21218 .... Emmons MR Brandon W
& Savage MS E Pauline G de T L D
Baltimore .... 21218 .... Goodwin MRS Charles
Baltimore .... 21218 .... Griffin MR & MRS J Clarke JR
Baltimore .... 21218 .... Hill DR & MRS (DR) George J
Baltimore .... 21218 .... Patterson MISS Shirley C
Baltimore .... 21218 .... Payne DR & MRS John W
Baltimore .... 21224 .... Barroll MS M Keene
Baltimore .... 21224 .... Conze MISS Nichola C
Baltimore .... 21224 .... Matthai MS E Chandler
Baltimore .... 21224 .... Rivera MR & MRS Dennis
Baltimore .... 21229 .... McKenna MR & MRS John M
Baltimore .... 21230 .... Apgar MR & MRS Mahlon IV
Baltimore .... 21230 .... Ayers MISS Eliza B
Baltimore .... 21230 .... Kelley MR & MRS James T III
Baltimore .... 21230 .... Matthai MR W Schuyler
Baltimore .... 21230 .... Thomas MR & MRS Robert J JR
Baltimore .... 21231 .... Schnupp DR & MRS Kevin A
Baltimore .... 21231 .... Vaughan MR & MRS Todd K
Bel Air .... 21014 .... Chapman MR & MRS James P
Bel Air .... 21014 .... Harvey MRS F Barton JR
Bel Air .... 21014 .... Haywood MRS D Bergman
Bel Air .... 21015 .... Hopkins MRS James E T
Beltsville .... 20705 .... Sterling MR & MRS Duncan D
Benson .... 21018 .... Pons MRS John P
Berlin .... 21811 .... Bounds MR & MRS James H III
Berlin .... 21811 .... Perry MS Linda S
Bethesda .... 20814 .... Anderson MR David P
Bethesda .... 20814 .... Ballman MR & MRS B George JR
Bethesda .... 20814 .... Bowles MR & MRS W Alexander L
Bethesda .... 20814 .... Grosvenor MR & MRS Edwin S
Bethesda .... 20814 .... Grosvenor MRS Melville Bell
Bethesda .... 20814 .... Hefter MR & MRS J Scott
Bethesda .... 20814 .... Hosmer DR Stephen T
Bethesda .... 20814 .... Huebner MR & MRS J Stephen
Bethesda .... 20814 .... Hyson DR & MRS Charles D
Bethesda .... 20814 .... Kiracofe MR & MRS Bruce E
Bethesda .... 20814 .... Kramer MISS Natasha D
Bethesda .... 20814 .... Lombardo MR & MRS Steven Paul
Bethesda .... 20814 .... Magary MR & MRS Andrew S

Bethesda.......................... 20814......... Mitchell MR & MRS George B
Bethesda.......................... 20814......... Petty MRS Lee M
Bethesda.......................... 20814......... Reed MR & MRS John
Bethesda.......................... 20814......... Roberts MR & MRS Steven V
Bethesda.......................... 20814......... Stauffer MR John Christian
Bethesda.......................... 20814......... Vickery MR & MRS Hugh B 3D
Bethesda.......................... 20814......... Washington MR John A
Bethesda.......................... 20814......... Wyckoff MR & MRS John S
Bethesda.......................... 20816......... Anderson MR Robert B & Powers MS Lynn R
Bethesda.......................... 20816......... Anderson MRS Michael H
Bethesda.......................... 20816......... Ballard MRS Frederic L JR
Bethesda.......................... 20816......... Barrett MR & MRS John J III
Bethesda.......................... 20816......... Benziger MRS Peter H
Bethesda.......................... 20816......... Bird MR & MRS W Lawrence JR
Bethesda.......................... 20816......... Blundon DR & MRS Montague 3D
Bethesda.......................... 20816......... Brown MR Stanley N JR
Bethesda.......................... 20816......... Burke MR & MRS Malcolm A McM
Bethesda.......................... 20816......... Cobb MR & MRS Calvin H III
Bethesda.......................... 20816......... Coe MR Peter G & Finch MS (DR) Elizabeth L
Bethesda.......................... 20816......... Costello MR & MRS John C
Bethesda.......................... 20816......... Ernst MR & MRS Robert A
Bethesda.......................... 20816......... Farnum MR & MRS Samuel E
Bethesda.......................... 20816......... Ford DR & MRS Christopher A
Bethesda.......................... 20816......... Grace MR & MRS Eugene
Bethesda.......................... 20816......... Gries MR & MRS David D
Bethesda.......................... 20816......... Hamilton MR & MRS Christopher B
Bethesda.......................... 20816......... Hewes MR & MRS Laurence I 3D
Bethesda.......................... 20816......... Hunsiker MISS Melissa L
Bethesda.......................... 20816......... Hyde MRS James F C JR
Bethesda.......................... 20816......... Johnston MR & MRS Oswald L JR
Bethesda.......................... 20816......... King MR & MRS Matthew H
Bethesda.......................... 20816......... Leary MR David W JR & Perretta MR Seth T
Bethesda.......................... 20816......... Linke MR & MRS Gordon F
Bethesda.......................... 20816......... Livingood DR & MRS (DR) John M
Bethesda.......................... 20816......... Maginnis MR & MRS Gordon H 2D
Bethesda.......................... 20816......... Mathews MR & MRS Alexander S
Bethesda.......................... 20816......... McClellan MR & MRS Maxwell C
Bethesda.......................... 20816......... McGehee MRS Kristine
Bethesda.......................... 20816......... McGloon MR & MRS Kevin J
Bethesda.......................... 20816......... Meier MRS Louis L
Bethesda.......................... 20816......... Meima MR & MRS Stephen H
Bethesda.......................... 20816......... Miller MR Michael
Bethesda.......................... 20816......... Muir MR & MRS John D JR
Bethesda.......................... 20816......... Nickerson MR & MRS Joshua B
Bethesda.......................... 20816......... Prezioso MR & MRS Giovanni P
Bethesda.......................... 20816......... Randall MR Sean J O SR
Bethesda.......................... 20816......... Randolph MRS Pickett D
Bethesda.......................... 20816......... Robinson MR & MRS Michael W
Bethesda.......................... 20816......... Russell MR John Mosby
Bethesda.......................... 20816......... Sands MS Elizabeth D
Bethesda.......................... 20816......... Smith MR & MRS Emery P
Bethesda.......................... 20816......... Snow MR & MRS J Roberts
Bethesda.......................... 20816......... Sterrett MR & MRS Malcolm M B
Bethesda.......................... 20816......... Stroh MR & MRS Frederic C
Bethesda.......................... 20816......... Symington MRS Lloyd
Bethesda.......................... 20816......... Turner MS Jennifer L
Bethesda.......................... 20816......... Walsh MRS Robert L JR
Bethesda.......................... 20816......... White MR & MRS Lawrence P JR
Bethesda.......................... 20816......... Witt MR & MRS Richard J
Bethesda.......................... 20817......... Anderson MR & MRS Mark A
Bethesda.......................... 20817......... Béguelin MR & MRS Robert D
Bethesda.......................... 20817......... Crans MRS Robert R
Bethesda.......................... 20817......... Darneille MR & MRS Hopewell H III
Bethesda.......................... 20817......... Heppe MR Christopher W
Bethesda.......................... 20817......... Horner MR & MRS J W Maitland
Bethesda.......................... 20817......... Jodrey MR & MRS Donald S Cox
Bethesda.......................... 20817......... Johnson MR R Tenney
Bethesda.......................... 20817......... Keech MISS Virginia W
Bethesda.......................... 20817......... Lee MR & MRS Robert E IV
Bethesda.......................... 20817......... McAdoo MRS Malcolm R JR
Bethesda.......................... 20817......... McIntosh MR & MRS Brent J
Bethesda.......................... 20817......... Moffat MRS Nathaniel C
Bethesda.......................... 20817......... Monroe MR Kendyl K
Bethesda.......................... 20817......... Moravec MR & MRS F Joseph
Bethesda.......................... 20817......... Murray MR & MRS Albert F 3D
Bethesda.......................... 20817......... Nanof MR & MRS Timothy P
Bethesda.......................... 20817......... Orme MR & MRS Nathaniel L
Bethesda.......................... 20817......... Redmond MRS J Woodward
Bethesda.......................... 20817......... Sainty MS Elizabeth F
Bethesda.......................... 20817......... Salomon MR & MRS Robert S 3D
Bethesda.......................... 20817......... Sheldon MRS Elizabeth W
Bethesda.......................... 20817......... Shepard MISS Josephine R
Bethesda.......................... 20817......... Stevenson MR & MRS Eric Van C
Bethesda.......................... 20817......... Tustian MR & MRS Richard E
Bethesda.......................... 20817......... Vietor MR & MRS G F Trevor
Bowie.............................. 20715......... Moffat MR & MRS Jay P
Bowie.............................. 20715......... Moffat MR Nathaniel C
Boyds.............................. 20841......... Obolensky PRC & PRCSS Dimitri S
Boyds.............................. 20841......... Woodward MR & MRS Robert F JR
Bozman............................ 21612......... Holt MR & MRS Ivan L 3D
Brookeville....................... 20833......... Doyle MR & MRS Geoffrey C JR
Brooklandville.................. 21022......... Pilgrim MRS James F
Brooklandville.................. 21022......... Semans MR & MRS Truman T
Butler.............................. 21023......... Boyce MR & MRS John C G JR
Butler.............................. 21023......... Brooke MR & MRS Brian W
Butler.............................. 21023......... Dorsey MRS Matilda W
Butler.............................. 21023......... Goodall MISS Mary E
Butler.............................. 21023......... McGuirk MR & MRS Hugh D
Butler.............................. 21023......... Winn MR & MRS James J JR
Cabin John....................... 20818......... Johnston MRS Portner
Cabin John....................... 20818......... King MR Jerome S II
Cabin John....................... 20818......... Thompson MR Charles W JR
Callaway.......................... 20620......... Sherman MR & MRS Christopher R
Cambridge....................... 21613......... Radcliffe MR & MRS George M
Cambridge....................... 21613......... Robertson MR & MRS John T 3D
Cambridge....................... 21613......... Shertenlieb MR & MRS William B
Cambridge....................... 21613......... Shertenlieb MR & MRS William B JR
Cambridge....................... 21613......... Wright MR & MRS Jeffrey W
Catonsville....................... 21228......... Wilds MISS Adrienne A
Cecilton........................... 21913......... Sawyer MR & MRS Hilary G
Centreville....................... 21617......... Ill MISS Jeannette H
Centreville....................... 21617......... Ill MRS Charles L
Centreville....................... 21617......... Kramer MR & MRS Daniel F JR
Centreville....................... 21617......... Long MRS Paul M
Centreville....................... 21617......... Reed MRS Adrian P
Centreville....................... 21617......... Sellers MR & MRS Coleman VI
Centreville....................... 21617......... Tubman MR & MRS S Alexander IV
Centreville....................... 21617......... Young DR J Kent H
Chesapeake City............. 21915......... Merryman MRS Nicholas B 3D
Chestertown.................... 21620......... Bainbridge MRS Anne M
Chestertown.................... 21620......... Barton MRS H Hudson 4TH
Chestertown.................... 21620......... Carell MR & MRS Walter S JR
Chestertown.................... 21620......... Clarke MR & MRS Garry E
Chestertown.................... 21620......... Collins MRS Susan B
Chestertown.................... 21620......... Councell MR & MRS Brian A
Chestertown.................... 21620......... Cowenhoven MISS Margaretta R
Chestertown.................... 21620......... Ellsworth MRS Robert F
Chestertown.................... 21620......... Hatfield MR & MRS Edward R
Chestertown.................... 21620......... Havemeyer MR Christian
Chestertown.................... 21620......... Jennings MR & MRS Christopher R
Chestertown.................... 21620......... Kloman MR & MRS Erasmus H
Chestertown.................... 21620......... Maxcy MR Edward Ellis

To nominate a candidate for the Social Register Association, please email: SRCommittee@thesocialregister.org

Chestertown, MD—Easton, MD

Chestertown	21620	May MRS William B JR
Chestertown	21620	McCown MS Susan G
Chestertown	21620	Morison MRS Elting E
Chestertown	21620	Neff MR Morton Gibbons JR
Chestertown	21620	Purnell MRS John Hurst JR
Chestertown	21620	Robbins MR & MRS Hanson C
Chestertown	21620	Ryon MRS Mortimer
Chestertown	21620	Sharpe MRS William P
Cheverly	20785	Sinclair MR & MRS Ryan S
Chevy Chase	20815	Abell MR & MRS William S
Chevy Chase	20815	Adler MR & MRS Mark A
Chevy Chase	20815	Allen DR & MRS Yorke III
Chevy Chase	20815	Anderson MR & MRS Ashby D
Chevy Chase	20815	Barker MR & MRS John F
Chevy Chase	20815	Bartlett MR & MRS Edmund 3D
Chevy Chase	20815	Beale MR & MRS John S JR
Chevy Chase	20815	Bellinger MRS Dunn
Chevy Chase	20815	Bowles MR & MRS John L
Chevy Chase	20815	Breed MR & MRS James H
Chevy Chase	20815	Carlson MR & MRS Richard W
Chevy Chase	20815	Chapoton MR & MRS John Edgar
Chevy Chase	20815	Cochran MRS Carlyle Van D
Chevy Chase	20815	Coerper MR & MRS Milo G
Chevy Chase	20815	Coleman MR & MRS John R
Chevy Chase	20815	Conger MR & MRS Stephen McC
Chevy Chase	20815	Crocker MRS (DR) Diane W
Chevy Chase	20815	de Fontnouvelle CTSS
Chevy Chase	20815	Debevoise MR & MRS Eli Whitney 2D
Chevy Chase	20815	Dial MISS Diana
Chevy Chase	20815	Dietrich MR & MRS H Richard III
Chevy Chase	20815	Dodds MRS Deborah D
Chevy Chase	20815	Eldridge MR & MRS Thomas R
Chevy Chase	20815	Felder MR & MRS Wilson N 2D
Chevy Chase	20815	Fessenden MISS Abbe
Chevy Chase	20815	Gaillard DR & MRS (DR) William Davis
Chevy Chase	20815	Gooding MR Frederic JR
Chevy Chase	20815	Gordon DR & MRS Spencer JR
Chevy Chase	20815	Grassi MR & MRS Temple
Chevy Chase	20815	Griebel MR & MRS Webster A
Chevy Chase	20815	Hamberger MR & MRS Edward R
Chevy Chase	20815	Hart MRS Frederick E
Chevy Chase	20815	Hauck MR & MRS Graham S
Chevy Chase	20815	Hughes HON & MRS Thomas L
Chevy Chase	20815	Jones MRS Carleton S
Chevy Chase	20815	Joyce MR & MRS H Sherman
Chevy Chase	20815	Joyce MRS William R JR
Chevy Chase	20815	Keech MR & MRS Gilbert W JR
Chevy Chase	20815	Kilborne MR & MRS Allerton W
Chevy Chase	20815	King MS Damaris W
Chevy Chase	20815	Knopes MR & MRS Christopher A
Chevy Chase	20815	Lamson MR & MRS Donald N
Chevy Chase	20815	Lamson MR Samuel L
Chevy Chase	20815	Lee MRS E Brooke JR
Chevy Chase	20815	Lloyd MR & MRS Robin M
Chevy Chase	20815	Lloyd MR & MRS Thomas L
Chevy Chase	20815	Lukens MR & MRS Alan W
Chevy Chase	20815	Mallory MR & MRS C King 3D
Chevy Chase	20815	Marshall MR & MRS Harry Reinhard JR
Chevy Chase	20815	McBride MR & MRS Jonathan E
Chevy Chase	20815	Merrifield MRS D Bruce
Chevy Chase	20815	Meyer DR & MRS Richard S
Chevy Chase	20815	Millspaugh MRS S Kirk
Chevy Chase	20815	Minichello MS Susan Winans
Chevy Chase	20815	Mitchell MISS Suzanne Rees
Chevy Chase	20815	Moorhead MR & MRS James B
Chevy Chase	20815	Morgan DR & MRS (DR) Seth A
Chevy Chase	20815	Parker MR & MRS Jonathan W
Chevy Chase	20815	Pascoe MR & MRS Llewellyn Patrick
Chevy Chase	20815	Pate MR William E II & Burden MS (DR) Frances F
Chevy Chase	20815	Price MISS Mary-Stuart Montague
Chevy Chase	20815	Price MR & MRS Allen I JR
Chevy Chase	20815	Prouvost MR & MRS Amédée S
Chevy Chase	20815	Putnam MR & MRS David E
Chevy Chase	20815	Robbins MISS Virginia W
Chevy Chase	20815	Saul MR & MRS B Francis 2D
Chevy Chase	20815	Schafer MISS Elizabeth King
Chevy Chase	20815	Sharon MRS Corsini
Chevy Chase	20815	Smith MRS Walter Burges 2D
Chevy Chase	20815	Stirling MRS E Tillman
Chevy Chase	20815	Sullivan MR & MRS Leonard
Chevy Chase	20815	Thorpe MRS Merle JR
Chevy Chase	20815	Van Nice DR & MRS Paul S
Chevy Chase	20815	Van Sant MR & MRS John F JR
Chevy Chase	20815	Walsh MR & MRS Brian M
Chevy Chase	20815	Webster MR & MRS Hugh K
Chevy Chase	20815	West MRS Millard F
Chevy Chase	20815	Whitehead MR & MRS Charles E 2D
Chevy Chase	20815	Williams MR Phillip L
Chevy Chase	20815	Wilson MR & MRS Russell P
Chevy Chase	20815	Winstead MR & MRS David L
Chevy Chase	20815	Wooten MRS Sidney C
Chevy Chase	20815	Wright MRS Ian Michael
Chevy Chase	20815	Zimmerman MR & MRS Landis P
Church Hill	21623	Raffetto REV & MRS Edward C JR
Churchton	20733	Yates LT CDR Richard M
Claiborne	21624	Garrity MR & MRS Devin A JR
Claiborne	21624	Nigra DR & MRS Thomas P
Clarksburg	20871	Morgan MRS LeRoy Tuttle
Cockeysville	21030	Fox MRS George Chandler
Cockeysville	21030	Heller MR & MRS John F 3D
Cockeysville	21030	Herrmann MR Robert H
Cockeysville	21030	Melia MR & MRS James E
Cockeysville	21030	Merrick MR & MRS Charles P III
Cockeysville	21030	Parsons MR & MRS I Manning 3D
Cockeysville	21030	Proctor MRS Kenneth C
Cockeysville	21030	Riepe MR & MRS James S
Cockeysville	21030	Spears MR & MRS Daniel B
Cockeysville	21030	Spragins DR & MRS Melchijah
Cockeysville	21030	von Kessler DR & MRS Kirby L C
Cockeysville	21030	Whedbee MR & MRS Thomas C
Cockeysville	21030	Wilson MRS Anna O'D
Cockeysville	21030	Wright MR & MRS Vernon H C
Cockeysville	21030	Young MR & MRS Thomas G III
Columbia	21044	Carchidi MR Bruce G
Columbia	21044	Dinning MISS Kathleen G
Columbia	21045	Staples MR Jeffrey K & Eliot MS
Columbia	21046	Santy MR & MRS Albert C JR
Columbia	21046	Taylor MS Laura P
Daisy	21797	Ross MRS B Lloyd
Damascus	20872	Brown DR & MRS James C
Davidsonville	21035	Biddle MR & MRS William B
Derwood	20855	Willard MR & MRS Daniel S
Dunkirk	20754	Doswell MR & MRS Joseph W
Earleville	21919	de Garbolewski MR & MRS C Edward T S
Easton	21601	Baer MRS Gordon R JR
Easton	21601	Ballantine MS Katherine
Easton	21601	Barney MS Katherine L
Easton	21601	Bartlett MISS Elizabeth M
Easton	21601	Beebe MRS Tod H
Easton	21601	Brown MR & MRS Clinton S
Easton	21601	Clifford MRS Susan L Burr
Easton	21601	Cox MR David M

Easton .... 21601 .... Cox MRS C Paul 2D
Easton .... 21601 .... Dent MR & MRS Daniel S
Easton .... 21601 .... Driggs MR & MRS Laurence La T III
Easton .... 21601 .... Driggs MRS M Barton
Easton .... 21601 .... Duer MR A Adgate
Easton .... 21601 .... Duer MRS A Adgate
Easton .... 21601 .... Garrett MRS Richard G
Easton .... 21601 .... Guinness MR & MRS Sean StL L
Easton .... 21601 .... Harris MRS Montgomery
Easton .... 21601 .... Haythe MRS Madison H
Easton .... 21601 .... Huddleston MRS C Elsworth
Easton .... 21601 .... Hughes MR & MRS Thomas R JR
Easton .... 21601 .... Hyatt MRS John K JR
Easton .... 21601 .... Hynson MR & MRS Richard JR
Easton .... 21601 .... Kegan MR & MRS R Adam
Easton .... 21601 .... King MR & MRS Clarence H JR
Easton .... 21601 .... Kingman MR & MRS Abner
Easton .... 21601 .... Lavin MRS Charles V
Easton .... 21601 .... Lee MR & MRS P O'Donnell
Easton .... 21601 .... Macaire MR & MRS David R J F
Easton .... 21601 .... McCall MR & MRS Thomas C
Easton .... 21601 .... McConnel MR & MRS W Bruce
Easton .... 21601 .... Nobel MR & MRS (DR) Robert D
Easton .... 21601 .... Noble MR & MRS John W JR
Easton .... 21601 .... Passano MR L Baldwin
Easton .... 21601 .... Robson MRS Robert K
Easton .... 21601 .... Rose MR & MRS C Bowie
Easton .... 21601 .... Smith MR & MRS Hugh M
Easton .... 21601 .... Straub MR & MRS (DR) William Watson
Easton .... 21601 .... Thorington MRS James II
Easton .... 21601 .... Tilghman MS Joanna L
Edgewater .... 21037 .... Marinakis DR & MRS Peter G
Edgewater .... 21037 .... Shanahan MR & MRS Daniel P
Edgewater .... 21037 .... Trowbridge MR Calvin D JR
Edgewater .... 21037 .... Wyrough MR Peter S
Ellicott City .... 21042 .... Fowler MR Hunter A
Ellicott City .... 21042 .... Seidel DR Edward A & Imperial MS Lorna Q
Ellicott City .... 21043 .... Stafford MR & MRS James S
Ellicott City .... 21043 .... Wehland MR Matthew H C & Lynch MR John J
Ellicott City .... 21043 .... Wendell MR James F
Euston .... 21601 .... Kramer MR & MRS Alexis E
Fallston .... 21047 .... Coyne MR & MRS James M
Finksburg .... 21048 .... Howard MR & MRS Barry C
Frederick .... 21701 .... Maniha MR John C & Carattini MS Amy M
Frederick .... 21702 .... True MR & MRS Jeffrey R
Friendship .... 20758 .... Clagett MR John Brice
Friendship .... 20758 .... Clagett MRS Brice McAdoo
Ft Washington .... 20744 .... Mason MR & MRS Charles E
Ft Washington .... 20744 .... Satterthwaite COL (RET) George 2D
Gaithersburg .... 20877 .... George MS Kathryn E
Galesville .... 20765 .... Brewer MRS William C
Galesville .... 20765 .... Simons MR & MRS S Stoney JR
Galesville .... 20765 .... Wilkie MR & MRS John McNeil
Gibson Island .... 21056 .... Bond MR & MRS T Talbott
Gibson Island .... 21056 .... Simpson MR & MRS Charles J JR
Gibson Island .... 21056 .... Slack MR & MRS W Cameron
Gibson Island .... 21056 .... Stein MRS Charles F 3D
Gibson Island .... 21056 .... Walton MRS Robert E
Gibson Island .... 21056 .... Wilbur MR & MRS LeRoy A JR
Glen Arm .... 21057 .... Cost DR & MRS (DR) R Scott
Glen Burnie .... 21061 .... Miller MR Joseph O'Donnell
Glencoe .... 21152 .... Jermakian MRS Joan C
Glenwood .... 21738 .... Harrison MR & MRS Charles C 5TH
Glyndon .... 21071 .... Boykin MS Rebecca E
Glyndon .... 21071 .... Collins MR & MRS Mark McC JR
Glyndon .... 21071 .... Fenwick MR & MRS Charles C
Glyndon .... 21071 .... Fenwick MR & MRS Peter R
Glyndon .... 21071 .... Foster MR & MRS Franklin Whittington
Glyndon .... 21071 .... Offutt MR & MRS Robert L Bentley
Glyndon .... 21071 .... Sands MR & MRS S Stevens JR
Glyndon .... 21071 .... Stonesifer MR & MRS Geary L III
Glyndon .... 21071 .... Tubman MR Joseph R B
Glyndon .... 21136 .... Iglehart MR & MRS Philip C
Glyndon .... 21136 .... Watriss MRS James B
Glyndon .... 21136 .... Williams MRS Rufus M G
Glyndon .... 21136 .... Zouck MR & MRS John H II
Hagerstown .... 21740 .... Williamson MR & MRS Peter
Harwood .... 20776 .... Clagett MISS Christine F
Harwood .... 20776 .... Link MR & MRS Roger W
Harwood .... 20776 .... Purdon MR Edward S
Havre De Grace .... 21078 .... Thompson MRS Josiah Van K
Hunt Valley .... 21030 .... Baker MR & MRS William W
Hunt Valley .... 21030 .... Cromwell MR & MRS M Jenkins JR
Jarrettsville .... 21084 .... Ober MRS Philip L
Kennedyville .... 21645 .... Williamson MR & MRS John F
Kensington .... 20895 .... Craig MR & MRS Robert L
Kensington .... 20895 .... Hamilton MR & MRS John Craig
Kensington .... 20895 .... Haskell MR & MRS Benjamin B
Kensington .... 20895 .... Lee MR & MRS Bruce H R H
Kensington .... 20895 .... Rienzo MR & MRS Matthew C
Kensington .... 20895 .... Sanders MR & MRS William B 3D
La Plata .... 20646 .... Turner MRS Edward Clarence
Landover .... 20785 .... Rogers MR Joseph Shepperd
Laurel .... 20707 .... Haight MR Jonathan O
Laurel .... 20707 .... Rice MRS Richard C
Lothian .... 20711 .... Wyrough MR & MRS Richard R P
Lutherville .... 21093 .... Baker DR Benjamin M
Lutherville .... 21093 .... Barroll MRS Richard S W
Lutherville .... 21093 .... Blue MR & MRS William F
Lutherville .... 21093 .... Chapin MRS Bedford
Lutherville .... 21093 .... Christhilf MRS Bryson G
Lutherville .... 21093 .... Colwill MR Stiles Tuttle & Gargiulo MR Jonathan J
Lutherville .... 21093 .... Denebeim MS Nancy A
Lutherville .... 21093 .... Dunbar MR & MRS James A
Lutherville .... 21093 .... Floyd MR George R
Lutherville .... 21093 .... French MR G Ross
Lutherville .... 21093 .... Gavin MR & MRS Kevin P
Lutherville .... 21093 .... Hahn DR & MRS Davis M
Lutherville .... 21093 .... Hays MRS Thomas A 5TH
Lutherville .... 21093 .... Hebert MRS Frances H
Lutherville .... 21093 .... Jarrett MRS John D
Lutherville .... 21093 .... Knox MR William A Read
Lutherville .... 21093 .... Long MR & MRS John D
Lutherville .... 21093 .... Owen MRS David R
Lutherville .... 21093 .... Renaud MR & MRS Stuart A
Lutherville .... 21093 .... Riggs MRS Richard C
Lutherville .... 21093 .... Saint MR & MRS Kelsey Y
Lutherville .... 21093 .... Whalen MR & MRS John J III
Lutherville .... 21093 .... Wing MRS S Bryce
Lutherville .... 21093 .... Witherbee MRS Mary O
Lutherville .... 21093 .... Young MRS Andrew J 3D
Lutherville Timonium . 21030 .... Hopkins MR & MRS Alexander McL
Lutherville Timonium . 21093 .... Carson MR & MRS William C
Lutherville Timonium . 21093 .... von Stade MR & MRS John T
Millersville .... 21108 .... Donovan MR & MRS Lee M
Mitchellville .... 20721 .... Bever DR & MRS Christopher T
Mitchellville .... 20721 .... French MRS Joseph W
Mitchellville .... 20721 .... Vickery MRS Hugh B
Monkton .... 21111 .... Constable MR & MRS James W
Monkton .... 21111 .... Drayton MRS Mary Millspaugh
Monkton .... 21111 .... Easter MR & MRS James M 2D
Monkton .... 21111 .... Fisher MR & MRS Jack O'D

To nominate a candidate for the Social Register Association, please email: SRCommittee@thesocialregister.org

Monkton, MD—Severna Park, MD

Monkton	21111	French MISS Virginia D
Monkton	21111	French MR & MRS George R JR
Monkton	21111	Gregory MRS John D
Monkton	21111	Hopkins MR & MRS Robert D
Monkton	21111	Lawrence MRS Suzanne
Monkton	21111	Maher MR & MRS Ronald L O'D JR
Monkton	21111	McIntosh MISS Ann L
Monkton	21111	Ober MRS Frank B JR
Monkton	21111	Pearce MR & MRS Ross R
Monkton	21111	Pitts MR & MRS Henry C
Monkton	21111	White MRS S Bonsal
Monkton	21111	Worcester MR & MRS R O Colt
Monkton	21111	Young MR & MRS Albert J A
Monrovia	21770	Gage MR & MRS John V
Nanjemoy	20662	Stokes MR Turner van C
Newburg	20664	Bowton MR & MRS Bradley J
North Bethesda	20852	Melby MR & MRS Scott E
North East	21901	Kamihachi MR & MRS James D
North Potomac	20878	TriandaFilou MR Nicholas M
		& Palermo MS Nancy M
Ocean City	21842	Marshall MR Linton S JR
Odenton	21113	Etter MR & MRS Paul C
Owings Mills	21117	Athey MR & MRS Preston G
Owings Mills	21117	Beese MR J Carter JR
Owings Mills	21117	Bond MRS Nelson L JR
Owings Mills	21117	Bonsal MR & MRS Frank A III
Owings Mills	21117	Doub MR & MRS George C III
Owings Mills	21117	Doub MR & MRS George C JR
Owings Mills	21117	Groff MR & MRS William D III
Owings Mills	21117	Groff MR & MRS William D IV
Owings Mills	21117	Hardy MR & MRS G Ridgely
Owings Mills	21117	Hathaway MRS E Phillips
Owings Mills	21117	Iglehart MR & MRS Philip L
Owings Mills	21117	Jensen MRS Philip J
Owings Mills	21117	Koppelman MR & MRS Baker R
Owings Mills	21117	Levering MR & MRS Edwin W 4TH
Owings Mills	21117	Levine MR & MRS Andrew S
Owings Mills	21117	Newhall MR & MRS Charles W 3D
Owings Mills	21117	Riggs MR & MRS Francis Graham
Owings Mills	21117	Rockwell MR & MRS Steven A
Owings Mills	21117	Stichel MRS Frances
Owings Mills	21117	Trimble MR & MRS William C JR
Owings Mills	21117	Wilbanks MR Thomas A
Owings Mills	21117	Wilmerding MR & MRS David R 3D
Owings Mills	21117	Worthington MR & MRS Edward H III
Owings Mills	21117	Worthington MRS Henry M
Oxford	21654	Collins MS Alice O
Oxford	21654	Hemphill MRS Alexander
Oxford	21654	Nolan MR & MRS Gaillard R
Oxford	21654	Vaughan MR & MRS Roger E
Oxford	21654	Walbridge MR & MRS Ryckman R
Oxford	21654	Walker MS Lee Telford
Oxford	21654	Welch MR & MRS W Perry
Parkton	21120	Baran DR Mark S
		& Kramer-Baran MRS (DR) Marie Alicia
Parkton	21120	Smithwick MR & MRS A Patrick JR
Phoenix	21131	Blake MISS Elizabeth C
Pocomoke City	21851	Shettle MR & MRS William M 2D
Poolesville	20837	Gilmour MR & MRS (DR) Andrew S
Potomac	20854	Berggren MRS P Dow
Potomac	20854	Bowen MR Brooks Jefferson
Potomac	20854	Bull MR & MRS Stephen B
Potomac	20854	Dressler MR & MRS David C
Potomac	20854	Farrington MR & MRS Phillips Todd
Potomac	20854	Hurd MR & MRS Bruce W
Potomac	20854	Kaplan MRS Sheldon Z
Potomac	20854	King MR Ludlow 3D
Potomac	20854	Knable MR & MRS John P 2D
Potomac	20854	Macsherry MR Bernard S JR
Potomac	20854	Macsherry MS Helen D
Potomac	20854	Meyer MRS Robert B JR
Potomac	20854	Parker MR & MRS Ellis J 3D
Potomac	20854	Peter MR & MRS Phillips S
Potomac	20854	Pfeiffer MR Leonard IV
		& Gunnarsson Pfeiffer MS Anna
Potomac	20854	Pflieger MRS John Ely
Potomac	20854	Proffitt MRS Claire B M
Potomac	20854	Raymond MR & MRS David A
Potomac	20854	Russell MR & MRS A Douglas JR
Potomac	20854	Spencer MR & MRS Matthew C
Potomac	20854	Webster MRS John R
Queen Anne	21657	Lea MR & MRS Robert C JR
Queenstown	21658	Carroll MRS John L
Queenstown	21658	Houghton MRS Arthur A JR
Reisterstown	21136	Bonsal MR & MRS Frank A JR
Reisterstown	21136	Cameron MR & MRS Patrick K
Reisterstown	21136	Felton MRS Henry D IV
Reisterstown	21136	Foster MRS Lucy C S
Reisterstown	21136	Hebb MR & MRS Donald B JR
Reisterstown	21136	Huppman MR & MRS L Reed JR
Reisterstown	21136	Koppelman MR & MRS Jay Van C
Reisterstown	21136	Marié MR Richard M
Reisterstown	21136	Parr MR & MRS Thomas D R
Reisterstown	21136	Plummer MR Robert S
Reisterstown	21136	Seymour MR & MRS Cregg R
Reisterstown	21136	Tuxill MAJ GEN & MRS Bruce F
Relay	21227	McKean MR & MRS Paul F
Riderwood	21139	Brett MRS Mary Lynn
Rock Hall	21661	Biddle MR & MRS Anthony J Drexel III
Rock Hall	21661	Collyer MRS Eleanor T
Rock Hall	21661	Dinning MR & MRS E Lawrence 4TH
Rock Hall	21661	Durocher DR & MRS John R
Rock Hall	21661	La Motte MR Ferdinand IV
Rock Hall	21661	Totten MRS Michael W
Rockville	20850	Achtmeyer MR & MRS Robert G MacM
Rockville	20850	Congdon MR & MRS A Edward
Rockville	20850	Hunton MR & MRS Christopher
Rockville	20852	Gottenberg MR & MRS Lawrence A
Rockville	20852	Kramer MR Alfred Schoellkopf
Rockville	20852	Schechter DR & MRS Stephen L
Rockville	20852	Walker MRS Monique Briend
Rockville	20855	Applegate MR Robert D
Rockville	20855	Scheck MR & MRS John F
Royal Oak	21662	Springs MRS Richard A
Royal Oak	21662	Throop MR & MRS Enos T 5TH
Ruxton	2124	Pistell MR & MRS Christopher A
Ruxton	21204	Baker MR & MRS Daniel
Ruxton	21204	Bell MRS M Ramsay
Ruxton	21204	Classen MR & MRS H Ward
Ruxton	21204	Hill COL (RET) & MRS John F P
Ruxton	21204	Iodice MR & MRS Scott C
Ruxton	21204	Pierson DR & MRS Richard N III
Ruxton	21204	Price DR & MRS Thomas Ransone
Ruxton	21204	Smith DR & MRS Philip L II
Ruxton	21204	Talmage MR & MRS John E
Ruxton	21204	Van Metre MRS Thomas E JR
Ruxton	21204	Walser MRS Mackenzie
Ruxton	21204	Yellott MRS Richard E
Salisbury	21801	Mastin MRS Charles O'F
Sandy Spring	20860	Schneider MR & MRS Thomas J
Sevensville	21666	King MS Margo Miller
Severna Park	21146	Auchincloss MR & MRS Leonard M

Severna Park 21146 Hopkins MRS William R
Severna Park 21146 Wyrough MRS (DR) Misty W
Shady Side 20764 Morgan MR & MRS John A JR
Silver Spring 20901 de Formigny MR & MRS Adrien C H R
Silver Spring 20901 Hazard MISS Caroline H
Silver Spring 20902 Stuart MISS Elizabeth A
Silver Spring 20904 Devens MR & MRS Richard M JR
Silver Spring 20904 Eliot MR & MRS John
Silver Spring 20904 Haight MR Daniel L
Silver Spring 20904 Packard MR Thomas W
Silver Spring 20905 Benson DR & MRS James E
Silver Spring 20906 Coel MR & MRS M Richard
Silver Spring 20910 Adkins MR & MRS William B
Silver Spring 20910 Carney MR & MRS Daniel J
Silver Spring 20910 Crawford MR Victor L JR
Silver Spring 20910 Newbold MISS Jennifer H
Silver Spring 20910 Penovich MR & MRS John R
Silver Spring 20910 Williams MR & MRS David H
Sparks 21152 Conaway MR & MRS Howard H JR
Sparks 21152 Hammann MR & MRS C Gordon III
Sparks 21152 Hundley MR & MRS Charles B
Sparks 21152 McDonough MR & MRS Henry C
Sparks 21152 Montague MR & MRS Alexander B
Sparks 21152 Ramberg MR & MRS Walter D
Sparks 21152 Robinson MR & MRS Randall S
Sparks 21152 Smith MRS J Marshall
Sparks 21152 Watriss MR Michael B
Sparks 21152 Watriss MRS Denckla
Sparks Glencoe 21152 Cromwell MR Josias J 2D
Sparks Glencoe 21152 Horenkamp MR John K
St Leonard 20685 Brown MR & MRS George Stewart
St Michaels 21663 Hopkinson MR & MRS Francis JR
St Michaels 21663 Talbot MR & MRS Timothy R III
Stevenson 21153 Arnot MR & MRS Oden Bowie
Stevenson 21153 Barnhill MR & MRS Gregory H
Stevenson 21153 Glynn MR Thomas A JR
Stevenson 21153 Lawrence DR & MRS James III
Stevenson 21153 Merryman MRS Adrian H
Stevenson 21153 Mickle MISS Anne R
Stevenson 21153 Rich MR & MRS George S
Stevenson 21153 Rockwell MR & MRS Jason M
Stevenson 21153 Whitehead MR & MRS Thomas F
Stevensville 21666 Crocker MR & MRS Christopher L
Still Pond 21667 Pepper MR & MRS T Sergeant
Sykesville 21784 Williams MRS Robert Hugh
Takoma Park 20912 Lancaster MS Alden
Takoma Park 20912 Masland MR Michael S
Takoma Park 20912 Rawson MR & MRS Carter C
Takoma Park 20912 Ross MR & MRS Samuel S
Takoma Park 20912 Waring MR Benjamin A
Taneytown 21787 Lea MR & MRS Robert C 3D
Tilghman 21671 Caplan MR Thomas M
Timonium 21093 Cook MRS Thomas McK 3D
Timonium 21903 McComas MR Louis G JR
Towson 21204 Anderson MRS William G
Towson 21204 Barton MRS Alexander K
Towson 21204 Byram MRS Elizabeth W
Towson 21204 Carroll MR & MRS Robert B
Towson 21204 Collie MRS Alastair MacR
Towson 21204 Conkling MRS William H
Towson 21204 Deering MR C Randall
Towson 21204 Dugan DR & MRS Francis Markoe
Towson 21204 Ewing MRS Gordon R
Towson 21204 Fisher MISS Caroline T
Towson 21204 Fisher MRS William A JR
Towson 21204 Fritz DR William F
Towson 21204 Gray MRS Anne B
Towson 21204 Hanna MR & MRS Matthew J
Towson 21204 Hilgenberg MR & MRS John C
Towson 21204 Lamblé MRS William E
Towson 21204 Marty MR & MRS Kenneth M
Towson 21204 McGill MR & MRS Peter R 3D
Towson 21204 McMillan MR & MRS William JR
Towson 21204 Montague MRS Albert C W
Towson 21204 Nuttle MR & MRS John C
Towson 21204 O'Rourk MRS Thomas R
Towson 21204 Palmer MR & MRS Alastair W R
Towson 21204 Perry MRS Oliver H
Towson 21204 Purinton MR & MRS Harold G
Towson 21204 Rowland MRS James H JR
Towson 21204 Sherley MR Thomas H
Towson 21204 TenHoopen MR & MRS Carl A JR
Towson 21204 Wilbur MR & MRS Scott E
Towson 21204 Woody MR & MRS Lee P JR
Towson 21286 Colyer MS Ellen B
Towson 21286 Craig MISS Sally K
Towson 21286 McCarthy MR & MRS Louis B JR
Towson 21286 Persons MR & MRS Alexander D
Towson 21286 Smith MRS Marion S
Towson 21286 von Lunz MR & MRS Robert C
Towson 21286 Wood MR Frederick William III
Tracys Landing 20779 Gagné MR Philip B
Trappe 21673 Christ MR John R
Trappe 21673 Firth MR & MRS Douglas L
Trappe 21673 Fuguet MR & MRS Stephen G
Trappe 21673 Jelich MR & MRS John Milton 2D
Trappe 21673 Pierce REV Nathaniel W
Travilah 20878 Warren MR & MRS Benjamin S 3D
University Park 20782 Ogilvie MR Nigel R & Woodville MS Louisa
Upper Marlboro 20772 Roberts MR & MRS Eugene B JR
Upperco 21155 Beckley MR & MRS John W
Upperco 21155 Morris MR & MRS J L Malcolm
Upperco 21155 O'Donovan MISS Achsah S
Warwick 21912 Sawyer MR R Curtis JR
West River 20778 Murray MRS William T 3D
Westminster 21157 Darcy MR & MRS Cornelius P
Westminster 21157 Webb MR & MRS Alexander D
Westminster 21158 Jenne MR & MRS Arthur K
Westminster 21158 Stevens MR & MRS Bradley D
White Hall 21161 Knott MR & MRS Francis X
White Hall 21161 McKnight MR & MRS H Turney JR
White Hall 21161 Wilmer MR & MRS William Holland 2D
Whitehall 21161 Riker MISS Audrey
Woodstock 21163 Francis MR & MRS Peter T
Worton 21678 Duemling MRS Robert W
Worton 21678 Murphy MR & MRS Harris P
Wye Mills 21679 Kramer MR & MRS Daniel Frederick SR

MASSACHUSETTS

Acton 01720 Faville MR & MRS Jonathan N L
Acton 01720 Garnett MR & MRS William J
Acton 01720 Holt MR & MRS Andrew J JR
Acton 01720 Hutchinson MR & MRS Peter
Acton 01720 Lagunowich MR & MRS Mark J
Acton 01720 Tolley MR & MRS Christopher S
Acton 01720 Tornga MR & MRS Todd A
Acton 01720 Toulmin MR & MRS John H
Alford 01230 Rose MR & MRS Mason C
Allston 02134 McKinney MR Reynold M
Allston 02134 Vanden-Eykel MR & MRS Steven G
Amherst 01002 Belt MR & MRS Edward S

Amherst, MA—Boston, MA

Amherst	01002	Bentley MR & MRS Richard N
Amherst	01002	Liversidge MR & MRS Horace P 3D
Amherst	01002	Steinway MRS Frederick
Andover	01810	Blaxter MR George H JR
Andover	01810	Dallett MR & MRS Matthew C
Andover	01810	Day MR & MRS John C
Andover	01810	Grady MR & MRS Todd E
Andover	01810	McIntyre MR & MRS James B JR
Andover	01810	Millar MR Robert G 3D
Andover	01810	Miller MR & MRS Michael JR
Andover	01810	Neissa MR & MRS Peter A
Andover	01810	Rollins MR & MRS Alger
Andover	01810	Vandermeer MR & MRS Paul D
Andover	01810	Wood MRS Cornelius Ayer
Andover	01810	Woodward MR & MRS George S 4TH
Andover	01810	Youngman MR & MRS Thomas M
Annisquam	01930	Lawrence MR & MRS Peter G
Arlington	02474	Du Bois MISS Abigail
Arlington	02474	McKinney MR & MR Laurence O
Arlington	02474	McKinney MR Laurence O
Arlington	02474	Todd MISS Kathryn S
Arlington	02474	Willoughby MR & MRS David W
Arlington	02476	Holcombe MR & MRS Shepherd M JR
Arlington	02476	Kopper MISS Lula B
Ashfield	01330	Walker MR & MRS Norman S
Ashland	01721	Billings MR & MRS Richard W JR
Attleboro	02703	Leach MR & MRS Edwin F II
Auburn	01501	Butterworth MR & MRS John JR
Barnstable	02630	Boocock MR & MRS Roger B
Barnstable	02630	Cummings MR & MRS Sean H
Barnstable	02630	Hunsaker MRS J Peter
Barnstable	02630	Rueter MRS William G JR
Bedford	01730	Barbour MRS William E JR
Bedford	01730	Brainerd MRS Anne E
Bedford	01730	Clapp MRS Nathaniel D
Bedford	01730	Lovejoy MISS Janet P
Bedford	01730	Motley MRS Herbert J
Bedford	01730	Paine MR & MRS Richard P JR
Bedford	01730	Thomas MR & MRS Donald W
Bedford	01730	Wade MRS Jeptha H
Bedford	01730	Welch MRS E Sohier
Belchertown	01007	Marsh MOST REV & MRS Brian R
Belmont	02478	Boyden MR & MRS W Lincoln
Belmont	02478	Chianese MR & MRS Edward V
Belmont	02478	Dunham MR & MRS William P JR
Belmont	02478	Fremont-Smith MR & MRS Phillip H
Belmont	02478	Glines MR & MRS Stephen R
Belmont	02478	Hamann MR & MRS Charles M
Belmont	02478	Herrick MR Peter B
Belmont	02478	Howe MRS Richard O
Belmont	02478	Kimball MRS Daniel M
Belmont	02478	Lombard MR & MRS Langdon F
Belmont	02478	Maier MR & MRS Nicholas W
Belmont	02478	McDonald MR & MRS Matthew S
Belmont	02478	Ogilby MRS L Phippen
Belmont	02478	Oliveira MR & MRS George R
Belmont	02478	Osborne MRS (DR) Maurice M JR
Belmont	02478	Pearson MR & MRS Arthur N
Belmont	02478	Pool MR & MRS Eugene H
Belmont	02478	Pullman MR & MRS Daniel N
Belmont	02478	Rhinelander MRS Nicholas T
Belmont	02478	Simonds MR & MRS Robert L
Belmont	02478	Stanton DR & MRS Vincent P JR
Belmont	02478	Thayer MR & MRS Philip K
Belmont	02478	Treat MR & MRS Jonathan B II
Belmont	02478	Valette MR & MRS Pierre A

Beverly	01915	Bacon MR Daniel C
Beverly	01915	Connolly MRS G Peter 3D
Beverly	01915	Crossan MISS Constance W
Beverly	01915	Dewart MR & MRS Timothy R
Beverly	01915	Dixon MISS Caroline C
Beverly	01915	Galacar MR & MRS Frederic L
Beverly	01915	Guenther MR & MRS William H
Beverly	01915	Hammond MRS Isabel D
Beverly	01915	Iler MRS William M
Beverly	01915	Lawrence MR & MRS Wayne B
Beverly	01915	Lodge MR & MRS George C JR
Beverly	01915	Reynders MR & MRS (DR) Charlton III
Beverly	01915	Ryland MR & MRS G Neal
Beverly	01915	Seamans MRS Robert C JR
Beverly Farms	01915	Buchanan MRS Eustace W
Beverly Farms	01915	Cabot MR & MRS Christopher
Beverly Farms	01915	Cabot MR & MRS Samuel III
Beverly Farms	01915	Clayman MR & MRS John M
Beverly Farms	01915	Curtis MR & MRS William G 5TH
Beverly Farms	01915	Cushing MR Edward B
Beverly Farms	01915	Dane MR & MRS Charles E
Beverly Farms	01915	Hewson DR & MRS James Stokes
Beverly Farms	01915	Loring MR & MRS William C JR
Beverly Farms	01915	Lyman MR & MRS R Jeffrey
Beverly Farms	01915	MacEwen MR & MRS Peter W
Beverly Farms	01915	Metcalf MR & MRS Robert Treat Paine
Beverly Farms	01915	Peltz DR William L
Beverly Farms	01915	Polese MR & MRS James K
Beverly Farms	01915	Pruett DR & MRS Ronald C
Beverly Farms	01915	Rogers MR & MRS Arthur M III
Beverly Farms	01915	Rowell MR & MRS Bradford V
Beverly Farms	01915	Seamans MR & MRS Robert C 3D
Beverly Farms	01915	Sherrill MR & MRS Charles H
Beverly Farms	01915	Smith MR & MRS Forrester C JR
Beverly Farms	01915	Welles MR & MRS Christopher S
Beverly Farms	01915	Williams MR Benjamin J
Bolton	01740	Henderson MISS Roberta C
Bolton	01740	Rezac MR & MRS Ronald J
Bolton	01740	Smith MISS Margaret F
Bolton	01740	Smith MR A Ledyard JR
Bolton	01740	Wells MR & MRS Warren M JR
Boston	01778	Hammer MR Joseph W & Hamlen MRS Margery M
Boston	02108	Adams REV Thomas E JR & Roosevelt MRS Candace
Boston	02108	Baker MRS Hope Lincoln
Boston	02108	Batchelder MR & MRS Richard D JR
Boston	02108	Cabot MR & MRS Lewis P
Boston	02108	Cabot MRS Maud
Boston	02108	Cadwalader MRS Cynthia W
Boston	02108	Carmany MR & MRS George W 3D
Boston	02108	Claflin MR & MRS Thomas M 2D
Boston	02108	Claflin MRS R Morton
Boston	02108	Clyde MR & MRS Thomas M
Boston	02108	Coolidge MR & MRS Lawrence
Boston	02108	de Bragança MR & MRS Miguel
Boston	02108	Devens MR & MRS Robert S
Boston	02108	Fisher MR & MRS David J A
Boston	02108	Gilligan MR Francis S
Boston	02108	Goriansky MR Alexander Yale
Boston	02108	Grote MR William A
Boston	02108	Harris MR & MRS John M JR
Boston	02108	Ireland MR & MRS George R
Boston	02108	Jeffries MR & MRS Stephen B
Boston	02108	Kenyon MR & MRS Geoffrey R T
Boston	02108	Ketterson MR & MRS Robert C
Boston	02108	Kornack MR & MRS Evan F
Boston	02108	Lee MR Henry

Boston............................. 02108......... Llewellyn MR & MRS Parker B
Boston............................. 02108......... Mahoney MR & MRS Robert F
Boston............................. 02108......... Meaders MRS Phyliss Pumroy
Boston............................. 02108......... O'Toole MR & MRS John J III
Boston............................. 02108......... Parker MR & MRS James S
Boston............................. 02108......... Peabody MRS Endicott
Boston............................. 02108......... Pope MR & MRS John A
Boston............................. 02108......... Reidy MR John S
Boston............................. 02108......... Righter MR & MRS James V
Boston............................. 02108......... Score MR & MRS Stephen
Boston............................. 02108......... Shay MR Brent E
Boston............................. 02108......... Shiland MR Scott DeF
Boston............................. 02108......... Stockwell MR & MRS William A
Boston............................. 02108......... Swain MRS Anthony
Boston............................. 02108......... Thaler MR Thomas W
Boston............................. 02108......... Tilney DR & MRS Nicholas L
Boston............................. 02108......... Townsend MR & MRS Thomas H
Boston............................. 02108......... Wagner MR & MRS H Whitney
Boston............................. 02108......... Walcott MS Diana Perry
Boston............................. 02108......... Walsh MR & MRS E Denis
Boston............................. 02108......... White MRS Constance V R
Boston............................. 02108......... Wick MR & MRS Tyler S
Boston............................. 02108......... Wilmerding MR Patrick R
Boston............................. 02108......... Winthrop MR & MRS Jonathan
Boston............................. 02109......... Ball MR & MRS Thomas J
Boston............................. 02109......... Black MISS Sophie C
Boston............................. 02110......... Armstrong MR & MRS Rodney
Boston............................. 02110......... Leland MR & MRS Timothy
Boston............................. 02110......... Loring MR & MRS Peter B
Boston............................. 02110......... Luquer MS Brenda P
Boston............................. 02110......... Lyman MR Arthur T 3D
Boston............................. 02110......... Penrose MR & MRS John R
Boston............................. 02111......... Carroll MS Megan E
Boston............................. 02111......... Colburn MR & MRS Kenneth H
Boston............................. 02111......... Donovan MISS Catharine-Mary
Boston............................. 02111......... Halpin MR & MRS Gerard A III
Boston............................. 02111......... Strawbridge MR & MRS Andrew V
Boston............................. 02111......... Vietor MISS Barbara G
Boston............................. 02111......... Wiehl MR & MRS Richard V
Boston............................. 02113......... Butterworth MR D Gardner JR
Boston............................. 02113......... Cluett MR Christopher B
Boston............................. 02114......... Brown MR & MRS Charles D
Boston............................. 02114......... Burnham MR David H
Boston............................. 02114......... Colburn MR & MRS Oliver C
Boston............................. 02114......... de Rham MR J Christopher
Boston............................. 02114......... Duryee MISS Cynthia A G
Boston............................. 02114......... Flight MR & MRS Curtis C
Boston............................. 02114......... Greenfield DR & MRS Paul S
Boston............................. 02114......... Hole MR & MRS Edward D
Boston............................. 02114......... Johnson MR & MRS Edward C 3D
Boston............................. 02114......... Jones MR Franklin D
Boston............................. 02114......... Lawrence MRS Virginia M
Boston............................. 02114......... Loizeaux MISS Sonia
Boston............................. 02114......... Morse MR & MRS David H
Boston............................. 02114......... Nagy MR & MRS Gregory B
Boston............................. 02114......... Pingree MR & MRS Eben H
Boston............................. 02114......... Potter MR & MRS Spencer W
Boston............................. 02114......... Quinn MR John B
Boston............................. 02114......... Rhein MR Peter V
Boston............................. 02114......... Walton MR Richard C
Boston............................. 02114......... White MR & MRS Christopher M
Boston............................. 02114......... Winter MR & MRS Anthony R
Boston............................. 02115......... French MR Seth B 4TH
Boston............................. 02115......... Kearney MR & MRS Gary P
Boston............................. 02115......... Smith MRS Henry J
Boston............................. 02115......... Spear MR & MRS Steven D
Boston............................. 02115......... Steward MR Scott C
Boston............................. 02115......... Streeter MRS Nina
Boston............................. 02115......... Taylor REV DR Nancy S
Boston............................. 02116......... Baker MR & MRS William R JR
Boston............................. 02116......... Beekman MR & MRS Hugo H L
Boston............................. 02116......... Bell MR & MRS Anderson Z
Boston............................. 02116......... Blua MISS Turchese d'A J B
Boston............................. 02116......... Borden MR & MRS Robert R IV
Boston............................. 02116......... Buddenhagen MR & MRS Paul S
Boston............................. 02116......... Campbell MR & MRS Benjamin K
Boston............................. 02116......... Carton MS Barbara Wells
Boston............................. 02116......... Coburn MISS Priscilla S
Boston............................. 02116......... Coogan MR & MRS David F
Boston............................. 02116......... Dabney MS Fay
Boston............................. 02116......... Doud MR & MRS Daniel H
Boston............................. 02116......... Gardiner MR & MRS Ian H
Boston............................. 02116......... Gay MR & MRS Andrew W
Boston............................. 02116......... Goodyear MRS (DR) Austin
Boston............................. 02116......... Grace MISS Maureen
Boston............................. 02116......... Grew RT REV & MRS J Clark II
Boston............................. 02116......... Hall MRS Elizabeth B
Boston............................. 02116......... Harmsworth HON Esmond V
Boston............................. 02116......... Haydock MR & MRS Charles T
Boston............................. 02116......... Henderson MRS Cassandra H
Boston............................. 02116......... Higgins MRS R Scott
Boston............................. 02116......... Hodges MR & MRS Arthur C
Boston............................. 02116......... Hubby MR Nicholas M
Boston............................. 02116......... Huber MR & MRS Timothy B
Boston............................. 02116......... Jackson MR & MRS F Gardner JR
Boston............................. 02116......... Jacobs MR & MRS (DR) George M
Boston............................. 02116......... Jerauld MR & MRS Anthony B
Boston............................. 02116......... Jones MR Brian E
Boston............................. 02116......... Kimber MISS Karen Beecher
Boston............................. 02116......... Loring MR & MRS R Gardner
Boston............................. 02116......... Lovejoy MR Philip W & Moses MR James A
Boston............................. 02116......... Mann MR & MRS Thomas D JR
Boston............................. 02116......... Marshall MR & MRS Jeffrey E
Boston............................. 02116......... McGinty MRS (DR) John E
Boston............................. 02116......... McIntire MR & MRS Peter T
Boston............................. 02116......... Metcalf MISS Lucy D
Boston............................. 02116......... Mormoris MR Stephen C & Cornell MR Robert L
Boston............................. 02116......... Patterson MR & MRS Robert E
Boston............................. 02116......... Payne MR Brooks E
Boston............................. 02116......... Pedersen MR Shaun F & Abbott MS Alexandra G
Boston............................. 02116......... Plimpton MR & MRS Samuel
Boston............................. 02116......... Plum MR & MRS Matthias JR
Boston............................. 02116......... Radloff MR & MRS Robert A
Boston............................. 02116......... Rayport MR & MRS Jeffrey F
Boston............................. 02116......... Scullin MR & MRS John R
Boston............................. 02116......... Sibley MR & MRS Thomas
Boston............................. 02116......... Singer MR & MRS Thomas E
Boston............................. 02116......... Sizer MRS Sandra
Boston............................. 02116......... Smith MR & MRS Winston C
Boston............................. 02116......... Sprayregen MR & MRS Benjamin F
Boston............................. 02116......... Taylor MRS William O
Boston............................. 02116......... Thompson MR Richard H P
Boston............................. 02116......... Tiffany MR & MRS Edwin P
Boston............................. 02116......... Trautman MR Courtney L
Boston............................. 02116......... Treco MR & MRS James D
Boston............................. 02116......... Van Alen MR & MRS James L JR
Boston............................. 02116......... Vandam MRS Carolyn
Boston............................. 02116......... Vivanco MR & MRS Eduardo
Boston............................. 02116......... Warburg MR & MRS Jonathan F
Boston............................. 02116......... Wellington MR & MRS Roger U III
Boston............................. 02116......... Whitney MR Andrew G C
Boston............................. 02116......... Wilmerding MR & MRS Michael R

Boston, MA—Cambridge, MA

Boston 02116 Wilson MR Samuel W
Boston 02116 Winter MRS Katherine B
Boston 02116 Withington MS Sara G
Boston 02116 Yaworsky MR Paul John
Boston 02117 Sack MR & MRS A Albert VI
Boston 02118 Behling MR & MRS Larry C
Boston 02118 Berg MR Dana S
Boston 02118 Clapp MR & MRS Eugene H 4TH
Boston 02118 Crocker MR & MRS Nicholas B
Boston 02118 DesPrez MR & MRS John D IV
Boston 02118 Henderson MR & MRS John T
Boston 02118 Logan MR & MRS Prescott H
Boston 02118 Madsen MR Peter E & Linehan MR Timothy R
Boston 02118 McGehee MR Edward McD
Boston 02118 Minturn MR Robert B
Boston 02118 Mitchell MR Douglas B & Brooker MS Berret A
Boston 02118 Simons MR D Brenton
Boston 02118 Taber MR & MRS Stephen H
Boston 02118 White MR & MRS Ogden III
Boston 02118 Wilson MR & MRS William F
Boston 02127 Eagleton DR & MRS Mark C
Boston 02127 Gagarin MR & MRS Serge A
Boston 02127 Hamill MR Robert B JR
Boston 02129 Yoh MISS Margaret F
Boston 02130 DiCamillo MR Curt J G
Boston 02130 England MR & MRS Sanford H
Boston 02130 Welch MR John H 2D
Boston 02132 Haight MR & MRS Robert S
Boston 02196 Kaye MR Howard JR
Boston 02199 de Laire MRS Antoine R
Boston 02199 Mason MRS Austin B
Boston 02199 Ogilby MR & MRS Henry McF
Boston 02199 Perera MR & MRS Lawrence T
Boston 02210 Cox MR Howard E JR
Boston 02210 Grant MR & MRS Newell McI JR
Boston 02210 Merrill MS Nina K
Boston 02210 Thompson MR & MRS Jeffrey L
Boston 02215 Coffin MR & MRS G Jarvis IV
Boston 02215 Cornell MR & MRS James K
Boston 02215 Earle MISS Witney D
Boxborough 01719 Martin MRS Lynn A
Boxborough 01719 Morse MRS Thomas R
Boxford 01921 Birdsall MISS Marie
Boxford 01921 Cox MRS Ila S
Boxford 01921 Goriansky MR Michael Eliot
Boxford 01921 Heidinger MR & MRS C Webb
Boxford 01921 Papin MR & MRS Gerard A
Braintree 02184 Allison MR & MRS Stephen D
Braintree 02184 Ego MR & MRS John J
Brewster 02631 Caviston MRS Sarah
Brewster 02631 Dillon MR George C
Brewster 02631 Lincoln MR & MRS L W Thompson JR
Brewster 02631 Lincoln MRS B Tyler
Brighton 02135 Harty MISS Hilary P
Brookline 02445 Albright DR & MRS Nile L
Brookline 02445 Balboni MS Margot N
Brookline 02445 Boden MRS Katharine
Brookline 02445 Boit MR & MRS Charles-Frederick D
Brookline 02445 Bourne MRS William N JR
Brookline 02445 Chapman MR & MRS Richard P JR
Brookline 02445 Comstock MISS Mary B
Brookline 02445 Cook MR & MRS John Ransom JR
Brookline 02445 Cox MRS J Dempsey
Brookline 02445 Dana MR & MRS Richard M
Brookline 02445 Dick MR & MRS Will K
Brookline 02445 Doran MR & MRS Robert W
Brookline 02445 Freeman MR & MRS Joseph S
Brookline 02445 Frost MRS Thomas B
Brookline 02445 Gerrity MR & MRS Daniel W
Brookline 02445 Hallowell MR & MRS Roger H III
Brookline 02445 Hollister MR & MRS Buell 4TH
Brookline 02445 Knapp MR & MRS Whitman E
Brookline 02445 Lawson MR & MRS Robert F A
Brookline 02445 Little DR & MRS John B
Brookline 02445 Morgan MISS Laura K
Brookline 02445 Pluhar MR & MRS (DR) James A
Brookline 02445 Richardson MR & MRS Maurice H III
Brookline 02445 Richardson MRS Harris S JR
Brookline 02445 Talbot MRS Nathan B
Brookline 02445 Thorndike MR & MRS W Nicholas
Brookline 02445 Ursul MRS George R
Brookline 02445 Walling MR & MRS Willoughby G 2D
Brookline 02445 Walton MR & MRS J Hunter JR
Brookline 02446 Ames MR Peter J
Brookline 02446 Earle MR & MRS Frank T III
Brookline 02446 Lane MR George Bliss JR
Brookline 02446 Lipson MR & MRS Paul
Brookline 02446 Lord MISS Ann O
Brookline 02446 McClean MR J Devereux E
Brookline 02446 Reed MISS Wrenn Dabney
Brookline 02446 Rothschild MR & MRS Adam D P
Brookline 02446 Sargent MISS Cornelia E
Brookline 02446 Smith MR & MRS Trevor L
Brookline 02446 Stokes MR & MRS Colin S
Brookline 02446 Thors MR & MRS Reginald F
Brookline 02446 Widing MR & MRS Bradway G
Brookline 02467 Rosenblatt MR David T & Doelger MS (DR) Emily M
Burlington 01803 Bradford MRS Judith R
Byfield 01922 Blanchard MR & MRS W Scott
Cambridge 02138 Alford MISS Dorothea B
Cambridge 02138 Ambler MR & MRS Peter W
Cambridge 02138 Ambler MRS L Todd
Cambridge 02138 Ames MR & MRS David JR
Cambridge 02138 Bartholet MRS Elizabeth
Cambridge 02138 Beaty MRS Ann Huff
Cambridge 02138 Biddle MRS Barbara K
Cambridge 02138 Black MRS Linda C
Cambridge 02138 Bodman MR & MRS Taylor S
Cambridge 02138 Bolton MR & MRS Kenyon C III
Cambridge 02138 Boudin HON Michael & Field MS Martha A
Cambridge 02138 Bower MR Joseph L & Potter MRS Elizabeth F
Cambridge 02138 Boyd MS Rebecca M
Cambridge 02138 Burnett MRS Dunn
Cambridge 02138 Cabot MR & MRS Timothy P
Cambridge 02138 Conlin MR & MRS Kelly P
Cambridge 02138 Connor MR & MRS Geremy E
Cambridge 02138 Davis MR Robert F
Cambridge 02138 Davol DR & MRS (DR) Peter B
Cambridge 02138 de Neufville MR & MRS Richard
Cambridge 02138 DeNormandie MR Philip Y
Cambridge 02138 DeNormandie MRS Tina
Cambridge 02138 Dickerson MR Thomas P
Cambridge 02138 Driscoll MISS (DR) Sonya Elizabeth
Cambridge 02138 Dupree MRS Frederick F JR
Cambridge 02138 Edmonds MRS George P JR
Cambridge 02138 Emmons MISS Catherine D
Cambridge 02138 Fairman MISS Helen A
Cambridge 02138 Fleming MR Ronald Lee
Cambridge 02138 Forney MR G David Jr & Coxe MS Elizabeth D
Cambridge 02138 Fox MISS (DR) Elizabeth M
Cambridge 02138 Fulweiler MR & MRS Hull P
Cambridge 02138 Gates MR & MRS John Davis JR

Cambridge........02138........Goodale MISS Kate D
Cambridge........02138........Goodhue MR H Shippen
Cambridge........02138........Gund MR & MRS Graham de Conde
Cambridge........02138........Holleran MS Lauren S & Salter MS Katherine N
Cambridge........02138........Hornblower MRS Rosalie
Cambridge........02138........Huber MR & MRS Horst W
Cambridge........02138........Huddleston MISS Margaret M
Cambridge........02138........Jackson MR & MRS Patrick G
Cambridge........02138........Kaneb MR & MRS Christopher P
Cambridge........02138........Kellogg MR Edward Blagden
Cambridge........02138........Kennedy MRS Sheila R
Cambridge........02138........Laconi MR Christopher M
Cambridge........02138........Leness MR & MRS Anthony H
Cambridge........02138........Lincoln MR & MRS Richard K
Cambridge........02138........Little MR & MRS Warren M
Cambridge........02138........Lloyd MR & MRS Boardman
Cambridge........02138........Lord MR & MRS Hambleton D
Cambridge........02138........MacCallum MRS Helen H
Cambridge........02138........Macdonald MR & MRS Demarest L
Cambridge........02138........Matisse MRS S Barrett
Cambridge........02138........McFerran MR & MRS Alexander Y JR
Cambridge........02138........Morris MRS Priscilla P
Cambridge........02138........Moulton MR Henry H
Cambridge........02138........Oliva MR & MRS Mark
Cambridge........02138........Paine MRS Stephen D
Cambridge........02138........Parkman MRS Samuel
Cambridge........02138........Phillips MR & MRS (REV) Daniel Anthony
Cambridge........02138........Pier MRS Arthur S
Cambridge........02138........Pierce MRS Allen B
Cambridge........02138........Porter MR & MRS Frank B JR
Cambridge........02138........Pratt MR & MRS Harold I
Cambridge........02138........Ravenel MR & MRS Ramsay M
Cambridge........02138........Reardon MR Matthew & Hunter MS Dorothy S
Cambridge........02138........Reece MR & MRS Franklin A III
Cambridge........02138........Sawyer MR Edward C 2D
Cambridge........02138........Scull MS Anna C
Cambridge........02138........Shields MISS Hilary W
Cambridge........02138........Spurr MR & MRS Robert J D
Cambridge........02138........Sunderland MRS Cynthia H
Cambridge........02138........Thomson LADY
Cambridge........02138........Tittmann MR & MRS Barclay
Cambridge........02138........van Buren MRS Elizabeth P
Cambridge........02138........Ward MR & MRS Eric N
Cambridge........02138........Warren MR Hugh L
Cambridge........02138........Watson MRS Robert B
Cambridge........02138........Wetherell MR & MRS D Bradford JR
Cambridge........02138........Whitney MRS Caroline H B
Cambridge........02139........Baldwin MR & MRS Blair F
Cambridge........02139........Biddle MR & MRS Edward L
Cambridge........02139........Bohlen MS Elizabeth H
Cambridge........02139........Burley MR & MRS Benjamin T
Cambridge........02139........Cummins MR & MRS Thomas B F
Cambridge........02139........Hatfield MR & MRS Jason D
Cambridge........02139........Howe MISS Emily D
Cambridge........02139........Ireland MR James D IV
Cambridge........02139........Swartwood MRS Judith F
Cambridge........02139........Wheeler MR Murray JR
Cambridge........02139........Young MR John D JR
Cambridge........02140........Blaine MRS Graham B JR
Cambridge........02140........Brown MR & MRS James Oliver JR
Cambridge........02140........Crocker MR & MRS Robert G
Cambridge........02140........de Rham MISS Elizabeth M
Cambridge........02140........Elliott MR David R
Cambridge........02140........Frentzel MR & MRS David G
Cambridge........02140........Moriarty MRS E Moore
Cambridge........02140........Sloane MR & MRS James R W
Cambridge........02140........Wright MISS Anson E
Cambridge........02142........Clark MR H Nichols B
Cambridge........02142........Jernigan MR Charles Carter
Cambridge........02142........Ziegler MR & MRS Henry S
Cambridge........02238........Moore MR & MRS John W JR
Canton........02021........Beck MR Cameron W
Carlisle........01741........Endicott MISS Katharine L
Carlisle........01741........Jewell MR & MRS Pliny 3D
Carlisle........01741........Livens MR & MRS John H JR
Carlisle........01741........Nash MR & MRS Peter W II
Carlisle........01741........Strugnell MR Tod D & McGee MS Kelleen C
Carlisle........01741........Valentine MR & MRS John H
Cataumet........02534........Ware MR & MRS William
Centerville........02632........Clark MR & MRS Carrington JR
Centerville........02632........Robinson MR & MRS Paul J
Charlestown........02129........Campbell MR & MRS Bradley McA
Charlestown........02129........Carver MR & MRS Ian B
Charlestown........02129........Cheston MR & MRS Morris JR
Charlestown........02129........Foster MR & MRS Tyler M
Charlestown........02129........Gillespie MR Duncan M
Charlestown........02129........Maynard MR & MRS Todd T
Charlestown........02129........Rogerson MR William G
Charlestown........02129........Slocum MR & MRS Jason B
Chatham........02633........Davis MRS James H
Chatham........02633........Higgins MR & MRS James H 3D
Chatham........02633........Mack MRS John D
Chatham........02633........Seybolt MISS Edwina P
Chestnut Hil........02467........Aretz DR & MRS (DR) H Thomas
Chestnut Hill........02467........Adams MRS Nancy
Chestnut Hill........02467........Bass MR George S
Chestnut Hill........02467........Boardman MR & MRS William H JR
Chestnut Hill........02467........Booth MR & MRS William N
Chestnut Hill........02467........Carroll MRS James A JR
Chestnut Hill........02467........Carter MR Peyton F III
Chestnut Hill........02467........Clarkson DR & MRS (DR) Bayard D JR
Chestnut Hill........02467........Coffin MR & MRS Peter B
Chestnut Hill........02467........Cutler MRS Donald F JR
Chestnut Hill........02467........Donovan MRS Alfred L
Chestnut Hill........02467........Elwood MR & MRS Michael W
Chestnut Hill........02467........Evans MR & MRS C Frazier
Chestnut Hill........02467........Finley MR & MRS John H 3D
Chestnut Hill........02467........Fogg MR & MRS George P III
Chestnut Hill........02467........Fox MR & MRS Thomas B
Chestnut Hill........02467........Fritze MRS Gunther E A
Chestnut Hill........02467........Gates MR & MRS Peter R
Chestnut Hill........02467........Gilbane MR & MRS Thomas F III
Chestnut Hill........02467........Harding MR L Branch 4TH
Chestnut Hill........02467........Havemeyer MR William MacG & Schulman MS Rebecca E
Chestnut Hill........02467........Haydock MRS Candace S
Chestnut Hill........02467........Hebard MR & MRS Charles W
Chestnut Hill........02467........Hobbs MR & MRS Franklin W
Chestnut Hill........02467........Hunnewell MR & MRS Ogden McC
Chestnut Hill........02467........Hurd MR & MRS Richard M IV
Chestnut Hill........02467........Johnson MR Richard I
Chestnut Hill........02467........Lawrence MR & MRS David T
Chestnut Hill........02467........Lee MR & MRS David S
Chestnut Hill........02467........Lloyd MR & MRS Francis V 3D
Chestnut Hill........02467........McGugan MR & MRS Vincent J
Chestnut Hill........02467........Metcalf MR & MRS Jonathan M
Chestnut Hill........02467........Moriarty MR & MRS G Marshall
Chestnut Hill........02467........Peabody MRS Francis W
Chestnut Hill........02467........Pellegrino MRS Joseph P
Chestnut Hill........02467........Perry MR & MRS E Lee
Chestnut Hill........02467........Perry MR Samuel D
Chestnut Hill........02467........Plimpton MRS Hollis W JR

Chestnut Hill, MA—Dedham, MA

Chestnut Hill	02467	Pollard MR & MRS Charles F JR
Chestnut Hill	02467	Pyle MR & MRS Russell T
Chestnut Hill	02467	Reece MR & MRS J Brooks JR
Chestnut Hill	02467	Riemer MRS Karl
Chestnut Hill	02467	Rowe MR & MRS William S 2D
Chestnut Hill	02467	Ryerson MISS Maria D
Chestnut Hill	02467	Thompson MR & MRS Neil L
Chestnut Hill	02467	Tonissi MR & MRS M Pierre
Chestnut Hill	02467	Walker MR & MRS David E
Chestnut Hill	02467	Walker MR & MRS Douglass E
Chestnut Hill	02467	Westcott MR & MRS John McM JR
Chestnut Hill	02467	Wheelock MR & MRS M Dix III
Chestnut Hill	02467	Whitman MRS Edward B 2D
Chestnut Hill	02467	Woolverton MR & MRS William H III
Chestnut Hill	02467	Wyman MRS Franklin JR
Chilmark	02535	Cammann MR Hamilton F
Chilmark	02535	Keith MR & MRS Allan R
Chilmark	02535	Lidgerwood MR William van V
Cohasset	02025	Berns MR & MRS Jordan C
Cohasset	02025	Bleakie MRS John M
Cohasset	02025	Borden MR & MRS James P
Cohasset	02025	Dean MR & MRS John S
Cohasset	02025	Dean MRS Patricia C
Cohasset	02025	Kerr MR & MRS Christopher W
Cohasset	02025	Manchester MR & MRS Eli
Cohasset	02025	Minot MR Winthrop G & Chenault Minot MRS Marilyn
Cohasset	02025	Narten MISS Martha C
Cohasset	02025	Narten MR Thomas N
Cohasset	02025	Palmer MR & MRS Lansing R JR
Cohasset	02025	Pile MR & MRS Wilson H JR
Cohasset	02025	Potter MR Nicholas B
Cohasset	02025	Potter MS Laura A
Cohasset	02025	Richardsson MR & MRS Peter K
Cohasset	02025	Richardsson MR & MRS Richmond H
Cohasset	02025	Swartwood MR & MRS Alexander B
Cohasset	02025	Thomas MR Bradford G
Cohasset	02025	Tuckerman MR & MRS Edward M
Cohasset	02025	Weedon MR & MRS D Reid JR
Concord	01742	Allen MS Eleanor L
Concord	01742	Alvarez de Toledo MRS Fernando
Concord	01742	Becton MR & MRS Henry P JR
Concord	01742	Béguelin MR & MRS W Drury
Concord	01742	Biglow DR John R
Concord	01742	Boynton MR & MRS John W IV
Concord	01742	Brockway MRS Genevieve
Concord	01742	Buttrick MRS Stedman
Concord	01742	Cabot MR Andrew L
Concord	01742	Callen MR & MRS Andrew B
Concord	01742	Campbell MR & MRS Levin H
Concord	01742	Chartener MR & MRS Robert V
Concord	01742	Cross MRS William R JR
Concord	01742	Davis MR & MRS Glenn E
Concord	01742	Dean MR Edwin P
Concord	01742	Diffenbach MRS John E
Concord	01742	Eddy MRS Morris R 2D
Concord	01742	Elliott MR & MRS Benjamin T
Concord	01742	Emerson MR & MRS Raymond III
Concord	01742	Evarts MR & MRS Thomas W M
Concord	01742	Forbes MRS Natalie S
Concord	01742	Goltra MR & MRS Alexis O
Concord	01742	Goud MR & MRS Richard B
Concord	01742	Gregory MR & MRS William D 3D
Concord	01742	Gustafson MR & MRS Dalton L
Concord	01742	Harding MISS Margaret C
Concord	01742	Hays DR F Whiting
Concord	01742	Hines MISS Carolyn
Concord	01742	Hines MRS Roy H JR
Concord	01742	Homans MRS George C
Concord	01742	Hornblower MR & MRS James W
Concord	01742	Houghton MRS Henry O JR
Concord	01742	Hoyt MR & MRS Coleman W JR
Concord	01742	Huggins MR & MRS John R
Concord	01742	Kent MRS Eleanor
Concord	01742	Keyes MR Jonathan M
Concord	01742	Ladd MR & MRS Gregory L
Concord	01742	Langan MR & MRS John J
Concord	01742	Le Roy MR & MRS Robert Otis
Concord	01742	Lease MR & MRS Christian A
Concord	01742	Livingston MR & MRS Kipp B
Concord	01742	Mast MR & MRS Robert D JR
Concord	01742	Mattson MS (DR) Louisa Hasen
Concord	01742	Megowen MR & MRS William Jacob
Concord	01742	Mudge MR & MRS Webster T
Concord	01742	Niles MRS Robert L
Concord	01742	Nimick MRS Thomas M H JR
Concord	01742	Palmer MR & MRS Charles D 3D
Concord	01742	Peck MR & MRS Philip F W 3D
Concord	01742	Potter MR & MRS Jeffrey D
Concord	01742	Rackemann MR Ford S
Concord	01742	Renshaw MISS Jeannette W
Concord	01742	Reynders MS Alys Ames
Concord	01742	Robb MR & MRS Russell
Concord	01742	Roddy MR & MRS Gilbert M JR
Concord	01742	Ross MRS J Martin
Concord	01742	Schermerhorn MR & MRS James IV
Concord	01742	Sherrill MISS Jane W
Concord	01742	Swartwood MR & MRS Thayer F
Concord	01742	Tilney MR & MRS John S JR
Concord	01742	Wasley MRS John S W
Concord	01742	White DR & MRS Benjamin Winthrop
Concord	01742	Whitman MR & MRS Robert F
Concord	01742	Wilking REV DR & MRS Spencer Van B
Concord	01742	Wilson MRS Anne Sears
Conway	01341	Endicott MS Eve
Conway	01341	Hardigg MR James McC
Cotuit	02635	Churbuck MR & MRS David C
Cotuit	02635	Parks MISS Frances S
Cotuit	02635	Swartwood MR Charles B 3D
Cummaquid	02637	Nichols MR Mark K & Massey MR Lowell R
Cummaquid	02637	Thébaud MR & MRS Charles G
Cummaquid	02637	Thompson REV & MRS Paul M
Cummaquid	02637	Walters MR Frederick L
Cummington	01026	Tesoro MR & MRS Michael R JR
Danvers	01923	Willcox MR J Keating
Dartmouth	02747	Rantoul-Hazard MR & MRS John E
Dartmouth	02748	Whitney MR & MRS William T JR
Dedham	02026	Adams MR & MRS William E
Dedham	02026	Adams MR Mitchell
Dedham	02026	Alexandre MR & MRS J Henry 5TH
Dedham	02026	Baldini MR & MRS (DR) Edward Bolles
Dedham	02026	Barrett MR & MRS C Redington 3D
Dedham	02026	Buffum MR & MRS Robert C JR
Dedham	02026	Bussey MR & MRS William Cook
Dedham	02026	Cabot MR & MRS Chilton L
Dedham	02026	Cabot MR & MRS Christopher S
Dedham	02026	Cabot MR & MRS Mitchell W
Dedham	02026	Cavallo MR & MRS Benjamin F
Dedham	02026	Cheever MR & MRS Christopher W
Dedham	02026	Chick MR & MRS Peter C
Dedham	02026	Colby MR & MRS Robert L
Dedham	02026	Corkery MR & MRS David P

Dedham	02026	Coughlin MR & MRS W Read
Dedham	02026	Detweiler MISS Anne L
Dedham	02026	Devens MR Charles 3D
Dedham	02026	Dunning MR & MRS William S
Dedham	02026	Durfee MR & MRS Allison B
Dedham	02026	Durocher MR & MRS John F
Dedham	02026	Games MRS Edmund B JR
Dedham	02026	Gifford MR & MRS Stephen N
Dedham	02026	Hollyday MR & MRS Thomas J
Dedham	02026	Holmes MR & MRS Gordon
Dedham	02026	Hornblower MR Henry 3D
Dedham	02026	Howard MR & MRS John L
Dedham	02026	Jarrett MR & MRS John D JR
Dedham	02026	Jenkins MR & MRS A Diehl
Dedham	02026	Knapp MR & MRS Richard C
Dedham	02026	Knox MR & MRS Northrup R JR
Dedham	02026	Lambert MR & MRS Adrian JR
Dedham	02026	LeBreton MR & MRS David H
Dedham	02026	Leith MR & MRS Alexander K
Dedham	02026	Lloyd MR & MRS R McAllister 3D
Dedham	02026	Logan MR & MRS James P 3D
Dedham	02026	McCleary MR & MRS Benjamin P
Dedham	02026	McKelvy MRS John E JR
Dedham	02026	Nichols MR & MRS George Q JR
Dedham	02026	Oates MRS William A JR
Dedham	02026	Parker MR & MRS George F
Dedham	02026	Pierce MRS Daniel
Dedham	02026	Pope MR & MRS Christopher M
Dedham	02026	Raymond MR & MRS Edward H
Dedham	02026	Roell REV Rudolph
Dedham	02026	Russell MR Charles T 3D
Dedham	02026	Ryerson MR & MRS Joseph T 3D
Dedham	02026	Siphron MR & MRS John R
Dedham	02026	Snow MRS E Douglas
Dedham	02026	Stone MR & MRS Galen L
Dedham	02026	Sweeny MR & MRS Michael Buckner
Dedham	02026	Torres MR & MRS Jorge
Dedham	02026	Van Oot MISS Betsy
Dedham	02026	Watts MR & MRS Edward E 3D
Dedham	02026	Watts MR Hardy G
Dedham	02026	Whitney MR & MRS Thomas H P JR
Dedham	02026	Williams MR & MRS Hugo A Y
Dedham	02026	Wynne-Willson MRS Michael F
Deerfield	01342	Ardrey MR & MRS Robert G
Deerfield	01342	Morsman MR & MRS Joseph J 3D
Dennis	02638	Dupuy MRS Christine G
Dover	02030	Adams MR & MRS David G
Dover	02030	Adams MR & MRS John W
Dover	02030	Adams MRS Charles F
Dover	02030	Adams MRS John Q
Dover	02030	Bailey DR & MRS E Duff
Dover	02030	Blanchard MS Lesley F
Dover	02030	Carroll MRS Anne O
Dover	02030	Chute MRS Antonie R
Dover	02030	Cunningham MR & MRS Colin McA JR
Dover	02030	Cunningham MRS Colin McA
Dover	02030	Fullerton MRS Mary W
Dover	02030	Gernerd MR & MRS Frederick H
Dover	02030	Harris MR & MRS Peter W
Dover	02030	King MR & MRS Clarence H 3D
Dover	02030	Ladd MR Philip L & Fiske MRS Elaine W
Dover	02030	Lewis MR David W JR
Dover	02030	Lobkowicz MRS Martin G
Dover	02030	Lynch MR & MRS Case H
Dover	02030	Manice MR & MRS Robert G
Dover	02030	Mayfield MR & MRS E Scott
Dover	02030	Minot MR & MRS Henry W JR
Dover	02030	O'Keefe MR John E
Dover	02030	Ribeiro MRS Elpidio W
Dover	02030	Sargent MRS Francis W
Dover	02030	Stuart MR & MRS James M JR
Dover	02030	Thomas MR & MRS Gregory N
Dover	02030	Walker MR & MRS James A S
Dover	02030	Ward MR & MRS Evans S
Dover	02030	White MR & MRS Stephen H
Dover	02030	Young MR & MRS Mark E
Duxbury	02331	Barrett MR & MRS David A JR
Duxbury	02331	Bates MR & MRS Nicholas L
Duxbury	02331	Kane MR Charles F JR & Eldridge MS Anne W
Duxbury	02331	Keleher MRS Walter D
Duxbury	02331	Loring MR & MRS Robert W
Duxbury	02331	Mattes MR & MRS John B
Duxbury	02331	Tearse MRS C Selden
Duxbury	02331	Thompson MS Deborah Higgins
Duxbury	02331	Tucker MR & MRS Jesse W
Duxbury	02331	White MR Bradford P
Duxbury	02332	Babcock MR & MRS William N
Duxbury	02332	Barr MR & MRS James H
Duxbury	02332	Blaisdell MR & MRS Brian A
Duxbury	02332	Carnuccio MR & MRS Matthew J
Duxbury	02332	Davis MR & MRS Charles B
Duxbury	02332	Dunn MR & MRS Steven M
Duxbury	02332	Fearey MR & MRS Morton L 2D
Duxbury	02332	Fleming MR & MRS Steven B
Duxbury	02332	MacLean MRS Malcolm O
Duxbury	02332	Maxey MR & MRS Lee G
Duxbury	02332	McCormick MR & MRS Peter H
Duxbury	02332	McGoodwin MR & MRS Robert R III
Duxbury	02332	McGoodwin MR Robert R IV
Duxbury	02332	Millar MR Robert G JR
Duxbury	02332	Olney MR & MRS Alexander D
Duxbury	02332	Palfrey MR & MRS Peter W
Duxbury	02332	Riegel MRS William M
Duxbury	02332	Rogerson MR & MRS Thomas C
Duxbury	02332	Strong MR & MRS Benjamin B
Duxbury	02332	Wells MRS David H
East Dennis	02614	Butler MR & MRS Edward J
East Dennis	02641	Backus MR & MRS Dennis L
East Falmouth	02536	Simonds MR & MRS Jonathan O
East Harwich	02645	Scott REV DR Bonnie
East Orleans	02643	Clough MR & MRS Anson W
East Walpole	02032	Urban MR & MRS (DR) David P
East Walpole	02032	Urban MR & MRS George P 3D
Eastham	02642	Everett MR & MRS Oliver S
Easthampton	01027	White MRS Galen J JR
Easthampton	01027	White MS Caroline J
Edgartown	02539	Blake MRS Edith G
Edgartown	02539	Bostrom MR & MRS Robert Everett
Edgartown	02539	Bowring MRS E Bonner
Edgartown	02539	Brady MRS D Norman
Edgartown	02539	Carpenter MISS Frederica L
Edgartown	02539	Crafts MRS Sybille N
Edgartown	02539	Delaney MR Timothy G & Putnam MS Katherine E
Edgartown	02539	Dunlop MR G Thomas
Edgartown	02539	Eshleman MRS B Franklin 2D
Edgartown	02539	Fearey MR & MRS Morton JR
Edgartown	02539	Hitchings MRS Sinclair H
Edgartown	02539	Kiersted MR & MRS Christopher W
Edgartown	02539	Lovell MRS Lane
Edgartown	02539	Lowell MR & MRS Ralph JR
Edgartown	02539	Mattison MR Joseph IV
Edgartown	02539	Mattison MRS Joseph III

To nominate a candidate for the Social Register Association, please email: SRCommittee@thesocialregister.org

Edgartown, MA—Ipswich, MA

Edgartown........ 02539........ Palmer MR & MRS Reuben T 4TH
Edgartown........ 02539........ Potter MR & MRS Robert G JR
Edgartown........ 02539........ Stevenson MR & MRS Robert M McC JR
Edgartown........ 02539........ Thompson MR & MRS David C
Edgartown........ 02539........ Van Tassel MR Peter B
Edgartown........ 02539........ Vietor MR & MRS David B
Edgartown........ 02539........ Warriner MR & MRS Samuel D 2D
Essex........ 01929........ Crocker MR & MRS Peter B
Essex........ 01929........ Madsen MRS Betsy
Essex........ 01929........ Marron MR & MRS Gregory W
Essex........ 01929........ Nadai MR & MRS Christopher M
Essex........ 01929........ Peabody MR Henry L
Essex........ 01929........ Pennoyer MRS Paul G JR
Essex........ 01929........ Pratt MR & MRS Stuart F
Essex........ 01929........ Shotwell MR & MRS E Carle IV
Essex........ 01929........ Steinert MS Lucy P C
Essex........ 01929........ Storey MR & MRS Charles Mills
Essex........ 01929........ Talbot MRS Susan S
Essex........ 01929........ Warren MRS Samuel D
Fairhaven........ 02719........ Linzee MR & MRS Thomas E JR
Fairhaven........ 02719........ Wood MR & MRS Stephen J
Falmouth........ 02540........ Adams MISS Martha L
Falmouth........ 02540........ Kellogg MR & MRS Loren L
Falmouth........ 02540........ Martin MRS Alison C
Falmouth........ 02540........ Nelson MR & MRS Brad A
Falmouth........ 02540........ Robertson MR & MRS Michael S
Falmouth........ 02540........ Ruegg MR & MRS Edward L
Falmouth........ 02540........ Wheeler DR William M
Falmouth........ 02540........ Willett MR Herbert L III
Florence........ 01060........ Howat MISS Karen L
Foxboro........ 02035........ Halperson MR Michael A
Franklin........ 02038........ Strong MR Stewart W
Gardner........ 01440........ Greenwood MR & MRS Richard H
Gloucester........ 01930........ Baumann MR & MRS Harald R
Gloucester........ 01930........ Bjorlie MR & MRS (DR) John B
Gloucester........ 01930........ Bradford MR & MRS Standish JR
Gloucester........ 01930........ Cullen MRS Jane S
Gloucester........ 01930........ Dillen MS Tatiana
Gloucester........ 01930........ Dodge MR & MRS Frederic P
Gloucester........ 01930........ Hall MR & MRS Robert Townsend
Gloucester........ 01930........ Kimball MR & MRS Nicholas H
Gloucester........ 01930........ Rando MR John S JR
Gloucester........ 01930........ Rhinelander MRS John B
Gloucester........ 01930........ Sinkinson MR & MRS Mark C
Gloucester........ 01930........ Trotman MR & MRS Nicholas G
Gloucester........ 01930........ Wall MR & MRS R Michael
Granby........ 01033........ Clement MR & MRS (DR) Henry R
Great Barrington........ 01230........ Chase MISS Mary R
Great Barrington........ 01230........ Nickerson MR & MRS Samuel B
Great Barrington........ 01230........ Post MRS Sarah W
Great Barrington........ 01230........ Stookey MR & MRS John Hoyt
Great Barrington........ 01230........ Weld MR & MRS Christopher P
Groton........ 01450........ Barker MR & MRS John C
Groton........ 01450........ Goodale MR & MRS John B
Groton........ 01450........ Goodale MR John B
Groton........ 01450........ Gould MR Albert P
Groton........ 01450........ Maynard MR & MRS John
Groton........ 01450........ McCullagh MR & MRS G Gibson JR
Groton........ 01450........ Pierpont MR & MRS Daniel G
Groton........ 01450........ Prockop MR & MRS David J
Groton........ 01450........ Sackett MR & MRS L Hugh
Hadley........ 01035........ Adams MISS Frances E
Hamilton........ 01936........ Clark MR & MRS Russell B
Hamilton........ 01936........ Longnecker MRS H Reed
Hamilton........ 01936........ McIntyre MR & MRS A Duncan
Hamilton........ 01936........ Moseley MR & MRS Frederick S 3D
Hamilton........ 01936........ Moseley MRS James B
Hamilton........ 01936........ Mulcahy MRS Charles W JR
Hamilton........ 01936........ O'Hara MR & MRS David O
Hamilton........ 01936........ Sears MRS Francis P
Hamilton........ 01936........ Shaw MR Alexander A 2D
Hamilton........ 01936........ Spaulding MS Victoria R R
Hamilton........ 01936........ Weekes MRS Arthur D 3D
Hamilton........ 01936........ Wheaton MR & MRS William C
Hamilton........ 01936........ Wolcott MR & MRS Oliver JR
Hamilton........ 01936........ Zaldastani MR & MRS Alexander G B
Hamilton........ 01982........ Cadigan MR & MRS John R
Hamilton........ 01982........ Curtis MR & MRS Charles F JR
Hamilton........ 01982........ Sears MR & MRS Daniel H
Hamilton........ 01982........ Shaw MRS Sally
Hampden........ 01036........ Wood MR & MRS R Lyman JR
Hanover........ 02339........ Coogan MRS Margaret
Hanover........ 02339........ Currier MRS Robert B
Hanover........ 02339........ Stocker MR & MRS Marshall L
Harvard........ 01451........ Carley MR & MRS Malcolm McD
Harvard........ 01451........ Ells MR & MRS Jonathan R
Harvard........ 01451........ Hays MR & MRS Frederick W JR
Harvard........ 01451........ Jones MR & MRS Christopher W
Harvard........ 01451........ Waterhouse MR & MRS Jeffrey C
Harwich........ 02645........ DeWitt MR H Vincent 3D
& Dupuy-DeWitt MRS Mirande
Harwich Port........ 02646........ Billings MR & MRS Harry G
Harwich Port........ 02646........ Groves MR & MRS Benjamin A
Harwich Port........ 02646........ Karlson MR Douglas E
Hatchville........ 02536........ Dick DR & MRS Henry J B
Hatfield........ 01038........ Wurts MISS Caroline M
Haydenville........ 01039........ Johnson MRS Rollin M
Hingham........ 02043........ Butters MR & MRS Craig W
Hingham........ 02043........ Cushman MR & MRS Allerton JR
Hingham........ 02043........ Eaton MR & MRS Nathan L
Hingham........ 02043........ Egan MR & MRS Mark A
Hingham........ 02043........ Fairfield DR & MRS Scott R
Hingham........ 02043........ Guild MR & MRS Edward M JR
Hingham........ 02043........ Hutchinson MISS Emily B
Hingham........ 02043........ Isenstadt MR & MRS Tate D
Hingham........ 02043........ McLane MR & MRS Douglas W
Hingham........ 02043........ Minevitz MR & MRS Bruce H
Hingham........ 02043........ Naimi DR & MRS Shapur
Hingham........ 02043........ Palmer MISS Pamela G
Hingham........ 02043........ Rodiger MR & MRS Albert A
Hingham........ 02043........ Shields MRS Leighton
Hingham........ 02043........ Strekalovsky MR & MRS Vcevold O
Hingham........ 02043........ Woods MR Edward F
Holbrook........ 02343........ Haskins MR & MRS Thomas E S
Holbrook........ 02343........ Haskins MR Thomas E
Holden........ 01520........ Murphy DR & MRS (DR) James T
Holliston........ 01746........ Boyd MRS Peter L B
Holliston........ 01746........ Ewing MR & MRS Richard C
Holliston........ 01746........ King MR & MRS David W
Holliston........ 01746........ Perrott MR & MRS Jeffrey H
Hopkinton........ 01748........ Mazza MRS Jeffrey R
Hopkinton........ 01748........ Morrison MR Gordon M
Hull........ 02045........ Brander CAPT Douglas K
Hull........ 02045........ Graziano MR & MRS Anthony W III
Hull........ 02045........ More DR Alexander F M
Hyannis........ 02601........ Bodell MRS Joseph J JR
Hyannis Port........ 02647........ Isham MR & MRS F Lance
Hyannis Port........ 02647........ Kennedy MRS Robert F
Hyannis Port........ 02647........ Schneeberger MR & MRS John A
Hyannis Port........ 02647........ Singmaster MR & MRS Lawrence G
Ipswich........ 01938........ Bezamat MR & MRS Adolfo
Ipswich........ 01938........ Bistrian DR & MRS Bruce R

Ipswich .... 01938 .... Eddy MR & MRS Thomas P JR
Ipswich .... 01938 .... Flood MR & MRS David B
Ipswich .... 01938 .... Galston MR John W
Ipswich .... 01938 .... Greene MR & MRS Michael S
Ipswich .... 01938 .... Griswold MR & MRS Brehon S
Ipswich .... 01938 .... Hodgson MR & MRS Howard B JR
Ipswich .... 01938 .... Larson MRS Daniel L JR
Ipswich .... 01938 .... McIntyre MRS C Littlefield
Ipswich .... 01938 .... Phillips MRS Christopher H
Ipswich .... 01938 .... Pulsifer MR & MRS Nathaniel
Ipswich .... 01938 .... Richardson MRS Roberts
Ipswich .... 01938 .... Roberts MRS Eve Ross
Ipswich .... 01938 .... Rogers MR & MRS Marc
Ipswich .... 01938 .... Scudder MR & MRS David W
Ipswich .... 01938 .... Scully MR Benjamin P
Ipswich .... 01938 .... Thayer MRS John O
Ipswich .... 01938 .... Van Alen MR & MRS Alexander S
Ipswich .... 01938 .... Vohr MR & MRS Neal P
Ipswich .... 01938 .... Ward MR & MRS Seth C
Ipswich .... 01938 .... Winthrop MR & MRS Frederic
Jamaica Plain .... 02130 .... Bailey MR & MRS H Louis 2D
Jamaica Plain .... 02130 .... Braun MRS Andrew G
Jamaica Plain .... 02130 .... Child MR & MRS Christopher C
Jamaica Plain .... 02130 .... Farrington MR & MRS Roger D
Jamaica Plain .... 02130 .... Jones MR & MRS Walker H
Jamaica Plain .... 02130 .... Lawrence MR & MRS Abbott W
Kingston .... 02364 .... de Brun MR & MRS John B III
Lancaster .... 01523 .... Anthony MR Richard G D
Lancaster .... 01523 .... Streeter MR Frank S 2D
Lawrence .... 01840 .... Parry MR Rawdon M C
Lee .... 01238 .... Holt MR & MRS Henry B
Lee .... 01238 .... Johansen MRS Mary Lee
Lenox .... 01240 .... Baruch MR & MRS Philip K
Lenox .... 01240 .... Carhart MR & MRS Amory S JR
Lenox .... 01240 .... Fenn MR & MRS Henry A JR
Lenox .... 01240 .... Jackson MR & MRS Richard S JR
Lenox .... 01240 .... Schwartz MR & MRS Arthur W JR
Lenox .... 01240 .... Selke MR Whitney F
Lenox .... 01240 .... Selke MRS Christian P
Leverett .... 01054 .... Brownell MR & MRS Kenneth C
Lexington .... 02420 .... Anderson MRS Francesca S
Lexington .... 02420 .... Strong MR & MRS William S
Lexington .... 02420 .... Webb MR & MRS Charles A 3D
Lexington .... 02421 .... Boardman MRS Francis
Lexington .... 02421 .... Bohlen MR E U Curtis
Lexington .... 02421 .... Bundy MRS McGeorge
Lexington .... 02421 .... Cattier MR & MRS Henri R
Lexington .... 02421 .... Hausslein MR & MRS Robert W
Lexington .... 02421 .... Jackman MR & MRS George A
Lexington .... 02421 .... Lloyd MR & MRS Wingate
Lexington .... 02421 .... May DR & MRS George A JR
Lexington .... 02421 .... McAdoo MR & MRS Richard B
Lexington .... 02421 .... Merck MRS Albert W
Lexington .... 02421 .... Polk MR & MRS William M
Lexington .... 02421 .... Randolph DR & MRS Peter B F
Lexington .... 02421 .... Starkey MRS George W B
Lexington .... 02421 .... Streeter MRS (DR) Chris C
Lexington .... 02421 .... Trementozzi MR & MRS Jonathan L
Lexington .... 02421 .... Walker MR & MRS Christopher B
Lincoln .... 01773 .... Beal MRS Thomas Prince JR
Lincoln .... 01773 .... Carmody MR & MRS Christopher G
Lincoln .... 01773 .... Hallowell MR & MRS Andrew W
Lincoln .... 01773 .... Horne MR & MRS Benjamin
Lincoln .... 01773 .... Kimball MRS Richard A JR
Lincoln .... 01773 .... LaMothe MR & MRS John D JR
Lincoln .... 01773 .... McCarthy MR Stephen J
Lincoln .... 01773 .... Mendelson MR & MRS (DR) John T
Lincoln .... 01773 .... Orr MRS Henry S 2D
Lincoln .... 01773 .... Patterson MR & MRS Jeffrey H
Lincoln .... 01773 .... Perera MRS Guido R JR
Lincoln .... 01773 .... Perry MR & MRS Christopher D
Lincoln .... 01773 .... Pingeon MR & MRS Hendon C
Lincoln .... 01773 .... Reinhardt MR Nicholas & Bowdoin MS Helen M
Lincoln .... 01773 .... Smith MR & MRS Colin L M
Lincoln .... 01773 .... Taylor MR & MRS J Arthur
Lincoln .... 01773 .... Torti MR & MRS Maurice L JR
Lincoln .... 01773 .... Vitrouk MR & MRS Arkady A
Lincoln .... 01773 .... Williams MR & MRS Benjamin J JR
Lincoln .... 01773 .... Young MR & MRS G Stewart
Lincoln Center .... 01773 .... Sprayregen MR & MRS Peter H
Littleton .... 01460 .... Wrenn MRS Robert D
Longmeadow .... 01106 .... Cowie MR & MRS Paul F JR
Longmeadow .... 01106 .... Cropsey MR & MRS Henry C G
Longmeadow .... 01106 .... Heaphy MS C Wilder
Longmeadow .... 01106 .... Low MR & MRS E Holland
Lynnfield .... 01940 .... Doorly MR & MRS Adam P
Lynnfield .... 01940 .... La Marche MR & MRS Stephen W
Manchester .... 01944 .... Abbott MR Christopher C
Manchester .... 01944 .... Abbott MRS Gordon JR
Manchester .... 01944 .... Almy MRS David
Manchester .... 01944 .... Barker MR & MRS B Devereux 3D
Manchester .... 01944 .... Beinecke MR & MRS Walter 3D
Manchester .... 01944 .... Bradley DR & MRS (DR) Francis M
Manchester .... 01944 .... Bradley MR John M
Manchester .... 01944 .... Cabot MR & MRS John G L
Manchester .... 01944 .... Campbell MR & MRS Samuel R
Manchester .... 01944 .... Colburn MRS Irving W
Manchester .... 01944 .... Coues MR & MRS W Pearce
Manchester .... 01944 .... Creighton MR & MRS Albert M JR
Manchester .... 01944 .... Crocker MR & MRS Andrew G
Manchester .... 01944 .... Cross MR & MRS William R
Manchester .... 01944 .... Cutler MRS Tarrant
Manchester .... 01944 .... Dane MR & MRS Edward H
Manchester .... 01944 .... Dixon MR & MRS Dennis C
Manchester .... 01944 .... Dorr MR & MRS Glenn Bert III
Manchester .... 01944 .... Emmons MRS Diane Neal
Manchester .... 01944 .... Erdmann MR & MRS Robert H
Manchester .... 01944 .... Everitt MRS Charles B
Manchester .... 01944 .... Foster MR & MRS Reginald III
Manchester .... 01944 .... Gannett MR & MRS Benjamin H
Manchester .... 01944 .... Glaenzer MR & MRS Thomas A
Manchester .... 01944 .... Gratz MR Clifford B
Manchester .... 01944 .... Greenough MR & MRS Malcolm W
Manchester .... 01944 .... Hammond MR & MRS James R 3D
Manchester .... 01944 .... Holt MR & MRS Stephen R
Manchester .... 01944 .... Hutchinson MRS Anne
Manchester .... 01944 .... Kennelly MR & MRS Richard B JR
Manchester .... 01944 .... Leggett MR & MRS Anthony L
Manchester .... 01944 .... Loomis MRS Macleod
Manchester .... 01944 .... Lovett MR & MRS Robert A II
Manchester .... 01944 .... McIntyre DR Angus P JR
Manchester .... 01944 .... Mehlman DR & MRS Robert D
Manchester .... 01944 .... Moore MR & MRS J Stuart
Manchester .... 01944 .... Morris MR & MRS Frederic H
Manchester .... 01944 .... Nelson MRS Valle R
Manchester .... 01944 .... Noble MRS Carol T
Manchester .... 01944 .... Parker MRS John O
Manchester .... 01944 .... Porter MR & MRS Henry H JR
Manchester .... 01944 .... Potter DR & MRS Nicholas S
Manchester .... 01944 .... Putnam MRS George
Manchester .... 01944 .... Reeve MR & MRS Alfred Roosevelt
Manchester .... 01944 .... Reeve MRS Cintra Lowell

To nominate a candidate for the Social Register Association, please email: SRCommittee@thesocialregister.org

Manchester, MA—Nahant, MA

Manchester	01944	Rohner MR & MRS Henry John 3D
Manchester	01944	Rossetti MR & MRS Ronald L
Manchester	01944	Saltonstall MRS William L
Manchester	01944	Scott MR & MRS Robert G
Manchester	01944	von Metzsch MR & MRS Ernst H
Manchester	01944	Wallace MR & MRS W Leland H
Manchester	01944	Weld MRS Christopher
Manchester	01944	Willcox MRS Robin
Manchester	01944	Williams MRS David E 3D
Manchester	01944	Wisner MR & MRS Charles M
Manchester-by-the-Sea	01944	Allard MRS Herbert K
Manchester-by-the-Sea	01944	Brown MR & MRS Michael T
Manchester-by-the-Sea	01944	Fabyan MRS H Helliwell
Manchester-by-the-Sea	01944	Gates MR & MRS Timothy G
Manchester-by-the-Sea	01944	Glidden MR & MRS Roland W
Manchester-by-the-Sea	01944	Hall MRS Richard Loomer
Manchester-by-the-Sea	01944	Hovey MR & MRS Charles F JR
Manchester-by-the-Sea	01944	Huggins MRS Gordon
Manchester-by-the-Sea	01944	Jay MR & MRS John C
Manchester-by-the-Sea	01944	Lastavica MRS (DR) John
Manchester-by-the-Sea	01944	Noble MR George W
Manchester-by-the-Sea	01944	Panetta MR & MRS Vincent J JR
Manchester-by-the-Sea	01944	Randolph MR & MRS Evan 4TH
Manchester-by-the-Sea	01944	Siems MISS Shelby D
Manchester-by-the-Sea	01944	Smith MR & MRS (REV DR) George Putnam
Manchester-by-the-Sea	01944	Thomas MRS Lindsay R
Manchester-by-the-Sea	01944	Townsend MRS Gerard B
Marblehead	01945	Ayer MR & MRS Peter E
Marblehead	01945	Beaumont MR & MRS Robert E
Marblehead	01945	Benning MR & MRS John A
Marblehead	01945	Borggaard MR & MRS Andrew P
Marblehead	01945	Brauer MR & MRS Henry G
Marblehead	01945	Churchill MR Colin W JR
Marblehead	01945	Clark MR & MRS Laurance R
Marblehead	01945	Clough MR & MRS Anson C
Marblehead	01945	Cooper MRS Alexandra M
Marblehead	01945	Cox DR & MRS Duncan B JR
Marblehead	01945	Danforth MR & MRS John B
Marblehead	01945	Derringer MRS Pamela
Marblehead	01945	Dingle MR & MRS Jeffrey L
Marblehead	01945	Herman MR & MRS James S JR
Marblehead	01945	Hooper MRS John B
Marblehead	01945	Lake MR Peter A
Marblehead	01945	Lamb MR & MRS Dana L
Marblehead	01945	Leeson MR & MRS Robert 3D
Marblehead	01945	Livingston DR & MRS William H 3D
Marblehead	01945	Ludington MR Hoyt W
Marblehead	01945	Lufkin MR & MRS H Christopher
Marblehead	01945	Lynn MR & MRS Seth McC JR
Marblehead	01945	Niles MRS John Cutler
Marblehead	01945	Noyes MR & MRS B Pike
Marblehead	01945	Nutt MR & MRS William J
Marblehead	01945	Pendleton MR & MRS Charles K
Marblehead	01945	Reiniger MR & MRS Harlan deC
Marblehead	01945	Rowland MR & MRS Benjamin A JR
Marblehead	01945	Trowbridge MR & MRS Charles A III
Marblehead Neck	01945	Howard MRS Herbert G
Marion	02738	Baldwin MR & MRS Michael
Marion	02738	Barrett MR & MRS David A
Marion	02738	Crocker MS Evelyn T
Marion	02738	Gryska MR & MRS Alexander von R
Marion	02738	Leonard MISS Cynthia Elyse
Marion	02738	Maier DR & MRS Ward R
Marion	02738	Mercer DR & MRS Richard J
Marion	02738	Nadler MR & MRS Charles F JR
Marion	02738	Noble MR & MRS Christopher
Marion	02738	Norweb MR & MRS R Henry 3D
Marion	02738	Perkins MR & MRS Mark C
Marion	02738	Rathborne MR & MRS J Cornelius IV
Marion	02738	Talbott MR Harold E III
Marion	02738	von Zweck MR & MRS Heimart
Marion	02738	Wakeman MR & MRS G Wiley
Marshfield	02050	Parker MR & MRS Allan D 3D
Marshfield	02050	Pyle MR Stuart H
Mashpee	02649	MacColl MR & MRS J Roberton 4TH
Mattapoisett	02738	Beams MR & MRS Robert C
Mattapoisett	02739	Burr MRS Carleton
Mattapoisett	02739	Cannell MR & MRS James C
Mattapoisett	02739	Drew MR & MRS John F
Mattapoisett	02739	Gibbons MRS John D
Mattapoisett	02739	Grummon MR John H & Chapin MS Elizabeth M
Mattapoisett	02739	Jolliffe MRS Michael J A H
Mattapoisett	02739	Parker MR & MRS James W C
Mattapoisett	02739	Rice MR & MRS Donald S
Mattapoisett	02739	Roberts MR & MRS Henry P
Mattapoisett	02739	Smith MRS George W H JR
Maynard	01754	Hunt MRS Andrew D
Maynard	01754	Norris MR & MRS Kingsley F
Medfield	02052	Catlin DR & MRS Randolph JR
Medfield	02052	Fearing MR Travers
Medfield	02052	Lewis MR & MRS Arthur L 2D
Medfield	02052	Macleod MR & MRS Robert W
Medfield	02052	Martin MR & MRS Peter S
Medfield	02052	Meyer-Cushing MS Katherine D & Cushing MS Lauren A
Medfield	02052	Standley MR & MRS Burgess P
Medfield	02052	Taylor MR & MRS (DR) Michael R
Medfield	02052	Taylor MS Whitney S
Medfield	02052	Washburne MR & MRS Stephen H
Medfield	02052	Wirts MR & MRS Christopher N
Medford	02155	Boggess MR & MRS Boyd S
Medford	02155	Li MR & MRS (DR) Claudius Wu-Jen
Medford	02155	van Nierop MR & MRS Daniel S
Medford	02155	Wrangham MRS Josefa M
Medfordn	02155	Crawford MR & MRS Benjamin C
Melrose	02176	Fremont-Smith MR & MRS Thayer
Middleton	01949	Peterson MR David C
Millis	02054	Meyer MR John M
Milton	02186	Atwood MR & MRS William C
Milton	02186	Bray MR & MRS Robert C JR
Milton	02186	Carr MRS Samuel B
Milton	02186	Carter MR & MRS Nicholas
Milton	02186	Grant MR & MRS Thomas L
Milton	02186	Haggerty MR & MRS Bryan D
Milton	02186	Hall MR & MRS Newell N
Milton	02186	Heath MRS Richard B
Milton	02186	Lapey DR & MRS Allen
Milton	02186	Lyon MR & MRS Richard A M
Milton	02186	Millet MR Francis D
Milton	02186	Moriarty MR & MRS Bradley M
Milton	02186	Panarese MR & MRS Mark J
Milton	02186	Place MRS David E
Milton	02186	Pope MRS Ralph L JR
Milton	02186	Potter MR & MRS Stephen W
Milton	02186	Truslow MR & MRS Charles H
Milton	02186	Whiteside MR Alexander
Milton	02186	Williams MRS Helen R
Monument Beach	02553	Fenton MRS Eugénie H
Monument Beach	02553	Hammond DR & MRS Ogden H
Monument Beach	02553	Milliken MR & MRS Henry O 3D
Nahant	01908	Butler MR & MRS Thomas S K
Nahant	01908	Hunnewell MR & MRS H Hollis

Nahant	01908	Motley MR & MRS (REV) Herbert J JR
Nahant	01908	Motley MRS Pamela K
Nahant	01908	Richardson DR & MRS George S
Nahant	01908	Schepens MR & MRS Luc J
Nantucket	02554	de Zalduondo MRS J Antonio
Nantucket	02554	Dewez MR & MRS Patrick J
Nantucket	02554	Dillon MS Lucy S
Nantucket	02554	Hays MRS William Henry 3D
Nantucket	02554	Heintz MR & MRS Robert B D
Nantucket	02554	Holch MR & MRS Eric S
Nantucket	02554	Knox-Johnston MR & MRS John A
Nantucket	02554	McKechnie MR D Eric
Nantucket	02554	Northrop MR Johnston W
Nantucket	02554	Reade MR & MRS Arthur I JR
Nantucket	02554	Renwick MR & MRS John P 3D
Nantucket	02554	Riggs MRS Lawrason JR
Nantucket	02554	Stagg MRS Eduardo J
Nantucket	02554	Sutro MRS Peter C
Nantucket	02554	Thornewill MR & MRS Luke T
Nantucket	02554	Wagley MR & MRS John R
Nantucket	02554	Weld DR & MRS Francis M
Nantucket	02554	Weld MISS Caroline R
Nantucket	02554	Wickser MISS M Melissa
Nantucket	02554	Willauer MR Whiting R JR
Natick	01760	Bennet-Alder MR & MRS Grant
Natick	01760	Bradley DR Peter P
Natick	01760	Hellmuth MRS Joseph A
Natick	01760	Nelson MR Robert M
Natick	01760	Smith MR & MRS Eric D
Natick	01760	Stumpf MR Jason T & Funkhouser MS Margaret A
Natick	01760	Wheeler MR & MRS David W
Natick	01760	Woodworth MISS Barbara J
Needham	02492	Allen MR & MRS A Clinton 3D
Needham	02492	Forrester MRS Peter C
Needham	02492	Foster MR & MRS Charles H W
Needham	02492	Gay MR & MRS Paul G
Needham	02492	Grant MRS Frederic D
Needham	02492	Greenway MR & MRS Hugh D S
Needham	02492	Handler MR & MRS Steven B
Needham	02492	Hiland MR & MRS Christopher P
Needham	02492	Huntington MR & MRS A Peter
Needham	02492	Kistner MR & MRS Stephen B
Needham	02492	Lapsley MR & MRS Howard
Needham	02492	Millet MR & MRS Alexander C
Needham	02492	Millet MR & MRS David F
Needham	02492	Minott MR & MRS Owen W
Needham	02492	Moore MR & MRS James W
Needham	02492	O'Neill MRS W Paul JR
Needham	02492	Osborn MRS Katherine Page
Needham	02492	Payson MRS Samuel R
Needham	02492	Perry MR & MRS H Bradlee
Needham	02492	Place MR & MRS H Calvin JR
Needham	02492	Place MRS Julie L
Needham	02492	Pyle MRS Charles McA JR
Needham	02492	Reece MR & MRS Christopher S
Needham	02492	Reece MR & MRS F Thompson
Needham	02492	Wilson MR & MRS Peter A
Needham	02494	Chandler MR & MRS Stuart B
Needham	02494	Taylor MRS Jonathan V
Needham Heights	02494	Kuehn MRS Martha
New Bedford	02740	Zane MR & MRS Anthony M
Newbury	01922	Barrows MR & MRS William D
Newbury	01951	Holland MRS E Morton
Newbury	01951	Owen MR & MRS Hugo A
Newburyport	01950	Fremont-Smith MR & MRS Thomas D
Newburyport	01950	Graves MR & MRS Sidney C JR
Newburyport	01950	Hufnagel MR & MRS Frederick B
Newburyport	01950	Johnson MR & MRS Richard M W
Newburyport	01950	Lincoln MR & MRS William A JR
Newburyport	01950	Moore DR & MRS Sean D
Newburyport	01950	Weese MR & MRS William K
Newburyport	01950	Wells MR & MRS Jonathan G 3D
Newburyport	01950	White MR & MRS Alexander W
Newton	02458	McPherson MR & MRS Aaron F
Newton	02458	Meigs DR & MRS James B
Newton	02458	Raker MR & MRS Lee R
Newton	02458	Rex MR Daniel F II
Newton	02458	Stocker MRS Wendy T
Newton	02458	Thompson MS Phyllis E P
Newton	02459	Goodrich MRS Wendy
Newton	02459	Metcalf MR & MRS Stephen C
Newton	02459	Patterson MR & MRS David D
Newton	02465	Reynders MR & MRS John V W 3D
Newton	02467	Russo MRS Jeremy W
Newton Center	02459	Aylward MR & MRS Michael F
Newton Center	02459	Burdick MR & MRS Lalor
Newton Center	02459	Dober MR & MRS Patrick L
Newton Center	02459	Larkin MRS Marian R
Newton Center	02459	Mason MR & MRS John H
Newton Center	02459	Minot MRS Gale W
Newton Center	02459	Nelson MR Arthur H
Newton Center	02459	Pfaelzer MR & MRS Arthur Goodhue
Newton Highlands	02461	Clark MISS Claudia G
Newton Highlands	02461	Dorfman MR & MRS John R
Newton Highlands	02461	Lewis MR John G JR
Newtonville	02460	LeStage MR & MRS Gregory C
Newtonville	02460	Post MISS Dorothy S
Newtonville	02460	Thomsen MR & MRS Stewart G
Norfolk	02056	Wick MRS K Bryant JR
North Andover	01845	Donovan MR & MRS Doran W F
North Andover	01845	French MR & MRS Steven B
North Andover	01845	Gardiner MR & MRS Charles W
North Andover	01845	Hannum MR William E III & Schwartz MS Sara Goldsmith
North Andover	01845	Lincoln MR & MRS J Alden
North Andover	01845	Loring MRS William C
North Andover	01845	Perkins MRS Paul F JR
North Andover	01845	Smith MRS Marcel A
North Andover	01845	West MR & MRS Scott L
North Attleboro	02763	Bryant MR & MRS Glenn R JR
North Chatham	02650	Edgar MRS (REV) David L R
North Chatham	02650	Hessler MR & MRS Robert B
North Chatham	02650	Kearns MR & MRS Robert L
North Chatham	02650	Montross MRS Franklin 3D
North Eastham	02651	Hoag MR & MRS William K JR
North Easton	02356	Ames MR Frederick L
North Easton	02356	Ames MRS Oliver F
North Falmouth	02556	Wellington MR & MRS Benjamin B
Northampton	01060	Fraser MR Ian H
Northampton	01060	Lukens MR & MRS David C
Northampton	01060	Muspratt MR & MRS Matthew
Northampton	01060	Parsons DR & MRS John M
Northampton	01060	Scarborough MISS Julia C
Northampton	01060	Thorne MR Brinkley S & Cox MS Mazie L
Northampton	01060	Wickersham MRS Allison
Northampton	01060	Williams MR & MRS Staunton JR
Northampton	01060	Wolf MR & MRS John F III
Northborough	01532	Whittemore MRS H Lawrence JR
Northfield	01360	Ames MR & MRS William S
Norwell	02061	Bennett MRS (DR) Robert E
Norwell	02061	Freeman MRS Daniel A 3D
Norwell	02061	Landon MR & MRS Russell W

To nominate a candidate for the Social Register Association, please email: SRCommittee@thesocialregister.org

Norwell, MA—South Hamilton, MA

Norwell	02061	Paine MR & MRS Richard P
Norwood	02062	Hall MR Jonathan M
Onset	02558	Wheeler MR & MRS Richard C
Orleans	02653	Ford MR & MRS Daniel B JR
Orleans	02653	Kanaga MR & MRS Clinton R
Orleans	02653	La Cava MR & MRS Gregory
Orleans	02653	Shrady MR Theodore G N
Orleans	02653	Solley MRS Pamela
Osterville	02655	Ahn MR & MRS Sangwoo
Osterville	02655	Côté MR & MRS Mark C
Osterville	02655	Fallon MRS John T
Osterville	02655	Nickerson MRS E Carleton
Osterville	02655	Wells MRS C McGregory 3D
Peabody	01960	Barber MR & MRS Elliot H
Peabody	01960	Chick MRS Elizabeth L
Peabody	01960	Lundgren MR Richard J
Peabody	01960	Perrin MISS Gail
Peabody	01960	Preston MRS Richard
Peabody	01960	Slayne MR & MRS Brian G JR
Peabody	01960	Strater MRS Edward P
Peabody	01960	West MRS Richard S
Pembroke	02359	Ray MISS Susan E
Petersham	01366	Hinton MRS Longstreet
Pittsfield	01201	Hawkins MRS Lisa
Plymouth	02360	Amory MRS Walter
Plymouth	02360	Bartlett MR & MRS Samuel B
Plymouth	02360	Greenwood MISS Jennifer
Plymouth	02360	Greenwood MR Richard N 2d
Plymouth	02360	Russell MR & MRS Edward T JR
Plymouth	02360	Saltonstall MR & MRS Endicott P JR
Plymouth	02360	Withington MR & MRS Nathan N
Plymouth	02360	Withington MR Richard F
Pocasset	02559	Baker MR Talbot JR
Prides Crossing	01965	Cabot MR & MRS John R
Prides Crossing	01965	Carr MR & MRS Peter F II
Prides Crossing	01965	Fiske MR & MRS John N JR
Prides Crossing	01965	Garcia MR & MRS Adolfo R
Prides Crossing	01965	Loring MR Jonathan B
Prides Crossing	01965	Olney MR & MRS Richard III
Prides Crossing	01965	Richardson MRS Julian H
Prides Crossing	01965	Roosevelt MR & MRS John A
Prides Crossing	01965	Steele MRS Kilman
Prides Crossing	01965	Thorndike MR & MRS Richard K 3D
Prides Crossing	01965	Warren MRS David U
Princeton	01541	Thys MISS Anne C
Quincy	02171	Loring MR & MRS Thomas B
Reading	01867	Wilmer MR & MRS Christopher K
Richmond	01254	Frelinghuysen MR & MRS T Kinney R
Rockport	01966	Bogert MISS Joan L
Rockport	01966	Bogert MR & MRS Bruce P
Rockport	01966	Burden MRS Frances D
Rockport	01966	Pierson MRS Daniel H
Rockport	01966	Tew MR & MRS James D 3D
Roslindale	02131	Dabiri DR & MRS Borna E
Rowley	01969	Peabody MISS Virginia S
Salem	01970	Choate MRS Charles F
Salem	01970	Cox MR & MRS (DR) Duncan B 3D
Salem	01970	Goodhue MR & MRS Albert 3D
Salem	01970	Greer MR & MRS Andrew C
Salem	01970	Parker MR Charles D
Salem	01970	Phillips MISS Jane A
Salem	01970	Phillips MR Jeffrey B
Salem	01970	Putnam MISS Rebecca D
Salem	01970	Steward MR & MRS Nicholas
Salem	01970	Tew MR & MRS Jonathan B
Sandwich	02563	Austin MR & MRS Stephen D W
Sandwich	02563	Jones MR & MRS Stephen B
Sandwich	02563	Maxwell MISS Mary Brooke
Sandwich	02563	Moszka MR & MRS Stanley J
Saugus	01906	Richardson MRS Charles S JR
Scituate	02066	Cutler MR & MRS Aaron I
Scituate	02066	Vietor MR & MRS Andreas H
Sharon	02067	Doolittle MR & MRS Roy W III
Sharon	02067	Sillcocks MR Warren Barrows
Sharon	02067	Webster MR & MRS C Scott
Shebhorn	01770	Wiehl MR & MRS Ernest A JR
Sheffield	01257	Brady MRS Anne Dallett
Sheffield	01257	Reeves MRS Barbara
Sheffield	01257	Thornton MR & MRS Henry H M
Sherborn	01770	Ewing MR & MRS Stephen C
Sherborn	01770	Fiske MISS Abigail W
Sherborn	01770	Fiske MR George F JR
Sherborn	01770	George MR & MRS Robert J
Sherborn	01770	Gilfoy MR & MRS Peter G
Sherborn	01770	Hoffman MR & MRS Tyler P
Sherborn	01770	Holder MR & MRS Nicholas P
Sherborn	01770	Howland MR & MRS Edward M 2D
Sherborn	01770	LaBonte MR & MRS Walter O JR
Sherborn	01770	Larkin MR & MRS William P
Sherborn	01770	Morss MR Christopher
Sherborn	01770	Motley MR & MRS George B
Sherborn	01770	Niles MR & MRS Samuel V
Sherborn	01770	Plimpton MR & MRS Hollis W 3D
Sherborn	01770	Roberts MRS Cornelia C
Sherborn	01770	Storer MR & MRS Robert T P 3D
Sherborn	01770	Sturgis MRS Robert M
Sherborn	01770	Twining MR & MRS Edmund S 4TH
Sherborn	01770	Wallace MR & MRS Neil W
Shirley	01464	Bradstreet MR & MRS Austin R
Shrewsbury	01545	Marshall MR & MRS Claiborne T
Siasconset	02564	Felch MR & MRS Robert D
Siasconset	02564	Urbahn MRS Clara R
Somerville	02143	Herter MR & MRS Aaron B
Somerville	02143	Latorre MR Emilio & Tucker MS Sarah G
Somerville	02143	Miller MR Henry S JR
Somerville	02144	Bentley MR & MRS Nicholas N
Somerville	02144	Welch MR & MRS Thomas C
South Dartmouth	02748	Allen MR & MRS Frank A 3D
South Dartmouth	02748	Anderson MR & MRS Robert Alexander
South Dartmouth	02748	Carter MR & MRS Lewis A JR
South Dartmouth	02748	Davis MR & MRS Thomas G
South Dartmouth	02748	Gelette MR Grantland W
South Dartmouth	02748	Griffen COL (RET) & MRS William W JR
South Dartmouth	02748	Hall MR & MRS Elton W
South Dartmouth	02748	Hoyt MR & MRS H Austin A
South Dartmouth	02748	King MR & MRS Timothy P
South Dartmouth	02748	Leeson MR Richmond T
South Dartmouth	02748	Löfberg MR & MRS Per G H
South Dartmouth	02748	Murray MR & MRS F Wisner
South Dartmouth	02748	Phyfe MR & MRS James D
South Dartmouth	02748	Pryor MRS Luanne W
South Dartmouth	02748	Sommaripa MRS George
South Dartmouth	02748	Stone MR Alan N & Hill MS D Lesley
South Dartmouth	02748	West MR & MRS Christopher
South Deerfield	01373	Brown MR & MRS Wesley H
South Egremont	01258	Regendahl MR & MRS Edward R
South Hamilton	01982	Barton MR & MRS William R
South Hamilton	01982	Boardman MR & MRS William H III
South Hamilton	01982	Clark MR & MRS Forrester A JR
South Hamilton	01982	Colloredo-Mansfeld MR & MRS Ferdinand
South Hamilton	01982	Colloredo-Mansfeld MR & MRS Franz F
South Hamilton	01982	Crossan MR H James 3D

South Hamilton............ 01982......... Everitt MR & MRS Timothy S
South Hamilton............ 01982......... Gardner MR John L
South Hamilton............ 01982......... Gould MR & MRS Robert R
South Hamilton............ 01982......... Kistner MR & MRS Timothy H
South Hamilton............ 01982......... McKean MR & MRS Robert W
South Hamilton............ 01982......... Merck MR Wilhelm M & Brady MS J Nonie
South Hamilton............ 01982......... Miller MR & MRS Jonathan R
South Hamilton............ 01982......... Morrill MR Benjamin B
South Hamilton............ 01982......... Richardson MR & MRS Peter W
South Hamilton............ 01982......... Ryus MRS David D 3D
South Hamilton............ 01982......... Sutro MR & MRS Thomas W
South Hamilton............ 01982......... Thayer MRS R Thruston H
South Hamilton............ 01982......... Thissell MR & MRS John A
South Hamilton............ 01982......... Ward MRS Hugh C JR
South Hamilton............ 01982......... Werner MR & MRS Edward L 2D
South Hamilton............ 01982......... Whitman MR & MRS Peter M JR
South Hamilton............ 01982......... Yonce MR & MRS S McClay JR
South Lee .... 01260......... Potter MRS Hitt
South Natick.................. 01760......... Cruickshank MR William H
South Natick.................. 01760......... Davidson MR & MRS Malcolm
South Natick.................. 01760......... Hunnewell MR & MRS Arnold W JR
South Natick.................. 01760......... Reitter MR & MRS Frank R
South Yarmouth........... 02664......... Sheridan MR John Edward
South Yarmouth........... 02664......... Woods MR & MRS David P
Southborough............... 01772......... Heiserman MR & MRS (DR) Hewitt JR
Southborough............... 01772......... Noble MR & MRS Richard E
Southborough............... 01772......... Norris MR & MRS Kingsley C 2D
Southborough............... 01772......... Perkins MR & MRS Francis E JR
Southborough............... 01772......... Rosenwald MR & MRS Stuart H
Southborough............... 01772......... Warren MR & MRS John C
Southfield....................... 01259......... Flintoft MR & MRS Richard A
Springfield .... 01108......... Lovell MISS Katherine G
Squantum .... 02171......... Freeman MR & MRS Peter S
Stockbridge.................... 01262......... Deely MR & MRS Philip S
Stockbridge.................... 01262......... Pulitzer MR & MRS Michael E JR
Stockbridge.................... 01262......... Schwartz MISS Julia C
Stockbridge.................... 01262......... Schwartz MR & MRS Arthur W
Stockbridge.................... 01262......... Sprague MR Carl J
Stoneham....................... 02180......... Wilson MR & MRS Anthony M W
Stow............................... 01775......... Mattison MR & MRS Peter D
Sudbury.......................... 01776......... Fearey MR & MRS Peter S
Sudbury.......................... 01776......... Griffin MR & MRS Paul E
Sudbury.......................... 01776......... Hawley MR & MRS Shervin B
Sudbury.......................... 01776......... Kashem MR & MRS Anwar P
Sudbury.......................... 01776......... McCabe MRS Annett P
Sudbury.......................... 01776......... McGuire MR & MRS Edward L
Sudbury.......................... 01776......... Parker MR & MRS John O JR
Sudbury.......................... 01776......... Rodiger MR & MRS William K
Sudbury.......................... 01776......... Sluder DR & MRS (DR) Greenfield
Swampscott................... 01907......... Myers MR & MRS Rem Van A JR
Swansea......................... 02777......... Mohn MISS Susan W
Topsfield........................ 01983......... Coffin MR & MRS Timothy J
Topsfield........................ 01983......... Goltra MR & MRS Edward S
Topsfield........................ 01983......... Peirce MR John W
Topsfield........................ 01983......... Perkins MR & MRS Richard S JR
Topsfield........................ 01983......... Steward MR Campbell
Topsfield........................ 01983......... Wilkinson MR & MRS Robert A
Truro.............................. 02666......... Grant MR Frederic D JR
& Lemperly Grant MS Barbara
Truro.............................. 02666......... Watson MR & MRS Thomas A D
Tyringham..................... 01264......... Gilder MR & MRS George F
Tyringham..................... 01264......... Kittredge MRS Charles J
Tyringham..................... 01264......... Palmer MR & MRS Anthony G W
Upton............................. 01568......... Billings MR & MRS Christopher C
Vineyard Haven............ 02568......... Cabral MR & MRS Douglas A
Vineyard Haven............ 02568......... Fulton MR James M JR
Vineyard Haven............ 02568......... Furst MS Suzanne
Vineyard Haven............ 02568......... Gillette MISS Mary D
Vineyard Haven............ 02568......... Kennedy MRS Kevin
Vineyard Haven............ 02568......... Mullins MR Thomas D II
Vineyard Haven............ 02568......... Potter MR & MRS Robert L C
Vineyard Haven............ 02568......... Roosevelt MR Tweed
Vineyard Haven............ 02568......... Yacubian MR Job A
Waban .... 02468......... Bauer MR & MRS Joseph A JR
Waban .... 02468......... Cox MR & MRS Peter B
Waban .... 02468......... Johnson MR & MRS Kevin P
Waban .... 02468......... Lyons MR & MRS William B
Waban .... 02468......... Ross DR Donald F JR
Wakefield .... 01880......... Robinson MR George H
Walpole .... 02081......... Davis MR R Neville
Walpole .... 02081......... Hunter MRS Robert D
Waltham .... 02451......... Kneen MRS Alfred T JR
Waltham .... 02452......... Barron MRS Timothy R
Waltham .... 02453......... Malcom MS Diana B
Waltham .... 02453......... Phelps MR & MRS Christopher M W
Waltham .... 02453......... Sears MR Frederick F JR
Ware............................... 01082......... Schaefer MR & MRS Peter M
Wareham .... 02571......... Fay MRS Eliot
Wareham .... 02571......... Gray MR & MRS Samuel P M
Watertown..................... 02472......... Abdulrazak MR & MRS Fawzi
Watertown..................... 02472......... Bering MR & MRS Charles C
Watertown..................... 02472......... Coner MR & MRS Christopher O
Watertown..................... 02472......... Constable MR & MRS Timothy C
Watertown..................... 02472......... Crissman MR & MRS James H
Watertown..................... 02472......... Richardson MISS Anna-Constantia DeQ
Watertown..................... 02472......... Stewart MRS Zeph
Watertown..................... 02472......... Teel MS Mary-Marshall
Wayland .... 01778......... Davlin MR & MRS William E B
Wayland .... 01778......... Garfield MR & MRS Michael R
Wayland .... 01778......... Hanson MR & MRS Harry A III
Wayland .... 01778......... La Farge MR & MRS Christopher G F
Wayland .... 01778......... Lowry MR & MRS Ritchie P
Wayland .... 01778......... Moore MR & MRS Charles P
Wayland .... 01778......... Myles MRS Thomas F
Wayland .... 01778......... Simpkins MR Willard Ritchie
Wellesley .... 02481......... Bates MR & MRS Gregory S
Wellesley .... 02481......... Clothier Moses MS Christina
Wellesley .... 02481......... Plumb MR & MRS Robert J 3D
Wellesley .... 02481......... Usen MR Nicholas F
Wellesley .... 02481......... Usen MRS Peter J
Wellesley .... 02482......... Beaver MR & MRS Bentley H
Wellesley .... 02482......... Boyd DR David P
Wellesley .... 02482......... Broberg MR & MRS (DR) Richard H
Wellesley .... 02482......... Butcher MR & MRS Arthur C
Wellesley .... 02482......... Carlson MR & MRS David G
Wellesley .... 02482......... Clark MRS Grenville JR
Wellesley .... 02482......... Clay MR & MRS Peter E
Wellesley .... 02482......... Crosier MR & MRS Louis P
Wellesley .... 02482......... Davis MR & MRS Joshua M
Wellesley .... 02482......... de Fontnouvelle DR & MRS Patrick Y de F
Wellesley .... 02482......... de Peyster MR & MRS Nicholas L M
Wellesley .... 02482......... Hansen MR & MRS Thomas S
Wellesley .... 02482......... Hill MR & MRS Robert B
Wellesley .... 02482......... Hunnewell MR & MRS F Oakes JR
Wellesley .... 02482......... Hunnewell MR & MRS Walter JR
Wellesley .... 02482......... Hunnewell MRS Francis O
Wellesley .... 02482......... Hunnewell MRS Walter
Wellesley .... 02482......... Lawrence MR & MRS John H
Wellesley .... 02482......... Leonard MR & MRS Danford C
Wellesley .... 02482......... Petrasch MRS John G
Wellesley .... 02482......... Powers MRS H Burton
Wellesley .... 02482......... Riley MR & MRS C Madison III

To nominate a candidate for the Social Register Association, please email: SRCommittee@thesocialregister.org

Wellesley, MA—Westport Harbor, MA

Wellesley	02482	Smith MR & MRS Trevor G
Wellesley	02482	Soule MISS Martha R
Wellesley	02482	Waldron MISS Dorothy W
Wellesley	02482	West MRS Ralph O'Neal
Wellesley	02482	Whitman MRS R Eugene
Wellesley	02482	Wickersham MR Walter M
Wellesley Farms	02481	Sargent MR & MRS Thomas A
Wellesley Hills	02481	Bleakie MR & MRS J Maxwell JR
Wellesley Hills	02481	Brown MR & MRS Eric C
Wellesley Hills	02481	Corsini MR & MRS Russell V JR
Wellesley Hills	02481	Dunne CAPT & MRS Maurice F III
Wellesley Hills	02481	Gardner MRS Wilfred E
Wellesley Hills	02481	Harrison MR & MRS Justin H
Wellesley Hills	02481	Hurley MR Stephen Nash
Wellesley Hills	02481	Johannsen MR & MRS Peter G
Wellesley Hills	02481	Marx MR & MRS Alexander R
Wellesley Hills	02481	Paine MR & MRS Thomas M
Wellesley Hills	02481	Parkinson MR & MRS A Troup
Wellesley Hills	02481	Place MR & MRS H Calvin
Wellesley Hills	02481	Washburn MR & MRS Alexander D
Wellesley Hills	02481	Weedon MR & MRS Alexander R
Wellesley Hills	02481	Zabriskie MR & MRS Charles JR
Wellfleet	02667	Wilkinson MRS Kirk C
Wenham	01984	Ayer MR & MRS Richard R C
Wenham	01984	Charman MR & MRS William O
Wenham	01984	Colhoun MRS Patricia R
Wenham	01984	Colt MRS James D
Wenham	01984	Dodge MR E Stanley JR
Wenham	01984	Ebling MR & MRS R Hilliard
Wenham	01984	French MR & MRS Hollis 3D
Wenham	01984	Gilmor MR & MRS William Gavin
Wenham	01984	Howland MR & MRS Llewellyn III
Wenham	01984	Hoyt MRS Diana C
Wenham	01984	Hunsaker MR & MRS Jerome C III
Wenham	01984	Huntoon MS Louise W
Wenham	01984	Jones MR & MRS Christopher B
Wenham	01984	Malabre MR Richard C
Wenham	01984	Mark MR & MRS James D
Wenham	01984	Marsh MR & MRS Colin W
Wenham	01984	McConnell MR & MRS (DR) William C IV
Wenham	01984	McGinness MR & MRS Robert A
Wenham	01984	Morgan MRS Hewitt JR
Wenham	01984	Page MR & MRS Andrew D
Wenham	01984	Polese MR & MRS James Sargent
Wenham	01984	Roberts MR & MRS T Williams III
Wenham	01984	Streeter MRS Henry S
Wenham	01984	Villa MR & MRS L Blair
Wenham	01984	Waller LT COL (RET) & MRS Littleton W T II
Wenham	01984	Waller MRS Wendy W
Wenham	01984	West MR & MRS R Angus
Wenham	01984	Whitman MR & MRS Peter T
Wenham	01984	Wolcott MR & MRS Oliver III
West Acton	01720	Perkins MRS Gladys Lovering
West Boylston	01583	Wellington MR & MRS Roger U JR
West Falmouth	02574	Funkhouser DR John J
West Falmouth	02574	Riddiford MR & MRS David T JR
West Newton	02465	Fox MR & MRS John B JR
West Newton	02465	Seth MR & MRS Raj K
West Peabody	01960	Cook MISS Joan M
West Roxbury	02132	Devine MR & MRS (DR) Henry C
West Roxbury	02132	Muspratt MRS Sara McGuire
West Roxbury	02132	Watts MRS Hardy G
West Somerville	02144	Woods MR & MRS Ryan J
West Stockbridge	01266	Boyd MR & MRS B Stephen JR
West Stockbridge	01266	Graulty MR & MRS William W JR
West Tisbury	02575	Cutler MR & MRS Michael W
West Tisbury	02575	MacKenzie MR & MRS Jared D
West Yarmouth	02673	Cushman DR & MRS Paul JR
West Yarmouth	02673	Rathbone MR & MRS Peter B
Westfield	01085	Stroud MR & MRS (REV) William D II
Westford	01886	Andrews MR & MRS Charles W H
Westford	01886	Huff MR J Craig 3D
Weston	02493	Alcock MR & MRS George L JR
Weston	02493	Alcock MR Peter L
Weston	02493	Becker MR & MRS John C
Weston	02493	Burns MR & MRS Tyler A
Weston	02493	Carlton-Foss MR & MRS John A
Weston	02493	Cheston MR & MRS James 2D
Weston	02493	Constable MR & MRS Philip S
Weston	02493	Crafts MR Frederic A III
Weston	02493	Davies DR & MRS John A K
Weston	02493	de Jong DR & MRS John H
Weston	02493	Faucett MR & MRS Benjamin M
Weston	02493	Fiske MR & MRS John N
Weston	02493	Frothingham MRS Diana S
Weston	02493	Fulenwider MR & MRS Michael C
Weston	02493	Gardiner MR & MRS J Matthew
Weston	02493	Gerrity MR & MRS James Francis 3D
Weston	02493	Grant MR & MRS Halcott G
Weston	02493	Grape MR & MRS Thomas Hamilton
Weston	02493	Grape MRS Anne Egbert
Weston	02493	Haines MR & MRS (DR) James B 6TH
Weston	02493	Hanser MR & MRS S Albert III
Weston	02493	Hastings MR Caryl C B
Weston	02493	Kelly MR & MRS Francis J 3D
Weston	02493	Kendrick MR & MRS Marvin H JR
Weston	02493	Lathrop MR & MRS John E
Weston	02493	Lobel MR & MRS Elliot D
Weston	02493	Lysak MR & MRS Eugene S A
Weston	02493	McDaniel MR & MRS James A
Weston	02493	McDonald MRS Samuel J
Weston	02493	Nelson MRS Warren G
Weston	02493	Newell MR & MRS John O 4TH
Weston	02493	Pell MR & MRS Anthony D
Weston	02493	Phillips MR & MRS Asa E III
Weston	02493	Quinn MR & MRS Daniel L
Weston	02493	Reeder MR & MRS Henry S
Weston	02493	Stanton MR & MRS Peter W
Weston	02493	Stonestreet MR & MRS John P
Weston	02493	Stubbs MRS John D
Weston	02493	Tubman MR John Barry
Weston	02493	Tucker MR & MRS D Stewart
Weston	02493	Van Nest MR & MRS Jeffrey C
Weston	02493	Walek MR David B & Gibson MRS Elizabeth Roberson
Weston	02493	Welles MR Christopher S
Weston	02493	Williams MR Charles D
Weston	02493	Williams MS Rosamond K
Weston	02493	Willis MRS Harold B JR
Weston	02493	Wiseman MRS William F
Westport	02790	Brown MR & MRS Bernard L
Westport	02790	Cooper MR & MRS Harold B 3D
Westport	02790	Dawson MR & MRS Alec B
Westport	02790	Griswold MRS Roger P
Westport	02790	Lee MR & MRS J Philip
Westport	02790	Morton MR & MRS W Hugh M
Westport	02790	O'Brien MR & MRS Jonathan B
Westport	02790	Tuckerman MRS Bayard
Westport	02790	Wise MR & MRS Christopher T
Westport Harbor	02790	Barnum MR & MRS William M
Westport Harbor	02790	Borden MR & MRS Robert R III
Westport Harbor	02790	Findlay MRS Charles W JR

Westport Point............... 02791.......... Guy MR & MRS Benjamin W 3D
Westport Point............... 02791.......... Hill MR Freeman W JR
Westwood....................... 02090......... Ames MRS David
Westwood....................... 02090......... Blodget MRS Alden S JR
Westwood....................... 02090......... Bodman MRS Helene D
Westwood....................... 02090......... Cabot MRS Paul C JR
Westwood....................... 02090......... Clark MRS Lewis H
Westwood....................... 02090......... Cutler MR & MRS Thomas P JR
Westwood....................... 02090......... de Marneffe DR Francis
Westwood....................... 02090......... Flynn MR & MRS Christopher J JR
Westwood....................... 02090......... Fuller MR William C JR
Westwood....................... 02090......... Gay MR & MRS Bradford F
Westwood....................... 02090......... Greppin MR & MRS Ernest H JR
Westwood....................... 02090......... Guild MR & MRS Henry R JR
Westwood....................... 02090......... Hall MS Kirke T
Westwood....................... 02090......... Harding MRS John L
Westwood....................... 02090......... Harris MRS P Randolph
Westwood....................... 02090......... Heckscher MR & MRS (DR) Christopher A
Westwood....................... 02090......... High MISS Margaret P
Westwood....................... 02090......... Hines MRS Marion E
Westwood....................... 02090......... Howe MRS James C
Westwood....................... 02090......... Hunnewell MR & MRS Arnold W
Westwood....................... 02090......... Husted MR & MRS John S
Westwood....................... 02090......... Irwin MRS Henry M
Westwood....................... 02090......... Johnston MR & MRS Douglas C
Westwood....................... 02090......... Jones MRS Richard 3D
Westwood....................... 02090......... Lawrence MR & MRS Robert A
Westwood....................... 02090......... Leonard MR & MRS Daniel
Westwood....................... 02090......... Linderman MR & MRS Robert P 3D
Westwood....................... 02090......... Martin MRS Richard S
Westwood....................... 02090......... Maynard DR Edwin P
Westwood....................... 02090......... McDowell MR & MRS Putnam B
Westwood....................... 02090......... McFarland MR & MRS Duncan M
Westwood....................... 02090......... Norton MRS Lawrence A
Westwood....................... 02090......... Olney MRS William S
Westwood....................... 02090......... Pellegrino MR & MRS Stephen J
Westwood....................... 02090......... Provost MR N Thomas & Gutowski DR Andrew
Westwood....................... 02090......... Provost MRS Pierre E IV
Westwood....................... 02090......... Reed MRS P Loring JR
Westwood....................... 02090......... Richardson MRS Edward P JR
Westwood....................... 02090......... Ricketson MRS Scott
Westwood....................... 02090......... Robinson MR & MRS Edward T
Westwood....................... 02090......... Sanel MR & MRS Scott
Westwood....................... 02090......... Saunders MR & MRS Preston H
Westwood....................... 02090......... Stokes MRS Richard W
Westwood....................... 02090......... Storey MRS Patricia P
Westwood....................... 02090......... Sunderland MRS Edwin S S
Westwood....................... 02090......... Talcott MR & MRS Hooker JR
Westwood....................... 02090......... Thorndike MR John L
Westwood....................... 02090......... Weld MRS Christopher M
Westwood....................... 02090......... West MR & MRS Thomas H
Westwood....................... 02090......... Wheeler MR & MRS James G
Westwood....................... 02090......... Whitman MR & MRS Stephen L
Westwood....................... 02090......... Yeager MRS John G
Williamstown................ 01267.......... Craig MR Thomas K & Rork MS Jennifer
Williamstown................ 01267.......... Fernandez MRS Rafael A
Williamstown................ 01267.......... Geier DR & MRS Philip O 3D
Williamstown................ 01267.......... Gibbons MR & MRS James C
Williamstown................ 01267.......... Grant MR William C JR
Williamstown................ 01267.......... McKnight MR & MRS Philip R
Williamstown................ 01267.......... Sprague MR & MRS John L
Williamstown................ 01267.......... Wassenar MR & MRS Winthrop M
Winchester..................... 01890.......... Abdulrazak MISS Caroline Earle
Winchester..................... 01890.......... Blodget MR & MRS Dudley F
Winchester..................... 01890.......... Foster MR & MRS Franklin H
Winchester..................... 01890.......... Goodrich MR & MRS Paul W JR
Winchester..................... 01890.......... Morris MR & MRS F Halsey JR
Winchester..................... 01890.......... Noble MR & MRS George W JR
Winchester..................... 01890.......... Richardson MR & MRS Edward D
Winchester..................... 01890.......... Williams MR & MRS Walworth B
Woburn.......................... 01801.......... Kuehn MR Alfred L
Woburn.......................... 01801.......... Newell MR & MRS Clifford A JR
Woods Hole.................... 02543.......... Brown MR David D S
& Meigs-Brown MRS Anne L
Woods Hole.................... 02543.......... Bruce MR John G JR
Woods Hole.................... 02543.......... Glazebrook MRS James G
Woods Hole.................... 02543.......... Hocker MR & MRS Lon
Woods Hole.................... 02543.......... Jeffrey MR & MRS Peter J
Woods Hole.................... 02543.......... Lineaweaver MR & MRS Timothy H
Woods Hole.................... 02543.......... Lyman MRS Huntington
Woods Hole.................... 02543.......... Rea MR & MRS C Cary
Woods Hole.................... 02543.......... Reynolds MRS Bartow
Woods Hole.................... 02543.......... Swift MRS E Kent JR
Woods Hole.................... 02543.......... Wagner MR & MRS Stephen P
Woods Hole.................... 02543.......... Wickersham MRS A A Tilney
Woodshole...................... 02543.......... Chappell DR Richard L
Woodville....................... 01784.......... Mazza MR Jeffrey R
Worcester....................... 01606.......... Williams MR & MRS Holden B
Yarmouth Port.............. 02675.......... Dyett MR E Granger 3D
Yarmouth Port.............. 02675.......... Gutterson MR & MRS Herbert L
Yarmouth Port.............. 02675.......... Murray MR & MRS William T JR
Yarmouth Port.............. 02675.......... Painter MRS William H
Yarmouth Port.............. 02675.......... Perera MR & MRS Ronald C
Yarmouth Port.............. 02675.......... Thompson MRS George W

MICHIGAN

Ann Arbor..................... 48103.......... Marshall MRS Ruth S
Ann Arbor..................... 48103.......... Tribou MR Douglas D & McQuilkin MS Hilary B
Ann Arbor..................... 48104.......... Butz MR & MRS David A
Ann Arbor..................... 48104.......... Fresco DR & MRS David M
Ann Arbor..................... 48104.......... Parker DR & MRS Walter R
Ann Arbor..................... 48104.......... Price MISS Margaret B
Ann Arbor..................... 48104.......... von Meister MR & MRS Rudolph W
Ann Arbor..................... 48105.......... Morgan MR & MRS Jonathan C
Ann Arbor..................... 48105.......... Price MR & MRS Richard H SR
Baroda.......................... 49101.......... Lobaugh MR & MRS Garry M
Belmont......................... 49306.......... Humm MR & MRS William W
Beverly Hills.................. 48025.......... Elledge MR Michael S
Beverly Hills.................. 48025.......... Laimbeer MR & MRS Richard B
Beverly Hills.................. 48025.......... Meehan MR Albert J & Rawls MS Anne W
Big Rapids..................... 49307.......... Mullet MR & MRS Daniel
Birmingham................... 48009.......... Ford MR & MRS Madison Lewis
Birmingham................... 48009.......... Noser MR & MRS Keith W
Birmingham................... 48009.......... Ward MR & MRS James C
Bloomfield Hills............ 48301.......... Levin MS Carolyn E B
Bloomfield Hills............ 48302.......... Fischer MR & MRS David T
Bloomfield Hills............ 48304.......... Danaher REV DR & MRS William J JR
Bloomfield Hills............ 48304.......... Goldberg MR & MRS Tom J
Bloomfield Hills............ 48304.......... Holmes MR & MRS Sidney S
Bloomfield Hills............ 48304.......... Ingold MRS John Arthur
Brighton........................ 48114.......... Lugar MRS Norman O JR
Burt Lake...................... 49717.......... O'Malley MRS John P
Canton........................... 48188.......... Cannon MR & MRS Michael C
Cedar............................ 49621.......... Cochran MR & MRS Philip Lee JR
Clarkston....................... 48346.......... Sherman MS Ingrid A
Coldwater...................... 49036.......... Marso MR & MRS Robert D JR
Commerce Township... 48390.......... Grotz MR & MRS William A 3D
East Grand Rapids........ 49506.......... Koeze MR & MRS Jeffrey S
Farmington Hills.......... 48331.......... Callahan MR & MRS Thomas D
Farmington Hills.......... 48331.......... Stockly MRS John G
Fenton........................... 48430.......... Sutherland MISS Maryanne B

Fort Gratiot, MI—Greenville, MS

Fort Gratiot ..... 48059 ..... Aiken DR & MRS Timothy B
Galien ..... 49113 ..... Mix MR B John JR
Glen Arbor ..... 49636 ..... Cochran MISS Corinne
Glen Arbor ..... 49636 ..... Moore MR & MRS Robert J
Grand Rapids ..... 49506 ..... Judson MR & MRS Gilbert H
Grand Rapids ..... 49506 ..... Levings MR Nelson T
Grand Rapids ..... 49546 ..... Dallman MRS James H
Grosse Pointe ..... 48230 ..... Camden MR & MRS Andrew L
Grosse Pointe ..... 48230 ..... Crenshaw MR & MRS D Kerry
Grosse Pointe ..... 48230 ..... Peck MR & MRS Jeffrey E
Grosse Pointe ..... 48230 ..... Wilkinson MRS Warren S
Grosse Pointe ..... 48236 ..... Maycock MR & MRS Joseph F JR
Grosse Pointe ..... 48236 ..... McMullen MRS George R
Grosse Pointe Farms ..... 48236 ..... Barroll MR & MRS F Lewis
Grosse Pointe Farms ..... 48236 ..... Begg MR & MRS Charles B JR
Grosse Pointe Farms ..... 48236 ..... Birgbauer MR & MRS Bruce D
Grosse Pointe Farms ..... 48236 ..... Booth MRS John L
Grosse Pointe Farms ..... 48236 ..... Broderick MR & MRS Kevin P A
Grosse Pointe Farms ..... 48236 ..... Campbell MR & MRS Duncan MacColl
Grosse Pointe Farms ..... 48236 ..... Campbell MRS Douglas JR
Grosse Pointe Farms ..... 48236 ..... Clark MRS Caulkins
Grosse Pointe Farms ..... 48236 ..... Conway MR & MRS John 4TH
Grosse Pointe Farms ..... 48236 ..... Cunningham MISS Caroline McFaddin
Grosse Pointe Farms ..... 48236 ..... Dow MR & MRS Peter A
Grosse Pointe Farms ..... 48236 ..... Hatch MR & MRS Thomas F
Grosse Pointe Farms ..... 48236 ..... Higbie MR & MRS Mark Scherer
Grosse Pointe Farms ..... 48236 ..... Hudson MR & MRS Joseph L JR
Grosse Pointe Farms ..... 48236 ..... Morris MRS Charles W JR
Grosse Pointe Farms ..... 48236 ..... Obolensky MRS Serge
Grosse Pointe Farms ..... 48236 ..... Perkins MR & MRS John M
Grosse Pointe Farms ..... 48236 ..... Platt MR & MRS Richard B
Grosse Pointe Farms ..... 48236 ..... Remick MR Fenton M
Grosse Pointe Farms ..... 48236 ..... Stroh MR & MRS John William III
Grosse Pointe Farms ..... 48236 ..... Warren MR & MRS John B JR
Grosse Pointe Farms ..... 48236 ..... Whitney MS Bethine S II
Grosse Pointe Park ..... 48230 ..... Manoogian MR & MRS Richard A
Grosse Pointe Shores ..... 48236 ..... Booth MR & MRS John Lord II
Grosse Pointe Shores ..... 48236 ..... Endicott MRS Charles M
Grosse Pointe Woods ..... 48236 ..... Fisher MR & MRS Thomas K
Grosse Pointe Woods ..... 48236 ..... McMullen MR George R JR
Harbor Springs ..... 49740 ..... Carruthers MRS Thomas H IV
Harbor Springs ..... 49740 ..... Glass MR & MRS Charles F
Harbor Springs ..... 49740 ..... Shafer MRS Cynthia C
Hickory Corners ..... 49060 ..... Richardson DR & MRS William C
Holland ..... 49423 ..... Skvarch MR & MRS Jeffrey P
Holland ..... 49424 ..... Gamble MR & MRS Robert B
Houghton ..... 49931 ..... Rose MR & MRS William I
Huntington Woods ..... 48070 ..... Platt MR & MRS R Booth JR
Ipswich ..... 01938 ..... Reid MR & MRS Andrew C
Lake Orion ..... 48362 ..... Lord MR Raymond W
Maple City ..... 49664 ..... Cochran MR & MRS George N
Milford ..... 48381 ..... Gregg MRS John M
Mt Pleasant ..... 48850 ..... Fuller MR G Gary
Muskegon ..... 49441 ..... Day MRS John MacL
Northport ..... 49670 ..... White MR & MRS William T III
Petoskey ..... 49770 ..... Moran MR & MRS John P
Plymouth ..... 48170 ..... Baker MR & MRS Brinton E
Plymouth ..... 48170 ..... Browne MRS Kathy F
Portage ..... 49024 ..... Balaguer MR & MRS Roberto JR
Royal Oak ..... 48067 ..... McConnell MR & MRS Hans K
St Clair Shores ..... 48080 ..... Higbie MISS Faye T
St Clair Shores ..... 48080 ..... Kogel MR & REV DR
Temperance ..... 48182 ..... McLean REV DR & MRS Alexander R
Three Oaks ..... 49129 ..... Thompson MRS Sandra H
Traverse City ..... 49686 ..... Peters MS M Gores

MINNESOTA

Afton ..... 55001 ..... Hayman MR & MRS Jonathan C
Austin ..... 55912 ..... Wood DR Harrison W JR
Bloomington ..... 55420 ..... Sinkler MR Wharton 3D
Bloomington ..... 55438 ..... Hensel MRS Carl N
Edina ..... 55410 ..... Farrell MR & MRS J Michael
Edina ..... 55424 ..... Hunnewell MR & MRS Willard P JR
Edina ..... 55435 ..... Ducar MR & MRS Michael P
Edina ..... 55436 ..... Scott MR & MRS James D
Edina ..... 55436 ..... Wellborn MR & MRS John Bennett
Edina ..... 55439 ..... Hardy MRS Rodney D
Golden Valley ..... 55422 ..... Walker MRS George G JR
Hinckley ..... 55037 ..... Ostheimer MR & MRS J Gibson
Long Lake ..... 55356 ..... Crosby MRS Thomas M JR
Long Lake ..... 55356 ..... Muldoon MR & MRS Paul D
Mankato ..... 56001 ..... Drake DR & MRS Thomas F
Maple Grove ..... 55369 ..... Davis MR & MRS (REV) Scott J
Maple Grove ..... 56311 ..... Alcott MR & MRS Michael B
Mendota Heights ..... 55118 ..... Painter MR & MRS Richard W
Minneapolis ..... 55401 ..... Mondale MR Walter F
Minneapolis ..... 55403 ..... Ketchum MR & MRS Perry D
Minneapolis ..... 55403 ..... MacDonald MR & MRS Reid V
Minneapolis ..... 55405 ..... Coe MISS Alexandra C
Minneapolis ..... 55409 ..... Harris MR & MRS (DR) Louis M JR
Minneapolis ..... 55409 ..... Willegalle MR & MRS Michael A
Minneapolis ..... 55410 ..... Bortolot DR & MRS Alexander I
Minneapolis ..... 55410 ..... Murray MR Timothy B
Minneapolis ..... 55414 ..... Dunham MR & MRS Lawrence B 3D
Minneapolis ..... 55414 ..... Smela DR & MRS (DR) Stephen J
Minneapolis ..... 55416 ..... Klopp MR & MRS David W
Minneapolis ..... 55424 ..... Smith MR & MRS Bradley R
Minnetonka ..... 55345 ..... Glover MR & MRS Jonathan L
Minnetrista ..... 55364 ..... Pidot MR Whitney D JR
Orono ..... 55356 ..... Lowe MR & MRS James R III
Pelican Rapids ..... 56572 ..... Harris MR Scott S
Plymouth ..... 55441 ..... Merriam MR & MRS Michael W
Plymouth ..... 55446 ..... Hulting MR & MRS Frederick L
Plymouth ..... 55447 ..... Wilbor MR A Wells
Prior Lake ..... 55372 ..... Poling MR & MRS Chandler H
Rochester ..... 55902 ..... Drake DR & MRS (DR) Matthew T
St Paul ..... 55101 ..... Webb MR Lucian A
St Paul ..... 55105 ..... Seifert MR & MRS Timothy E
St Paul ..... 55116 ..... Drake MR & MRS Mark H
St Paul ..... 55116 ..... Motter MRS William C
St Paul ..... 55104 ..... Brown MR & MRS Lawrance A JR
Stillwater ..... 55082 ..... Swisher MR Michael Scott
Wayzata ..... 55391 ..... Hannaford MR & MRS Jule M IV
Wayzata ..... 55391 ..... Mitchell MR & MRS Kirk F
Wayzata ..... 55391 ..... Osborn MR & MRS Steele Bartley
Wayzata ..... 55391 ..... Pidot MRS Ellison
Wayzata ..... 55391 ..... Pillsbury MRS John S JR
Winona ..... 55987 ..... Richardson MR & MRS Steven M

MISSISSIPPI

Biloxi ..... 39530 ..... Miller DR & MRS (DR) Jule P 3D
Biloxi ..... 39530 ..... Miller DR Jule P JR
Brookhaven ..... 39601 ..... Henderson MRS (DR) Anne Atkinson
Cleveland ..... 38732 ..... Jacobs MR & MRS Charles Clark JR
Columbia ..... 39429 ..... Jordan LTC (RET) Horace R
Columbia ..... 39429 ..... Simmons MR & MRS William E 3D
Columbus ..... 39701 ..... Garzon LT & MRS George H
Columbus ..... 39705 ..... Clark MR & MRS B Conner
Diberville ..... 39540 ..... Brinkley MR Brandon Lemmon A
Greenville ..... 38701 ..... Mixson MRS James Franklin JR

Gulfport 39501 Little DR & MRS Robert A
Hattiesburg 39401 Heidelberg MR & MRS R Webster 3D
Hattiesburg 39401 Rutland MRS Gregory W
Hattiesburg 39402 Stevens MR & MRS Benjamin McC III
Hattiesburg 39402 Thomson MR & MRS Richard S JR
Jackson 39206 Duke MR & MRS Frank M
Jackson 39211 Becker MR & MRS Edward W
Jackson 39211 Jabaley DR & MRS Michael E
Jackson 39211 Jones MR Ben B B II
Jackson 39211 Kientz MR & MRS William A 3D
Jackson 39211 McClendon MR & MRS Burwell B JR
Jackson 39211 Walker MR & MRS Harry M
Jackson 39211 Wells MR & MRS Calvin L
Jackson 39216 Butler MR & MRS Thorne G
Jackson 39216 Simmons DR & MRS Heber S JR
Jackson 39216 Winter MR & MRS William F
Long Beach 39560 Fairbank MR David Ezekiel & Smith DR Judith W
Madison 39110 Wells MR Gordon Menard
Meridian 39305 Dohan MRS Thomas R JR
Natchez 39120 Calhoun DR & MRS William Felix
Natchez 39120 Eidt MR & MRS Edward Duncan
Natchez 39120 Peale MR & MRS William Allen 3D
Natchez 39120 Pierrepont MISS Peggy
Natchez 39120 Scott MR & MRS Bobby Clay
Natchez 39120 Smith MR & MRS William Marion
Natchez 39120 Taylor MRS John Martin
Natchez 39120 Tillman DR & MRS C Randolph
Oxford 38655 Bartholomew MR & MRS Niles E
Pass Christian 39571 Whitlock MS Suzanne de L
Port Gibson 39150 Crisler MR & MRS Edgar Theodore JR
Port Gibson 39150 Lum MR & MRS William Douglas JR
Ridgeland 39157 Ferrell MR & MRS Wayne E JR
Tupelo 38804 DeMoville MS Margaret Jock
Woodville 39669 Sturgeon MR & MRS A Holmes III

MISSOURI

Ballwin 63011 Williams MR W Grant
Brentwood 63144 Baldwin MR & MRS Richard 3D
Cape Girardeau 63703 Snow MRS Robert B
Chesterfield 63005 Garlich MR & MRS Greg A
Chesterfield 63017 Harris MR & MRS Christopher J
Chesterfield 63017 Houser MR & MRS James G
Chesterfield 63017 Lewis MR Robert D 2D
Chesterfield 63017 Liggett MRS Hiram S JR
Chesterfield 63017 Meyer MRS Robert J
Chesterfield 63017 Parker MR & MRS John E JR
Chesterfield 63017 Pernoud DR & MRS Michael J
Chesterfield 63017 Rabenberg MR & MRS Steven N
Chesterfield 63017 Waterbury MR Jackson D
Clayton 63105 Aguado MR & MRS Michael H
Clayton 63105 Battram MRS Richard L
Clayton 63105 Chalfant MR & MRS Holland F JR
Clayton 63105 Frank MR Terrence D
Clayton 63105 Jones MR & MRS Herbert N
Clayton 63105 Lawton MR William J
Clayton 63105 Mattis MR Richard B
Columbia 65203 Huxley MISS Virginia H
Columbia 65203 Terry DR & MRS James H 3D
Creve Coeur 63141 Francis MR & MRS James A
Des Peres 63131 Forster MR Gerald M
Des Peres 63131 Saxton MR & MRS A Clifford JR
Florissant 63031 Desloge MRS Joseph JR
Florissant 63031 Fordyce MR S Wesley 5TH
Frontenac 63131 James MRS Christy F
Glencoe 63038 Stewart MISS Amy H
Glendale 63122 Bell MRS John H
Huntleigh 63131 Niedringhaus MR & MRS George W 3D
Joplin 64801 Fuller MR & MRS Stephen W
Kansas City 64111 Welles MRS Edward R 2D
Kansas City 64112 Seabaugh MR & MRS Kevin P
Kansas City 64113 Buffum MRS Charles G 3D
Kansas City 64114 Lewis MR & MRS James E 3D
Kansas City 64137 Van der Leur MISS Suzanne
Kansas City 64152 Engelbert MR & MRS David G
Kirkwood 63122 Condie MRS Churchill C
Kirkwood 63122 Doyle MR & MRS Thomas J
Kirkwood 63122 Shands MR & MRS Courtney JR
Labadie 63055 Leschen MR & MRS Harry J III
Ladue 63124 Bryan MRS Henry C JR
Ladue 63124 Day MR & MRS Laurence Clark
Ladue 63124 Marshall MR & MRS John A
Louisiana 63353 Hoover MR F Herbert
Nevada 64772 Hader MISS Karla S
O'Fallon 63368 Pernoud DR & MRS (DR) Michael J
Springfield 65804 Amberg MR & MRS Richard H III
St Louis 63102 Day MR Spencer D
St Louis 63104 Hale MR & MRS Stephen F
St Louis 63105 Archie REV & MRS Andrew J
St Louis 63105 Bryant MISS Ruth Alyne
St Louis 63105 Claggett MR & MRS Charles E JR
St Louis 63105 Corley MRS Robert C JR
St Louis 63105 Fletcher MRS Paul F
St Louis 63105 Fordyce MRS William C
St Louis 63105 Gallagher MR Arthur C MacV
St Louis 63105 Galt MR & MRS Martin E 3D
St Louis 63105 Gerdine DR & MRS Leigh
St Louis 63105 Haffenreffer MR & MRS John D
St Louis 63105 Harrison MRS Donald L
St Louis 63105 Humphreys DR & MRS (DR) Michael H
St Louis 63105 Jacobi MR & MRS Jan de G
St Louis 63105 Krone MRS Robert C
St Louis 63105 Lionberger MRS John S JR
St Louis 63105 Matthews MR & MRS F Maury
St Louis 63105 Newman MR & MRS Andrew R
St Louis 63105 Pantaleoni MR & MRS Jonathan R
St Louis 63105 Rava MR & MRS John A
St Louis 63105 Raven MRS Tamra E
St Louis 63105 Roberts MISS Lila L
St Louis 63105 Scott MRS Ann R Cady
St Louis 63105 Sears MR & MRS Robert M
St Louis 63105 Symington MR & MRS Stuart JR
St Louis 63105 Tregellas MRS A Smith
St Louis 63105 Voges MRS Shelton C
St Louis 63105 Walker-Said MR & MRS Maher R
St Louis 63105 Wightman MR & MRS Orrin S III
St Louis 63105 Witherspoon MR & MRS James T
St Louis 63105 Wolfsberger MR & MRS Donald L
St Louis 63108 Barry MR François Benoist
St Louis 63108 Bush MR & MRS Marc W
St Louis 63108 Carpenter MR & MRS Clarkson 3D
St Louis 63108 Corley DR & MRS Robert C
St Louis 63108 Cunningham MR & MRS C Baker
St Louis 63108 Humphreys DR & MRS Benjamin D
St Louis 63108 McGowan MR & MRS William J
St Louis 63108 McKay MR George F JR
St Louis 63108 Morrison MRS George H
St Louis 63108 O'Connor MRS Richard D
St Louis 63108 Pulitzer MRS Joseph JR
St Louis 63108 Sawyer MISS Eloise McLaran
St Louis 63108 Sayad MR E W Gentry
St Louis 63108 Schlafly MR & MRS J Joseph III

St Louis, MO—St Louis, MO

St Louis........................... 63108......... Schlafly MR & MRS Thomas F
St Louis........................... 63108......... Spencer MR & MRS Robert A
St Louis........................... 63108......... Teasdale MRS Elizabeth
St Louis........................... 63108......... Tompkins MR & MRS Frederick K
St Louis........................... 63108......... Van Luven MR & MRS William R
St Louis........................... 63108......... Wilson MR & MRS Andrew B
St Louis........................... 63109......... Drain MISS Caroline E M
St Louis........................... 63109......... Drain MR James N
St Louis........................... 63112......... Dunn MR & MRS Robert C 3D
St Louis........................... 63112......... Fehlig MR & MRS Edward K
St Louis........................... 63112......... Garnett MR & MRS Anthony T
St Louis........................... 63117......... Bermingham MR & MRS John R JR
St Louis........................... 63117......... Hartung MR & MRS Cory McC
St Louis........................... 63117......... Smith MR & MRS Emmet Carter
St Louis........................... 63117......... Smith MR & MRS R Andrew
St Louis........................... 63119......... Bruns MR & MRS David J
St Louis........................... 63119......... Hughes REV DR John Jay
St Louis........................... 63119......... Kennedy MRS Nancy K
St Louis........................... 63119......... Schmitz MR & MRS Walter Douglas
St Louis........................... 63119......... Sumner MR & MRS (DR) Paul E
St Louis........................... 63122......... Anthon MR & MRS Donald W JR
St Louis........................... 63122......... Barry DR & MRS Robert A 3D
St Louis........................... 63122......... Cramer MRS John E III
St Louis........................... 63122......... Demerath MR & MRS Jeffrey T
St Louis........................... 63122......... Garrick MRS Marguerite
St Louis........................... 63122......... Jones MR Maury F
St Louis........................... 63122......... Kniest MRS Bernard J
St Louis........................... 63122......... MacVeagh MR Charles P 3D
St Louis........................... 63122......... Metcalfe MR & MRS James W
St Louis........................... 63122......... Meyer MR & MRS George F 3D
St Louis........................... 63122......... Moppert MR & MRS Philip E
St Louis........................... 63124......... Allen MR & MRS Charles C JR
St Louis........................... 63124......... Anthon MR & MRS Donald W
St Louis........................... 63124......... Bade MR & MRS Christopher M
St Louis........................... 63124......... Ballinger MRS Walter F 2D
St Louis........................... 63124......... Barnes MR & MRS Charles Le F
St Louis........................... 63124......... Behan MR & MRS Patrick J JR
St Louis........................... 63124......... Benoist DR Walter F
St Louis........................... 63124......... Benoist MR & MRS W Elliot
St Louis........................... 63124......... Bitting MR & MRS George C JR
St Louis........................... 63124......... Black MR & MRS Van-Lear 3D
St Louis........................... 63124......... Brauer MR & MRS Blackford F
St Louis........................... 63124......... Brauer MR & MRS Stephen F
St Louis........................... 63124......... Broughton MR & MRS Donald A
St Louis........................... 63124......... Bundy MR & MRS Graham L
St Louis........................... 63124......... Cann MR & MRS William F JR
St Louis........................... 63124......... Carruthers MR & MRS John D
St Louis........................... 63124......... Carruthers MRS Letah H
St Louis........................... 63124......... Chouteau MRS Pierre P
St Louis........................... 63124......... Ciapciak MR & MRS Robert J
St Louis........................... 63124......... Collins MR & MRS Richard J JR
St Louis........................... 63124......... Cornwell MR & MRS Alexander M JR
St Louis........................... 63124......... Danforth MRS Donald JR
St Louis........................... 63124......... Dexter MR & MRS Philip
St Louis........................... 63124......... Douglass MR & MRS Thomas Edward
St Louis........................... 63124......... Dowd MR & MRS Edward L JR
St Louis........................... 63124......... Dozier MR & MRS John O JR
St Louis........................... 63124......... Drescher MR & MRS John M JR
St Louis........................... 63124......... Duhme MRS H Richard JR
St Louis........................... 63124......... Elliott MR & MRS Howard JR
St Louis........................... 63124......... Engler MR & MRS J Curtis
St Louis........................... 63124......... Ferriss MR & MRS Franklin
St Louis........................... 63124......... Flanigan MR & MRS Peter Allen
St Louis........................... 63124......... Flanigan MR Christopher A
St Louis........................... 63124......... Fouke MR & MRS Lucien R JR
St Louis........................... 63124......... Fusz MR & MRS Louis J JR
St Louis........................... 63124......... Goessling MR & MRS John G JR
St Louis........................... 63124......... Haffner MR & MRS David M
St Louis........................... 63124......... Hailand MR & MRS Arthur G III
St Louis........................... 63124......... Hailand MR Jeffress B
St Louis........................... 63124......... Hall MR & MRS Stephen J
St Louis........................... 63124......... Hawes MR & MRS Frederick L
St Louis........................... 63124......... Hermann MR & MRS Robert R JR
St Louis........................... 63124......... Hiemenz MR & MRS A Charles III
St Louis........................... 63124......... Hiemenz MR & MRS A Charles IV
St Louis........................... 63124......... Holloway MRS Jerome K
St Louis........................... 63124......... Holmes MR & MRS Fielding L
St Louis........................... 63124......... Holmes MR & MRS Warren C C
St Louis........................... 63124......... Holmes MR John A III & Eastwood MR Hugh A
St Louis........................... 63124......... Holmes MRS John A JR
St Louis........................... 63124......... Holton MR & MRS Richard C JR
St Louis........................... 63124......... Igleheart MRS Edgar A
St Louis........................... 63124......... Imbs MR & MRS R Christopher
St Louis........................... 63124......... Jenks MRS M Mathews
St Louis........................... 63124......... Johnson MR & MRS James Lee III
St Louis........................... 63124......... Johnston MR & MRS Henry O
St Louis........................... 63124......... Jones MR & MRS Stephen C
St Louis........................... 63124......... Jones MRS Edwin S
St Louis........................... 63124......... Keefer MRS Victoria A
St Louis........................... 63124......... Knight MRS Charles F
St Louis........................... 63124......... Kobusch MRS Richard B
St Louis........................... 63124......... Lammert MR & MRS Martin 5TH
St Louis........................... 63124......... Lammert MR & MRS Warren B JR
St Louis........................... 63124......... Lejeune MR & MRS Peter L
St Louis........................... 63124......... Lindburg MR & MRS A Clinton
St Louis........................... 63124......... Maricle MR John F
St Louis........................... 63124......... McAlpin MR & MRS Charles N
St Louis........................... 63124......... McDonnell MR & MRS James S 3D
St Louis........................... 63124......... McLean MR & MRS Edward B 4TH
St Louis........................... 63124......... McMullin MR & MRS Kimball R
St Louis........................... 63124......... Meyer MR & MRS George F JR
St Louis........................... 63124......... Mikulec DR & MRS (DR) Anthony A
St Louis........................... 63124......... Niedringhaus MR & MRS Charles H
St Louis........................... 63124......... Obermeyer MRS Louise T
St Louis........................... 63124......... Otto MR & MRS Robert E JR
St Louis........................... 63124......... Pettus MR & MRS Robert C
St Louis........................... 63124......... Reed MR & MRS Lawrence A
St Louis........................... 63124......... Roberts MR & MRS John R
St Louis........................... 63124......... Rogers MR & MRS M Weldon III
St Louis........................... 63124......... Sant MR & MRS John T
St Louis........................... 63124......... Schaperkotter MR & MRS John D
St Louis........................... 63124......... Scherrer MR & MRS Frederick W
St Louis........................... 63124......... Schlafly MR & MRS David K
St Louis........................... 63124......... Schmid MR & MRS Leo B
St Louis........................... 63124......... Schock MRS William C
St Louis........................... 63124......... Schwering MR & MRS Harley E
St Louis........................... 63124......... Seddon MRS James A
St Louis........................... 63124......... Selkirk MRS Bruce B JR
St Louis........................... 63124......... Shepley MR & MRS John
St Louis........................... 63124......... Shinkle MR & MRS Jackson J
St Louis........................... 63124......... Smith MR & MRS Gregory R
St Louis........................... 63124......... Smith MR & MRS Nicholas E
St Louis........................... 63124......... Smith MR & MRS Stephen A
St Louis........................... 63124......... Smith MRS George D
St Louis........................... 63124......... Snowden MR & MRS James M JR
St Louis........................... 63124......... Sommer MR & MRS Charles S
St Louis........................... 63124......... Stephens MRS John Krey
St Louis........................... 63124......... Stevens MR & MRS Gregory T
St Louis........................... 63124......... Sumner MR & MRS Lawrence C JR
St Louis........................... 63124......... Terry MR & MRS Whitelaw T JR
St Louis........................... 63124......... Veeder MRS Nicholas P
St Louis........................... 63124......... Warren MR & MRS Peter W

St Louis 63124 Wees MRS Charles A
St Louis 63124 Wehrle MR John S
St Louis 63124 Wells MR & MRS David Q JR
St Louis 63124 White MR & MRS Thomas W 5TH
St Louis 63124 Whitelaw MR & MRS George P III
St Louis 63124 Whitelaw MRS George P JR
St Louis 63124 Williams MR & MRS J Carter
St Louis 63124 Williams MRS Eugene F
St Louis 63124 Wulfing MR Charles 4TH
St Louis 63126 Bundy MRS Judith C
St Louis 63126 Greene MR & MRS Jon R
St Louis 63126 Jones MRS Maury A
St Louis 63129 Shands MR & MRS E F Berkley
St Louis 63130 Drain MRS Frederick J JR
St Louis 63130 Griffin MR & MRS Nathaniel M
St Louis 63130 Kiefer DR & MRS William F JR
St Louis 63130 Law MR & MRS Hugh R
St Louis 63130 Lucas MR & MRS Morton J 3D
St Louis 63130 Neilson MISS Margaret J
St Louis 63130 Torno MR & MRS Laurent J JR
St Louis 63131 Berger MRS John Torrey JR
St Louis 63131 Berger MS Helen Elizabeth
St Louis 63131 Clark MRS John D
St Louis 63131 Clithero MR & MRS Michael A
St Louis 63131 Feldmeir MR & MRS Christopher T
St Louis 63131 Ittner MRS Susan Shepherd
St Louis 63131 MacKenzie MR & MRS James C
St Louis 63131 McEnery MR & MRS Charles J 3D
St Louis 63131 Miller MR & MRS Stuart H
St Louis 63131 Murphy MR & MRS E Evan C
St Louis 63131 Murphy MR & MRS Russell W JR
St Louis 63131 Roudebush MR George S JR
St Louis 63131 Samuel MR & MRS James R JR
St Louis 63131 Thompson MRS Tandy C
St Louis 63132 Bock MR & MRS Kent H
St Louis 63132 Curtis MRS Robert M
St Louis 63132 Douglass MR & MRS Richard T
St Louis 63132 Drain MR Kevin R
St Louis 63132 Grote MR & MRS Richard T
St Louis 63132 Imbs MR Joseph F III
St Louis 63132 Johnson MRS James L JR
St Louis 63132 O'Reilly MRS Mary E
St Louis 63132 Remington MRS Thomas R
St Louis 63132 Shepley MRS Ethan A H JR
St Louis 63132 Smith CAPT & MRS John H 3D
St Louis 63132 Werner MR & MRS Joseph L 2D
St Louis 63141 Anstey MR Christopher L
St Louis 63141 Bakewell MR Edward L 3D
St Louis 63141 Bealke MR & MRS Linn H
St Louis 63141 Carpenter MISS Sophie E C
St Louis 63141 Chamberlain MR & MRS Philip G
St Louis 63141 Condie MR & MRS Parker B JR
St Louis 63141 Culver MISS Elizabeth
St Louis 63141 Goodman MRS Stanley J
St Louis 63141 Hall MRS George H
St Louis 63141 Hanser MR & MRS Timothy F
St Louis 63141 Hellauer MR & MRS Joseph F 3D
St Louis 63141 Ittner MR & MRS H Curtis JR
St Louis 63141 Kaiser MRS Franck Hyatt
St Louis 63141 Loyd MR & MRS Mark R
St Louis 63141 MacMillan MRS A Bryan
St Louis 63141 Niedringhaus MR & MRS W Delafield JR
St Louis 63141 Schneithorst MR & MRS James E
St Louis 63141 Wetzel MR & MRS Robert B
St Louis 63141 Wetzel MR & MRS Rolla K
St Louis 63141 Wilkinson MR & MRS Bruce S
St Louis 63143 Drain MR & MRS Eugene K
St Louis 63143 Morrissey MR Robert N
St Louis 63144 Barbieri MR & MRS Albert J
St Louis 63144 Hiemenz MR Jonathan E
St Louis 63144 Strelinger MR & MRS Richard W SR
St Louis 63144 Sumner MR & MRS Lawrence C
St Louis 63146 Corwin MR & MRS David E
St Louis 63146 Harney MR John M
St Louis 63146 Nelidow MISS Irina
St Louis 63146 Smith COL & MRS Charles F
Town & Country 63017 Waterbury MR & MRS Jackson D III
Town & Country 63131 Glascock MR & MRS John W
University City 63132 Lawton MR & MRS Frank B
Webster Groves 63119 Gibbs MRS Harry C
Webster Groves 63119 von Weise MR & MRS W Gage JR
Webster Groves 63119 Zimmerman MR & MRS Scott E
Weldon Spring 63305 Balding MRS Ivor David
Wildwood 63005 Belt MRS Charles Banks JR
Wildwood 63038 McCoy MR & MRS Timothy J

MONTANA

Absarokee 59001 Cox MR & MRS Millard
Absarokee 59001 Duke MR & MRS A St George B
Belgrade 59714 Werner MR & MRS Peter G D
Big Timber 59011 Blake MR & MRS Francis JR
Bigfork 59911 Meyer MR & MRS Ferdinand C JR
Billings 59102 Taylor MR & MRS James H
Billings 59103 Sample MR Joseph S
Billings 59105 Thomas MRS Hilda E
Bozeman 59715 Davis MR & MRS Ian S
Bozeman 59715 Hammer MR & MRS James S
Bozeman 59715 Hemingway MR & MRS Patrick
Bozeman 59715 Heminway MR & MRS John H JR
Bozeman 59715 Kerr MR & MRS John D
Bozeman 59715 Martin MRS Robert W
Bozeman 59715 Minton MR Dwight C
Bozeman 59715 Tilt MR & MRS Whitney C
Bozeman 59715 Totten MR & MRS Charles A L
Bozeman 59715 Webster MR & MRS (REV) James G 4TH
Bozeman 59718 Schurz MR Franklin D JR
Bozeman 59719 Hanes MR & MRS John W JR
Busby 59016 Taylor MISS Margaret J
Dillon 59725 Fick MR & MRS Ronald G
Dillon 59725 Mee MISS Catherine
Edgar 59026 Duke MR George StGeorge Biddle
Gallatin Gateway 59730 de Rham MRS William
Gallatin Gateway 59730 von Stade MR & MRS Charles S
Great Falls 59405 Fulton MR James R
Hamilton 59840 Patterson MR & MRS Mark
Helena 59601 Cordingley MR & MRS William A
Helena 59601 Hood MR & MRS Barry G
Huson 59846 Evarts MRS Maxwell
Livingston 59047 Hallowell MR & MRS Morris L 4TH
Livingston 59047 Tewell MR & MRS Aaron H
Lolo 59847 Moorhead MR & MRS Dudley T III
Missoula 59802 Lewis MR & MRS Winslow III
Missoula 59802 Tucker MISS Frances M
Missoula 59808 Maus MRS William D JR
Sheridan 59749 Wood MR & MRS Stephen H
Stevensville 59870 Holt MRS Robert d'A
Stevensville 59870 Hunter MR & MRS Nicholas S
Victor 59875 Draper MR & MRS Lawrence A
Victor 59875 Merrell MRS Cyrus W JR
Whitefish 59937 Munson MS Laura A
Whitefish 59937 Pulsifer MR & MRS Nathaniel M

To nominate a candidate for the Social Register Association, please email: SRCommittee@thesocialregister.org

Wilsall, MT—Hampstead, NH

Wilsall .... 59086 .... Pew MR & MRS Richard Ford
Wilsall .... 59086 .... Potter MR & MRS Horatio R
Winston .... 59647 .... Hoeffner MR & MRS Jeff D

NEBRASKA

Lincoln .... 68502 .... Baylor MR John R
Lincoln .... 68502 .... Grew MR & MRS Edward S
Lincoln .... 68516 .... Kiechel MR & MRS Frederic 4TH
Omaha .... 68124 .... Vandeveer MRS Jay W
Omaha .... 68152 .... Batchelder MRS Anne S

NEVADA

Genoa .... 89411 .... Donohoe MR William J JR
Glenbrook .... 89413 .... Bliss MR William W
Henderson .... 89052 .... Saltonstall MR & MRS John L 2D
Incline Village .... 89450 .... Wood MR & MRS Christopher W
Incline Village .... 89451 .... Gerken MR & MRS M Edward
Incline Village .... 89451 .... Harris MR J Andrews 5TH
Jean .... 89019 .... Stannard MR Ralph E
Las Vegas .... 89117 .... Painter MR William H
Las Vegas .... 89121 .... Lee MRS Jacqueline
Las Vegas .... 89134 .... Mailliard MR & MRS Howard
Las Vegas .... 89135 .... Brooks MR & MRS Brian McKinley
Las Vegas .... 89135 .... Lowry MR & MRS Arthur S
Las Vegas .... 89140 .... Brown MISS Melissa
Las Vegas .... 89141 .... Sciarratta MS Cynthia
Las Vegas .... 89147 .... Pinnicchia MR & MRS Gino
Las Vegas .... 89148 .... Chalkley MR James E II & Cushman MS Susan
Minden .... 89423 .... Schilling MR Robert E
Reno .... 89509 .... Burton MISS Virginia Todd
Reno .... 89509 .... Burton MR & MRS C Thomas JR
Reno .... 89509 .... Laughton MR & MRS Mitchell C
Reno .... 89510 .... Jones MRS Russell C
Reno .... 89511 .... Atkins MR & MRS Victor K JR
Reno .... 89511 .... Souza MR & MRS David A
Reno .... 89513 .... Rick MRS Alan J
Reno .... 89515 .... de Peyster MR & MRS F van Cortlandt
Reno .... 89519 .... Pirie MS Heather A
Reno .... 89521 .... Fox MISS Marie-Etienne C
Reno .... 89523 .... McNabb MR Mark Hopkins
Smith .... 89430 .... Fulstone MR & MRS Richard N
Smith .... 89430 .... Fulstone MR & MRS Steven A
Washoe Valley .... 89704 .... Eyre MRS Edward E JR
Washoe Valley .... 89704 .... King MR & MRS MacLellan E JR
Zephyr Cove .... 89448 .... Robertson MR Charles S 3D
Zephyr Cove .... 89448 .... Tornga MR & MRS Thomas H

NEW HAMPSHIRE

Acworth .... 03601 .... Phinizy MR & MRS James G
Atkinson .... 03811 .... Churchman MR & MRS Joseph S
Bedford .... 03110 .... Curran MR Jeffrey P & Harding MS Marie P
Bedford .... 03110 .... Richmond DR & MRS Stewart S
Bedford .... 03110 .... Richmond MR & MRS Stewart S JR
Bedford .... 03110 .... Upton MRS J Gordon
Bennington .... 03442 .... Brown MR Jeremy P
Bow .... 03304 .... Burton MRS John R 3D
Bow .... 03304 .... Hibbard MRS William M
Bow .... 03304 .... Mosle MISS Cornelia B
Bow .... 03304 .... Soucy MR & MRS Benjamin I
Bradford .... 03221 .... Kincaid MRS Margaret Gray
Brentwood .... 03833 .... Austin MR & MRS Charles R
Brentwood .... 03833 .... Austin MR & MRS James E
Brentwood .... 03833 .... Storm MRS Jane S
Bristol .... 03222 .... Bryan MISS Anne de L
Campton .... 03223 .... Dent MISS Deborah du V
Canaan .... 03741 .... Clark MR J Dudley 3D
Canaan .... 03741 .... Gray MR & MRS Alexander L
Canaan .... 03741 .... Paine DR Michael P W H
Center Harbor .... 03226 .... Dane MR & MRS Edward Nathan
Center Ossipee .... 03814 .... Fahy CDR Richard H JR
Center Ossipee .... 03814 .... Fahy MRS Richard H
Center Sandwich .... 03227 .... Carega MR & MRS Paolo F
Center Sandwich .... 03227 .... Donald MRS Elizabeth H
Center Sandwich .... 03227 .... Dunnell MR & MRS William W 3D
Center Sandwich .... 03227 .... Hathaway MISS Mallory
Center Sandwich .... 03227 .... Klein MR Gilbert W
Center Sandwich .... 03227 .... Speers MRS T Guthrie JR
Center Sandwich .... 03227 .... Van Winkle MR & MRS Peter K
Center Sandwich .... 03227 .... Whyatt MR & MRS Nicholas M A
Center Tuftonboro .... 03816 .... Hackl MR & MRS George C S
Center Tuftonboro .... 03816 .... Lyon MR William W 3D
Charlestown .... 03603 .... Webb MR & MRS Richard C L
Chocorua .... 03817 .... Lloyd MRS Robert McA JR
Claremont .... 03743 .... Roy MR & MRS Leo V
Concord .... 03301 .... Armstrong MR & MRS Richard M III
Concord .... 03301 .... Doak MR Kenelm W
Concord .... 03301 .... Duncan MR & MRS Andrew P
Concord .... 03301 .... McCain MR & MRS David W
Concord .... 03301 .... Porter MRS Richard P
Concord .... 03301 .... Tolles MR & MRS Bryant F JR
Concord .... 03301 .... Wadsworth MRS Burton G
Cornish .... 03745 .... Newbold MR & MRS J Cheston M
Danville .... 03819 .... Howland MRS John S
Deering .... 03244 .... Neville MISS Betsey B
Dover .... 03820 .... Hamilton MS Evelyn de Zouche
Dover .... 03820 .... Mulligan MR & MRS Charles A
Dublin .... 03444 .... Bastedo MR & MRS P Russell
Dublin .... 03444 .... Guth MR & MRS John H J
Dublin .... 03444 .... Handy MR Albert M
Dublin .... 03444 .... Pool MRS Beekman H
Durham .... 03824 .... Fahy MR J Carter
Durham .... 03824 .... Mulhern MR & MRS Michael J
East Kingston .... 03827 .... Morrison MISS Joan Van D
Etna .... 03750 .... Bedford MR & MRS Frederick T 3D
Etna .... 03750 .... Harjes MR & MRS Henry H JR
Etna .... 03750 .... Kinsolving MRS Monique
Etna .... 03750 .... Morgan MR & MRS Chauncey G
Exeter .... 03833 .... Alling MRS Charles B JR
Exeter .... 03833 .... Baker DR & MRS George P JR
Exeter .... 03833 .... Coffin MR David D
Exeter .... 03833 .... Mason MRS Robert C
Exeter .... 03833 .... Sears MR & MRS Herbert T
Exeter .... 03833 .... Worthington MRS Arthur L
Fitzwilliam .... 03447 .... Beckwith MR & MRS E Kenneth
Francestown .... 03043 .... Alsop MRS Reese F
Francestown .... 03043 .... Pyle MR & MRS Charles McA 3D
Franconia .... 03580 .... de Rham MRS Anne McK
Franconia .... 03580 .... Foss MR & MRS Paul W
Franconia .... 03580 .... Grote MR & MRS G Peter
Franconia .... 03580 .... Holder DR & MRS Jonathan D
Franconia .... 03580 .... Nicodemus DR & MRS Christopher F
Freedom .... 03836 .... Morrow MRS Lorraine B
Gilmans Corner .... 03777 .... Parsons MR Stephen C
Grantham .... 03753 .... Ballantine DR & MRS Percy 2D
Grantham .... 03753 .... Evans MR & MRS George J JR
Grantham .... 03753 .... Keller DR & MRS (DR) William R
Greenfield .... 03047 .... Pennoyer MR & MRS Sheldon K
Greenfield .... 03047 .... Thomson DR & MRS George G III
Hampstead .... 03841 .... Evans MR & MRS Jeremy A M

Hancock, NH—Sugar Hill, NH

Hancock	03449	Coffin MR & MRS G Jarvis III
Hancock	03449	Gregg MR Robert E JR
Hanover	03755	Appell MRS Frederick W
Hanover	03755	Ball MR & MRS Stephen F W
Hanover	03755	Brown CAPT (RET) John Willoughby
Hanover	03755	Burchenal MRS Joseph Holland
Hanover	03755	Dodson MR & MRS Robert H T
Hanover	03755	Edgar MR & MRS Antony
Hanover	03755	Farrington MRS Phillips
Hanover	03755	Helm MR & MRS William L JR
Hanover	03755	Hemenway MR Henry J
Hanover	03755	Higgerson MR & MRS Richard McI
Hanover	03755	Lubrano MR & MRS Steven D
Hanover	03755	McCulloch MRS Andrew C
Hanover	03755	Meyer MR Charles H
Hanover	03755	Miller DR & MRS Donald McE
Hanover	03755	Napier MR & MRS James C 3D
Hanover	03755	Piasecki MR & MRS Gregory W
Hanover	03755	Pietsch THE REV DR Louise Parsons
Hanover	03755	Rueckert DR & MRS Frederic
Hanover	03755	Smith MR & MRS Dudley Renwick
Hanover	03755	Strasenburgh MRS J Griffin
Hanover	03755	Swett MR & MRS Steven C
Hanover	03755	Turner MR & MRS Arthur N
Hanover	03755	Ufford MR & MRS Charles W JR
Hanover	03755	Weeks MR John T
Hanover	03755	White MR & MRS C Stuart JR
Harrisville	03450	Appel MR & MRS Kenneth G
Harrisville	03450	Raley MR Robert L
Holderness	03245	Garesché MR & MRS Thomas K
Hollis	03049	MacMillan MR & MRS Donald S
Hollis	03049	MacMillan MR & MRS Richard J
Hopkinton	03229	Frank MRS Walter N JR
Hopkinton	03229	Trafton MR & MRS Stephen D
Hudson	03051	Brucker MR & MRS Willis Howard
Intervale	03845	Tilney MISS Heather W
Jackson	03846	Tilney DR & MRS Robert W 3D
Jaffrey	03452	Hollister MR & MRS G Clay 2D
Jefferson	03583	Ward MRS Winifred S
Keene	03431	Gooding MRS Judson
Keene	03431	Hansel MR & MRS J Parker JR
Keene	03431	Shaw MISS Emily T
Keene	03431	Sutherland MR & MRS Robert B JR
Kingston	03848	Coffin CAPT & MRS Peter D
Laconia	03246	LeRoy MR & MRS Newbold 3D
Landaff	03585	Cooper MR & MRS Charles Terrell
Langdon	03602	Fowler MR & MRS Lucius L
Lebanon	03766	Lascell MR Joshua A & Martin DR Isabella W
Lebanon	03766	Phyfe MS Edith A
Lebanon	03766	Rode MR John B G
Lee	03861	Whitney MS Cynthia F
Litchfield	03052	Calawa DR Steven P
Loudon	03307	Truesdale MR & MRS Joseph R IV
Lyme	03768	Cummings DR & MRS Harlan G
Lyme	03768	Smithers MR & MRS Austin L
Lyme	03768	Van Vleck MR & MRS Roy T
Lyndeborough	03082	Cullen MR & MRS Barry A
Madbury	03820	Calzone MR & MRS Antonio
Madbury	03823	Dickerson MS D Anne
Madbury	03823	Norling MR & MRS John C
Manchester	03104	Reno DR & MRS Stephen J
Marlborough	03455	Frost MR & MRS Rufus S 3D
Marlborough	03455	Hale MRS William M
Marlborough	03455	MacVeagh MR & MRS Charlton
Marlborough	03455	Mead MR & MRS Frederick G
Melvin Village	03850	Walker DR & MRS Peter F R
Meredith	03253	Crowell MR & MRS Donald E
Meriden	03770	Bonney MR & MRS James K
Merrimack	03054	Pierce MISS Anne
Mirror Lake	03853	Elkins MR & MRS George W
Montpelier	05602	Scharnberg MR & MRS Eric C
Moultonborough	03254	Robinson MR & MRS Kevin T C
Nashua	03060	Bender MR Peter M
Nashua	03062	Blagden MR & MRS George
Nashua	03063	Burks MR & MRS D Parker
Nashua	03064	Buttrick MS Kathryn L
New Castle	03854	Lynch DR & MRS Gregory M
New Castle	03854	Tarbell MR & MRS Charles A
New London	03257	Curtis MISS Judith A
New London	03257	Denny MRS Charles S
New London	03257	Jones MRS Charles P
New London	03257	Leach MR & MRS Richard M
New London	03257	Phillips MR & MRS R Wendell JR
New London	03257	von Heisermann MRS Marion A
New London	03257	Wagner MR & MRS
New London	03257	Webster MRS David Z
Newbury	03255	Reynders MR & MRS Charlton JR
Newmarket	03857	Malone MR & MRS Mark J
North Hampton	03862	Boies MRS David
North Hampton	03862	Field MR & MRS Robert B JR
North Hampton	03862	Garnett MR & MRS Richard N A
North Hampton	03862	Jeffery MR Patrick G
North Hampton	03862	Schoettler MR & MRS James R
North Sandwich	03259	Blodgett MISS Victoria F
Orford	03777	Karol MR John J JR & Fitzhugh MS Portia L
Peterborough	03458	Bass MR & MRS Alexander
Peterborough	03458	Bass MRS Perkins
Peterborough	03458	Coffin MRS G Jarvis JR
Peterborough	03458	Crocker MRS (DR) Augustus T
Peterborough	03458	Gerard MR & MRS Peter H
Peterborough	03458	Graves MRS John H
Peterborough	03458	Grinnell MR Lawrence I 2D
Peterborough	03458	Mead MRS James G
Peterborough	03458	Mundy MR & MRS Gardner M
Peterborough	03458	Taylor MRS E Hope
Peterborough	03458	Troussoff MRS George B
Peterborough	03458	Weir MRS David R
Peterborough	03458	Whitney MRS Craig W
Plainfield	03781	Binger MR & MRS David G
Plymouth	03264	Overaker DR Lewis J
Portsmouth	03801	Childs MR J Brentley
Portsmouth	03801	Clark DR & MRS Geoffrey E
Portsmouth	03801	De Chard MR & MRS Richard J
Portsmouth	03801	Gardner MRS Henry Alfred
Portsmouth	03801	Kean MRS Hamilton F
Portsmouth	03801	Osgood MR Edward R
Portsmouth	03801	Smith MR & MRS Winthrop D
Portsmouth	03801	Thompson MR & MRS Edward P
Portsmouth	03802	Evans REV John Miles & Allen MR Douglas M
Rindge	03461	Bourdelais MR & MRS David A
Rye	03870	Eaton MR & MRS Robert G
Rye	03870	Fenner MR & MRS Clarke J
Rye	03870	Wilich MS Clare S
Rye Beach	03871	Bottomley MR & MRS John T
Salem	03079	Magro MISS Nancy L
Sandown	03873	Noble MISS Susan Weare
Somersworth	03878	McLean CDR (RET) & MRS Michael A
Spofford	03462	Clarkson MR & MRS Robert L 3D
Stratham	03885	Langenberg MR Roy T
Stratham	03885	Reath MR & MRS Thomas JR
Sugar Hill	03586	Jostrom CDR (RET) & MRS Eric H
Sugar Hill	03586	Poole MR & MRS Peter A

To nominate a candidate for the Social Register Association, please email: SRCommittee@thesocialregister.org

Sugar Hill, NH—Edison, NJ

Sugar Hill........ 03586........ Weiler MR & MRS Milton C F
Sunapee........ 03782........ Anthony MR Austin T
Sunapee........ 03782........ Cooper MR Alan A
Sunapee........ 03782........ Cooper MR Douglas C
Tamworth........ 03886........ Stafford MR & MRS Hansel B
Temple........ 03084........ Holmes MISS (REV) Olivia
Tilton........ 03276........ Cropsey MR & MRS James M G
Walpole........ 03608........ Burr DR & MRS I Tucker 3D
Walpole........ 03608........ Montgomery DR & MRS Charles H
Walpole........ 03608........ Philson MR & MRS J Gibbs
Walpole........ 03608........ Trundle MRS Sidney A JR
Warner........ 03278........ Glendinning MR & MRS David P
Warner........ 03278........ Karrick MR & MRS David B JR
Warner........ 03278........ Welch MRS Stuart C
Washington........ 03280........ Bissonnette MR & MRS James P
Waterville Valley........ 03215........ Fairchild MR & MRS Peter T
Weare........ 03281........ Tiffany MR & MRS Henry D III
West Lebanon........ 03784........ Carleton MR & MRS Bukk G III
West Lebanon........ 03784........ Gallaway MS Grace B P
Whitefield........ 03598........ Craig MRS Peggie-Louise
Wilmot........ 03287........ Kerr MR & MRS E Coe 3D
Wolfeboro........ 03894........ French MR & MRS Peter S
Wolfeboro........ 03894........ Haskell MR & MRS Richard L JR
Wolfeboro........ 03894........ Muir DR & MRS Warren R

NEW JERSEY

Annandale........ 08801........ Ballantine MR & MRS Robert D
Atlantic Highlands........ 07716........ Blaisdell MISS Susan C
Atlantic Highlands........ 07716........ Ellis MRS Joan F
Basking Ridge........ 07920........ Clark MR & MRS Charles R
Basking Ridge........ 07920........ Corbin MRS Horace K III
Basking Ridge........ 07920........ Corson MR & MRS William C
Basking Ridge........ 07920........ Dillon MRS Hardenbergh
Basking Ridge........ 07920........ Dougherty MRS Kenneth W
Basking Ridge........ 07920........ Fotouhi DR & MRS Nader
Basking Ridge........ 07920........ Gifford MRS Garfield
Basking Ridge........ 07920........ Heller MRS Charles R
Basking Ridge........ 07920........ Hetherington MRS James A 2D
Basking Ridge........ 07920........ McLean MRS William H
Basking Ridge........ 07920........ Ross MR & MRS Amory L
Basking Ridge........ 07920........ Taft MR Timothy E
Basking Ridge........ 07920........ Taft MR William P
Basking Ridge........ 07920........ Walsh MR & MRS Alexander T
Basking Ridge........ 07920........ White MRS Sumner W 3D
Bay Head........ 08742........ Clark MR & MRS Robert G
Bay Head........ 08742........ Harris MISS Ann B
Bay Head........ 08742........ Nunan MR Alfred B
Bedminster........ 07921........ Bellis MR & MRS James L JR
Bedminster........ 07921........ Caspersen MR & MRS Finn M W JR
Bedminster........ 07921........ Clarke MR & MRS Peter L
Bedminster........ 07921........ Enos MR & MRS Alanson T IV
Bedminster........ 07921........ Forbes MR & MRS Malcolm S JR
Bedminster........ 07921........ Giordano MR & MRS John C 3D
Bedminster........ 07921........ Macdonald MRS Neil M
Bedminster........ 07921........ Mathewson MR & MRS William G
Bedminster........ 07921........ Putnam MR & MRS Sumner C
Bedminster........ 07921........ Ridder MR & MRS Eric JR
Bedminster........ 07921........ Robinson MR & MRS Samuel S JR
Bedminster........ 07921........ Tansey MR & MRS Douglas W
Bedminster........ 07921........ Thompson MR & MRS Charles K
Belle Mead........ 08502........ Bates MR & MRS (DR) Michael T
Belle Mead........ 08502........ Strong MR & MRS Benjamin W
Belmar........ 07719........ Sommerfield MRS Mark J
Belvidere........ 07823........ Ellis MR Arthur L JR
Belvidere........ 07823........ Wade MR & MRS Robert E
Bernardsville........ 07924........ Buck MR & MRS C Austin
Bernardsville........ 07924........ Chubb MRS Percy 3D
Bernardsville........ 07924........ Dahler MR & MRS Donald L JR
Bernardsville........ 07924........ Diemar MR & MRS Thomas S
Bernardsville........ 07924........ Dillon MRS Milton S JR
Bernardsville........ 07924........ Dixon MR & MRS (DR) Richard W
Bernardsville........ 07924........ Fenwick MRS Leigh E
Bernardsville........ 07924........ Galpin MR & MRS Stephen K JR
Bernardsville........ 07924........ Gibson MR & MRS William L
Bernardsville........ 07924........ Kean MR & MRS John JR
Bernardsville........ 07924........ Lincoln MR & MRS Daniel W
Bernardsville........ 07924........ Melchionni MR & MRS Keith V
Bernardsville........ 07924........ Parker MR & MRS (DR) Stephen W
Bernardsville........ 07924........ Peterson MR & MRS George 3D
Bernardsville........ 07924........ Ross MR & MRS (DR) Benson T
Bernardsville........ 07924........ Savage MR & MRS Thomas C
Bernardsville........ 07924........ Scott MR & MRS Andrew F
Bernardsville........ 07924........ Valentine MRS Kara Mulcahy
Bernardsville........ 07924........ Ward MR & MRS James W C
Bernardsville........ 07924........ West MR & MRS Stephen K
Bernardsville........ 07924........ Wiedenmayer MR & MRS Christopher M
Bernardsville........ 07924........ Winder MR & MRS Miles S III
Blairstown........ 07825........ Thors MISS Virginia Averell
Bloomfield........ 07003........ Merriman MR & MRS John C
Bloomingdale........ 07403........ Galbraith MR Evan G III
Boonton........ 07005........ Sculley MR & MRS Arthur B
Boonton Township........ 07005........ Turben MR & MRS Nicholas A
Bordentown........ 08505........ Hall MS Elizabeth S
Bordentown........ 08505........ Kuser MR & MRS Lawrence deQ
Brick........ 08723........ Burns MR Kevin W
Brick........ 08724........ Kennard MISS Anne M
Bridgewater........ 08807........ Witt MR & MRS Roger A JR
Brigantine........ 08203........ Phelps MISS Ann Naile
Caldwell........ 07006........ Pryor MR William B
Califon........ 07830........ Bassett MISS Nancy L
Califon........ 07830........ Klipstein MR & MRS Kenneth H II
Califon........ 07830........ Mesnard DR & MRS (DR) William J
Califon........ 07860........ Spaeth MRS Victoria
Cape May........ 08204........ Flershem MR Gerald B
Cape May........ 08204........ Swoyer MRS George R
Cape May Courthouse.. 08210........ Crunden MR Warren C JR
Chatham........ 07928........ Baker MR & MRS Hayden S
Chatham........ 07928........ de Neufville MR John P
Chatham........ 07928........ Lowe MR & MRS Kevin E
Chatham........ 07928........ Nichols MR & MRS Brett E
Chatham........ 07928........ Radsch MRS Richard T
Chatham........ 07928........ Ross MR & MRS George S
Chatham........ 07928........ Ross MR & MRS George S 3D
Chatham........ 07928........ Shirley MRS Homer C III
Chatham........ 07928........ Wilson MRS William N
Cherry Hill........ 08003........ Hopkins MR & MRS Holt E
Chester........ 07930........ Aronson MR & MRS Robert A
Chester........ 07930........ Saltus MR & MRS Seymour S
Chester........ 07930........ Valentine MR & MRS H Stuart IV
Chesterfield........ 08515........ Lohmann MR & MRS Richard P
Clark........ 07066........ Gates MR & MRS Geoffrey McNair
Clarksboro........ 08020........ Hollingshead MR & MRS Wickliffe
Clarksboro........ 08020........ Hollingshead MR William Keith
Clifton........ 07013........ Schwefel MR Charles A
Clinton........ 08809........ Spencer MR & MRS Scott R
Cranbury........ 08512........ Goodfellow MRS Emily C
Cranbury........ 08512........ Harvey MR & MRS Thomas B JR
Cranbury........ 08512........ Suttmeier MR & MRS Stephen W
East Windsor........ 08520........ Sharples MR & MRS Russell P
East Windsor........ 08520........ Taussig MR & MRS Wayne H
Edison........ 08820........ Moore MISS Caroline D

Elmer, NJ—Locust, NJ

Elmer	08318	Read DR & MRS John Harleston 6TH
Englewood	07631	Barrett DR & MRS C Redington JR
Englewood	07631	Carson MR & MRS Robert R JR
Englewood	07631	Downes MRS Katherine Y
Englewood	07631	James MRS Denis N R
Englewood	07631	Lattimer MRS John K
Englewood	07631	Svensson MR & MRS Sten G
Essex Fells	07021	Newman MRS Charles I
Ewing	08638	Bassett MR George P 4TH & Wilson MS Nancy H
Fair Haven	07704	Boyle MR & MRS Michael G
Fair Haven	07704	Miltenberger MRS Eugene F JR
Fanwood	07023	Coxe MR & MRS Henry B 4TH
Far Hills	07931	Alexandre MR & MRS DeWitt L JR
Far Hills	07931	Allen MR & MRS Philip D
Far Hills	07931	Allport MR & MRS George N
Far Hills	07931	Biedron MR & MRS Scott P
Far Hills	07931	Boyer MR & MRS Georges C
Far Hills	07931	Brady MR & MRS James C
Far Hills	07931	Brady MR & MRS James C III
Far Hills	07931	Brady MR & MRS Nicholas F
Far Hills	07931	Carter MRS Elizabeth Ketterson
Far Hills	07931	Cochran MR & MRS Thomas N
Far Hills	07931	Crawford MR & MRS Harden L 3D
Far Hills	07931	Daly MRS Winston
Far Hills	07931	Dwyer MR & MRS Denis R
Far Hills	07931	Ely MR & MRS B Danforth
Far Hills	07931	Escaravage MR & MRS Phillip O'H
Far Hills	07931	Falivene MR & MRS Philip J
Far Hills	07931	Filley MR Oliver D
Far Hills	07931	Forbes MR & MRS Christopher C
Far Hills	07931	Gardiner MRS Robert M
Far Hills	07931	Jeanes MRS Marshall M
Far Hills	07931	Kean MR & MRS Thomas H
Far Hills	07931	Krag MR W Brace JR
Far Hills	07931	Lorillard MR & MRS Screven Peter
Far Hills	07931	Matthews MR Donald J & Bowers-Matthews MRS Ann Lind
Far Hills	07931	McNamara MR & MRS John J JR
Far Hills	07931	Mellon MRS Charles H 3D
Far Hills	07931	Pyne MRS Percy R 3D
Far Hills	07931	Richards MR & MRS Reuben F
Far Hills	07931	Schley MRS Kenneth B JR
Far Hills	07931	Smith MR & MRS Michael S
Far Hills	07931	Smith MR & MRS Philip W III
Far Hills	07931	Smith MR & MRS Philip W JR
Far Hills	07931	Turpin MR & MRS John K
Far Hills	07931	Vartanian MR & MRS Paul D
Flemington	08822	Adam MR & MRS K Bruce
Flemington	08822	Kendall MRS Gloria G
Gladstone	07934	Dillon MR Sidney G
Gladstone	07934	Durling MR & MRS C Chapin
Gladstone	07934	La Costa MR Tomás R
Gladstone	07934	Mackay MRS Ian D
Gladstone	07934	Shanley MRS Kevin
Glen Gardner	08826	Huston MR Andrew R
Glen Ridge	07028	Jenkins MRS George P
Glen Ridge	07028	Molin MR & MRS Karl T II
Glen Ridge	07028	Provost MRS Lloyd JR
Glen Ridge	07028	Theodorou MR & MRS Jeffrey J
Green Village	07935	du Pont MR & MRS E Paul III
Green Village	07935	Simon MR & MRS J Peter
Hackensack	07601	Zilli MR Richard R
Hackettstown	07840	Byrnes MR Joseph T
Hackettstown	07840	Stewart MR Michael C
Hackettstown	07840	Vilas REV & MRS Franklin E JR
Haddonfield	08033	Churchill MRS Edward D JR
Haddonfield	08033	Hodges MRS June J
Haddonfield	08033	Hopkins MRS Anthony C
Haddonfield	08033	Thayer MR & MRS Nelson S T JR
Haworth	07641	Ogden DR & MRS (DR) Alfred T III
Highland Park	08904	Minott MISS Elizabeth
Highlands	07732	Burnett MRS W Griffin
Hightstown	08520	DiLorenzo MR & MRS Renato A
Hightstown	08520	Hull MRS Philip G
Hightstown	08520	Kraft MR Peter A
Hoboken	07030	Baer MRS Theodore C III
Hoboken	07030	Cooke MR & MRS Frederick P H
Hoboken	07030	Kopp MR & MRS Duncan R
Hoboken	07030	Richards MISS Holly L
Hoboken	07030	Taylor MR & MRS Herbert H IV
Hoboken	07030	Thibault MR & MRS Carrow III
Holmdel	07733	Smith MR & MRS H Cortelyou
Hopewell	08525	Carter MRS David L
Hopewell	08525	Chappell MR & MRS Hayward H
Hopewell	08525	Griswold MR & MRS Hector W JR
Hopewell	08525	Hodge MRS Edward B
Hopewell	08525	Preston MISS Frances L
Howell	07731	Ott MR Anthony E
Jackson	08527	Hitchcock MRS Peter T
Jersey City	07202	Henderson MR Peter III
Jersey City	07302	Jobson MR Mark deV
Jersey City	07302	Lippe MR Christopher G & Drachlis MS Jennifer C
Jersey City	07302	Ross MR & MRS T Eliot JR
Jersey City	07307	Jones MR Andrew Berrien
Jersey City	07307	Williams MRS Alan D
Jersey City	07310	Drew REV & MRS (DR) Charles D
Jersey City	07310	Forbes MR & MRS Timothy C
Jersey City	07310	Teasdale MS Anne C Ware
Jersey City	07310	Ward MISS Bleecker B
Kingston	08528	Rulon-Miller MR Patrick
Kinnelon	07405	Hicks MR & MRS Harry C
Lake Hiawatha	07034	Rianhard MRS M Bensh
Lakewood	08701	Phillips MRS Francis F
Lambertville	08530	Barnett MR & MRS Benjamin H III
Lambertville	08530	Hatfield MR & MRS Charles J III
Lawrence Township	08648	Hammond MR & MRS Benjamin C
Lawrenceville	08648	Cooke MR & MRS R Caswell JR
Lawrenceville	08648	Gruen MRS Peter J
Lawrenceville	08648	Harman MR & MRS Daniel H III
Lawrenceville	08648	Holdsworth MRS David G
Lawrenceville	08648	Huston MR & MRS John J JR
Lawrenceville	08648	Johnson MRS F Coit II
Lawrenceville	08648	Potter MR Hamilton F III
Lawrenceville	08648	Stackpole MRS William
Lawrenceville	08648	Taunay MR & MRS Pierre-Yves C R
Lebanon	08833	Howard MR & MRS Reese Evans JR
Lebanon	08833	Koven MRS Theodore Gustav
Lebanon	08833	Rose MR & MRS William Duncan
Lebanon	08833	Stransky MR & MRS Thomas M
Lincoln Park	07035	Walker MRS John Y G JR
Linwood	08221	Schaut MR & MRS Norman F
Little Silver	07739	Becker MRS Sherburn M 3D
Little Silver	07739	Biddle MR & MRS Packard
Little Silver	07739	Dale MRS John D
Little Silver	07739	Hazlett MRS James V JR
Little Silver	07739	Hertz MR & MRS Daniel L JR
Little Silver	07739	Huber MRS Pehr C
Little Silver	07739	Landreth MRS Diana C
Little Silver	07739	Lawrence MR & MRS Robert C III
Locust	07760	Brooks MR & MRS Douglas A
Locust	07760	Flinn MR Larsen H
Locust	07760	Flinn MRS George H II

Locust, NJ—Perth Amboy, NJ

Locust	07760	Gulden MR & MRS Paul I JR
Locust	07760	Halsey MR & MRS Alexander Van R
Locust	07760	Riker REV & MRS William C
Locust	07760	Timolat MR Paul F
Lutherville	21093	Galleher DR & MRS Earl P JR
Madison	07940	Allen MISS Edith M
Madison	07940	Almond MR & MRS Weston M F
Madison	07940	Benjamin MR & MRS Park IV
Madison	07940	Gnichtel MR & MRS Edwin M
Madison	07940	MacMaster MR & MRS Donald F
Madison	07940	Rambusch MR & MRS (DR) Edwin P
Madison	07940	Scattergood MR & MRS J Henry
Madison	07940	Sullivan MR & MRS Michael A
Madison	07940	Thayer MRS Nelson S T
Mantoloking	08738	Dougherty MRS Geoffrey B
Mantoloking	08738	O'Malley MR & MRS Edwin J JR
Mantoloking	08738	Pilling MRS John F
Maplewood	07040	Eddy MR John S
Maplewood	07040	Morris MR & MRS Richard T
Maplewood	07040	Paynter MR & MRS Nathaniel C
Marlton	08053	Ringe MR & MRS Henry Ralph 2D
Matawan	07747	Rianhard MR Edward N
Medford	08055	Gnichtel MR & MRS William Van O
Medford	08055	Morris MR & MRS Robert F JR
Medford	08055	Pennink MR & MRS Karel B
Mendham	07945	Brunet MR & MRS Stuart
Mendham	07945	Corbett MR & MRS (DR) Kevin S
Mendham	07945	Donaldson MISS Beirne
Mendham	07945	Farrelly MR & MRS Louis C R
Mendham	07945	Green MRS Thomas M 3D
Mendham	07945	Hinckley MR & MRS David M
Mendham	07945	Lamb MR & MRS James R
Mendham	07945	Ludlow MR & MRS George C JR
Mendham	07945	Ross MRS Andrea C
Merchantville	08109	Rogers MR Frank L
Middletown	07748	Brewer MR & MRS Lee R
Middletown	07748	West MR & MRS Nicholas Stuart
Millville	08332	Crompton DR Thomas F
Monroe	08831	Taussig MRS Thomas K
Montclair	07042	Eddy MRS John P B
Montclair	07042	Friend MR & MRS Pierson
Montclair	07042	Hansell MR & MRS (DR) Robert L
Montclair	07042	Nammack MR & MRS Thomas W
Montclair	07042	Nelson MR Joseph H & Griffinger Nelson MRS Tracy
Montclair	07042	Rand MR & MRS Frank C IV
Montclair	07042	Talbot MISS Margaret H
Montclair	07043	Nagy MR & MRS J Estep
Montclair	07043	Stevenson MRS G Barnes
Montville	07045	Spencer MR & MRS Jack
Moorestown	08057	Collins MR Daniel Wills
Moorestown	08057	Decker MRS Arnold F A
Moorestown	08057	Doyle MR & MRS Andrew C R
Moorestown	08057	Giordano HON & MRS Frank
Moorestown	08057	Henry MR & MRS Clement M
Moorestown	08057	Webster MR & MRS Andrew F
Morristown	07960	Courtemanche MR & MRS Robert H
Morristown	07960	Cutler MR Timothy G
Morristown	07960	Cutler MRS Elizabeth Lee
Morristown	07960	Cutler MS Alice D
Morristown	07960	Dougherty DR Sarah B
Morristown	07960	Frelinghuysen MR & MRS Rodney P
Morristown	07960	Gordon MRS Patricia P
Morristown	07960	Hoyt MRS Henry M
Morristown	07960	Krementz MRS Richard
Morristown	07960	MacAusland MR W Russell
Morristown	07960	Magyar MR Mark J & Parker MS Elizabeth K
Morristown	07960	Morhouse MR Sanford W & Hogan MS Patricia M
Morristown	07960	Moronski MR & MRS Sean F
Morristown	07960	Nash MR Paul Le N
Morristown	07960	Rhinelander MR & MRS John R
Morristown	07960	Saunders MR & MRS Charles T
Morristown	07960	Scarlett MR & MRS Lindley C
Morristown	07960	Sharretts MR & MRS Amos B JR
Morristown	07960	Thompson MR & MRS Benjamin R
Morristown	07960	Urfer MR & MRS Richard P
Morristown	07960	Whitehead MR & MRS Brent R
Morristown	07963	Fiske MRS William E
Mountain Lakes	07046	Foth MR & MRS Robert F
Mountain Lakes	07046	Parker MR & MRS Ellis Stuart
Mountainside	07092	Gardiner MR & MRS J Brooke
Mountainside	07092	Hamway MS Julia
Mountainside	07092	Peter MR & MRS Phillips S JR
Mountainside	07092	Vari MISS Christina E
Mt Laurel	08054	Parry MRS H Frazer
New Providence	07974	Mickel MR Paul J
New Providence	07974	Ogden MRS Robert M 3D
New Providence	07974	Zerweck MR & MRS Jeffrey W
New Vernon	07976	Aspero MR & MRS Benedict V SR
New Vernon	07976	Aspero MR Alexander M
New Vernon	07976	Bartlett MR & MRS Marshall P
New Vernon	07976	Granbery MR & MRS W Preston
New Vernon	07976	Irwin MRS D King
New Vernon	07976	Markey MR Bernard B
New Vernon	07976	McCarthy MR & MRS David G
New Vernon	07976	Miller MRS Paul L
New Vernon	07976	Rooke MRS Christopher D
New Vernon	07976	Weldon MR & MRS William H IV
North Bergen	07047	Downer MR & MRS William T
North Plainfield	07062	Laidlaw MR & MRS Douglas B
Norwood	07648	Gillon MR & MRS Christopher T
Norwood	07648	Peltz MR & MRS George M Dallas
Ocean City	08226	Thornton MR John R
Ocean Grove	07756	Perkowski MR & MRS J Douglas
Oldwick	08858	Annis MR & MRS Craig
Oldwick	08858	Chapin MR & MRS Charles M 3D
Oldwick	08858	Connor MRS (DR) M Pyne
Oldwick	08858	Dillon MR & MRS Charles H
Oldwick	08858	Dillon MRS Thomas H
Oldwick	08858	Goss MR & MRS Robert E
Oldwick	08858	Moyer MR & MRS Timothy B
Oldwick	08858	O'Connor MR Michael J
Oldwick	08858	Prouty MS Hilary J
Oldwick	08858	Stewart MRS William T JR
Peapack	07977	Higgins MR & MRS James C 2D
Peapack	07977	Mason MRS Eugene W JR
Peapack	07977	Slack MR & MRS Henry R
Peapack	07977	Terry MR Walter B JR
Peapack	07977	Terry MRS Walter Bliss
Peapack	07977	van den Bergh MR & MRS Adriaan M
Peapack	07977	Villa MR & MRS Anthony G
Peapack	07977	Villa MR & MRS Peter L
Peapack	07977	Villa MR Nicholas G
Peapack	07977	Walton MR & MRS James M JR
Peapack	07979	Walsh MRS Philip C
Pennington	08534	Bartholomew MR & MRS James R
Pennington	08534	Berglund MRS B Quintal
Pennington	08534	Blair MR & MRS Wolcott R
Pennington	08534	McCall MR & MRS David B JR
Pennington	08534	Meneghin MR & MRS Brian C
Pennington	08534	Sproul MR & MRS George F
Perth Amboy	08861	Bryan MISS Olive M

Pitman	08071	Potter MR & MRS Gregory C
Pittstown	08867	Levick MISS Stephanie S
Pittstown	08867	Warner MR Nicholas H
Plainfield	07060	Finch MISS Anne W
Pompton Plains	07444	Armstrong MR & MRS Richard W
Pottersville	07979	Connor MR Geoffrey M
Pottersville	07979	von Meister MR & MRS Joseph P
Pottersville	07979	Ward MRS Elmer L JR
Princeton	08540	Ammidon MR & MRS Hoyt III
Princeton	08540	Anderson MR & MRS Ellis B
Princeton	08540	Anderson MRS Harry B JR
Princeton	08540	Anderson MRS Warren H
Princeton	08540	Balavoine MR & MRS Olivier G
Princeton	08540	Barfield MRS Alice Guthrie
Princeton	08540	Barrows MR & MRS Thomas S
Princeton	08540	Bartlett MR & MRS John P
Princeton	08540	Bush MR Alfred L
Princeton	08540	Clark MS Linda G
Princeton	08540	Colt MRS C Learned
Princeton	08540	Crane MRS Edward M JR
Princeton	08540	Delafield MRS B Reed
Princeton	08540	Dennison MRS Charles E P
Princeton	08540	Eggers MR & MRS Lawrence C B
Princeton	08540	Ellison MR & MRS David A
Princeton	08540	Fenton MR & MRS Lewis D
Princeton	08540	Ford MR Jeremiah 3D
Princeton	08540	Frelinghuysen MISS Jessica R
Princeton	08540	French MRS Dorothy F
Princeton	08540	Ganoe MR Charles S
Princeton	08540	Gerry MR Peter G
Princeton	08540	Gerry MRS (DR) Alexandra W
Princeton	08540	Gillin MR & MRS Peter J
Princeton	08540	Hagen MR & MRS Lee R
Princeton	08540	Hamill MR Samuel M JR
Princeton	08540	Hawkes MRS (REV) Dudley F
Princeton	08540	Holt MR & MRS Philetus H 3D
Princeton	08540	Hutchinson DR & MRS George F JR
Princeton	08540	Irving MR & MRS John E D JR
Princeton	08540	Irving MRS John E duP
Princeton	08540	Kuser MR & MRS John E
Princeton	08540	Lambert MR & MRS Samuel W III
Princeton	08540	Long MR & MRS David A
Princeton	08540	Longshaw MR & MRS Nigel P
Princeton	08540	Machold MR & MRS Roland M
Princeton	08540	McKinnon MR & MRS James M
Princeton	08540	McLaughlin MR & MRS George H 2D
Princeton	08540	Mecray MR & MRS Christopher H
Princeton	08540	Miller MS Karla Sue
Princeton	08540	Moore MRS Barton
Princeton	08540	Morgan DR & MRS Robert F
Princeton	08540	Morgan MR & MRS Jonathan E H
Princeton	08540	Morgan MRS Margaret C
Princeton	08540	Morris MR & MRS Robert Fitler
Princeton	08540	Paine MR & MRS Peter S III
Princeton	08540	Reid MRS John
Princeton	08540	Rippin MR Charles
Princeton	08540	Rivkin MR & MRS Harold J
Princeton	08540	Robins MR & MRS William R III
Princeton	08540	Roebling MR & MRS William S
Princeton	08540	Ross MR Llewellyn G
Princeton	08540	Ryan MR & MRS Dudley D
Princeton	08540	Santy MR & MRS Ross C
Princeton	08540	Sayer MR & MRS John D
Princeton	08540	Scott MR & MRS David R
Princeton	08540	Scott MRS David J
Princeton	08540	Sharretts MRS Amos B
Princeton	08540	Sidamon-Eristoff MR & MRS Andrew
Princeton	08540	Siebens MRS Allen C
Princeton	08540	Speir MR R Wade JR
Princeton	08540	Stockman MR & MRS Robert B
Princeton	08540	Stockwell MR & MRS D Hunt JR
Princeton	08540	Tatnall MRS Henry C JR
Princeton	08540	Taylor MR Joseph McC JR
Princeton	08540	Trowbridge MR & MRS James W
Princeton	08540	Wachter MR & MRS John F III
Princeton	08540	Wainwright MS Christine
Princeton	08540	Wetherill MR & MRS David C
Princeton	08540	White MR & MRS Robert D 3D
Princeton	08540	Wiley MR & MRS Laurence D
Princeton	08540	Winant DR & MRS John G JR
Princeton	08540	Wynne MR John MacD JR & Richardson MS Juliet
Princeton	08542	Frederick REV DR John B M
Princeton	08542	Mittnacht MR Stewart JR
Pt Pleasant	08742	Baird MISS Abi A
Ramsey	07446	Drowne MRS Lisa D
Randolph	07869	Saliba MR & MRS Robert G
Randolph	07869	Shuford MR & MRS Sydney H
Red Bank	07701	Harper MR James A
Red Bank	07701	Strong MR & MRS William L 3D
Ridgewood	07450	Clothier DR & MRS James G JR
Ridgewood	07450	McKay MR & MRS Thomas A
Ridgewood	07450	Serritella MR & MRS James R
Ridgewood	07450	Stewart MR & MRS Victor E
Ridgewood	07450	Sullivan DR & MRS Brendan P
Ringoes	08551	Gardner MR & MRS Frederick
Ringoes	08551	Thompson MR & MRS W Bryce IV
Ringoes	08551	Woodfield MRS Denis B
Rocky Hill	08553	Dean BRIG GEN (RET) & MRS Guy K III
Rocky Hill	08553	Olson DR & MRS Robert M
Rumson	07760	Arlinghaus DR Frank H JR
Rumson	07760	Baugh MR & MRS Alexander R
Rumson	07760	Brighton MR & MRS Christopher S
Rumson	07760	Friedel DR & MRS Steven P
Rumson	07760	Gilbertson MRS Francis E
Rumson	07760	Hemphill MR & MRS Joseph K
Rumson	07760	Henning MR & MRS William P
Rumson	07760	Jones MR & MRS Charles H III
Rumson	07760	Jordan MRS John D
Rumson	07760	Lawrence MR & MRS Robert C IV
Rumson	07760	McKean MRS Q A Shaw JR
Rumson	07760	Metcalf MS Deirdre T E
Rumson	07760	Nixon MR & MRS Jeffrey S
Rumson	07760	Olson DR & MRS Ty J
Rumson	07760	Reiss MR & MRS Carl A
Rumson	07760	Reiss MR & MRS Theodore J
Rumson	07760	Riker MISS Elizabeth Q
Rumson	07760	Riker MRS William I
Rumson	07760	Slingluff MRS Charles H JR
Rumson	07760	Stewart MRS John G
Rumson	07760	Trent MR & MRS Allan A
Rumson	07760	Van Nice MR & MRS Cole S
Rumson	07760	Winmill MRS Bassett S
Rumson	07760	Wolfe MR & MRS Howard D III
Saddle River	07458	Plum MR & MRS John E
Salem	08079	Carpenter MR & MRS John S JR
Scotch Plains	07076	Pearson MR & MRS Stanley W III
Scotch Plains	07076	Ritchie MR & MRS Robert B
Sea Bright	07760	Blaisdell MR Bruce F
Sea Bright	07760	Smith MR & MRS Stephen J
Sea Girt	08750	Squarcy MS Charlotte Van Horne
Secaucus	07094	Gynn MR & MRS Edward J
Secaucus	07094	Hills MR & MRS Thomas C

Ship Bottom, NJ—Santa Fe, NM

Ship Bottom	08008	Cammann MR William Bayard
Short Hill	07078	Beatty MR & MRS Calvin C
Short Hills	07078	Fraser MR & MRS James W
Short Hills	07078	Hatab MR & MRS John O
Short Hills	07078	Haverstick MR & MRS S Alexander II
Short Hills	07078	Laplante MRS Paul A
Short Hills	07078	McGraw MR & MRS David D
Short Hills	07078	McGraw MR & MRS James H 4TH
Short Hills	07078	Umbdenstock MR & MRS Tyler J
Short Hills	07078	Welch MR & MRS James O JR
Shrewsbury	07702	Karlinski MR & MRS Frank J 3D
Shrewsbury	07702	Thurber MR & MRS Alfred E JR
Shrewsbury	07702	Thurber MR & MRS Edward C
Sicklerville	08081	Pritchard MRS Anne L S
Skillman	08558	Brush MRS Graham M
Skillman	08558	Burch MR & MRS Philip H
Skillman	08558	Egan MR & MRS William C III
Skillman	08558	Gerry MR & MRS Christopher W
Skillman	08558	Johnson MRS Hallett JR
Skillman	08558	Leonard MR & MRS Richard H
Skillman	08558	Parmele MRS Charles Roome III
Skillman	08558	Vehslage MRS Ramsay W
South Orange	07079	Niles MR & MRS David T
Southampton	08088	Reichner MRS C Fraser
Spring Lake	07762	Schoettle MR Philip A
Springfield	07081	Doble MS Sheilah J
Stockton	08559	Smith MR & MRS Paul R
Stone Harbor	08247	Conrad MRS James W
Stone Harbor	08247	Hardy MISS Amy S
Stone Harbor	08247	Hardy MISS Lisa M
Summit	07901	Brittain MR & MRS John S JR
Summit	07901	Chick MR & MRS Timothy C
Summit	07901	Dougherty MR & MRS G Bromley JR
Summit	07901	Fowler MR & MRS Robert S
Summit	07901	Gillin MR & MRS James B
Summit	07901	Hatfield MR & MRS Edward R 3D
Summit	07901	Hayford MR & MRS Matthew W
Summit	07901	Hedley MR & MRS Peter C
Summit	07901	Ogden MR & MRS Henry M
Summit	07901	Outwater MR & MRS Gregory M
Summit	07901	Peterson MR & MRS Clark Gamble
Summit	07901	Sheehan MR & MRS Arthur W
Summit	07901	Speas MR & MRS Wade T
Summit	07901	Vostal MR & MRS Kenneth N
Summit	07901	Yerkes MRS William H J
Tenafly	07670	Huguley MR & MRS Martin C
Titusville	08560	Epperly DR Corinne D
Titusville	08560	Fielding MR & MRS H Page
Titusville	08560	Lippincott MR Walter H
Titusville	08560	Lippincott MRS C Seebohm
Toms River	08753	Van Arsdale MR John H
Trenton	08691	Knipe MRS Peter R
Union City	07087	Sparrow MS Katherine M
Upper Montclair	07043	Cerf MR & MRS William Montgomery
Upper Montclair	07043	Deehan MR & MRS Alan C
Upper Montclair	07043	Schramm MR & MRS Frank E III
Vernon	07462	Gerard MRS C H Coster
Verona	07044	Fabend MR & MRS E Carl
Verona	07044	Walter MR & MRS William Todd
Wall	07719	Dunn MISS Helen C
Wall	07719	Kimm MR Walter E III
Wall	07719	Mathews MR & MRS Richard A
Warren	07059	Ehrenclou MR & MRS Alfred M
Warren	07059	Strong MRS Nancy J
Watchung	07069	Gardiner MR & MRS Blair L
Watchung	07069	Sayan MR & MRS George J
Weehawken	07086	Miller MS Carolyn D
Wenonah	08090	Lader MR & MRS Paul J
West New York	07093	Evenbeck MR Scott E
West Orange	07052	Day MRS Jerome C
Westfield	07090	Sands MISS Edith K
Westfield	07090	Verga MR & MRS Joseph C
Whitehouse	08888	Durling MR Henry A
Whitehouse	08888	Schley MR & MRS Reeve 3D
Whitehouse Station	08889	Drain DR & MRS (DR) Charles Michael
Whitehouse Station	08889	Norkeliunas MR Philip A
Woodbury	08096	Shoemaker DR & MRS B Dawson
Wyckoff	07481	King REV & MRS Jonathan LeR
Wyckoff	07481	Staller MR Peter D & Puzio DR Christopher M

NEW MEXICO

Albuquerque	87104	Chavez MR & MRS Fernando
Albuquerque	87105	Savage MR William H JR
Albuquerque	87106	Connors MR Andrew L
Albuquerque	87107	Clotworthy MR & MRS C Baker JR
Albuquerque	87111	Ely MRS Alfred
Albuquerque	87111	Hayes MR & MRS Geoffrey N
Albuquerque	87122	Ely MR & MRS William Brewster
Albuquerque	87122	Harrison MR & MRS Peter D'A
Albuquerque	87123	Hale MR William Manning JR
Albuquerque	87199	Schwab MRS Stuart T
Corrales	87048	Ponce MRS Joseph L
Des Moines	88418	Wolfe MR & MRS Joseph V
Dixon	87527	Lynch MISS Mary B
El Prado	87529	Rose MR & MRS Peter H
Galisteo	87540	Fleming MR & MRS Edward S JR
Lamy	87540	Burling MR & MRS David L Winslow
Lamy	87540	Morrow MRS S Roy
Madrid	87010	Anderson MR Clinton R G
Pecos	87552	Truesdale MISS Suzanne C
Roswell	88202	McQuiddy MR Arthur R
Rowe	87562	Cowles MR William S JR
Ruidoso	88345	Davis MR & MRS Samuel Riker JR
Ruidoso	88345	Davis MRS Sharon M
Santa Fe	87501	Dennis MR & MRS Landt
Santa Fe	87501	Dulles LT (RET) Allen M
Santa Fe	87501	Duncan DR & MRS Donn G
Santa Fe	87501	Ellis MS Elizabeth D
Santa Fe	87501	Hilbert MISS Elspeth R
Santa Fe	87501	Lummis MR Dayton M JR
Santa Fe	87501	Massey MRS Paul H
Santa Fe	87501	Mitchell MR & MRS Timothy L P
Santa Fe	87501	Osgood MR & MRS Thomas H
Santa Fe	87501	Richardson GOV & MRS William B
Santa Fe	87501	Rogers MR John A
Santa Fe	87501	Toland MR & MRS David A
Santa Fe	87501	Weiser REV & MRS Ivan
Santa Fe	87501	Werner MISS Anne K F D
Santa Fe	87502	La Farge DR & MRS C Grant
Santa Fe	87504	Dunnington MRS (DR) Jacqueline
Santa Fe	87504	Herbert MR & MRS William A
Santa Fe	87504	Herbert MR William A
Santa Fe	87504	Parsons MR & MRS Jack
Santa Fe	87504	Stirling MS (DR) Elizabeth Cole
Santa Fe	87504	Trapnell MR Baylor H
Santa Fe	87505	Barclay MR & MRS Rutgers
Santa Fe	87505	Bullock MISS Sabrina C
Santa Fe	87505	Caldwell DR & MRS David W
Santa Fe	87505	Carey MR James Bayard
Santa Fe	87505	Dechert MR Peter
Santa Fe	87505	Dodds MR & MRS Robert J 3D

Santa Fe 87505 Ennis MRS Bruce J JR
Santa Fe 87505 Furlanetto MR & MRS Michael R
Santa Fe 87505 Geer MRS Mariana Griswold
Santa Fe 87505 La Farge MR John Pendaries
Santa Fe 87505 Love MISS (DR) Lily Pierrepont
Santa Fe 87505 Love MISS Nathalie C P
Santa Fe 87505 Marsh MR & MRS Charles S
Santa Fe 87505 McGonagle MR Milo L & Dunaway MRS Gwendolyn F
Santa Fe 87505 Neuhaus MR & MRS William O 3D
Santa Fe 87505 Van Sant MR James A
Santa Fe 87505 Veenstra MR & MRS David E
Santa Fe 87505 Ward MR Michael E A
Santa Fe 87505 Wright MR T Spencer
Santa Fe 87506 Donnell MR Bruce B
Santa Fe 87506 Gubelmann MR & MRS Wyeth S McC
Santa Fe 87506 Harrison MR & MRS Charles M
Santa Fe 87506 McDougal DR & MRS David B JR
Santa Fe 87506 Parker DR & MRS Thomas D
Santa Fe 87506 van der Hoeven MR & MRS Bernard J C JR
Santa Fe 87507 Dillard MR Tyree 3D
Santa Fe 87507 Klimczuk-Massion MR & MRS Stephen J
Santa Fe 87507 Preucel MISS Ruth B G
Santa Fe 87508 Graves MR & MRS Eugene F JR
Santa Fe 87508 McMahon MR & MRS Bernard J JR
Santa Fe 87508 Warren MR & MRS Christopher D
Santa Fe 87508 Wolff MISS Gerry P
Santa Fe 87594 Parker MR & MRS Michael S
Santa Fe 87594 Walden MR & MRS Russell T
Silver City 88062 Brown MS Susan C

NEW YORK

Accord 12404 Flam MR & MRS Morris
Albany 12210 Eaton MR & MRS F Newell
Albany 12210 Letteron MR Henry
Albany 12210 Litchfield MR William G
Amagansett 11930 Heppenheimer MR & MRS William S
Amenia 12501 Howard MISS Catherine Alger
Amenia 12501 Kim MR & MRS Soohyung
Amenia 12501 Thorne MR & MRS Oakleigh
Amenia 12501 Wetmore MR & MRS William T JR
Amherst 14226 Naylon MR Peter C
Ancram 12502 Wanzenberg MR Alan C
Ancramdale 12503 Meigs MR & MRS S Jonathan
Ardsley-on-Hudson 10503 Steffens MR & MRS Daniel C
Armonk 10504 Ogden MR & MRS Elliott M III
Astoria 11103 Kelly MS Anne F
Astoria 11103 McNair MS Clarissa
Astoria 11105 Carter MR Stephen W
Auburn 13021 Osborne MR & MRS Frederik R-L
Baldwinsville 13027 Stearns MRS David G
Ballston Spa 12020 Freeman MR & MRS (DR) Harry B III
Barrytown 12507 Aldrich MR & MRS Richard
Barrytown 12507 Jenrette MR Richard H
Bayville 11709 Fisher MR & MRS Julian P II
Bayville 11709 Mulry MR & MRS Sean F
Bedford 10506 Borner MR & MRS Steven P
Bedford 10506 Brouder MRS Bernard P
Bedford 10506 Brown MR & MRS C Leonard 2D
Bedford 10506 Chase MR & MRS Cornelius Crane
Bedford 10506 Clark MRS Florence W
Bedford 10506 Côté MRS Storrs
Bedford 10506 Crater MR & MRS Douglas E
Bedford 10506 Durfee MR & MRS Sherman B
Bedford 10506 Edgar MR & MRS James A JR
Bedford 10506 Ewing MRS J G Blaine JR
Bedford 10506 Finn MR & MRS Robert M
Bedford 10506 Firth MR & MRS Nicholas L D
Bedford 10506 Foulke MR & MRS William G JR
Bedford 10506 Grand MR & MRS Harry S
Bedford 10506 Grubb MR & MRS David J
Bedford 10506 Harrington MR & MRS Edward A
Bedford 10506 Husted MR William A
Bedford 10506 Johnson MR & MRS Broaddus
Bedford 10506 Kernan MRS Francis K JR
Bedford 10506 Knoblauch MR & MRS Loring W JR
Bedford 10506 Lounsbery MRS Phillips
Bedford 10506 Mas MR & MRS Paul J
Bedford 10506 Morley MR & MRS Christopher J
Bedford 10506 Olds MR & MRS John T
Bedford 10506 Olney MISS Katrina
Bedford 10506 Quinn MR & MRS Bruce M
Bedford 10506 Randol MR & MRS Jeremy B
Bedford 10506 Root MRS Oren
Bedford 10506 Sachs MR & MRS Samuel 2D
Bedford 10506 Sednaoui MR & MRS M Kent
Bedford 10506 Swift MR & MRS H Steel
Bedford 10506 Waters MR William H
Bedford 10506 Weld MR & MRS William N
Bedford Corners 10549 Heilman MR & MRS Colin S
Bedford Corners 10549 Johnston MR & MRS Scott C
Bedford Corners 10549 La Motte MR & MRS Gardner H
Bedford Corners 10549 Lawrence MR & MRS James R
Bedford Corners 10549 Woodward MR & MRS Gordon H
Bedford Hills 10507 Bogert MR & MRS Jeremiah M
Bedford Hills 10507 Combes MRS Abbott C IV
Bedford Hills 10507 Durfee MR & MRS S Brayton JR
Bedford Hills 10507 El Bouhali MRS Abdelouahab
Bedford Hills 10507 Foster MR & MRS Herbert H 3D
Bedford Hills 10507 Jackson MR & MRS William M
Bedford Hills 10507 Kernan MS Sophia R
Bedford Hills 10507 Ledes MR & MRS George M
Bedford Hills 10507 Lowe MRS James J
Bedford Hills 10507 McKenna MR & MRS Brian V S
Bedford Hills 10507 McLanahan MR & MRS William Duer
Bedford Hills 10507 Meyer MR & MRS Thomas H
Bedford Hills 10507 Polk MR & MRS Samuel H
Bedford Hills 10507 Riegel MR & MRS Richard E III
Bedford Hills 10507 Robinson MR & MRS J Howland
Bedford Hills 10507 Vincent MR & MRS Roger B
Bedford Hills 10507 West MR & MRS George S JR
Bedford Hills 10507 Whitman MRS Harold C III
Bedford Hills 10607 Zahl THE REV & MRS John A
Bellport 11713 Paige MRS Peter
Billings 12510 Voges MR & MRS Shelton C JR
Bloomingdale 12913 Verner MR & MRS Elliott K
Bohemia 11716 Berry MISS Lucinda B
Bolton Landing 12814 Boericke DR & MRS Ralph R
Bolton Landing 12814 Defty MRS S Bixby
Bolton Landing 12814 Hoopes MR & MRS Samuel P
Boston 14025 Killeen MR & MRS Henry W III
Brewster 10509 Ballantine MRS John H
Brewster 10509 Farrington MRS Harold P
Briarcliff Manor 10510 Aldrich MR & MRS Richard R
Briarcliff Manor 10510 Forbes MR Wallace F
Briarcliff Manor 10510 Mischenko MR & MRS Paul B
Bridgehampton 11932 Kinney MR & MRS Christopher F
Bridgehampton 11932 McAuliffe MR & MRS Edward T
Bridgehampton 11932 Ryan MR & MRS Allan A 3D
Bridgehampton 11932 Thompson MISS Sarah B
Bronx 10461 Capato MR & MRS David A

Bronx, NY—Brooklyn, NY

Bronx .... 10463 .... Ryan MR John T
Bronx .... 10463 .... Spencer MR & MRS G Parke
Bronx .... 10463 .... Van der Leur MS Michelle
Bronx .... 10464 .... Swett MS C Catherine H
Bronx .... 10471 .... Lynch MR & MRS Robert F 3D
Bronx .... 10471 .... Willis MR & MRS Philip L
Bronxville .... 10708 .... Abbott MS Andrea N
Bronxville .... 10708 .... Allison MR & MRS William E III
Bronxville .... 10708 .... Almy MRS William 3D
Bronxville .... 10708 .... Anderson MR & MRS Robert Gardner JR
Bronxville .... 10708 .... Baxter MR James A
Bronxville .... 10708 .... Bender MR & MRS Andreas J V M
Bronxville .... 10708 .... Burgin MR & MRS Nicholas F
Bronxville .... 10708 .... Cameron MRS Donald J
Bronxville .... 10708 .... Castillo MS Paulette L
Bronxville .... 10708 .... Clay MR & MRS Jonathan C
Bronxville .... 10708 .... Cummings MR & MRS Alexander B
Bronxville .... 10708 .... Donohue MISS Claire B
Bronxville .... 10708 .... Eimicke MRS Victor W
Bronxville .... 10708 .... Gelpi-Toro MR & MRS William R
Bronxville .... 10708 .... Gemes MR & MRS Kenneth E
Bronxville .... 10708 .... George MR & MRS Quintín H JR
Bronxville .... 10708 .... Gill MR & MRS Peter T
Bronxville .... 10708 .... Gourd MR & MRS Henri N
Bronxville .... 10708 .... Harrington MR & MRS Matthew J
Bronxville .... 10708 .... Horn MR & MRS Anthony G
Bronxville .... 10708 .... Humphreys MR & MRS William F
Bronxville .... 10708 .... Klimley MR & MRS Brooks J
Bronxville .... 10708 .... Logan MISS Edith S
Bronxville .... 10708 .... Mack MR & MRS (DR) George M
Bronxville .... 10708 .... MacLachlan MR & MRS Charles D
Bronxville .... 10708 .... McFadden MR & MRS Ashton S dos S
Bronxville .... 10708 .... Meaders MR Paul Le S 3D
Bronxville .... 10708 .... Millard MR & MRS J Alden JR
Bronxville .... 10708 .... Moore MR & MRS Thomas W
Bronxville .... 10708 .... Peale MR James
Bronxville .... 10708 .... Potter MRS Eugene W JR
Bronxville .... 10708 .... Preis MR & MRS (DR) Phillip W JR
Bronxville .... 10708 .... Raymond MR & MRS Peter D
Bronxville .... 10708 .... Shapard MR W Allen 4TH & Sierck MS Carsten W
Bronxville .... 10708 .... Stebbins MRS H Lyman
Bronxville .... 10708 .... Sullivan MR & MRS Holland A JR
Bronxville .... 10708 .... Twining MR & MRS Alexander C
Bronxville .... 10708 .... Vietor MR & MRS Richard R
Bronxville .... 10708 .... Welch MR & MRS Leighton B
Bronxville .... 10708 .... Yerkes MR & MRS Harry E IV
Brooklyn .... 11201 .... Alvarado MR & MRS Marcos
Brooklyn .... 11201 .... Atenasio MR & MRS Adam A
Brooklyn .... 11201 .... Baldwin MR & MRS Murray H
Brooklyn .... 11201 .... Baltzell MR & MRS W Hewson V
Brooklyn .... 11201 .... Beha MR & MRS James Joseph II
Brooklyn .... 11201 .... Bernbach MRS Paul
Brooklyn .... 11201 .... Brooke MR & MRS Peter F
Brooklyn .... 11201 .... Browne MR & MRS Whitney R
Brooklyn .... 11201 .... Chase MR & MRS (DR) Warren S
Brooklyn .... 11201 .... Clement MR & MRS Theodore D
Brooklyn .... 11201 .... Coryell MISS Allegra O
Brooklyn .... 11201 .... Coulson MR & MRS Crocker
Brooklyn .... 11201 .... De La Cour MR Willis S JR
Brooklyn .... 11201 .... Dowling MR John W
Brooklyn .... 11201 .... Everdell MR & MRS William R
Brooklyn .... 11201 .... Fawcett MRS Polly O
Brooklyn .... 11201 .... Ferrer MR & MRS Andrew K
Brooklyn .... 11201 .... FitzGerald MR & MRS William H C II
Brooklyn .... 11201 .... Friend MR & MRS Theodore P
Brooklyn .... 11201 .... Fruin MR & MRS Thomas E
Brooklyn .... 11201 .... Haines MR & MRS Thomas D JR
Brooklyn .... 11201 .... Hodges MR & MRS Sewall F
Brooklyn .... 11201 .... Ingle MR & MRS Phillip H
Brooklyn .... 11201 .... Jones MR & MRS Oliver H
Brooklyn .... 11201 .... Kline MR & MRS John R
Brooklyn .... 11201 .... Long MR & MRS Tarlton H JR
Brooklyn .... 11201 .... MacKay MR & MRS Malcolm
Brooklyn .... 11201 .... Massey MR & MRS Daniel M
Brooklyn .... 11201 .... Morris MR & MRS Whitten McC
Brooklyn .... 11201 .... Paumgarten-Hohenschwangau-Erbach MR & MRS Harald
Brooklyn .... 11201 .... Phillips MS Abigail S
Brooklyn .... 11201 .... Pool MR & MRS James D
Brooklyn .... 11201 .... Robertson MR & MRS J Spencer
Brooklyn .... 11201 .... Robinson MR & MRS Guy N
Brooklyn .... 11201 .... Roosevelt MR & MRS Theodore 4TH
Brooklyn .... 11201 .... Silver MR & MRS Pierson H
Brooklyn .... 11201 .... Swain MR & MRS Thomas S
Brooklyn .... 11201 .... Whelan MR Reid A
Brooklyn .... 11205 .... Bainbridge MISS Julia V
Brooklyn .... 11205 .... Cogan MR & MRS Daniel F
Brooklyn .... 11205 .... McKown MISS Alice B
Brooklyn .... 11205 .... Peterson MR & MRS James C
Brooklyn .... 11205 .... Starbuck MR & MRS Joshua B
Brooklyn .... 11205 .... Summers MR & MRS Phillip T
Brooklyn .... 11205 .... Wood MR Paul S & English MS Katharine J
Brooklyn .... 11206 .... Winkler MR & MRS Thomas P
Brooklyn .... 11211 .... Gieskes MR & MRS Joost J
Brooklyn .... 11211 .... Oliphant MRS Katherine Holland
Brooklyn .... 11211 .... Schoder MR William A
Brooklyn .... 11211 .... Weld MR & MRS George F III
Brooklyn .... 11211 .... Windsor MR & MRS Robert G JR
Brooklyn .... 11211 .... Yocum MR & MRS Samuel C II
Brooklyn .... 11215 .... Allen MR & MRS Douglas F III
Brooklyn .... 11215 .... Beller MR & MRS Alan L
Brooklyn .... 11215 .... Ellis MR Freddie JR
Brooklyn .... 11215 .... Harvey MR & MRS (DR) Robert E
Brooklyn .... 11215 .... Kimball-Stanley MR & MRS David C
Brooklyn .... 11215 .... Kuflik DR Arthur & Day MS Allison P
Brooklyn .... 11215 .... Machold MR & MRS Robert P
Brooklyn .... 11215 .... Mendelsohn MR & MRS David M R
Brooklyn .... 11215 .... Montour MR & MRS Brandt A
Brooklyn .... 11215 .... Mudannayake DR & MRS Louis M
Brooklyn .... 11215 .... Nevius MRS John G
Brooklyn .... 11215 .... Osborne MR Duncan T
Brooklyn .... 11215 .... Prochnow MR Thomas H & Lin MS Anita
Brooklyn .... 11215 .... Ripley MR & MRS Peter H
Brooklyn .... 11215 .... Rodd MR & MRS F Morgan JR
Brooklyn .... 11215 .... Rogers MR & MRS Nathaniel F R
Brooklyn .... 11215 .... White DR & MRS Arthur P
Brooklyn .... 11215 .... Willis MRS Emily K
Brooklyn .... 11216 .... Gansa MR & MRS Charles R vonS
Brooklyn .... 11217 .... Armstrong MR Robert K
Brooklyn .... 11217 .... Beekman MR Gerard J & Kaminsky MR Michael S
Brooklyn .... 11217 .... Bowditch MR & MRS Richard L 3D
Brooklyn .... 11217 .... Davol MR & MRS Samuel B
Brooklyn .... 11217 .... Jackson MR & MRS Henry W A
Brooklyn .... 11217 .... Morgan MR & MRS Andrew R
Brooklyn .... 11217 .... Parsons MS Michele A
Brooklyn .... 11217 .... Schwab MR George B & Lodi MS Monique P
Brooklyn .... 11217 .... Soule MR & MRS Richard H JR
Brooklyn .... 11218 .... Pitou MR David W
Brooklyn .... 11220 .... Keegan MRS (DR) Warren J
Brooklyn .... 11222 .... Edwards MR & MRS Oliver VII
Brooklyn .... 11222 .... Elliott MR & MRS T Scott
Brooklyn .... 11222 .... Kirk MISS Lisa S

Brooklyn .... 11222 .... Roessler MR Peter C
Brooklyn .... 11225 .... Hornblower MR Samuel R
& Allen-Hornblower DR Emily
Brooklyn .... 11226 .... De Witt MISS Jessica S
Brooklyn .... 11226 .... Hoyt MR & MRS Winthrop S
Brooklyn .... 11226 .... Meyer MR & MRS Robert P
Brooklyn .... 11226 .... Parker MR & MRS Thomas B
Brooklyn .... 11226 .... Potter MR Robert B
Brooklyn .... 11226 .... Prisant MR & MRS M Barden
Brooklyn .... 11231 .... Ayers MISS Frances McK
Brooklyn .... 11231 .... Bierman MR & MRS Frederick C
Brooklyn .... 11231 .... Campbell MR & MRS Peter B
Brooklyn .... 11231 .... Mullan MR & MRS Peter D
Brooklyn .... 11231 .... Nalley MR & MRS Richard V
Brooklyn .... 11231 .... Roberts MR & MRS John A
Brooklyn .... 11231 .... Talbot MR & MRS James S
Brooklyn .... 11231 .... Walley MR & MRS Noah J
Brooklyn .... 11238 .... Bain MR Michael J & Wood MS Penelope B
Brooklyn .... 11238 .... Butler MR & MRS Jonathan R
Brooklyn .... 11238 .... Cox MR & MRS Samuel R
Brooklyn .... 11238 .... Crawford MR & MRS James E IV
Brooklyn .... 11238 .... Humes MR & MRS W Hans
Brooklyn .... 11238 .... Naudé MR Philip W
Brooklyn .... 11238 .... Sachs MR & MRS Alexander J A
Brooklyn .... 11238 .... Weir MR & MRS Richard IV
Brooklyn .... 11249 .... Pai MR Ashok S
Brooklyn .... 11249 .... Rutgers MR & MRS Heimata K M
Brooklyn .... 11249 .... Senior MS Fern D & Thomas MS Kristin A
Brooklyn .... 11249 .... Stiglitz MR & MRS Michael E
Brooklyn Heights .... 11201 .... Bland MR & MRS Frederick A
Brookville .... 11545 .... Evans MR & MRS Johnston L
Buchanan .... 10511 .... Draper MR & MRS Thayer P JR
Buffalo .... 14202 .... Bigelow MR & MRS Ernest A JR
Buffalo .... 14202 .... Strachan MR & MRS Malcolm 2D
Buffalo .... 14209 .... Ambrus DR Julian L
Buffalo .... 14209 .... Bean MR & MRS Edwin T JR
Buffalo .... 14209 .... Cowles MRS Chauncey D
Buffalo .... 14209 .... Cowles MS Julia K
Buffalo .... 14209 .... Doolittle MRS Roy W JR
Buffalo .... 14209 .... Fryer MRS Appleton
Buffalo .... 14209 .... Houston MR & MRS Frederic K
Buffalo .... 14209 .... Johnston MR & MRS Edwin McC 3D
Buffalo .... 14209 .... Kashin DR & MRS Jeffrey D
Buffalo .... 14209 .... Kellogg MR & MRS Stephen
Buffalo .... 14209 .... McGowan MRS Gerard F
Buffalo .... 14209 .... Pierce MRS Frederick S
Buffalo .... 14209 .... Williamson MRS William J JR
Buffalo .... 14209 .... Wyckoff MR & MRS Kevin B
Buffalo .... 14214 .... Hemenway MRS Brewster R
Buffalo .... 14214 .... Mollenberg MR & MRS Henry Van
Buffalo .... 14214 .... Oshei MRS Mary B
Buffalo .... 14214 .... Pearce MR & MRS William H JR
Buffalo .... 14215 .... Williams MR & MRS Keith H
Buffalo .... 14216 .... Banta MR & MRS Charles W
Buffalo .... 14216 .... Braen DR & MRS G Richard
Buffalo .... 14216 .... Duryea MRS George R JR
Buffalo .... 14216 .... Flickinger MRS (DR) Bonnie G
Buffalo .... 14216 .... Hettrick MR & MRS John L JR
Buffalo .... 14216 .... Jewett MRS Edgar B 3D
Buffalo .... 14216 .... Johnston MR Edwin M JR
Buffalo .... 14216 .... Knox MR & MRS Seymour H IV
Buffalo .... 14216 .... Marcy MRS William L JR
Buffalo .... 14216 .... Rupp MR William R
Buffalo .... 14216 .... Sears MR & MRS R Buford
Buffalo .... 14216 .... Stevenson MR & MRS Robert L
Buffalo .... 14216 .... Weathers MRS Suzanne J
Buffalo .... 14221 .... Prentice DR & MRS Theodore C
Buffalo .... 14222 .... Call MR & MRS Dennis R
Buffalo .... 14222 .... Clarkson MR & MRS William M E
Buffalo .... 14222 .... Cummings MRS Robert C
Buffalo .... 14222 .... de Castro MRS J Edmund JR
Buffalo .... 14222 .... Hamlett MR & MRS Samuel L
Buffalo .... 14222 .... Irey MISS Annabelle V
Buffalo .... 14222 .... Kellogg MR & MRS Justin K
Buffalo .... 14222 .... Marlette MR John E JR
Buffalo .... 14222 .... Morris MS Jane C
Buffalo .... 14222 .... Otto MRS John 3D
Buffalo .... 14222 .... Regan MR & MRS William J JR
Buffalo .... 14222 .... Richards MR & MRS Rowland JR
Buffalo .... 14222 .... Rumsey MRS R Douglas
Buffalo .... 14222 .... Sawyer MRS William B H
Buffalo .... 14222 .... Wadsworth DR & MRS John M
Buffalo .... 14222 .... Wettlaufer MRS (DR) C Penn
Buffalo .... 14226 .... Frenning MR Alfred B
Burnt Hills .... 12027 .... Haskell REV & MRS Robert F
Cambridge .... 12816 .... Kittell DR & MRS John C
Camillus .... 13031 .... Whitney MR & MRS Mark R
Campbell Hall .... 10916 .... Glendening CAPT Sean D
Canandaigua .... 14424 .... D'Amore DR & MRS (DR) John J
Canandaigua .... 14424 .... Greenleaf MISS Sara W
Canandaigua .... 14424 .... Montgomery MR & MRS Parker Gilbert
Cape Vincent .... 13618 .... Bragdon MR Brooks J
Carmel .... 10512 .... Peters MR & MRS Merz K
Cazenovia .... 13035 .... Evans MR & MRS James F 3D
Cazenovia .... 13035 .... Kane DR & MRS Peter B
Cazenovia .... 13035 .... Knapp MS Camilla T
Cazenovia .... 13035 .... MacVeagh MR Colin L
Cazenovia .... 13035 .... Sullivan MR & MRS Michael J
Centerport .... 11721 .... Allen MR Freeman Towne
Centre Island .... 11771 .... Benjamin MR & MRS Park III
Chappaqua .... 10514 .... Guerney MR & MRS Paul M
Chappaqua .... 10514 .... Hart MR & MRS Lewis J JR
Chappaqua .... 10514 .... Jorgensen MRS Amoret T
Chappaqua .... 10514 .... Kiernan MR & MRS Gregory F
Chatham Center .... 12184 .... Gerrity MR & MRS Robert T
Chatham Center .... 12184 .... Kennedy MISS Catharine C
Cherry Plain .... 12040 .... Fosburgh MRS Pieter W
Chester .... 10918 .... Knapick MR & MRS (DR) Gary J
Claverack .... 12513 .... Ackert MR Stanley M III
Claverack .... 12513 .... Post MR & MRS Christopher C
Clinton Corners .... 12514 .... Braga MR & MRS David J
Clinton Corners .... 12514 .... Garcia MR & MRS Andrew A
Cold Spring .... 10516 .... Bickford MR & MRS Robert C
Cold Spring .... 10516 .... Cabot MRS Francis H
Cold Spring .... 10516 .... Florke MR Randy G & Maloney MR Sean P
Cold Spring .... 10516 .... Knapp MRS Cleaver L
Cold Spring .... 10516 .... Silva-Sadder MR & MRS Adolfo
Cold Spring Harbor .... 11724 .... Babcock MR & MRS Henry D JR
Cold Spring Harbor .... 11724 .... Cullen MR & MRS Denis D
Cold Spring Harbor .... 11724 .... Dohan MR & MRS Michael R
Cold Spring Harbor .... 11724 .... Donohue MR & MRS Mark P
Cold Spring Harbor .... 11724 .... Elder MRS R Duncan
Cold Spring Harbor .... 11724 .... Feder MR & MRS Andrew M
Cold Spring Harbor .... 11724 .... Hadden MRS John W
Cold Spring Harbor .... 11724 .... Hewitt MR & MRS C F Lindsay
Cold Spring Harbor .... 11724 .... Ingraham MR Frederic B
Cold Spring Harbor .... 11724 .... MacKay MR & MRS Robert B
Cold Spring Harbor .... 11724 .... Megear MR & MRS Thomas J
Cold Spring Harbor .... 11724 .... Pratt MRS Richardson
Cold Spring Harbor .... 11724 .... Prugh MR & MRS Clayton A
Cold Spring Harbor .... 11724 .... Walton MR & MRS Robert P
Cooperstown .... 13326 .... Gotwald MR & MRS Stephen McC

Cooperstown, NY— Glen Head, NY

Cooperstown	13326	Hamilton DR & MRS Lewis L
Cooperstown	13326	Kegelman MR & MRS Brian J
Cooperstown	13326	Schau MR Jonathan D
Cooperstown	13326	Smythe MR & MRS Christopher W
Cooperstown	13326	Vincent MR & MRS Gilbert T
Cooperstown	13326	Weldon MR & MRS William J III
Coram	11727	Pigott MR Richard I
Cornwall-on-Hudson	12520	Stillman MR Mark C
Cornwall-on-Hudson	12520	Stillman MRS John S
Cornwall-on-Hudson	12520	Tobin MR & MRS (DR) Bradford J
Cornwall-on-Hudson	12520	von Estorff MISS (DR) Irene
Cortlandt Manor	10567	Carmen DR Ira H & Putnam MS Lawrence Lowell
Crestwood	10707	Coleman MR & MRS F Daniel Le V
Cross River	10518	Colley MR & MRS Bryan O
Cross River	10518	Wood MRS Peter H
Crugers	10521	Norman MISS Jessye
Delmar	12054	Foss MR & MRS Edward C
Delmar	12054	Ledbetter DR T Mark & Cumings MS (DR) Susan G
Delmar	12054	Martin MR & MRS Christopher J
Derby	14047	Esty MR John A
Dobbs Ferry	10522	Hoff MR & MRS William B
Downsville	13755	Martin MR & MRS Robert I M
Dryden	13053	Vincent MR & MRS Roger B JR
Dundee	14837	Jensen MR & MRS Eric J
East Amherst	14051	Tingley MISS Priscilla A
East Amherst	14051	Urban MR & MRS Henry Z JR
East Aurora	14052	Dewart MR & MRS Alan
East Aurora	14052	Hatrick MR & MRS David W
East Aurora	14052	Herrick MR & MRS Sherlock A JR
East Aurora	14052	Morris MR & MRS George C
East Hampton	11937	Booth MRS Winifred M
East Hampton	11937	Breckenfeld MR & MRS William Gurney
East Hampton	11937	Dayton MR & MRS Peter P
East Hampton	11937	Dillard DR James N
East Hampton	11937	Edwards MRS James C
East Hampton	11937	Feid MR & MRS Stephen B
East Hampton	11937	Gorman MRS Kernan F
East Hampton	11937	Hopkinson MR & MRS Peter
East Hampton	11937	Hyatt MR & MRS Frederick E III
East Hampton	11937	McAuliffe MR & MRS E Timothy JR
East Hampton	11937	Millard MR & MRS Richard D
East Hampton	11937	Murray MR & MRS Henry L
East Hampton	11937	Paton DR & MRS David
East Hampton	11937	Peddy MR & MRS Jackson E
East Hampton	11937	Pool MR & MRS James L S
East Hampton	11937	Robert MR & MRS Yves H
East Hampton	11937	Robertson MR & MRS Jaquelin T
East Hampton	11937	Savage MR Charles C
East Hampton	11937	Smith MR & MRS Richard W
East Hampton	11937	Timpson MR & MRS James JR
East Hampton	11937	Tyson MR & MRS Anthony N
East Hampton	11937	Wainwright MR & MRS D Walker
East Hampton	11937	Wainwright MR & MRS Stuyvesant 3D
East Hampton	11937	Wiegand MRS Michael D
East Hills	11577	Corey MR & MRS R William
East Islip	11730	Williams DR & MRS Howard C
East Norwich	11732	Duke MR & MRS Anthony D JR
East Norwich	11732	Floyd-Jones MR & MRS William JR
East Norwich	11732	Kimmick MR & MRS Adam O
East Norwich	11732	Lihme MISS Heidi L
East Quogue	11942	de Ropp MRS Zoé Van Wyck
East Rochester	14445	Horne MR & MRS Theodore L
Eastchester	10709	Hale MR & MRS Tyler B
Eden	14057	Spaulding MR & MRS Frederick A
Eden	14057	Walters MR Seymour G
Eden	14057	Wolf MRS John F JR
Elma	14059	Harper MR & MRS Stuart L
Elmsford	10523	Lighty MS Nylia E
Essex	12936	Irwin MRS David M
Evans Mills	13637	Forbes DR William I 3D
Fairport	14450	Connard MR Frank L JR
Fairport	14450	Perkins MS Rebecca D
Fayetteville	13066	Ewart MR & MRS Craig K
Fishers Island	06390	Parker MR & MRS Harry S 3D
Fishers Island	06390	Sanger MR & MRS Penn du P
Fishkill	12524	Bartow MR & MRS Clarence W JR
Forest Hills	11375	Irwin MISS Maria B
Forest Hills	11375	Paine MR Andrew S
Forest Hills	11375	Paine MR William D
Forest Hills	11375	Schott MR Steven G
Forest Hills	11375	Smith DR Robert G & Chiappelloni MS Silvana
Ft Johnson	12070	Cecil DR & MRS (DR) Russell N A
Garden City	11530	Bowden MISS Emily M
Garden City	11530	Gillespie MRS Edward A
Garden City	11530	Magovern MR & MRS Frederick J
Garden City	11530	Munn MR & MRS Douglas J
Garden City	11530	Tully MR & MRS Christopher J
Garrison	10524	Banker MR & MRS Douglas H
Garrison	10524	de Rham MR Pierre R
Garrison	10524	Felder MAJ & MRS William L
Garrison	10524	Frazier MISS Julia R
Garrison	10524	Geer REV & MRS Francis H
Garrison	10524	Lansbury MR & MRS George W
Garrison	10524	Osborn MR & MRS Frederick H 3D
Garrison	10524	Platt MR & MRS Geoffrey JR
Garrison	10524	Potts DR & MRS Daniel T
Garrison	10524	Spalding MRS Charles F
Garrison	10542	Cutler MR Robert B JR
Geneseo	14454	Chanler MRS Oliver H
Geneseo	14454	Kelley MR & MRS Stephen M
Geneseo	14454	McClellan MR Gordon B
Geneseo	14454	Wadsworth MS Martha C
Geneseo	14454	Wood MRS William P
Germantown	12526	Davidson MR & MRS Benjamin Q
Germantown	12526	Livingston MS Isabel C
Germantown	12526	Perry MRS Hart
Getzville	14068	Putnam MRS John G JR
Ghent	12075	Black MR David & Weisberg MS Barbara
Gilbertsville	13776	Elbrick MR & MRS Alfred J
Glen Cove	11542	Banker MR & MRS Vincent C
Glen Cove	11542	Bartow MR & MRS Philip K JR
Glen Cove	11542	Belt MR & MRS John H K
Glen Cove	11542	Carton MRS Sybil B
Glen Cove	11542	Cattier MRS Jean
Glen Cove	11542	Clark MR & MRS Frederick S
Glen Cove	11542	Duryea MRS James M
Glen Cove	11542	Gimbel MR & MRS Thomas S T
Glen Cove	11542	Heyes MRS Fred L
Glen Cove	11542	Hilbert MR & MRS Lawrence P
Glen Cove	11542	Lynch MR & MRS Edmund C III
Glen Cove	11542	Marshall MR & MRS Peter E
Glen Cove	11542	McLanahan MR & MRS Morgan C
Glen Cove	11542	Miller MR & MRS Edward M
Glen Cove	11542	Nolte MRS Ann L
Glen Cove	11542	Sutherland MRS Donald J
Glen Cove	11542	Thurber MRS A Edward JR
Glen Head	11545	Bostwick MR & MRS James F C
Glen Head	11545	Choremi MR & MRS A Michael JR
Glen Head	11545	Geisel MR & MRS Andrew F
Glen Head	11545	Hooton MRS Bruce D
Glen Head	11545	Huwiler MR & MRS John E
Glen Head	11545	Kelsey MR & MRS Parker B

Glen Head .... 11545 .... Lardi MR Paul F
Glen Head .... 11545 .... Mason MRS Grey
Glen Head .... 11545 .... Pilkington MR & MRS Robert
Glen Head .... 11545 .... Polk MRS Frank L JR
Glen Head .... 11545 .... Ponomarev MR & MRS Paul C
Glen Head .... 11545 .... Ross MRS Walter L II
Glen Head .... 11545 .... Webel MR & MRS Peter C
Glenwood Landing .... 11547 .... McGovern MR & MRS James W
Goldens Bridge .... 10526 .... Evarts MR & MRS John R H
Grand View-on-Hudson 10960 .... Brown MR & MRS Howard H JR
Grand View-on-Hudson 10960 .... Figg MR James A III
Granville .... 12832 .... Hicks MR & MRS Matthew B
Granville .... 12832 .... Schieffelin MR & MRS Lindsay
Great Neck .... 11021 .... Coddington MR & MRS Stewart G
Great Neck .... 11021 .... Russell MR & MRS Hollis F
Greenport .... 11944 .... Lewis MRS Ogden Northrop
Greenport .... 11944 .... McIntyre MRS Angus P
Greenport .... 11944 .... Reynal MR & MRS Eric Y
Greenport .... 11944 .... Righter MR & MRS Brewster A McN
Greenport .... 11944 .... Tessier MR John S
Greenport .... 11944 .... Ulman MR & MRS Stephen Van R
Greenvale .... 11548 .... Gallatin MR & MRS Thomas G JR
Greenwich .... 12834 .... Poor MS Penelope
Hamburg .... 14075 .... Windebank MRS Charles S
Hampton Bays .... 11946 .... Beale MR & MRS N Ridgely
Hampton Bays .... 11946 .... Zimmerman MRS Robert W JR
Harrison .... 10528 .... Arquit MR & MRS Kevin J
Harrison .... 10528 .... Grant MR & MRS Francis C III
Harrison .... 10528 .... McCooey MR & MRS Mark J
Harrison .... 10528 .... Rees MR & MRS Timothy M
Hastings-on-Hudson .... 10706 .... Bernard MR & MRS André P
Hastings-on-Hudson .... 10706 .... Brent MR & MRS Steven C
Hastings-on-Hudson .... 10706 .... Dent MR Thomas A 3D
Hastings-on-Hudson .... 10706 .... Maxwell MISS Elizabeth C
Hicksville .... 11801 .... Whitlock DR Prentice E
Highland .... 12528 .... Persinger MR & MRS Philip B
Hillsdale .... 12529 .... Nouri MR & MRS Guy K
Hinsdale .... 14743 .... Dahar MR & MRS William J
Holmes .... 12531 .... Andrews MR & MRS Peter F
Hudson .... 12534 .... Eyre MRS Henry N JR
Hudson .... 12534 .... Furse MR William R
Hudson .... 12534 .... Livingston MR & MRS Richard H B
Hudson .... 12534 .... Livingston MRS Henry H
Hudson .... 12534 .... Welles MR & MRS David W
Hughsonville .... 12537 .... Reese MR & MRS Alexander S
Huntington .... 11743 .... Dean MRS William Tucker
Huntington .... 11743 .... Fowler MR & MRS Scudder T
Huntington .... 11743 .... Fuchs MR & MRS David C
Huntington .... 11743 .... Grace MR & MRS D Richard
Huntington .... 11743 .... Hamersley MR Nicholas B
Huntington .... 11743 .... Hargraves MRS Gordon Sellers
Huntington .... 11743 .... MacKay MR & MRS John F III
Huntington .... 11743 .... MacLean MR & MRS Babcock
Huntington .... 11743 .... Marshall MR & MRS Thornton W
Huntington .... 11743 .... Merritt MR & MRS Christopher J
Huntington .... 11743 .... Mitchell MR Robert P
Huntington .... 11743 .... Parks MR & MRS Gregory G
Huntington .... 11743 .... Pugsley MR & MRS William J
Huntington .... 11743 .... Riley MR & MRS J Gregory
Huntington .... 11743 .... Wardell MRS Cathie B
Huntington Bay .... 11743 .... Perrell MR & MRS Franklin H
Huntington Bay .... 11743 .... Schueler MR & MRS Charles R JR
Hurley .... 12443 .... Bailey MR & MRS James G
Irvington .... 10533 .... Knudson MR & MRS David N
Island Park .... 11558 .... Snyder MR Philip M JR
Islip .... 11751 .... Unger MR & MRS Toby
Ithaca .... 14850 .... Biloski DR & MRS Alan J
Ithaca .... 14850 .... Cox MRS Gerard H
Ithaca .... 14850 .... Dewart MISS Elizabeth A
Ithaca .... 14850 .... Dewart MR Brian
Ithaca .... 14850 .... Franciscus MISS Monica
Ithaca .... 14850 .... Miller MR & MRS Philippus III
Ithaca .... 14850 .... Pollock MR & MRS Christopher H
Ithaca .... 14850 .... White MR & MRS William D
Jackson Heights .... 11372 .... Jones MR Robert A W
Jamesport .... 11947 .... Hargrave MS Louisa Thomas
Katonah .... 10536 .... Bennett MR & MRS Matthew G
Katonah .... 10536 .... Biddle MR & MRS Edward E
Katonah .... 10536 .... Bostwick MR & MRS James F C JR
Katonah .... 10536 .... Bueti MR & MRS John P
Katonah .... 10536 .... Clymer MR & MRS Robert H 3D
Katonah .... 10536 .... Dewing MISS Martha F
Katonah .... 10536 .... Frelinghuysen MR & MRS Nicholas L
Katonah .... 10536 .... Lamb MR & MRS Lawton S
Katonah .... 10536 .... Ledes MR John G
Katonah .... 10536 .... Pachios MR & MRS Christopher H
Katonah .... 10536 .... Potter MR & MRS Winslow Ward
Katonah .... 10536 .... Simpson MR William K
Katonah .... 10536 .... Straton MR & MRS John C JR
Katonah .... 10536 .... Talbot MR & MRS Harold R
Katonah .... 10536 .... Walsh MR & MRS Brian R
Keene Valley .... 12943 .... Dennis MRS Anne P
Keene Valley .... 12943 .... Kernan MR Benjamin T
Kerhonkson .... 12446 .... Nichols MR C Walter 4TH
Kerhonkson .... 12446 .... Nichols MRS Corinna
Kew Gardens .... 11415 .... Lonergan MR Michael G
Kinderhook .... 12106 .... Anderson MRS Alexandra C
Kingston .... 12401 .... Post MR & MRS Waldron K 2D
Lagrangeville .... 12540 .... Collins MR & MRS Henry Lafayette III
Lagrangeville .... 12540 .... Klose MISS Victoria
Lake Clear .... 12945 .... Duncan MRS Ransom H
Lake Katrine .... 12449 .... Molyneux MRS Edward F
Lake Placid .... 12946 .... Master MRS Nancy S
Lake View .... 14085 .... Petri MR & MRS Pitt JR
Larchmont .... 10538 .... Brawer MR & MRS Nicholas A
Larchmont .... 10538 .... Brush MR & MRS Peter W
Larchmont .... 10538 .... Collins MR & MRS Dwight M
Larchmont .... 10538 .... Donnelly MS Allison C T
Larchmont .... 10538 .... Kippax MR & MRS John E
Larchmont .... 10538 .... Manice MR & MRS Charles DeForest
Larchmont .... 10538 .... Paddock MRS Anthony C
Larchmont .... 10538 .... Pardiwala MR & MRS Cyrus N
Larchmont .... 10538 .... Rogers MR & MRS Grant E
Larchmont .... 10538 .... Ryden MR & MRS Kurt V
Larchmont .... 10538 .... Snedeker MR & MRS Robert D
Larchmont .... 10538 .... Warren MR & MRS Michael J
Larchmont .... 10538 .... Weed MRS Barbara L
Larchmont .... 10538 .... Welden MR Wickford W
Larchmont .... 10538 .... Wray MR & MRS Michael B
Latham .... 12110 .... Townsend MRS Howard
Lattingtown .... 11560 .... Bancroft MRS William W
Lattingtown .... 11560 .... Franson MR & MRS Bjorn E
Lattingtown .... 11560 .... Sheldon MR & MRS John Stevens
Laurel Hollow .... 11791 .... Hopkinson MR & MRS Mark
Lawrence .... 11559 .... Bierwirth MRS John C
Lawrence .... 11559 .... Carpenter MRS Edward N
Lawrence .... 11559 .... Madsen MR & MRS Stephen S
Lawrence .... 11559 .... Mullally MRS Mandeville
Lawrence .... 11559 .... Nicol MR & MRS Arthur C A
Lawrence .... 11559 .... Ogden MR & MRS Gordon S
Lawrence .... 11559 .... Snyder MR Robert M
Lawrence .... 11559 .... Thayer MRS James L

To nominate a candidate for the Social Register Association, please email: SRCommittee@thesocialregister.org

Lindenhurst, NY—Milbrook, NY

Lindenhurst	11757	Nicholl MRS Helen Dale
Lloyd Harbor	11743	Jay MRS Robert D
Lloyd Harbor	11743	MacKay MR & MRS John F JR
Lloyd Harbor	11743	O'Connell MR & MRS Matthew McG
Locust Valley	11560	Ault MRS Lee A
Locust Valley	11560	Bard MRS Henry H
Locust Valley	11560	Benham MR & MRS David B
Locust Valley	11560	Body MR & MRS Louis F V
Locust Valley	11560	Bogart MR & MRS Adrian T JR
Locust Valley	11560	Boggess MR & MRS Russell T
Locust Valley	11560	Bonebrake MR & MRS Michael H
Locust Valley	11560	Braff MR & MRS Douglas P
Locust Valley	11560	Brinkley MR & MRS Sterling B JR
Locust Valley	11560	Brisbane MR & MRS Charles A
Locust Valley	11560	Burchfield MR & MRS William W
Locust Valley	11560	Byers MR & MRS W Russell G JR
Locust Valley	11560	Cannell MR & MRS Peter B
Locust Valley	11560	Chapman MR & MRS Gilbert W JR
Locust Valley	11560	Choate MRS Thomas H
Locust Valley	11560	Choremi MR & MRS Alec M
Locust Valley	11560	Clark MR & MRS E McMichael JR
Locust Valley	11560	Comfort MR & MRS William T
Locust Valley	11560	Conway MR & MRS Elliot S
Locust Valley	11560	Cooney MR & MRS Stephen M
Locust Valley	11560	Crary MR Robert C K & Murphy MRS Pia P G
Locust Valley	11560	Cushman MR & MRS Christoph von F
Locust Valley	11560	Danforth MRS Theodore N
Locust Valley	11560	Davidson MR Murat H & Peters MS Sally A
Locust Valley	11560	Davison MR & MRS Henry P II
Locust Valley	11560	Davison MRS Daniel P
Locust Valley	11560	Dejoux MR Edouard H G
Locust Valley	11560	Dick MR & MRS William C
Locust Valley	11560	Dillenbeck MRS Suzanne V
Locust Valley	11560	Dixon MR & MRS P Brooke JR
Locust Valley	11560	Ely MR & MRS Stephen
Locust Valley	11560	Farley MRS Edward I
Locust Valley	11560	Forman MR & MRS Edward J
Locust Valley	11560	Frick MRS Henry C II
Locust Valley	11560	Garde MRS John F
Locust Valley	11560	Geddes MR & MRS Robert A
Locust Valley	11560	Gerry MR & MRS Elbridge T JR
Locust Valley	11560	Gerry MR & MRS William F
Locust Valley	11560	Graham MR & MRS Gordon JR
Locust Valley	11560	Grant MR & MRS Thomas W
Locust Valley	11560	Gray MR & MRS Austen T JR
Locust Valley	11560	Gulden MR & MRS Christopher A
Locust Valley	11560	Hall MR & MRS Ransom F
Locust Valley	11560	Hartmeyer MR Stuart H
Locust Valley	11560	Havens MR & MRS John Paul
Locust Valley	11560	Hawkey MISS Elizabeth H
Locust Valley	11560	Hollingsworth MR & MRS William I 3D
Locust Valley	11560	Howard MISS Victoria B
Locust Valley	11560	Howe MRS Margaret Hamilton
Locust Valley	11560	Jackson MR Frost B
Locust Valley	11560	Johnson MR & MRS Douglas S
Locust Valley	11560	Jones MR & MRS Nicholas P
Locust Valley	11560	Kemper MR & MRS Antoine C JR
Locust Valley	11560	Key MR Timothy S
Locust Valley	11560	Knutsen MR & MRS Ragnar M
Locust Valley	11560	Lamb MR & MRS David R
Locust Valley	11560	Landreth MR & MRS Chase W
Locust Valley	11560	Lapsley MRS John W
Locust Valley	11560	Large MR & MRS James M JR
Locust Valley	11560	Leslie MRS James JR
Locust Valley	11560	Lindsay MR & MRS Robert D
Locust Valley	11560	Mackay MR & MRS Patrick H
Locust Valley	11560	McLane MR & MRS Robert M JR
Locust Valley	11560	McMillen MR & MRS Bryan
Locust Valley	11560	Merrill MR & MRS Robert A
Locust Valley	11560	Merrill MR Robert G
Locust Valley	11560	Meyer MR & MRS Douglas C
Locust Valley	11560	Meyer MR & MRS Edward B 3D
Locust Valley	11560	Michalis MR & MRS Clarence F
Locust Valley	11560	Morgan MR & MRS Alfred Y 4TH
Locust Valley	11560	Mortimer MR & MRS Richard I
Locust Valley	11560	Moseley-Rioux MRS Leslie M
Locust Valley	11560	Niven MISS Susan McK
Locust Valley	11560	Niven MRS John B
Locust Valley	11560	Parsons MR & MRS William JR
Locust Valley	11560	Pell MR Peter J SR
Locust Valley	11560	Pell MS Allison M
Locust Valley	11560	Pidot MR & MRS Philip M
Locust Valley	11560	Pierrepont MR & MRS R Stuyvesant III
Locust Valley	11560	Porter MR & MRS Grant A
Locust Valley	11560	Reese MR & MRS John R
Locust Valley	11560	Roosevelt MS Fay S
Locust Valley	11560	Salant MRS Robert S
Locust Valley	11560	Scully MR & MRS David B
Locust Valley	11560	Sincerbeaux MR & MRS Richard M
Locust Valley	11560	Slater MRS Alexander B
Locust Valley	11560	Smith MR & MRS H Brooks
Locust Valley	11560	Smith MR & MRS Herbert L IV
Locust Valley	11560	Smith MR & MRS Peter C
Locust Valley	11560	Snodgrass MR & MRS John D'Arcy
Locust Valley	11560	Staniford MRS Robert H JR
Locust Valley	11560	Tabler MR & MRS William B JR
Locust Valley	11560	Taylor MRS David S
Locust Valley	11560	Tilghman MR George H JR
Locust Valley	11560	Timpson MR & MRS Carl W 3D
Locust Valley	11560	Urry MR & MRS James A
Locust Valley	11560	Whitcraft MR Edward C R
Locust Valley	11560	Wolcott MR Samuel H
Locust Valley	11560	Woodhouse MR & MRS Henry M JR
Locust Valley	11560	Worth MR & MRS Peter J JR
Long Island City	11101	de Sanctis MR Pier F
Long Island City	11101	Fox MS Emily
Long Island City	11101	Griffith MR & MRS Paul Maxwell
Long Island City	11101	Jones MS Hope H
Long Island City	11101	Peel MR & MRS Bradley G
Long Island City	11109	Drachlis MR & MRS Eric B
Long Island City	11109	Kerr MR & MRS Ian A N MacD
Long Lake	12847	Roalsvig MR & MRS Paul H
Loudonville	12211	Berg MR H George S JR & Love MS Kathryn S
Loudonville	12211	Helm MR & MRS William L 3D
Loudonville	12211	Lewis MR & MRS Griffith E
Mahopac	10541	Kim MR & MRS Douglas
Malden Bridge	12115	Whitney MR Wheelock 3D & Cagnin MR Sandro
Mamaroneck	10543	Borst MR & MRS Alan W JR
Mamaroneck	10543	Findlay MR & MRS Joshua P
Mamaroneck	10543	Glick MR & MRS Ronald M
Mamaroneck	10543	Hearst MR & MRS John Augustine C
Mamaroneck	10543	Seymour MRS A Vaisière
Mamaroneck	10543	Sherrid DR & MRS Mark V
Manhasset	11030	Alsheimer MR & MRS Alan M JR
Manhasset	11030	Boone MR William H
Manhasset	11030	de Roulet MRS Vincent
Manhasset	11030	Snedeker MRS William A
Marcellus	13108	Casper MR & MRS Richard M
Matinecock	11560	Meyer MR & MRS Richard W JR
Mendon	14506	Farnam MR & MRS Henry W 3D
Middle Island	11953	Pool MR Charles Chauncey
Milbrook	12545	Block MR & MRS John D

Mill Neck........................ 11765.......... Balding MR Bruce E
Mill Neck........................ 11765.......... Biondi MR & MRS O Francis JR
Mill Neck........................ 11765.......... Colgate MR & MRS John K JR
Mill Neck........................ 11765.......... Dooley MR & MRS Timothy J
Mill Neck........................ 11765.......... Dunaway MR & MRS Carlyle M JR
Mill Neck........................ 11765.......... Garcia-Mansilla MRS Lucio S
Mill Neck........................ 11765.......... Harrison MR Randolph
Mill Neck........................ 11765.......... Humes MR F Cooper
Mill Neck........................ 11765.......... Jones MR & MRS Hoyle C
Mill Neck........................ 11765.......... Jones MR & MRS Parry von S
Mill Neck........................ 11765.......... Knott MR & MRS David M
Mill Neck........................ 11765.......... MacLeod MR Sayre 3D
Mill Neck........................ 11765.......... Marsh MR & MRS Howard D
Mill Neck........................ 11765.......... McNicol MR & MRS Paul M
Mill Neck........................ 11765.......... Murray MR & MRS Thomson C JR
Mill Neck........................ 11765.......... Murray MRS Thomson C
Mill Neck........................ 11765.......... Quick MR & MRS Peter
Mill Neck........................ 11765.......... Shea MRS Peter L
Mill Neck........................ 11765.......... Slocum MISS Suzanne
Mill Neck........................ 11765.......... Smith MR & MRS Alexander J
Mill Neck........................ 11765.......... Smith MR Herbert L III
Mill Neck........................ 11765.......... Teagle MR & MRS Walter C III
Mill Neck........................ 11765.......... von Briesen MR & MRS Edward F
Mill Neck........................ 11765.......... Wellner MR Karl G & Norville MS Deborah A
Millbrook........................ 12545.......... Brown MR & MRS Hobson JR
Millbrook........................ 12545.......... Bucove MRS Arnold D
Millbrook........................ 12545.......... Chapman MR & MRS Peter Herbert
Millbrook........................ 12545.......... Collins MR & MRS Farnham F
Millbrook........................ 12545.......... Corbin MR & MRS Peter S
Millbrook........................ 12545.......... Cox MR & MRS Thomas S
Millbrook........................ 12545.......... Galatti MR Stephen
Millbrook........................ 12545.......... Gillis MS Anne C
Millbrook........................ 12545.......... Howland MR & MRS Cornelius De F III
Millbrook........................ 12545.......... Lott MRS Carola K
Millbrook........................ 12545.......... Mandy MR & MRS David P
Millbrook........................ 12545.......... Möller MR & MRS Mikael C L
Millbrook........................ 12545.......... Perkins MRS George W JR
Millbrook........................ 12545.......... Place MR & MRS H Curtis
Millbrook........................ 12545.......... Sioussat MR & MRS Pierce S
Millbrook........................ 12545.......... Sloan MR & MRS David R
Millbrook........................ 12545.......... Smith MR J Kevin
Millbrook........................ 12545.......... Stahl MR & MRS William W JR
Millbrook........................ 12545.......... Thorne MR & MRS Oakleigh B
Millbrook........................ 12545.......... Toland MR & MRS Richard H R JR
Millbrook........................ 12545.......... Welles MR & MRS Caldwell Mead
Millerton........................ 12546.......... Curtis DR & MRS John P
Millerton........................ 12546.......... Drexel MR & MRS John R IV
Millerton........................ 12546.......... Winmill MR & MRS Mark C
Mineola........................ 11501.......... Madsen MR & MRS (DR) Stephen S JR
Montgomery........................ 10987.......... Coleman MR Michael R
Mount Vernon........................ 10552.......... Blodgett MR & MRS Thomas N
Mount Vernon........................ 10552.......... Hand MR & MRS William J
Mount Vernon........................ 10552.......... Kaiser MR Robert A JR
Mt Kisco........................ 10549.......... Chace MRS Minturn de S V
Mt Kisco........................ 10549.......... Hoguet MRS Elizabeth B
Mt Kisco........................ 10549.......... Keesee MRS Thomas W JR
Mt Kisco........................ 10549.......... Lawrence MR & MRS Philip S
Mt Kisco........................ 10549.......... Lawrence MR & MRS Richard H
Mt Kisco........................ 10549.......... Ryan MRS Evelyne H
Mt Kisco........................ 10549.......... Stanley MR & MRS Jonathan L
Mt Kisco........................ 10549.......... Stockbridge MR & MRS John J
Mt Kisco........................ 10549.......... Townsend MR & MRS William H
Mt Morris........................ 14510.......... Wadsworth MS Naomi W
Mt Vernon........................ 10552.......... Bobrinskoy CTSS
Mt Vernon........................ 10552.......... Duncan MRS Dyson
Mt Vernon........................ 10552.......... Ruhm MR & MRS Thomas F
Muttontown........................ 11791.......... Stebbins MR & MRS James F
New Berlin........................ 13411.......... Bassett MISS Phebe L
New Lebanon........................ 12125.......... Deely MISS Mary S
New Paltz........................ 12561.......... Conger THE REV & MRS George M
New Paltz........................ 12561.......... Smith MRS Roger D
New Rochelle........................ 10801.......... Delafield MR & MRS Walter B
New Rochelle........................ 10804.......... O'Connell MR & MRS J Ryan
New Rochelle........................ 10805.......... Cooke MR & MRS Bradford
New Rochelle........................ 10805.......... Heintz MR & MRS Edward S A
New Rochelle........................ 10805.......... Taney MRS John Charles 2D
New Windsor........................ 12553.......... Bingham MRS William L
New York........................ 10001.......... Davison MR & MRS Daniel P III
New York........................ 10001.......... Koen MR Kenneth F
New York........................ 10001.......... Miller MR George A
New York........................ 10001.......... Moore MR Thomas E 3D
New York........................ 10001.......... Spencer MRS F Gilman
New York........................ 10001.......... Whitney MR & MRS Jonathan B
New York........................ 10002.......... Brooke MR & MRS James B
New York........................ 10002.......... Cecil MR Alexander T
New York........................ 10002.......... Hanley MR John J
New York........................ 10002.......... Matuschak MR & MRS Mark G
New York........................ 10002.......... Nagraj MR & MRS Anil N
New York........................ 10002.......... Smith MR Aimery de F D
New York........................ 10003.......... Armstrong MR George W 3D
New York........................ 10003.......... Brandt MRS C Patteson
New York........................ 10003.......... Brickley MR Parker W
New York........................ 10003.......... Britton MR & MRS John D II
New York........................ 10003.......... Brown MR Peter Schuyler
New York........................ 10003.......... Carpenter MISS Dorothy M
New York........................ 10003.......... Casdin MR Eli D & Haythe MS (DR) Jennifer H
New York........................ 10003.......... Clark MR Christopher A
New York........................ 10003.......... Coker MISS Rachel L
New York........................ 10003.......... Connor MR Keith F
New York........................ 10003.......... Covington MISS S Amy
New York........................ 10003.......... de Coppet MISS Laura
New York........................ 10003.......... Duncan MISS Jean W
New York........................ 10003.......... Enthoven MR & MRS Nicholas G T
New York........................ 10003.......... Feldman MR & MRS Luke D
New York........................ 10003.......... Finch MR & MRS Charles B JR
New York........................ 10003.......... Gamble MISS Frederica G
New York........................ 10003.......... Goodrich MR & MRS John A JR
New York........................ 10003.......... Guare MR & MRS John
New York........................ 10003.......... Gubelmann MISS Phoebe G
New York........................ 10003.......... Hall MR Gregory J
New York........................ 10003.......... Hasse MR & MRS Thomas T Hasse
New York........................ 10003.......... Hodges MS Leslie F
New York........................ 10003.......... Howard MR & MRS Philip K
New York........................ 10003.......... Ingalls MR Redmond S
New York........................ 10003.......... Kelly MISS Elizabeth Lee
New York........................ 10003.......... Lombard MR Laurence M 2D
New York........................ 10003.......... Low MISS Jessica T
New York........................ 10003.......... MacNair MRS Cynthia P
New York........................ 10003.......... McGarry MR & MRS John P III
New York........................ 10003.......... Murray MS Felicia C
New York........................ 10003.......... Newbold MRS John L
New York........................ 10003.......... Nickoll MR Benjamin & Armstrong MS Christine M
New York........................ 10003.......... Nordeman MR & MRS Landon S
New York........................ 10003.......... Pike COL & MRS Thomas F JR
New York........................ 10003.......... Pike REV & MRS Thomas F
New York........................ 10003.......... Rodgers MS Sarah Ann
New York........................ 10003.......... Romero MR Pedro E V
New York........................ 10003.......... Royce MR Charles M JR
New York........................ 10003.......... Royce MRS Jacqueline C
New York........................ 10003.......... Salisbury MR & MRS D Austin JR
New York........................ 10003.......... Sanchez MR & MRS Francisco G
New York........................ 10003.......... Scheerer MR Thomas I

To nominate a candidate for the Social Register Association, please email: SRCommittee@thesocialregister.org

New York, NY—New York, NY

New York	10003	Scott MISS Sheila N
New York	10003	Scribner MR & MRS John
New York	10003	Shea MISS Adrienne B
New York	10003	Shyer MR Christopher D
New York	10003	Smith MISS Sallie Dorsey
New York	10003	Southwell MS Victoria Vanzandt
New York	10003	von Winterfeldt MR & MRS Caspar D
New York	10003	Wight MR Devereux Pinkus
New York	10003	Winkelman MR & MRS Mark O
New York	10003	Woods MR & MRS Anthony H
New York	10003	Wyatt MISS Susan A
New York	10004	Blaney MR & MRS Samuel
New York	10004	Keane MR Edward W
New York	10005	Richardson MR & MRS Ambrose M III
New York	10006	Abrahams MR & MRS Mark W
New York	10007	Baird MR & MRS Matthew 2D
New York	10007	Davis MR & MRS Henry Patterson
New York	10007	Delaney MR & MRS Christopher B
New York	10007	Dotson MR & MRS William J JR
New York	10007	Huray MR & MRS J Matthew
New York	10007	Kleinschmidt MR & MRS Paul J
New York	10007	Leisure MR & MRS Peter K
New York	10007	Minnis MR & MRS James S JR
New York	10008	Craig MR Michael S
New York	10009	Blair MR Alfred F III
New York	10009	Cort MRS John
New York	10009	Coxe MR Alexander B
New York	10009	Dick MR Anthony
New York	10009	Lovejoy MR Donald W R
New York	10009	Obolensky MISS Octavia W
New York	10009	Shettle MR & MRS Arthur F II
New York	10009	Wells MR George Breckinridge
New York	10010	Benenson MR & MRS James III
New York	10010	Benenson MR & MRS James JR
New York	10010	Bloch MR & MRS Godfrey C
New York	10010	Boothby MR & MRS Willard S
New York	10010	Breed MR Henry E III
New York	10010	Conlisk MR & MRS Patrick J
New York	10010	Curtis MS Sarah M
New York	10010	Griggs MR Remy E
New York	10010	Hatchett MR & MRS Michael E
New York	10010	Hess MR & MRS Adam P
New York	10010	Jackson MR Raymond S JR
New York	10010	Kean MR Christopher
New York	10010	Kemper MR & MRS R Crosby III
New York	10010	Kennedy MISS Martha C
New York	10010	Langenberg MRS Margaret M
New York	10010	Larochelle MR & MRS Ryan D
New York	10010	Lee MISS Sara M
New York	10010	Linke MR Gordon R
New York	10010	Littlejohn MR & MRS Angus C III
New York	10010	Meihuizen MR Nicolaas J van
New York	10010	Mellen MISS Abigail
New York	10010	Murray MISS Amanda M
New York	10010	Nash MS Daphne T
New York	10010	Paduano MR & MRS John P
New York	10010	Pope MR & MRS Charles T
New York	10010	Rowlands MR Eliot W & Stone MS Deborah A
New York	10010	Smith REV & MRS Jacob A
New York	10010	Thompson MR & MRS William McI III
New York	10010	van der Voort MR & MRS Michael V M
New York	10011	Aldea MR David M
New York	10011	Anderson DR John A & Forbes MS Moira S
New York	10011	Baldini MR Daniel H
New York	10011	Bell MR & MRS Byron
New York	10011	Bell MR & MRS Jefferson E
New York	10011	Benkert MR & MRS Edward R
New York	10011	Berlind MR & MRS William P
New York	10011	Bowditch MS (DR) Lucy L
New York	10011	Buice MR William T 3D
New York	10011	Burnett MISS Ryland
New York	10011	Chisholm MR Hugh A J & Prince MS Cynthia E
New York	10011	Chrystie MR James McD
New York	10011	Clarke MR John W
New York	10011	Corcoran MR & MRS Neil D
New York	10011	Cuddihy MR & MRS John M JR
New York	10011	Day MISS Rebecca B
New York	10011	de Vito Piscicelli Taeggi MR & MRS Carlo
New York	10011	Downer MR A Charles W JR
New York	10011	Field MR & MRS Christopher E
New York	10011	Fulenwider MISS Anne M
New York	10011	Githens MR John Lawrence
New York	10011	Hale MRS Nathan
New York	10011	Harding REV Stephen R & Swain MS
New York	10011	Hart MR & MRS Lewis J III
New York	10011	Hawkins MR & MRS Howard R JR
New York	10011	Hicks MR & MRS Stephen W
New York	10011	Hobbs MR & MRS Nicholas B
New York	10011	Huffman MRS Maria Ewing
New York	10011	Hurrion DR James R & Burdine MS Mary Catherine
New York	10011	Kearns MR & MRS James J III
New York	10011	Keevil MR & MRS Peter L
New York	10011	Kingston MRS C John
New York	10011	Klotz MISS Leslie R
New York	10011	Kroeger MS Joanne T
New York	10011	Kroeger MS Joanne T
New York	10011	Lambert MR Arthur G JR
New York	10011	Maclay MR John B III & Conradt MR Ken
New York	10011	Malcom MRS John W
New York	10011	Marder MR Jonathan A
New York	10011	Marzulli MR & MRS John A JR
New York	10011	McQuilkin MR Robert Rennie JR
New York	10011	Nichol MR & MRS Alasdair N M
New York	10011	Nusbaum MR Jack H & Wallace MS Nora Ann
New York	10011	Osnoss MR Daniel R & Howard MS Charlotte I C
New York	10011	Pierro DR Robert A & Coleman DR Eliza A
New York	10011	Provost MR Paul R
New York	10011	Ravenel MR & MRS Curtis de St Julien
New York	10011	Regan MR W Deering
New York	10011	Reibel MISS Katherine G
New York	10011	Richardson MR Seth F C & Herron MS Mary D
New York	10011	Rollins MR Richard III
New York	10011	Schiff MR & MRS James G
New York	10011	Seery MR John R
New York	10011	Stevens MISS Amber K
New York	10011	Stickney MISS Anna N
New York	10011	Storment MR & MRS Peter M
New York	10011	Sussman MR & MRS Charles T
New York	10011	Van Sciver MR Joseph B IV & Olson MS (DR) Katherine Q
New York	10011	Wilcox MR & MRS McClelland W
New York	10011	Winstead MR & MRS Trevor V
New York	10011	Zacharias MR John L
New York	10011	Ziegelasch MR Richard W
New York	10012	Adelaar MR Jesse D & Thomas MR Corrin
New York	10012	Beekman MR & MRS William B
New York	10012	Bennett MR John F JR
New York	10012	Danner MR & MRS William B
New York	10012	Firestone MRS Susan P
New York	10012	Fox MR & MRS Jason E
New York	10012	Heenan MR Charles
New York	10012	Holder MRS Geoffrey L

New York........................ 10012......... Hubbard MR Eliot
New York........................ 10012......... Jensen MR H Carter
New York........................ 10012......... Knapp MRS Whitman
New York........................ 10012......... Luce MR & MRS H Christopher
New York........................ 10012......... Malkiel MR & MRS Jonathan P
New York........................ 10012......... Mallery MISS (DR) Berrell E
New York........................ 10012......... Marburg MR & MRS Charles L
New York........................ 10012......... Mead DR & MRS Lawrence M 3D
New York........................ 10012......... Piasecki MR & MRS Frank W
New York........................ 10012......... Picard MR Peter W L
New York........................ 10012......... Prager MR & MRS Paul B
New York........................ 10012......... Shafer MR & MRS Daniel W E
New York........................ 10012......... Tobeason MR & MRS Peter F
New York........................ 10012......... Waterman MR George H III
New York........................ 10013......... Benedict MR & MRS Charles P
New York........................ 10013......... Clements MR & MRS Robert M JR
New York........................ 10013......... Corman MISS Catherine A
New York........................ 10013......... Crawford MS Bridget J
New York........................ 10013......... Darrell MR & MRS Andrew H
New York........................ 10013......... Day MR Lee G & Endlicher MS Ursula
New York........................ 10013......... Drew MISS Catherine L
New York........................ 10013......... Englund MISS Alixandra G
New York........................ 10013......... Friestedt MR & MRS Matthew M
New York........................ 10013......... Irving MR & MRS David D
New York........................ 10013......... Kadakia MR & MRS Rahul R
New York........................ 10013......... Kulukundis MR Manuel E
New York........................ 10013......... Lanier MR & MRS Henry D
New York........................ 10013......... Lawrence MISS Letitia O
New York........................ 10013......... Nève de Mévergnies MR & MRS Stanislas
New York........................ 10013......... Nigro MR John Walter
New York........................ 10013......... Pell MR & MRS Nicholas L
New York........................ 10013......... Radziwill MR & MRS Philip C W
New York........................ 10013......... Roosevelt MR & MRS Theodore 5TH
New York........................ 10013......... Rutgers MR Anthony L JR & Roth MR David J
New York........................ 10013......... Scott MR & MRS Stanley D
New York........................ 10013......... Tooker MISS Tracey
New York........................ 10013......... Turnure MR & MRS Richard L
New York........................ 10013......... Vetterlein MR & MRS Victor W
New York........................ 10013......... Ylvisaker MR & MRS Jon A
New York........................ 10014......... Barth MISS Giselle M
New York........................ 10014......... Benjamin MRS Samuel N
New York........................ 10014......... Block MR Alexander C
New York........................ 10014......... Boyce MISS M Gwendolyn B
New York........................ 10014......... Boyd MISS Brooke W
New York........................ 10014......... Bruckmann MR & MRS Bruce C
New York........................ 10014......... Burch MR J Christopher
New York........................ 10014......... Castaldi DR & MRS Mark W
New York........................ 10014......... Clark MISS A Elise C
New York........................ 10014......... Collins MR & MRS Michael P
New York........................ 10014......... Cooke MR Charles B IV
New York........................ 10014......... Coulson MR & MRS Robert Cromwell
New York........................ 10014......... Crimmins MR Thomas L & Davies MR Nicholas E
New York........................ 10014......... Crosby MR Henry A V
New York........................ 10014......... Fennebresque MR & MRS John D II
New York........................ 10014......... Fowler MISS Mary W G
New York........................ 10014......... Holbrook MR & MRS David D
New York........................ 10014......... Ingalls MR Bradley D
New York........................ 10014......... Kimball MR & MRS Samuel W
New York........................ 10014......... Lees MISS Aubrey
New York........................ 10014......... Merrill MRS Monique V
New York........................ 10014......... Moreland MISS Elaine S
New York........................ 10014......... Nadler MR Duncan H M
New York........................ 10014......... Peterson MR J B Wyeth
New York........................ 10014......... Roff MS (DR) Suzanne
New York........................ 10014......... Rowan MISS Dorothy G
New York........................ 10014......... Shamamian MR Oscar & Sinkler MS Llewellyn H
New York........................ 10014......... Sutherland MR & MRS Conor J
New York........................ 10014......... Sykes MR & MRS Ware
New York........................ 10014......... Taylor MR & MRS Willard B
New York........................ 10014......... Usnik MR William L JR & Bratcher MR Harlan R
New York........................ 10014......... Valentine DR Edward S
New York........................ 10014......... Werwaiss MR & MRS John A W
New York........................ 10014......... Wilkie MR John McN JR
New York........................ 10014......... Winthrop MISS Cornelia T
New York........................ 10016......... Brown MRS Elizabeth C
New York........................ 10016......... Buddenhagen MISS Eliza S
New York........................ 10016......... Clough MR W Jaques JR
New York........................ 10016......... Curry MR & MRS William J II
New York........................ 10016......... Doble MR & MRS William S
New York........................ 10016......... Greenough MISS Meredith H
New York........................ 10016......... Haynes-Dale MR Campbell J
New York........................ 10016......... Healy MR H Harris 3D
New York........................ 10016......... Hewson MRS Charlotte W
New York........................ 10016......... Hitchcock MR Nelson B
New York........................ 10016......... Holland MR & MRS David C
New York........................ 10016......... Hourihan MR & MRS Marc Anthony
New York........................ 10016......... Jordan MRS William JR
New York........................ 10016......... Jorgensen MR Edvard
New York........................ 10016......... Lewis MR James G
New York........................ 10016......... Loehr MR & MRS David J
New York........................ 10016......... Loud MR Douglass N
New York........................ 10016......... Moore MR Charles
New York........................ 10016......... Munn MS Linda
New York........................ 10016......... Nalywajko MS Katerina L
New York........................ 10016......... Nype MISS Caroline F
New York........................ 10016......... Peterkin MR Patrick O'B
New York........................ 10016......... Quick MISS Grace
New York........................ 10016......... Rabkin MR & MRS William
New York........................ 10016......... Radcliffe MR & MRS Charles C
New York........................ 10016......... Rafalski MR & MRS Brendan J
New York........................ 10016......... Rudman MR & MRS Stephen M
New York........................ 10016......... Vaughan MR Brian C
New York........................ 10016......... Westcott-Pitt MR & MRS Colin T
New York........................ 10017......... Armstrong MRS Thomas N III
New York........................ 10017......... Donaldson MR & MRS William H
New York........................ 10017......... Draper MR John W
New York........................ 10017......... Duncan MR Samuel MacF
New York........................ 10017......... Fuller MISS Elizabeth H
New York........................ 10017......... Gamble MR & MRS Theodore R JR
New York........................ 10017......... Gatje MISS Alexandra L
New York........................ 10017......... Gray MR & MRS James L
New York........................ 10017......... Jones MRS Caroline Chapin
New York........................ 10017......... Lang MR Peter
New York........................ 10017......... Leach MR & MRS Peter T
New York........................ 10017......... Madara MR & MRS Edward S III
New York........................ 10017......... Morse MRS Robert P
New York........................ 10017......... Rauch MR Benjamin Brewster
New York........................ 10017......... Thomas MRS B Brooks
New York........................ 10017......... Touchstone MS Mary B
New York........................ 10017......... Wagner MR Duncan E
New York........................ 10017......... Witter MRS William D
New York........................ 10018......... Devaney MR & MRS John G
New York........................ 10019......... Arrott MR & MRS Anthony S
New York........................ 10019......... Barlow MRS Victoria S
New York........................ 10019......... Becker MISS Ashley E
New York........................ 10019......... Canfield MRS Gabriella Befani
New York........................ 10019......... Curtis MR Daniel S
New York........................ 10019......... Dexter MR Charles E 3D
New York........................ 10019......... Disi MR & MRS David A
New York........................ 10019......... Elger MR & MRS Hermann W JR
New York........................ 10019......... Ferrell MR R Anderson
New York........................ 10019......... Finch MR Charles B III

To nominate a candidate for the Social Register Association, please email: SRCommittee@thesocialregister.org

New York, NY—New York, NY

New York........................ 10019.......... Havens MR David S
New York........................ 10019.......... Hill MISS Sarah K
New York........................ 10019.......... Hudson MR & MRS R Webber
New York........................ 10019.......... Hughes MR & MRS Robert A
New York........................ 10019.......... Kennedy MRS Michael
New York........................ 10019.......... Lumbard MR Dirk
New York........................ 10019.......... McCrary MR Dennis D
New York........................ 10019.......... Michahelles MRS Caroline Burton E
New York........................ 10019.......... Miller MR & MRS Richard J JR
New York........................ 10019.......... Moore MR & MRS James T C
New York........................ 10019.......... Moretz THE REV Matthew J & Brandt-Meyer MS Megan I
New York........................ 10019.......... Ohrstrom MISS Lysandra A
New York........................ 10019.......... Patterson DR & MRS Russel H JR
New York........................ 10019.......... Putnam MS Barbara
New York........................ 10019.......... Reger MR Robert J JR
New York........................ 10019.......... Reid MR David W
New York........................ 10019.......... Remmel MR H M Towson
New York........................ 10019.......... Rodocanachi MR Paul S
New York........................ 10019.......... Scrymgeour MRS John A
New York........................ 10019.......... Soule MR Christopher W
New York........................ 10019.......... Spivy MR & MRS Samuel O J
New York........................ 10019.......... Tabasso MR & MRS Martin A
New York........................ 10019.......... Tannahill MR James Stewart
New York........................ 10019.......... Tiné MR Christopher R
New York........................ 10019.......... Tiné MR Matthew D
New York........................ 10019.......... Wheelock MR Stephen B
New York........................ 10019.......... Yates MR & MRS Eames H
New York........................ 10020.......... Davis MR & MRS Christopher C
New York........................ 10021.......... Adams MR & MRS (DR) Benjamin Crowninshield
New York........................ 10021.......... Adler MR & MRS Allen
New York........................ 10021.......... Alfaro MR & MRS Francisco
New York........................ 10021.......... Alford MS Rebecca D
New York........................ 10021.......... Allen MR & MRS Christopher D
New York........................ 10021.......... Allen MS Alice
New York........................ 10021.......... Allison MR & MRS Donald G
New York........................ 10021.......... Altschul MR Arthur G JR
New York........................ 10021.......... Andersen MRS Louise McM
New York........................ 10021.......... Anderson MRS O Kelley JR
New York........................ 10021.......... Andrade MR & MRS José E
New York........................ 10021.......... Arnold MR & MRS Milton H
New York........................ 10021.......... Aston DR Sherrell J & Aston MS Muffie Potter
New York........................ 10021.......... Austin MS Barbara L
New York........................ 10021.......... Bacon MR & MRS Varick
New York........................ 10021.......... Baker MRS Harold d'O
New York........................ 10021.......... Baker MRS Marianna J
New York........................ 10021.......... Baldwin MR & MRS Townsend L
New York........................ 10021.......... Ballard MISS Elizabeth F R
New York........................ 10021.......... Bartlett MRS David F
New York........................ 10021.......... Bass MRS Anne H
New York........................ 10021.......... Bean MR & MRS Jonathan S
New York........................ 10021.......... Beatty MR & MRS William H
New York........................ 10021.......... Becker MRS A William J III
New York........................ 10021.......... Becker MS Alison Price
New York........................ 10021.......... Benedict MR William J JR & Sprague MS Dorothy Whitmarsh
New York........................ 10021.......... Bergstrom MR & MRS Craig G
New York........................ 10021.......... Berkowitz MR & MRS Mortimer III
New York........................ 10021.......... Bernstein MR Nathan A & Otto-Bernstein MRS Katharina
New York........................ 10021.......... Berry MR Samuel W
New York........................ 10021.......... Bessent MR Scott K H
New York........................ 10021.......... Bickford MR David G
New York........................ 10021.......... Bickford MS Laura S
New York........................ 10021.......... Biddle MISS Sheila
New York........................ 10021.......... Biggs MRS Jeremy H
New York........................ 10021.......... Bingham MR & MRS J Reid
New York........................ 10021.......... Boden MR Constantin R & Peters MS Petra
New York........................ 10021.......... Bolen MR & MRS Alexander L
New York........................ 10021.......... Bouriez MRS Philippe G
New York........................ 10021.......... Bowden MR Garrett R
New York........................ 10021.......... Bowers MRS Cynthia S-H
New York........................ 10021.......... Boyd MRS William Y II
New York........................ 10021.......... Brandi MR & MRS James H
New York........................ 10021.......... Breck MR & MRS Henry R
New York........................ 10021.......... Brennan MRS William J JR
New York........................ 10021.......... Brock DR Horace W
New York........................ 10021.......... Brock MR & MRS Charles Lawrence
New York........................ 10021.......... Brokaw MR & MRS George R
New York........................ 10021.......... Brooker MR & MRS T Kimball JR
New York........................ 10021.......... Brown MISS Christie Gardner
New York........................ 10021.......... Brush MISS (DR) Karen Alexandra
New York........................ 10021.......... Buddenhagen MR & MRS Frederick L
New York........................ 10021.......... Bullock MR & MRS Charles S JR
New York........................ 10021.......... Burke MRS Russell M
New York........................ 10021.......... Calder MR & MRS Donald G
New York........................ 10021.......... Camp MR Gregory Talcott
New York........................ 10021.......... Cappello MR & MRS Juan C
New York........................ 10021.......... Carling MR Francis & Hinkson-Carling MS Susan M
New York........................ 10021.......... Carroll MRS Robert E
New York........................ 10021.......... Castle MR & MRS John S
New York........................ 10021.......... Chaikin MR Eric B & Lamborn MRS Kathleen R
New York........................ 10021.......... Chase MRS Ryland E D
New York........................ 10021.......... Chen MRS Christopher C Y
New York........................ 10021.......... Chinn MR & MRS Garretson W
New York........................ 10021.......... Christy MRS Arthur H
New York........................ 10021.......... Colassano DR & MRS Francis M
New York........................ 10021.......... Colas-Thibouville MR & MRS Pierre H
New York........................ 10021.......... Coleman MR & MRS Kevin C
New York........................ 10021.......... Connor MR & MRS Ian C
New York........................ 10021.......... Corbett MR & MRS Andrew J III
New York........................ 10021.......... Cornell MR & MRS Joseph E
New York........................ 10021.......... Corroon MS Andrée B
New York........................ 10021.......... Cox MR & MRS Edward F
New York........................ 10021.......... Craigmyle MISS (DR) Lydia S
New York........................ 10021.......... Crandall MRS F William
New York........................ 10021.......... Crawford MR & MRS George
New York........................ 10021.......... Creel MR James R 4TH
New York........................ 10021.......... Creel MRS Jennifer C
New York........................ 10021.......... Crudge MRS Vernon G
New York........................ 10021.......... Cunningham MR C Seth
New York........................ 10021.......... Curtis MR & MRS Ashton M
New York........................ 10021.......... Cushing MISS Justine B
New York........................ 10021.......... Dalva MRS David L II
New York........................ 10021.......... David MR & MRS George A L
New York........................ 10021.......... Davidson MR & MRS William A
New York........................ 10021.......... Davis MISS Maude S
New York........................ 10021.......... Davis MR & MRS Andrew A
New York........................ 10021.......... Davis MR Duncan F
New York........................ 10021.......... Davis MRS Dwight F III
New York........................ 10021.......... Dawson MR & MRS John S W
New York........................ 10021.......... de Koning MR & MRS Joep M J
New York........................ 10021.......... de Portago MRS Barbara
New York........................ 10021.......... de Saint Phalle MR & MRS Marc
New York........................ 10021.......... de Saint Phalle MRS Elene C
New York........................ 10021.......... De Voe MRS Natalie S
New York........................ 10021.......... DeLuca MS (DR) Antoinette
New York........................ 10021.......... Dimsey MR & MRS Peter S P
New York........................ 10021.......... Dixon MR Mark C M & Lange MS Alexandra P
New York........................ 10021.......... Donner MR & MRS Joseph W
New York........................ 10021.......... Donovan MISS Christine P

New York.......................... 10021.......... Dorkey MR Charles E III & Rousseaux MS Andrea Rose
New York.......................... 10021.......... Dorland MR & MRS Dodge O
New York.......................... 10021.......... Druckenmiller MR & MRS Stanley F
New York.......................... 10021.......... Duer MR & MRS Beverley C
New York.......................... 10021.......... Edelman MR & MRS Thomas J
New York.......................... 10021.......... Edmonds MR & MRS E Alden
New York.......................... 10021.......... Egbert MR George Pennington III
New York.......................... 10021.......... Eitel MR & MRS Walter T
New York.......................... 10021.......... Embree MR & MRS Jeb N
New York.......................... 10021.......... Eyre MRS William H
New York.......................... 10021.......... Fair MS Sara Cheves
New York.......................... 10021.......... Fessenden MR Jerald D
New York.......................... 10021.......... Fingleton MR & MRS Anthony J
New York.......................... 10021.......... Fisher MISS Helen E
New York.......................... 10021.......... Flöttl MR & MRS Wolfgang K
New York.......................... 10021.......... Forbes MRS Wallace F
New York.......................... 10021.......... Fox MR & MRS Daniel MacGill
New York.......................... 10021.......... Fraise MR & MRS Adrien G
New York.......................... 10021.......... Freeman MR John F
New York.......................... 10021.......... Frelinghuysen MR & MRS Anson B
New York.......................... 10021.......... French MRS Marina K
New York.......................... 10021.......... Gales MRS Seaton
New York.......................... 10021.......... Galvis MR & MRS Sergio J
New York.......................... 10021.......... Gaston DR & MRS James P
New York.......................... 10021.......... Geary MR & MRS John W III
New York.......................... 10021.......... Gellert MR & MRS John M
New York.......................... 10021.......... Gerard MR & MRS (DR) James W 5TH
New York.......................... 10021.......... Gerard MRS Teresa Niki
New York.......................... 10021.......... Glass MR & MRS John B JR
New York.......................... 10021.......... Glover MR & MRS Thomas S
New York.......................... 10021.......... Goelet MISS Alexandra G
New York.......................... 10021.......... Goelet MR Robert G
New York.......................... 10021.......... Goodwin DR & MRS Charles B
New York.......................... 10021.......... Gottschalk MR Adam W H
New York.......................... 10021.......... Gowen MR & MRS George W 2D
New York.......................... 10021.......... Graev MR & MRS Lawrence G
New York.......................... 10021.......... Graham MRS Gordon
New York.......................... 10021.......... Graham MS Diane D
New York.......................... 10021.......... Grassi MR & MRS Marco
New York.......................... 10021.......... Greenan MISS Eleanor J
New York.......................... 10021.......... Grubstein MR Peter S H & Ripley MS Rosemary L
New York.......................... 10021.......... Grunwald MRS Henry A
New York.......................... 10021.......... Guerin MISS Anna J
New York.......................... 10021.......... Guernsey MR & MRS Peter E JR
New York.......................... 10021.......... Hackett MR Randall W
New York.......................... 10021.......... Hale MR Benton S & Rolfe MS Jennifer E
New York.......................... 10021.......... Halstead MR Clark P
New York.......................... 10021.......... Hamlin MR Jerome F
New York.......................... 10021.......... Hare MRS Martha M
New York.......................... 10021.......... Harnes DR & MRS Jack R
New York.......................... 10021.......... Harnes MR & MRS John F
New York.......................... 10021.......... Havemeyer MR & MRS Harry W
New York.......................... 10021.......... Heckscher MRS August
New York.......................... 10021.......... Hedberg MR & MRS Gregory S
New York.......................... 10021.......... Henckels MR & MRS Kirk
New York.......................... 10021.......... Henderson MR & MRS G L Cabot II
New York.......................... 10021.......... Hendrickson MRS Reiland
New York.......................... 10021.......... Hickox MR & MRS Charles C
New York.......................... 10021.......... Hill MR & MRS J Tomilson 3D
New York.......................... 10021.......... Hill MR Samuel R 2D
New York.......................... 10021.......... Hoar MR William P H
New York.......................... 10021.......... Hobbs MR & MRS Franklin W 4TH
New York.......................... 10021.......... Hodges MRS Lorin C
New York.......................... 10021.......... Hoerle MR & MRS Robert F
New York.......................... 10021.......... Holm MR & MRS Owen P
New York.......................... 10021.......... Holmes MR & MRS Peter B
New York.......................... 10021.......... Holterbosch MS Heidi M
New York.......................... 10021.......... Hoopes MR & MRS Joseph C JR
New York.......................... 10021.......... Hornick MR Louis III
New York.......................... 10021.......... Hunt MR David P
New York.......................... 10021.......... Huntington MR & MRS Lawrence S
New York.......................... 10021.......... Ijams MR W Seton
New York.......................... 10021.......... Ingham MRS Joy H
New York.......................... 10021.......... Ireland MR Robert L JR
New York.......................... 10021.......... Irwin MR C Russell
New York.......................... 10021.......... Jacobs MRS Ted S
New York.......................... 10021.......... James MR & MRS David F
New York.......................... 10021.......... Javelos MR Michael C D
New York.......................... 10021.......... Johns MR William Potter
New York.......................... 10021.......... Johnson MR & MRS Christopher W
New York.......................... 10021.......... Johnson MR & MRS Dudley D
New York.......................... 10021.......... Jordan MRS Michael H
New York.......................... 10021.......... Kaiser MR & MRS John JR
New York.......................... 10021.......... Kallop MRS Deborah Farber
New York.......................... 10021.......... Keesee MR & MRS Thomas W 3D
New York.......................... 10021.......... Keesee MR Christian & Keigwin MR Lawrence
New York.......................... 10021.......... Keith MRS Jayne T
New York.......................... 10021.......... Kiesel MR & MRS Michael T
New York.......................... 10021.......... Kinney MR & MRS Gilbert H
New York.......................... 10021.......... Koch MRS David H
New York.......................... 10021.......... Kroeger MISS A Gale
New York.......................... 10021.......... La Branche MS Trinka
New York.......................... 10021.......... LaBarre MR & MRS Dennis W
New York.......................... 10021.......... Landegger MR & MRS Gregory M
New York.......................... 10021.......... Lapham MR & MRS Lewis H 2D
New York.......................... 10021.......... LeFrak MR & MRS Richard S
New York.......................... 10021.......... Leonard MR & MRS Richard R
New York.......................... 10021.......... L'Esperance DR & MRS Francis A JR
New York.......................... 10021.......... Lewis MRS Carolyn C
New York.......................... 10021.......... Lewis MRS John B JR
New York.......................... 10021.......... Libby MRS John K
New York.......................... 10021.......... Lindgren MRS Victoria C
New York.......................... 10021.......... Lipscomb MRS Christine J
New York.......................... 10021.......... Livingston MISS Lorna M
New York.......................... 10021.......... Locke MISS Sallie C
New York.......................... 10021.......... Loening MR & MRS J Michael
New York.......................... 10021.......... López-Balboa MR & MRS Enrique
New York.......................... 10021.......... Los Arcos MR & MRS José Luis
New York.......................... 10021.......... Lynch MS Rose Peabody
New York.......................... 10021.......... MacLear MRS Frank R
New York.......................... 10021.......... MacRae MR & MRS Cameron F 3D
New York.......................... 10021.......... Malone MR & MRS Frederick R
New York.......................... 10021.......... Malone MR & MRS W Hughlett N
New York.......................... 10021.......... Manger MR Charles Seymour
New York.......................... 10021.......... Manice MR & MRS Christopher H
New York.......................... 10021.......... Mann MRS J Herbert
New York.......................... 10021.......... Manning MISS Alice V
New York.......................... 10021.......... Marron MR & MRS Donald B
New York.......................... 10021.......... Maxwell MR & MRS David B JR
New York.......................... 10021.......... McBean MS Edith
New York.......................... 10021.......... McCall MR & MRS Peter C
New York.......................... 10021.......... McCarthy MR & MRS Brian A
New York.......................... 10021.......... McCarthy MR Philip E II & Brodsky MR James S
New York.......................... 10021.......... McLanahan MRS Martha
New York.......................... 10021.......... McLaughlin MR & MRS I Andrew Van D
New York.......................... 10021.......... McMorris MR & MRS Howard II
New York.......................... 10021.......... McQuade MR & MRS Lawrence C
New York.......................... 10021.......... Meigher MR & MRS S Christopher III
New York.......................... 10021.......... Melhado MS Teresa Smith
New York.......................... 10021.......... Menges MR & MRS Carl B
New York.......................... 10021.......... Meyer MRS Averil Payson

New York, NY—New York, NY

New York........................ 10021.......... Meyer MS Elizabeth Alker
New York........................ 10021.......... Millard MR & MRS John A
New York........................ 10021.......... Millard MR & MRS Peter de F
New York........................ 10021.......... Miller DR & MRS David H
New York........................ 10021.......... Miller MISS Helen H
New York........................ 10021.......... Miller MS Elizabeth Adams
New York........................ 10021.......... Milliken MRS Minot K
New York........................ 10021.......... Moore MR & MRS George B
New York........................ 10021.......... Moore MRS Marian S
New York........................ 10021.......... Moore SIR Thomas R
New York........................ 10021.......... Moorhead MR & MRS Rodman W 3D
New York........................ 10021.......... Morgan MR Miles
New York........................ 10021.......... Morris MR & MRS Roland III
New York........................ 10021.......... Morris MR William B
New York........................ 10021.......... Mortimer MR & MRS Averell H
New York........................ 10021.......... Mosse MR & MRS (DR) Peter J C
New York........................ 10021.......... Mullen MRS Robert W
New York........................ 10021.......... Muma MRS John R
New York........................ 10021.......... Munn MR & MRS Orson D III
New York........................ 10021.......... Murphy MR & MRS Brian D
New York........................ 10021.......... Muzinich MR & MRS George M
New York........................ 10021.......... Neel MR & MRS Richard
New York........................ 10021.......... Neff MR & MRS James L
New York........................ 10021.......... Nicholas MRS Peter H
New York........................ 10021.......... Niven MR James G
New York........................ 10021.......... Niven MRS Fernanda W
New York........................ 10021.......... Nordeman MR & MRS John H
New York........................ 10021.......... Ocampo MR & MRS Juan M
New York........................ 10021.......... Ogden MR & MRS Alfred T II
New York........................ 10021.......... Ogilvie MR & MRS John G
New York........................ 10021.......... Older MR & MRS Eric A
New York........................ 10021.......... Olyphant MRS Tatyana D
New York........................ 10021.......... O'Neill MRS Grover JR
New York........................ 10021.......... Owen MR & MRS Stephen B
New York........................ 10021.......... Owen MR Stephen C JR
New York........................ 10021.......... Page MR & MRS Blakely C
New York........................ 10021.......... Pai MR & MRS Dhananjay M
New York........................ 10021.......... Pappas MR & MRS William
New York........................ 10021.......... Pattee MR & MRS Gordon B
New York........................ 10021.......... Peabody MRS James B
New York........................ 10021.......... Pearl MR & MRS Erwin
New York........................ 10021.......... Peaslee MISS Charlotte H
New York........................ 10021.......... Pemberton MR & MRS Louis W
New York........................ 10021.......... Pennoyer MR & MRS Peter M
New York........................ 10021.......... Perkin MRS Richard T
New York........................ 10021.......... Peterson MR & MRS William P
New York........................ 10021.......... Phillips DR & MRS Gerald B
New York........................ 10021.......... Phillips MRS Stephen
New York........................ 10021.......... Pignatelli di Montecalvo PRCSS
New York........................ 10021.......... Platt MR & MRS Nicholas
New York........................ 10021.......... Platt MR David N
New York........................ 10021.......... Plimpton MRS George A
New York........................ 10021.......... Plummer MR & MRS J Raymond
New York........................ 10021.......... Potter MRS Hamilton F JR
New York........................ 10021.......... Powers MRS John A
New York........................ 10021.......... Powers REV MR John Michael
New York........................ 10021.......... Pratt MR & MRS Derek W
New York........................ 10021.......... Price MR & MRS Joseph A
New York........................ 10021.......... Pulling MRS S Sonne
New York........................ 10021.......... Purcell MR & MRS Thomas W JR
New York........................ 10021.......... Pynchon MISS Patricia
New York........................ 10021.......... Pyne MR & MRS John S JR
New York........................ 10021.......... Quasha MRS Diana R
New York........................ 10021.......... Raby MR & MRS Victor
New York........................ 10021.......... Radziwill MR & MRS John S
New York........................ 10021.......... Randolph MRS Francis F JR
New York........................ 10021.......... Rawson MRS Kennett L
New York........................ 10021.......... Rayner MRS William
New York........................ 10021.......... Reese MR & MRS George B
New York........................ 10021.......... Reiner MR Clark B W
New York........................ 10021.......... Reiner MRS John Paul
New York........................ 10021.......... Renehan MR & MRS Peter L
New York........................ 10021.......... Richardson MRS Melody Sawyer
& Thomson MR Malcolm
New York........................ 10021.......... Richter MR & MRS John B
New York........................ 10021.......... Rieck MR John E
New York........................ 10021.......... Riegel MRS Lawrence M
New York........................ 10021.......... Ritchie MR Charles J III
New York........................ 10021.......... Roberts MISS Letitia
New York........................ 10021.......... Robertson MR & MRS William D
New York........................ 10021.......... Robinson MR & MRS Hamilton JR
New York........................ 10021.......... Rogers MRS H Scott
New York........................ 10021.......... Romaine MR & MRS Sigourney B JR
New York........................ 10021.......... Rose MR & MRS J Harden
New York........................ 10021.......... Rowley MRS Peter W
New York........................ 10021.......... Rugg MR & MRS Peter
New York........................ 10021.......... Rusch MISS (DR) Valerie W
New York........................ 10021.......... Rutherfurd MR & MRS James P
New York........................ 10021.......... Ryan MR & MRS Baird W
New York........................ 10021.......... Saltus MR & MRS Ralph W H
New York........................ 10021.......... Schaeffer MISS Georgina B
New York........................ 10021.......... Schiff MR & MRS David T
New York........................ 10021.......... Schiff MR David B
New York........................ 10021.......... Schifter MR & MRS Timothy W
New York........................ 10021.......... Schley MRS Stephanie T
New York........................ 10021.......... Schofield MR & MRS R Hayden JR
New York........................ 10021.......... Schorr MR & MRS Paul C IV
New York........................ 10021.......... Scribner MR & MRS Charles III
New York........................ 10021.......... Scull MR & MRS Theodore W
New York........................ 10021.......... Scully MR & MRS Dennis A
New York........................ 10021.......... Seherr-Thoss MR & MRS Henry W
New York........................ 10021.......... Selden MR & MRS George L
New York........................ 10021.......... Semple MR & MRS Robert B JR
New York........................ 10021.......... Serena di Lapigio BRN & BRNSS Ottavio
New York........................ 10021.......... Shapard MR & MRS Austin V
New York........................ 10021.......... Sheffield MRS Anne
New York........................ 10021.......... Sherrer MR & MRS Charles D
New York........................ 10021.......... Sherrill MISS Sarah B
New York........................ 10021.......... Sherrill MR & MRS Stephen C
New York........................ 10021.......... Shields MR & MRS David V
New York........................ 10021.......... Shiland MR William McA JR
New York........................ 10021.......... Shute MR & MRS Benjamin R JR
New York........................ 10021.......... Simons MR & MRS Albert 3D
New York........................ 10021.......... Sincerbeaux MRS Katherine C
New York........................ 10021.......... Skor MISS Barbara B
New York........................ 10021.......... Smith MR & MRS Gerard L
New York........................ 10021.......... Speight MRS Randolph L
New York........................ 10021.......... Spofford MR & MRS John S W
New York........................ 10021.......... Springhorn MISS Kathleen E
New York........................ 10021.......... Stearns MR & MRS Peter C
New York........................ 10021.......... Steffan MR & MRS Andrew P
New York........................ 10021.......... Sterne MR & MRS Richard J
New York........................ 10021.......... Stevenson MR & MRS Charles P JR
New York........................ 10021.......... Stone MR & MRS Timothy J
New York........................ 10021.......... Stoudemire MR & MRS Sterling Cranford
New York........................ 10021.......... Stratoudakis MR & MRS Alexander J
New York........................ 10021.......... Swift MS Nina E
New York........................ 10021.......... Sylvester MR & MRS Michael S
New York........................ 10021.......... Talamo MRS L Rutherfurd
New York........................ 10021.......... Talley MRS Truman M
New York........................ 10021.......... Taylor MRS Topsy E
New York........................ 10021.......... Teagle MR & MRS Clifton D

New York, NY—New York, NY

New York	10021	Topping MR & MRS Henry J 4TH
New York	10021	Tozer MS Katherine C
New York	10021	Tysen MRS John C
New York	10021	Uffelman MR & MRS Charles G
New York	10021	Ughetta MR & MRS William C JR
New York	10021	Van der Mije MISS Alexis
New York	10021	van Eck MRS John C
New York	10021	van Heerden MR & MRS Jan H
New York	10021	Van Pelt MR & MRS Guy F C
New York	10021	Vance MR & MRS Lee G
New York	10021	Villard MRS Vincent S JR
New York	10021	Wade MR & MRS George J
New York	10021	Wagner MR & MRS Edward F JR
New York	10021	Waud MR & MRS Sydney P
New York	10021	Weber DR John C
New York	10021	Weekes MR & MRS Christopher R
New York	10021	Weeks MS Patricia M
New York	10021	Whipple MRS Hope A
New York	10021	White MRS Edgar P E
New York	10021	Widener MR & MRS Ryan E
New York	10021	Wilkie MR Angus McN
New York	10021	Willkie MR Hall Francis
New York	10021	Wilson MR & MRS R Clifford 3D
New York	10021	Winn MR & MRS Michael P A
New York	10021	Wyper MISS Florence A
New York	10021	York MRS Janet B
New York	10021	Younes MR & MRS Mohamed S
New York	10021	Zeisler MR Richard S
New York	10021	Zieman MR John H & Mezzacappa MRS Jessica
New York	10021	Zilkha MS Donna S
New York	10021	Zirin MR & MRS James D
New York	10021	Zoullas MR & MRS Sophocles N
New York	10021	Zoullas MR Alexis P
New York	10021	Zoullas MR Nicholas S & Bates Zoullas MRS Susan H
New York	10022	Aalde MR & MRS Heilo
New York	10022	Allen MR C Edmonds 3D
New York	10022	Andrews MR & MRS Mark E III
New York	10022	Argenti MR & MRS John P
New York	10022	Ashdown MRS Cecil Spanton JR
New York	10022	Atterbury MR & MRS S Ward
New York	10022	Ayers MISS E Victoria M
New York	10022	Baker MR & MRS Stuart D
New York	10022	Banker MR David L
New York	10022	Baskett MRS Charles E
New York	10022	Beha MR & MRS James A II
New York	10022	Bergreen MR & MRS Laurence
New York	10022	Bidwell MR & MRS J Truman JR
New York	10022	Bishop MRS Louis Faugères III
New York	10022	Blair MRS William McC JR
New York	10022	Blum MR & MRS Andrew M
New York	10022	Bricker MRS Anne Tracy
New York	10022	Brown MR & MRS Jeffrey T
New York	10022	Byram MISS Elizabeth Nye
New York	10022	Callahan MR & MRS Peter H
New York	10022	Carr MR Dayton T
New York	10022	Carrington MISS Judith
New York	10022	Cartwright MR Carroll L
New York	10022	Clark MR & MRS Merrell E JR
New York	10022	Clarke MR & MRS John P H
New York	10022	Clarke MR & MRS Phillips H 3D
New York	10022	Clarkson DR & MRS Bayard D
New York	10022	Clothier MR Morris W
New York	10022	Cole MR & MRS Charles J
New York	10022	Coles MR & MRS Andrés
New York	10022	Cook MR & MRS William H
New York	10022	Cooke MRS Oakley W
New York	10022	Cushing MISS Margaret C
New York	10022	Dance MR Robert
New York	10022	Davis MR & MRS Blake T
New York	10022	de Kay MRS George C
New York	10022	de Liagre MR Nicholas
New York	10022	De Lorenzo MS Annette M
New York	10022	Diedrick MR & MRS Arthur H JR
New York	10022	Donner MR Alexander B
New York	10022	Dougherty MR Marcus J
New York	10022	Douglas MRS Camille J
New York	10022	Drake MRS Rodman L
New York	10022	Drexel MS Pamela
New York	10022	Duke MR William T & Badger MS Madonna L
New York	10022	Dye MR & MRS William N
New York	10022	Elwell MR & MRS Briggs S
New York	10022	Espy MS Amanda Stetson
New York	10022	Farias MR George L
New York	10022	Faux MR & MRS R Gordon III
New York	10022	Fennebresque MRS Deborah
New York	10022	Foss MR Christopher B
New York	10022	Foster MR & MRS David V
New York	10022	Foster MR & MRS Walter S II
New York	10022	Fownes MR & MRS Henry G
New York	10022	French MR & MRS John III
New York	10022	Fulrath MISS Irene
New York	10022	Gibson MISS Eleanor Mather
New York	10022	Gilbert MRS Thomas S
New York	10022	Gilhuley MR & MRS Stephen E
New York	10022	Giordano MR & MRS Mark V
New York	10022	Goelet MR & MRS Robert G
New York	10022	Hartnett MISS Elizabeth A
New York	10022	Havemeyer MR & MRS William E
New York	10022	Hildesley REV & MRS C Hugh
New York	10022	Hornblower MR & MRS Ralph III
New York	10022	Hughes MISS Caitlin C
New York	10022	Hughes MR & MRS Charles B III
New York	10022	Ingraham MR & MRS John W
New York	10022	Isham MR & MRS Ralph H
New York	10022	Kean MR & MRS Robert W JR
New York	10022	Kissinger DR & MRS Henry A
New York	10022	Kloter MR Owen A
New York	10022	Knight MR Hilary
New York	10022	Krieger DR & MRS Karl H
New York	10022	Krusen MR & MRS Charles B
New York	10022	Kush MR Justin R
New York	10022	Lamphere MRS Louise W
New York	10022	Lauder MS Frederica R
New York	10022	Lauder MS Leigh B
New York	10022	Leaycraft MR Matthew T & Cambron MR Steven B
New York	10022	Leness MR & MRS Anthony V
New York	10022	Low MR & MRS Christopher A M
New York	10022	Magee MRS Rice
New York	10022	Manning MR Michael J
New York	10022	Mascheroni MR & MRS Mark
New York	10022	McAndrew MR & MRS Matthew P
New York	10022	Mellgard MR & MRS David M
New York	10022	Meyjes MRS C Robert P
New York	10022	Millard MRS Amory H
New York	10022	Moken MS Merri C
New York	10022	Montgomery MR & MRS J Anthony
New York	10022	Morgan MR Frank E II
New York	10022	Moss MR & MRS George K
New York	10022	Mullins MR & MRS William E G
New York	10022	Mullins REV CANON & MRS Andrew J W
New York	10022	Murphy MR & MRS Richard W
New York	10022	Mürrle MR Christian & Martin MS Christine Miller

New York, NY—New York, NY

New York	10022	Naud DR & MRS Robert Armstead
New York	10022	Nordeman MR & MRS Jacques C
New York	10022	Northrop MRS J Weissinger
New York	10022	Nouri MRS Edmond J
New York	10022	Ostergard MR & MRS Derek E
New York	10022	Palmer MR & MRS Stewart L
New York	10022	Patterson MRS Susan H
New York	10022	Paynter MRS Grenville H
New York	10022	Peabody MISS Elizabeth T
New York	10022	Pershing MRS John W
New York	10022	Phelan MR & MRS William J
New York	10022	Poëkel MR & MRS Charles A JR
New York	10022	Pratt MR & MRS Charles McC
New York	10022	Prowell MISS Leonora P
New York	10022	Pujol MR Raoul H
New York	10022	Quasha MR & MRS Alan G
New York	10022	Rainey MRS John Crews
New York	10022	Reeser MR Philip A
New York	10022	Reid MR Bagley
New York	10022	Rockefeller MRS Rodman C
New York	10022	Roosevelt MR Andrew E
New York	10022	Ross MR Paul C
New York	10022	Sanders MR P Layton JR
New York	10022	Sanford MR Thomas McG
New York	10022	Sargent MRS John T
New York	10022	Sartorius MR & MRS John M JR
New York	10022	Scaife MRS Frances G
New York	10022	Schaefer MR & MRS Charles James IV
New York	10022	Schaeffer MRS Marcia M
New York	10022	Scott MR & MRS Edward B 5TH
New York	10022	Shafer MR & MRS Robert L
New York	10022	Shuman MR & MRS Stanley S
New York	10022	Slade MR & MRS Jarvis J
New York	10022	Spalding MS Jill
New York	10022	Stillman MR Alfred 3D
New York	10022	Stratford MS Nancy A
New York	10022	Thomas MRS Weston L
New York	10022	Thors MR & MRS Thor
New York	10022	Tilney MR & MRS Hugh J
New York	10022	Toland MISS Avery C
New York	10022	Trafelet MR Remy W
New York	10022	Train HON & MRS John
New York	10022	Truesdale MRS Mary S
New York	10022	Vahabzadeh MR Ali-Reza & Mujica MS Maryam A M
New York	10022	Van Sise MR Keith H & Hadik MS Stephanie M
New York	10022	Vitagliano MISS Maria T
New York	10022	Wallace MR & MRS Hugh C JR
New York	10022	Wallis MR Stephen F & Rowley MS Alexandra F
New York	10022	Ward MRS Ralph E
New York	10022	Warner MISS Elizabeth L
New York	10022	Weaver MR & MRS Richard L N
New York	10022	White MR & MRS James J JR
New York	10022	Wildenstein MR & MRS Guy
New York	10022	Wills MRS Elizabeth G S
New York	10022	Wolfe RT REV & MRS Dean E
New York	10022	Worthington MR Ralph 4TH
New York	10023	Agry MR Bradford W
New York	10023	Ames MISS Katrine W
New York	10023	Angell MR & MRS Christopher C
New York	10023	Barbey MR Henry I JR
New York	10023	Barton MR Reginald McCarroll JR
New York	10023	Beard MR Robert R & Mohapatra MR Bibhudutta
New York	10023	Brown MR & MRS Thatcher M 3D
New York	10023	Buck MR & MRS Walter H
New York	10023	Carr MR & MRS Richard R JR
New York	10023	Cashman MISS Josephine I
New York	10023	Clark MR Gordon T
New York	10023	Contiguglia MR & MRS Carl A
New York	10023	Crosby MRS Virginia D
New York	10023	Cummings MR Lawrence B
New York	10023	Diedrick MRS Age Buer
New York	10023	Diels MR & MRS William G
New York	10023	Doller MR Benjamin F
New York	10023	Downey MR & MRS Robert N
New York	10023	Eiswerth MR Jason A
New York	10023	Fowkes MR William I & Smith MR Stephen M
New York	10023	Geer MR & MRS John F
New York	10023	Hawkins MR Ashton & Hawkins MR Johnnie Moore
New York	10023	Hein MR Peter C SR & Farley MS Anne
New York	10023	Hinckley MRS Low
New York	10023	Jackson MISS Sarah R
New York	10023	Kennedy MR & MRS (DR) Kevin W
New York	10023	Laue MR & MRS Bruce A
New York	10023	Lowrey MR Charles F JR & Rodriguez MS Susan T
New York	10023	MacNair MS Caroline Prichitt
New York	10023	Manoff MR & MRS Morgan C E
New York	10023	Mantin MR Adam L & Breed MS Vail R
New York	10023	Mather MR & MRS Charles E 4TH
New York	10023	Maull MISS Diana
New York	10023	Melano MR Fabrizio
New York	10023	Mezrich MR & MRS Mark N
New York	10023	Miller MRS Robert
New York	10023	Nitze MISS Heidi
New York	10023	Oram MR Peter D
New York	10023	Quinlan MR & MRS Timothy C
New York	10023	Radsch MR & MRS Robert W
New York	10023	Ramsay MR Gustavus R
New York	10023	Ratto MR & MRS Alessandro
New York	10023	Read MS Cornelia
New York	10023	Roberts MS Catherine G
New York	10023	Rose MISS Lauren
New York	10023	Sanderson MR & MRS Ry C
New York	10023	Sanford MR & MRS Floyd Smith III
New York	10023	Sasso MR Anthony B
New York	10023	Schiff DR Andrew N
New York	10023	Schubert MS Lisa A
New York	10023	Sommer MR Graydon H
New York	10023	Sutherland MS Paige Cutting
New York	10023	Voorham MR & MRS Markus A B
New York	10023	Waters MR & MRS Somerset R III
New York	10023	Webb MR & MRS Elmon D
New York	10024	Allen MRS A Christine
New York	10024	Benenson MR & MRS Marcius K
New York	10024	Binkerd MISS Julia Stedman
New York	10024	Blanchard MR & MRS Richard F
New York	10024	Brown MR & MRS Peter Chase Hayden
New York	10024	Casey MS Edith B
New York	10024	Chase MR Kenneth H
New York	10024	Cobbs MR & MRS William W JR
New York	10024	Cowley MR & MRS Nicholas P T
New York	10024	Cox MR & MRS Brian W
New York	10024	Dale MISS Patricia B
New York	10024	Daley MR & MRS John P
New York	10024	Daniel MRS Margaret Carr
New York	10024	Daubin MR & MRS Michael S
New York	10024	Daviau MR & MRS Fabrice O
New York	10024	Davison MR & MRS George P
New York	10024	Dijols MR & MRS Frédéric
New York	10024	Drayton MR & MRS John W JR
New York	10024	Eastman MR & MRS John L JR

New York........................ 10024......... Franken MR & MRS Joseph P II
New York........................ 10024......... Gatch MR Milton McC
New York........................ 10024......... Hawkins MR & MRS Eliot D
New York........................ 10024......... Heckscher MR & MRS Morrison H
New York........................ 10024......... Hentic MR & MRS Frank H W
New York........................ 10024......... Heyn MR & MRS Edward B
New York........................ 10024......... Hill-Edgar MR & MRS (DR) W Keyes
New York........................ 10024......... Hoppin MR & MRS Charles S
New York........................ 10024......... Hughes MISS Nancy M
New York........................ 10024......... Johnson MR & MRS David C JR
New York........................ 10024......... Jones MR Winfield P
New York........................ 10024......... Jones MS S Henrietta H
New York........................ 10024......... Klebnikov MRS Paul
New York........................ 10024......... Knox MR & MRS Lewis C 4TH
New York........................ 10024......... Koob MR & MRS Daniel J
New York........................ 10024......... Krauss VERY REV Harry Edward
New York........................ 10024......... Larson MR & MRS Douglas E
New York........................ 10024......... Lawrence MR E Alexander
New York........................ 10024......... Leake MISS Joan A
New York........................ 10024......... Ledes MR & MRS Richard C
New York........................ 10024......... Lewis MR & MRS A Churchill R
New York........................ 10024......... Ludington MR Nicholas L
New York........................ 10024......... Lusk MR & MRS Andrew P
New York........................ 10024......... MacDonald MR Kirkpatrick
New York........................ 10024......... McAlpin MR & MRS David M
New York........................ 10024......... McCabe MR & MRS William L
New York........................ 10024......... McDonald MS Mia
New York........................ 10024......... McKown MR & MRS Alexander P
New York........................ 10024......... Meyer MISS Tara B
New York........................ 10024......... Mitchell MR & MRS David H
New York........................ 10024......... Morrison MR & MRS Bart W
New York........................ 10024......... Morse DR Stephen S
New York........................ 10024......... Morss MR & MRS Anthony W
New York........................ 10024......... Myles MRS Robert C III
New York........................ 10024......... Pantaleoni MR & MRS Anthony
New York........................ 10024......... Peters MR & MRS Frederick W
New York........................ 10024......... Phifer MR & MRS Thomas M 3D
New York........................ 10024......... Philip MR John Van Ness 3D
New York........................ 10024......... Pyne MR & MRS Benjamin N
New York........................ 10024......... Rafferty MR & MRS John P
New York........................ 10024......... Rea MISS Alison B
New York........................ 10024......... Roberts MRS Harold M
New York........................ 10024......... Robinson MR A Pitts 3D
New York........................ 10024......... Saccomano MR Anthony R
New York........................ 10024......... Selch MR & MRS Jason B
New York........................ 10024......... Sherrill MR & MRS M David
New York........................ 10024......... Small MRS Ann
New York........................ 10024......... Smith MR & MRS Mark P
New York........................ 10024......... Smith MR & MRS Scott F
New York........................ 10024......... Snee MR & MRS Henry T M
New York........................ 10024......... Stillman MR & MRS Waddell W
New York........................ 10024......... Sutton MR & MRS (DR) Robert H
New York........................ 10024......... Tanner DR & MRS Michael
New York........................ 10024......... Taylor MR & MRS Hugh Gibbs JR
New York........................ 10024......... Timpson MR & MRS Robert C L JR
New York........................ 10024......... Tisdale-Woods MR David N S
& Tisdale-Woods MR Gary L
New York........................ 10024......... Vanderwarker MR & MRS R Dean III
New York........................ 10024......... Vickery MR & MRS Alan B
New York........................ 10024......... Waxman MR & MRS Jonathan M
New York........................ 10024......... Welch MISS (DR) Martha G
New York........................ 10024......... Whitney MR & MRS Edward B
New York........................ 10024......... Wilcox MR Alexander D
New York........................ 10024......... Yates MRS John Sellers
New York........................ 10025......... Adam MR & MRS Laszlo
New York........................ 10025......... Adams MR & MRS John Brooks
New York........................ 10025......... Allen MISS Hadley
New York........................ 10025......... Almond MR & MRS Richard W
New York........................ 10025......... Auchincloss MRS Gordon 2D
New York........................ 10025......... Banhara MR Fernando S
& Whitney MRS Francine Douwes
New York........................ 10025......... Betekhtin MR & MRS Sergei O
New York........................ 10025......... Blodgett MR & MRS Thomas N JR
New York........................ 10025......... Bovet MISS Daria L
New York........................ 10025......... Brooks MR Arthur H 3D
New York........................ 10025......... Brown MRS Hope
New York........................ 10025......... Cardew MR & MRS Piers A
New York........................ 10025......... Davidge MR & MRS John W III
New York........................ 10025......... de Kay MR Thomas S
New York........................ 10025......... de Menocal DR & MRS Peter B
New York........................ 10025......... Di Pietro MR & MRS Luca
New York........................ 10025......... Dietsche RT REV & MRS Andrew M L
New York........................ 10025......... Edwards MISS Mary D
New York........................ 10025......... Ellis MS Katherine de S
New York........................ 10025......... Forsyth MR & MRS William H JR
New York........................ 10025......... Gately MR Michael D & Kent MS (DR) Laura K
New York........................ 10025......... Gatje MRS Barbara W
New York........................ 10025......... Gatto MR & MRS Philip R
New York........................ 10025......... Glueck MR William C
New York........................ 10025......... Gouge DR & MRS Thomas H
New York........................ 10025......... Haynes MRS Sophy P-Q
New York........................ 10025......... Hodges MR & MRS Fletcher III
New York........................ 10025......... Holmes MR & MRS Nicholas S
New York........................ 10025......... Hood MISS Christianna T
New York........................ 10025......... Horan MISS Honora
New York........................ 10025......... Hoyt MR & MRS W C Alexander
New York........................ 10025......... Hughes MR & MRS Michael C
New York........................ 10025......... Hyatt MR James K H
New York........................ 10025......... Hyatt MRS James P
New York........................ 10025......... Jenkins MR & MRS Evan A
New York........................ 10025......... Kates MRS Andrew K
New York........................ 10025......... Keehner MR & MRS Brigham M
New York........................ 10025......... Kelley MS (DR) Darcy B
New York........................ 10025......... Kumar MR & MRS Sunil P
New York........................ 10025......... Mayhew MR & MRS Timothy P JR
New York........................ 10025......... McAvoy MR & MRS Matthew G
New York........................ 10025......... McElhiney MR & MRS Richard L
New York........................ 10025......... McKinley DR & MRS George F
New York........................ 10025......... Moore MR & MRS Willard S
New York........................ 10025......... Morgan MRS William J
New York........................ 10025......... Nash MR & MRS Philip V
New York........................ 10025......... Neiger MR Henry M
New York........................ 10025......... Noonan MR Stephen M & Lowe MR Mark A
New York........................ 10025......... Palache MISS Lucy B
New York........................ 10025......... Parks MRS Mackenzie D
New York........................ 10025......... Pierson MR & MRS Joseph A
New York........................ 10025......... Polubinski MR & MRS Edmund 3D
New York........................ 10025......... Preston MR Percy JR
New York........................ 10025......... Purdy MR & MRS Peter J
New York........................ 10025......... Robins MR & MRS Seth S
New York........................ 10025......... Root MR Oren
New York........................ 10025......... Sakellariadis MR & MRS Nicholas J
New York........................ 10025......... Schoettle MR Douglas Abbott
New York........................ 10025......... Smith MR Edward Byron 3D
New York........................ 10025......... Taylor MR & MRS Randall Lenox
New York........................ 10025......... Thompson MR & MRS Lawrence B
New York........................ 10025......... Vaino MR & MRS Jaan E
New York........................ 10025......... Van Ingen MISS Anne H
New York........................ 10025......... Wiedemann MR & MRS Christopher B
New York........................ 10025......... Wilkie MR & MRS Austin T
New York........................ 10025......... Wuorinen MR Charles P
New York........................ 10025......... Zanger MR & MRS Jesse D

To nominate a candidate for the Social Register Association, please email: SRCommittee@thesocialregister.org

New York, NY—New York, NY

New York........................ 10026.......... Doughten MISS Lisa M
New York........................ 10026.......... Elkus MR & MRS James M
New York........................ 10026.......... Fradd MR R Brandon
New York........................ 10027.......... Blake MR & MRS Brian A
New York........................ 10027.......... Coll MR Stephen W & Griswold MS Eliza
New York........................ 10027.......... Curry MR Emerson Whitfield
New York........................ 10027.......... Duryea MR & MRS Robert A
New York........................ 10027.......... Thompson MR Schuyler S
New York........................ 10028.......... Ahern MR & MRS F Gregory
New York........................ 10028.......... Anthony MR & MRS Silas R JR
New York........................ 10028.......... Aspegren MR John B JR
New York........................ 10028.......... Auchincloss MRS Edward H
New York........................ 10028.......... Baker MR & MRS William T JR
New York........................ 10028.......... Barkus MR & MRS Paul R
New York........................ 10028.......... Bateson MR & MRS Douglas F
New York........................ 10028.......... Beinecke MR & MRS Frederick W
New York........................ 10028.......... Belford MR & MRS Ralph J III
New York........................ 10028.......... Benton MRS Nicholas
New York........................ 10028.......... Berlind MR & MRS Roger S
New York........................ 10028.......... Bierman MR & MRS Stephen K
New York........................ 10028.......... Bishop MR André S & Manning MR Peter
New York........................ 10028.......... Bliss MRS Richard M
New York........................ 10028.......... Bonner MR & MRS J Christopher JR
New York........................ 10028.......... Borges MR & MRS Luiz E A
New York........................ 10028.......... Borland MISS Anne J
New York........................ 10028.......... Bovet MR Robert E
New York........................ 10028.......... Bozorth MRS Squire N
New York........................ 10028.......... Brown MRS Francis C JR
New York........................ 10028.......... Brown MRS J Warren
New York........................ 10028.......... Brown MRS Thomas B Hynson JR
New York........................ 10028.......... Bullen MRS Richard H
New York........................ 10028.......... Burch MR & MRS Robert L III
New York........................ 10028.......... Burden MR & MRS Ordway P
New York........................ 10028.......... Butler MR & MRS Frederick J C
New York........................ 10028.......... Buxton MR & MRS George N
New York........................ 10028.......... Byron-Patrikiades MR & MRS Charles A
New York........................ 10028.......... Cahill MR & MRS Robert L JR
New York........................ 10028.......... Camacho MR Alejandro E & Rollins Camacho MS Pamela
New York........................ 10028.......... Cannell MR & MRS Michael T
New York........................ 10028.......... Caracappa MR & MRS David W
New York........................ 10028.......... Carragher MS Jenny
New York........................ 10028.......... Cattier MR & MRS Jacques E
New York........................ 10028.......... Chapman MR & MRS Duncan Anthony
New York........................ 10028.......... Childs MR & MRS David M
New York........................ 10028.......... Clark MR & MRS Brooks S
New York........................ 10028.......... Clark MR & MRS Robert G JR
New York........................ 10028.......... Clement MR & MRS Stephen M III
New York........................ 10028.......... Coleman MISS Constance M
New York........................ 10028.......... Collins MR & MRS Bradley I JR
New York........................ 10028.......... Comfort MR & MRS Stuyvesant P
New York........................ 10028.......... Cooke MISS (DR) Claudia M
New York........................ 10028.......... Coolidge MR & MRS Peter J
New York........................ 10028.......... Craigmyle MR & MRS Robert de R JR
New York........................ 10028.......... Cushing MR & MRS Howard G JR
New York........................ 10028.......... Davies DR & MRS Edward A
New York........................ 10028.......... Davis MR & MRS Douglas K
New York........................ 10028.......... de Vegh MR & MRS Pierre J
New York........................ 10028.......... Dean MRS Howard B
New York........................ 10028.......... Dearth MISS Deborah H
New York........................ 10028.......... Dowling MRS John L
New York........................ 10028.......... Doyle MR & MRS L F Boker
New York........................ 10028.......... Du Brul MRS Antonia P
New York........................ 10028.......... Duke MRS Anthony Drexel
New York........................ 10028.......... Eastman MR & MRS John L
New York........................ 10028.......... Eberhart MR & MRS Frank III
New York........................ 10028.......... Erensel MR & MRS Brent B
New York........................ 10028.......... Evarts MRS William M JR
New York........................ 10028.......... Fawcett MR & MRS Kipp M
New York........................ 10028.......... Fisher MS Nancy
New York........................ 10028.......... Fletcher MS Sarah P
New York........................ 10028.......... Fowlkes MR & MRS Gregory G
New York........................ 10028.......... Francombe MR Nigel I & De Rose MS Kathleen
New York........................ 10028.......... Frelinghuysen MR & MRS George L K
New York........................ 10028.......... Furniss MR & MRS R Vanneman
New York........................ 10028.......... Gambee MS Fay
New York........................ 10028.......... Garnett MR & MRS Charles H E
New York........................ 10028.......... Gatje MR Robert F
New York........................ 10028.......... Gavales MISS Diana H
New York........................ 10028.......... Grace MRS F Cecil S
New York........................ 10028.......... Grieco MR & MRS Matthew V
New York........................ 10028.......... Gross MR & MRS Rainer
New York........................ 10028.......... Gruber MR & MRS Matthew J
New York........................ 10028.......... Gundlach MR & MRS Andrew S
New York........................ 10028.......... Gutwillig MR & MRS Jacob H
New York........................ 10028.......... Hadden MR & MRS John W II
New York........................ 10028.......... Hall MISS Caroline C
New York........................ 10028.......... Hall MISS Hillary B
New York........................ 10028.......... Hallen MR & MRS John R JR
New York........................ 10028.......... Harbison MR & MRS James W JR
New York........................ 10028.......... Harper MRS Fletcher M
New York........................ 10028.......... Harvey MR & MRS John C
New York........................ 10028.......... Haskell MR & MRS John H F JR
New York........................ 10028.......... Hemingway MS Sylvia K
New York........................ 10028.......... Hitchcock MR & MRS Thomas 3D
New York........................ 10028.......... Hoagland MR & MRS Leigh W
New York........................ 10028.......... Hoar MR William R S
New York........................ 10028.......... Hoguet MS Nancy
New York........................ 10028.......... Holbrook MISS Christina E
New York........................ 10028.......... Holden MR & MRS W Hale
New York........................ 10028.......... Hutchins MR & MRS Winston W
New York........................ 10028.......... Hutchinson MRS (DR) Daniel L JR
New York........................ 10028.......... Jennison MR & MRS Peter H
New York........................ 10028.......... Johnson MR & MRS Francis E 3D
New York........................ 10028.......... Johnson MR & MRS Howard B
New York........................ 10028.......... Jones MR & MRS Peter C
New York........................ 10028.......... Junquera MR & MRS Oscar
New York........................ 10028.......... Keating MR Marshall P
New York........................ 10028.......... Kempner MR & MRS T Nathaniel
New York........................ 10028.......... Kimmelman MR & MRS Peter
New York........................ 10028.......... Kinlin MR & MRS Bruce D
New York........................ 10028.......... Kissel MRS Michael Case
New York........................ 10028.......... Kunhardt MRS Edith W
New York........................ 10028.......... Lansing MRS Gerrit L
New York........................ 10028.......... Larose MR & MRS Lawrence A
New York........................ 10028.......... Leddy MR Thomas F
New York........................ 10028.......... Legendre MS Bokara H
New York........................ 10028.......... Liddell MR & MRS D Roger B
New York........................ 10028.......... Little MR & MRS George F 2D
New York........................ 10028.......... Loomis MR Alfred F 2D
New York........................ 10028.......... Luers MR & MRS William H
New York........................ 10028.......... MacDonald MISS Patricia A
New York........................ 10028.......... Manger DR & MRS William Muir
New York........................ 10028.......... Marshall MRS Patricia T
New York........................ 10028.......... Matthews MR & MRS William O'C JR
New York........................ 10028.......... McCleary MS Katherine C
New York........................ 10028.......... Mills MRS Margaret A
New York........................ 10028.......... Montague MR & MRS Edward
New York........................ 10028.......... Moore MR Robert H II
New York........................ 10028.......... Moran MISS Thirza T
New York........................ 10028.......... Morgan MR & MRS Charles F
New York........................ 10028.......... Moss MR & MRS George Farrell

New York.......................... 10028.......... Murray MRS (DR) A Brean
New York.......................... 10028.......... Myers DR & MRS Robert A
New York.......................... 10028.......... Nadosy MR & MRS Peter A
New York.......................... 10028.......... Nelson MRS George A III
New York.......................... 10028.......... Niedermayer MR & MRS Theodore E
New York.......................... 10028.......... Nottebohm MR & MRS Johann D
New York.......................... 10028.......... Ohrstrom MR & MRS Wright R S
New York.......................... 10028.......... Ohrstrom MRS Rochelle
New York.......................... 10028.......... Overall MISS (REV) Martha R
New York.......................... 10028.......... Paschal MR & MRS Kent A
New York.......................... 10028.......... Patterson MR & MRS William C
New York.......................... 10028.......... Pendl MR & MRS Ulrich G
New York.......................... 10028.......... Pierce MR & MRS John V H
New York.......................... 10028.......... Pochna MRS Priscilla T
New York.......................... 10028.......... Potter MR & MRS Nicholas F
New York.......................... 10028.......... Pulling MR & MRS Edward L
New York.......................... 10028.......... Rappel MR R William JR
New York.......................... 10028.......... Reese MR & MRS Morgan C
New York.......................... 10028.......... Remmel MR & MRS H Lawrence
New York.......................... 10028.......... Ridder MR L Michael & Vance MS Linda S
New York.......................... 10028.......... Riley MR & MRS James W III
New York.......................... 10028.......... Roberts MR & MRS Donald M
New York.......................... 10028.......... Robinson MR & MRS Michael R
New York.......................... 10028.......... Rodeo DR Scott A & Frissora MS (DR) Christine L
New York.......................... 10028.......... Rogers MR & MRS Theodore O JR
New York.......................... 10028.......... Rohan MR & MRS Gregory J
New York.......................... 10028.......... Roosevelt MR Robert E
New York.......................... 10028.......... Rose DR & MRS Donald J
New York.......................... 10028.......... Rose MR & MRS Louis
New York.......................... 10028.......... Rothe MR & MRS Whitney Knowlton
New York.......................... 10028.......... Rowley MR & MRS John C
New York.......................... 10028.......... Rubin MR & MRS Howard
New York.......................... 10028.......... Saint-Amand MR & MRS Alexander
New York.......................... 10028.......... Scheerer MRS Idoline
New York.......................... 10028.......... Scheuermann MR & MRS Eric F
New York.......................... 10028.......... Schrade MISS Rhonda-Lee
New York.......................... 10028.......... Schrade MISS Rolisa M
New York.......................... 10028.......... Schrade MR & MRS Randolph R A
New York.......................... 10028.......... Schuster DR & MRS Derek V
New York.......................... 10028.......... Sevener MR & MRS Kent L
New York.......................... 10028.......... Seybolt MR & MRS G Crossan JR
New York.......................... 10028.......... Sidamon-Eristoff MRS Constantine
New York.......................... 10028.......... Smith DR & MRS Silas W
New York.......................... 10028.......... Smith MISS Alexandra G
New York.......................... 10028.......... Smith REV John Cutrer
New York.......................... 10028.......... Spagnoli MR & MRS Kevin L
New York.......................... 10028.......... Spellman MR & MRS John T
New York.......................... 10028.......... Sprague MR & MRS John A
New York.......................... 10028.......... Spring MR & MRS Robert E
New York.......................... 10028.......... Stanton MRS Phoebe R
New York.......................... 10028.......... Taft MR & MRS William H V
New York.......................... 10028.......... Tankoos MS Lisa S
New York.......................... 10028.......... Teryazos MR & MRS Christopher A
New York.......................... 10028.......... Thomas MR & MRS Jeremiah L 3D
New York.......................... 10028.......... Thornton MRS Daphne S
New York.......................... 10028.......... Toland MR John G
New York.......................... 10028.......... Triant MRS Theodore
New York.......................... 10028.......... Van Antwerp MR & MRS T Bragg JR
New York.......................... 10028.......... Van Leuven MRS Thomas C
New York.......................... 10028.......... Vogel MR & MRS William D 2D
New York.......................... 10028.......... von Boyens MRS Renate B
New York.......................... 10028.......... Vris MISS Courtney M
New York.......................... 10028.......... Walker MR & MRS James E C JR
New York.......................... 10028.......... Warner MR & MRS Miner H
New York.......................... 10028.......... Warren MRS William B
New York.......................... 10028.......... Westwood MR & MRS Christopher J
New York.......................... 10028.......... Wild MRS Anne Russell
New York.......................... 10028.......... Williams MR & MRS Jeffrey L
New York.......................... 10028.......... Willis MRS Gwendolyn H
New York.......................... 10028.......... Wilson MR Ransom C
New York.......................... 10028.......... Wilson MRS Henry T
New York.......................... 10028.......... Witter MRS Susan R
New York.......................... 10028.......... Wyeth MRS Christina L
New York.......................... 10028.......... Yang MR & MRS John F
New York.......................... 10029.......... Adelson MR & MRS Jonathan
New York.......................... 10029.......... Auchincloss MR & MRS Andrew S
New York.......................... 10029.......... Benedict MR & MRS Rodman W
New York.......................... 10029.......... Binger MRS S Storck
New York.......................... 10029.......... Brewster MR & MRS Richard W
New York.......................... 10029.......... Bristol MR & MRS Brian T
New York.......................... 10029.......... Burns MR & MRS Richard J
New York.......................... 10029.......... Butterworth MRS J Warner II
New York.......................... 10029.......... Carson MISS Georgia Chapin
New York.......................... 10029.......... Casaly MR John P & Parent MS Louise M
New York.......................... 10029.......... Chepiga MR & MRS Geoffrey R
New York.......................... 10029.......... Cooper MRS Mary L
New York.......................... 10029.......... Edgar MR & MRS Robert V
New York.......................... 10029.......... Farah MISS Adelaide P
New York.......................... 10029.......... Furlaud MR & MRS Richard M JR
New York.......................... 10029.......... Gallatin MRS James P
New York.......................... 10029.......... Guthrie MR & MRS Lucien Snowden Yokana
New York.......................... 10029.......... Hathaway MS Rebecca P
New York.......................... 10029.......... Healy MRS Harold H JR
New York.......................... 10029.......... Johnson MISS Wilhelmina C
New York.......................... 10029.......... Jones MR & MRS Adrian H
New York.......................... 10029.......... MacGill MR & MRS Gordon
New York.......................... 10029.......... Melnick MR & MRS James R
New York.......................... 10029.......... Miller MR & MRS Corbin R
New York.......................... 10029.......... Miller MR & MRS Leigh M
New York.......................... 10029.......... Moorhead MR & MRS J Upshur 2D
New York.......................... 10029.......... Morris MRS Peter V C
New York.......................... 10029.......... O'Connor MR & MRS Thomas E
New York.......................... 10029.......... Ogden MR & MRS Thomas P
New York.......................... 10029.......... Oswald MISS Diana S T
New York.......................... 10029.......... Pennoyer MR & MRS Russell P
New York.......................... 10029.......... Pettibone MR & MRS Peter J
New York.......................... 10029.......... Reboul MR & MRS John W
New York.......................... 10029.......... Rothe MR & MRS Ernst
New York.......................... 10029.......... Ryan MR & MRS Edward S
New York.......................... 10029.......... Smith MR & MRS Nicholas W
New York.......................... 10029.......... Tatnall MRS Samuel M V
New York.......................... 10031.......... Frazier MR Gibson
New York.......................... 10031.......... Miller MR & MRS Christopher Y
New York.......................... 10031.......... Perry MR & MRS Walter E 3D
New York.......................... 10032.......... Carse MRS Isabelle W
New York.......................... 10032.......... Dearie MR & MRS John C
New York.......................... 10032.......... Feigen MR & MRS Richard W B
New York.......................... 10033.......... Auchincloss MR & MRS Conrad McI
New York.......................... 10033.......... Brown MRS Henry S
New York.......................... 10033.......... Claflin MR Richard M II
New York.......................... 10033.......... Colt DR & MRS Edward W D
New York.......................... 10033.......... Dellenbaugh MR & MRS Samuel G
New York.......................... 10034.......... Franciscus MISS Alexandra
New York.......................... 10034.......... King MS Noëlle W
New York.......................... 10035.......... Mander MISS Melanie R
New York.......................... 10035.......... Rutherfurd MRS Morton A
New York.......................... 10035.......... Seyffert MR John R
New York.......................... 10036.......... Cushman MR Allerton 3D
New York.......................... 10036.......... Damon MR Sloan F
New York.......................... 10036.......... Forbes MR Douglas B
New York.......................... 10036.......... Gillespie MR Benson Bright
New York.......................... 10038.......... Erdreich MR & MRS Stanley M III

New York, NY—New York, NY

New York........................ 10038......... Hawkins MR Ira A 3D
New York........................ 10038......... Hughes MR & MRS Thomas M
New York........................ 10038......... Simon MR & MRS Timothy C
New York........................ 10038......... Soehner MR & MRS Kenneth
New York........................ 10040......... Hardy MR & MRS Jeffrey D
New York........................ 10040......... Sypher MR Francis J
New York........................ 10044......... Kimball MS Mary Eliza
New York........................ 10044......... Kimball-Stanley MR & MRS Arthur E
New York........................ 10061......... Hyman DR Louis R & Howe MS Katherine B
New York........................ 10065......... Allen MR & MRS Frederick H S
New York........................ 10065......... Altherr MR & MRS Mark R
New York........................ 10065......... Ambler MR & MRS Michael Nash
New York........................ 10065......... Anderson MR & MRS Courtenay B
New York........................ 10065......... Auchincloss MRS Reginald L G JR
New York........................ 10065......... Bancroft MR & MRS William W JR
New York........................ 10065......... Bard Varges MR Drew
New York........................ 10065......... Barr MR & MRS Thomas N
New York........................ 10065......... Becker MR Frank L
New York........................ 10065......... Becker MS Margaret W
New York........................ 10065......... Benedict MR & MRS Neil P
New York........................ 10065......... Benedict MRS William J
New York........................ 10065......... Bernhard MR & MRS Jason Ruggles
New York........................ 10065......... Bingham MRS A Walker III
New York........................ 10065......... Blackshaw MRS Roger S
New York........................ 10065......... Blair MR & MRS Michael W
New York........................ 10065......... Bland MR & MRS D Gerald JR
New York........................ 10065......... Bolton MR William G
New York........................ 10065......... Brand MR & MRS Martin J
New York........................ 10065......... Brawer DR & MRS Robert A
New York........................ 10065......... Breit MRS Ann L
New York........................ 10065......... Brokaw MR Clifford V 4TH & Taylor MS Amanda A C
New York........................ 10065......... Burch MS Tory
New York........................ 10065......... Buxton MRS Jorge N
New York........................ 10065......... Carnahan MR & MRS David H
New York........................ 10065......... Carr MR & MRS Michael J
New York........................ 10065......... Carr MRS Susanne Earls
New York........................ 10065......... Cates MRS Dudley F
New York........................ 10065......... Chapin MRS Schuyler G
New York........................ 10065......... Chen MRS Kendall G
New York........................ 10065......... Claghorn MR & MRS John W IV
New York........................ 10065......... Coleman MR & MRS Charles P III
New York........................ 10065......... Coleman MR & MRS Reed P
New York........................ 10065......... Collins MRS Daniel G
New York........................ 10065......... Connor MISS Amy
New York........................ 10065......... Corcos MRS Anne B
New York........................ 10065......... Cox MR & MRS Archibald JR
New York........................ 10065......... Crivelli MRS Gioconda M K
New York........................ 10065......... Curry MR Leigh S
New York........................ 10065......... Cushman MS Brooke Roberson
New York........................ 10065......... Dangremond MR Samuel P C
New York........................ 10065......... Darlington MRS Dorothea F
New York........................ 10065......... David-Weill MR & MRS Michel A
New York........................ 10065......... de la Renta MRS Oscar
New York........................ 10065......... de Neufville MR & MRS Peter B
New York........................ 10065......... de Sibour MRS Jacqueline
New York........................ 10065......... Detwiler MR William F
New York........................ 10065......... Devine MRS C Robert
New York........................ 10065......... Duff MR & MRS Louis D III
New York........................ 10065......... Duncan MR & MRS James A
New York........................ 10065......... Durgin MRS Don
New York........................ 10065......... Feldstein MRS (DR) Martin S
New York........................ 10065......... Fennebresque MR Quincy C
New York........................ 10065......... Fioratti MRS Nereo
New York........................ 10065......... Fiorilla di Santa Croce MR & MRS John Leopoldo
New York........................ 10065......... Firestone MRS Leonard K
New York........................ 10065......... Fleming MR & MRS Porter Farrar
New York........................ 10065......... Fleming MRS Charles L
New York........................ 10065......... Forgan MRS J Russell
New York........................ 10065......... Foster MR & MRS John H
New York........................ 10065......... Fox MR C Thayer
New York........................ 10065......... Fraser MRS John M JR
New York........................ 10065......... Frelinghuysen MS Adaline H
New York........................ 10065......... Galbraith MRS Evan G
New York........................ 10065......... Galbraith MS Christina M
New York........................ 10065......... Gault MS Mary Virginia
New York........................ 10065......... Gillmore MR & MRS Frederick H JR
New York........................ 10065......... Gimbel MR & MRS Mark P
New York........................ 10065......... Giroux MR & MRS Paul A
New York........................ 10065......... Glass MRS Frederick M
New York........................ 10065......... Gordon MR & MRS Peter A
New York........................ 10065......... Greeven MR & MRS Rainer N K
New York........................ 10065......... Gregor MR John B
New York........................ 10065......... Grew MR & MRS Robert R
New York........................ 10065......... Haas MR G William
New York........................ 10065......... Hackett MR & MRS Montague H JR
New York........................ 10065......... Hall MR & MRS James R P
New York........................ 10065......... Hanke MR & MRS G F Robert
New York........................ 10065......... Hansen MS Victoria D
New York........................ 10065......... Hardwick MR & MRS Robert Duncan
New York........................ 10065......... Harper MR & MRS Nelson V JR
New York........................ 10065......... Haynes-Dale MRS Amanda H
New York........................ 10065......... Heath MR Andrew G B
New York........................ 10065......... Henault MR Darren & Bassett MR Michael R
New York........................ 10065......... Heyman MR William H & Dietze MS Katherine E
New York........................ 10065......... Hines MR & MRS Edward M W
New York........................ 10065......... Hoguet MISS Denise M
New York........................ 10065......... Hoguet MR & MRS Geoffrey R
New York........................ 10065......... Hubbard MR & MRS William N 3D
New York........................ 10065......... Hupper MRS John R
New York........................ 10065......... James MR & MRS Hamilton E
New York........................ 10065......... James MR & MRS Robert R
New York........................ 10065......... Jeffries MR & MRS Andew H
New York........................ 10065......... Jessup MRS Philip C JR
New York........................ 10065......... Johnson MR & MRS Christopher M
New York........................ 10065......... Katona MR & MRS David L
New York........................ 10065......... Keber MR & MRS Christopher A
New York........................ 10065......... Kempner MR & MRS Michael C
New York........................ 10065......... Kennedy MR & MRS Gregory D
New York........................ 10065......... Kertess MR Hans William
New York........................ 10065......... Killian MR Justin P
New York........................ 10065......... King MR & MRS Henry L
New York........................ 10065......... Kittle MR & MRS Ralph W III
New York........................ 10065......... Koch MR Frederick R
New York........................ 10065......... Krimendahl MRS H Frederick II
New York........................ 10065......... La Branche MRS George M L III
New York........................ 10065......... Larm MR & MRS Richard P
New York........................ 10065......... Lawrence MR & MRS L Peter
New York........................ 10065......... Lawrence MR W Jeffrey
New York........................ 10065......... Lee MR & MRS Bruce
New York........................ 10065......... Lindley MR & MRS Daniel A JR
New York........................ 10065......... Lisman DR Richard D
New York........................ 10065......... Loreto MR & MRS Mario L F
New York........................ 10065......... Lyden DR & MRS John P
New York........................ 10065......... Maclean MISS Barbara J
New York........................ 10065......... Manice MR & MRS John H
New York........................ 10065......... March MR Clyde V 3D
New York........................ 10065......... Mariner MR & MRS Edward H
New York........................ 10065......... Maxwell MR George L
New York........................ 10065......... May MR & MRS Theodore A
New York........................ 10065......... McCallum MR & MRS David K
New York........................ 10065......... McClellan MR Gerald C
New York........................ 10065......... McCrary MR & MRS D Campbell

New York........................ 10065......... McKnight MR & MRS William G 3D
New York........................ 10065......... McLain MS Caroline
New York........................ 10065......... Meade MR & MRS Winston D
New York........................ 10065......... Metz MRS Richard E
New York........................ 10065......... Miles MR Reid R
New York........................ 10065......... Missett MR & MRS Joseph V 3D
New York........................ 10065......... Moeschlin MR George J III
New York........................ 10065......... Moore MRS William E JR
New York........................ 10065......... Mortimer MR Robert L & Simmons MS Tabitha
New York........................ 10065......... Nelson MR & MRS Norman R
New York........................ 10065......... Noyes MRS José W
New York........................ 10065......... O'Brien MRS Catherine L
New York........................ 10065......... O'Connor MAJ GEN (RET) & MRS Douglas J
New York........................ 10065......... Oliver MS Joan Duncan
New York........................ 10065......... O'Sullivan MR & MRS Ryan M
New York........................ 10065......... Owens MR & MRS Brian Ross
New York........................ 10065......... Owsley MR David T
New York........................ 10065......... Pace MR Eric D
New York........................ 10065......... Pagel MR & MRS Alex B
New York........................ 10065......... Palmer MR & MRS A Wright P
New York........................ 10065......... Pasquier MR Roger F
New York........................ 10065......... Patterson MR & MRS David C
New York........................ 10065......... Patterson MR & MRS David S
New York........................ 10065......... Patteson MR Charles J
New York........................ 10065......... Paul MR & MRS Douglas L
New York........................ 10065......... Pearman LADY
New York........................ 10065......... Pearman MRS Richard S L
New York........................ 10065......... Perkin MR & MRS Thorne L
New York........................ 10065......... Perry MR George S
New York........................ 10065......... Pfeifler MR & MRS Brian C
New York........................ 10065......... Pinto MR Maurice E
New York........................ 10065......... Piraino MR Leonel & Griscom MS Nina
New York........................ 10065......... Plowden-Wardlaw MR & MRS James C
New York........................ 10065......... Potter MRS Robert S
New York........................ 10065......... Pyne MR & MRS John S
New York........................ 10065......... Quasha MR & MRS Weston W
New York........................ 10065......... Reiss MS Jody Smith
New York........................ 10065......... Rich MR & MRS David B III
New York........................ 10065......... Roosevelt MRS Franklin D JR
New York........................ 10065......... Rowley MRS Henry N JR
New York........................ 10065......... Sailer MR & MRS Christopher A JR
New York........................ 10065......... Samet MR Roger H
New York........................ 10065......... Scharf MR & MRS Andrew Z
New York........................ 10065......... Schilling MR & MRS Charles H
New York........................ 10065......... Schwab MRS Hermann C
New York........................ 10065......... Scott MR & MRS Alfred L
New York........................ 10065......... Scribner MR Blair S
New York........................ 10065......... Simmons MR & MRS Donald M
New York........................ 10065......... Simon MR James E
New York........................ 10065......... Smith MS Elizabeth C
New York........................ 10065......... Smithers MRS Charles F
New York........................ 10065......... Snow MR & MRS Ian K W
New York........................ 10065......... Spurdle MR & MRS John William JR
New York........................ 10065......... Stanton MR & MRS Louis L
New York........................ 10065......... Stanton MR Fredrik S
New York........................ 10065......... Stetson MR & MRS Charles P JR
New York........................ 10065......... Stubbs MR & MRS Michael B
New York........................ 10065......... Swalm MR William K
New York........................ 10065......... Tashjian MR & MRS John C
New York........................ 10065......... Taylor MR David H JR & Rennie-Taylor MRS Milbrey
New York........................ 10065......... Terry MR & MRS Frederick A JR
New York........................ 10065......... Thalhimer MRS Charles G
New York........................ 10065......... Tober MR & MRS Donald G
New York........................ 10065......... Tompkins MR & MRS Russell C
New York........................ 10065......... Tompkins MS Evelyn Winthrop
New York........................ 10065......... Tozer MR & MRS W James JR
New York........................ 10065......... Tracy MRS Marylin N
New York........................ 10065......... Trafelet MRS Lara
New York........................ 10065......... Trott MISS Eugenie F
New York........................ 10065......... Tucker MRS Toinette
New York........................ 10065......... Tuckerman MRS Roger W
New York........................ 10065......... Tyree MR & MRS William B
New York........................ 10065......... Underwood MS Judith
New York........................ 10065......... Unger MRS Peter J
New York........................ 10065......... Van Rensselaer MRS Knauth
New York........................ 10065......... Warner MR & MRS Philip W
New York........................ 10065......... Wassenaar MR & MRS Julian S
New York........................ 10065......... Whitmarsh MRS Theodore F
New York........................ 10065......... Wickham MRS Robert D
New York........................ 10065......... Williams MR Francis H
New York........................ 10065......... Williams MRS Samuel D
New York........................ 10065......... Worth MR & MRS Theron O JR
New York........................ 10065......... Worth MR James H
New York........................ 10065......... Zilkha MR Ezra K
New York........................ 10065......... Zwack de Wahl MISS Gioia W
New York........................ 10069......... Ambler MISS Mary Cary
New York........................ 10075......... Aitken MRS Russell B
New York........................ 10075......... Allen MR & MRS Armin B
New York........................ 10075......... Anderson MRS Harry B 3D
New York........................ 10075......... Attfield MISS Gillian
New York........................ 10075......... Auerbach MR & MRS Jonathan A G
New York........................ 10075......... Bacon MR & MRS Louis M
New York........................ 10075......... Bartlett MR & MRS Stephen W
New York........................ 10075......... Benasuli MRS Alan
New York........................ 10075......... Benton MR & MRS Allan M
New York........................ 10075......... Bickford MR & MRS Nathaniel J
New York........................ 10075......... Birdsey MR & MRS Laurence H
New York........................ 10075......... Bomonti MRS Ralph M
New York........................ 10075......... Boughal MR & MRS Steven
New York........................ 10075......... Bowers MR & MRS Philip J 4TH
New York........................ 10075......... Branch MISS Suzanne
New York........................ 10075......... Brodsky MR & MRS Daniel J
New York........................ 10075......... Burke MR & MRS Coleman P
New York........................ 10075......... Campagna MR & MRS David W
New York........................ 10075......... Chase MRS Edward T
New York........................ 10075......... Chorske MR & MRS Michael W
New York........................ 10075......... Cisneros MR & MRS Gustavo A
New York........................ 10075......... Cobb MR & MRS Henry N
New York........................ 10075......... Coughlin MR & MRS Gerald W JR
New York........................ 10075......... Crawford MR & MRS Philip K
New York........................ 10075......... Creel MR Lawrence G
New York........................ 10075......... Cronson MR & MRS Paul
New York........................ 10075......... Cronson MRS Mary Sharp
New York........................ 10075......... Curley MRS Walter J
New York........................ 10075......... Cuyler DR G Grenville
New York........................ 10075......... Dalzell MR & MRS Robert F JR
New York........................ 10075......... Dance MR & MRS Andrew M
New York........................ 10075......... Dewey MR & MRS Thomas E JR
New York........................ 10075......... Diana MR Michael K
New York........................ 10075......... Dixon MRS Peter T
New York........................ 10075......... Fanjul MR & MRS J Pepe
New York........................ 10075......... Farr MR & MRS George III
New York........................ 10075......... Feigen MR & MRS Richard L
New York........................ 10075......... Fennebresque MR Kim Samuel
New York........................ 10075......... Foley MR & MRS Stephen P
New York........................ 10075......... Froelich MR Robert L
New York........................ 10075......... Gilbertson MR Mark Forrest
New York........................ 10075......... Gimbel MR S Stinor
New York........................ 10075......... Gooder MR & MRS Grenville MacD III
New York........................ 10075......... Goss MR Jared du P
New York........................ 10075......... Grace MRS Gerd Morris
New York........................ 10075......... Grinnell MR & MRS Alexander

To nominate a candidate for the Social Register Association, please email: SRCommittee@thesocialregister.org

New York, NY—New York, NY

New York........................ 10075......... Gubelmann MS Marjorie Barton
New York........................ 10075......... Hall MRS Mary Lou M
New York........................ 10075......... Harman MR & MRS William R
New York........................ 10075......... Harvey MS Christina McCarron
New York........................ 10075......... Hill MR Robert F
New York........................ 10075......... Holder MISS Heidi
New York........................ 10075......... Israel MR & MRS Thomas C
New York........................ 10075......... Izmirly DR Peter M & Farr MS Lucy W
New York........................ 10075......... James MRS Philip R
New York........................ 10075......... Jeffery MRS Ann Folliss
New York........................ 10075......... Kellner MR & MRS George A
New York........................ 10075......... Killian MISS Christiana I
New York........................ 10075......... Kotur MRS Robert K
New York........................ 10075......... Lamont MRS Lansing
New York........................ 10075......... Lash MR & MRS Stephen S
New York........................ 10075......... Laughlin MR & MRS Alexander M
New York........................ 10075......... Lawrence MR & MRS David B
New York........................ 10075......... Lincoln MR & MRS Edmond L
New York........................ 10075......... Lowerre MR & MRS Paul C
New York........................ 10075......... Macdonald MR & MRS Ian R
New York........................ 10075......... Maddock MR & MRS Paul L III
New York........................ 10075......... Mali MRS Frederick J
New York........................ 10075......... Maloney MR & MRS Robert B
New York........................ 10075......... Manger MR Stewart Sheppard
New York........................ 10075......... Martin MR & MRS Tucker E
New York........................ 10075......... Maund MR & MRS James S
New York........................ 10075......... McCarthy MR & MRS Thomas C
New York........................ 10075......... McCreery MR & MRS David A
New York........................ 10075......... Mehta MR & MRS Ved P
New York........................ 10075......... Meigher MISS Elizabeth T
New York........................ 10075......... Menken MRS Kenneth A
New York........................ 10075......... Mestres MR Ricardo A JR
New York........................ 10075......... Metcalf MR Manton B III
New York........................ 10075......... Montgomery THE REV & MRS Ian B
New York........................ 10075......... Moore MR Christopher S
New York........................ 10075......... Moore MRS George C
New York........................ 10075......... Neis MR & MRS Arnold H
New York........................ 10075......... Nicholls MR S Scott JR
New York........................ 10075......... Nickerson MR W Storm
New York........................ 10075......... O'Hara MR & MRS Robert S JR
New York........................ 10075......... Oldenburg MRS Richard E
New York........................ 10075......... Patel MR & MRS Sanjay H
New York........................ 10075......... Peek MR & MRS Jeffrey M
New York........................ 10075......... Petrides MR George
New York........................ 10075......... Philo MR & MRS John M
New York........................ 10075......... Post MR & MRS Joel S
New York........................ 10075......... Potter MRS C Nicholas
New York........................ 10075......... Reese MRS William Willis
New York........................ 10075......... Reid MR & MRS William R
New York........................ 10075......... Rentschler MISS Mary M
New York........................ 10075......... Reuben MR & MRS Michael B
New York........................ 10075......... Roosevelt MRS Jill
New York........................ 10075......... Rosen MR & MRS (DR) Aby J
New York........................ 10075......... Rybakoff MR & MRS James B
New York........................ 10075......... Schlangen MR Charles N W
New York........................ 10075......... Sechrest MR & MRS Jeffrey Ryan
New York........................ 10075......... Segura MS Jacqueline Derrey
New York........................ 10075......... Singleton MS M Pamela
New York........................ 10075......... Smith MR & MRS McKelden 3D
New York........................ 10075......... Stevenson MR & MRS William Wheeler
New York........................ 10075......... Talamo MR & MRS R Lupo
New York........................ 10075......... Thorne MR & MRS Nathan C
New York........................ 10075......... Thors MR & MRS Thor P
New York........................ 10075......... Tomenson MR Walter S III & Wettlaufer MS Virginia S
New York........................ 10075......... Tomlinson MS Joy A
New York........................ 10075......... Trinkle MRS Peter B
New York........................ 10075......... Trowbridge MR & MRS Thomas R 3D
New York........................ 10075......... Uzielli MRS Barbara B
New York........................ 10075......... Wagner MR & MRS Charles Havemeyer
New York........................ 10075......... Webster MRS Deborah
New York........................ 10075......... Weymouth MRS Elizabeth G
New York........................ 10075......... Whittemore MR Frederick B
New York........................ 10075......... Williams MR & MRS Eugene F III
New York........................ 10075......... Willkie MISS Julia F
New York........................ 10075......... Wilmerding MR John
New York........................ 10075......... Wilson MRS Robert C
New York........................ 10075......... Wise MR & MRS D Scott
New York........................ 10075......... Zilkha MISS Bettina L
New York........................ 10101......... Whittell MISS Mary K
New York........................ 10105......... Coleman MR James H
New York........................ 10128......... Abelow MR & MRS Justin D
New York........................ 10128......... Alexander MR & MRS David G
New York........................ 10128......... Allen MR & MRS Arthur Yorke
New York........................ 10128......... Allen MR & MRS Douglas F JR
New York........................ 10128......... Ambler MR & MRS William N
New York........................ 10128......... Anagnostopoulos DR & MRS Constantine E
New York........................ 10128......... Anderson MR & MRS Oscar K III
New York........................ 10128......... Anderson MR & MRS Sumner E
New York........................ 10128......... Armstrong MR & MRS Jeb S
New York........................ 10128......... Ashby MRS Elizabeth S C
New York........................ 10128......... Austin MRS C Lee JR
New York........................ 10128......... Baer MR & MRS Gregory H
New York........................ 10128......... Bailey MRS William P D
New York........................ 10128......... Ballard MR & MRS Robert F R
New York........................ 10128......... Bancroft MR & MRS Alexander C
New York........................ 10128......... Bannon MR & MRS Sean
New York........................ 10128......... Bardin DR & MRS C Wayne
New York........................ 10128......... Barrie MR John P & Smith MS Elizabeth A
New York........................ 10128......... Barton MR Thomas H
New York........................ 10128......... Bartow MR & MRS Francis D 2D
New York........................ 10128......... Bason MR & MRS George R JR
New York........................ 10128......... Bates MR & MRS Chapin C
New York........................ 10128......... Bateson MR William M
New York........................ 10128......... Bauer MR & MRS Gregory W
New York........................ 10128......... Beer MR David W
New York........................ 10128......... Bellas MR & MRS Albert C
New York........................ 10128......... Bellas MR & MRS Michael C
New York........................ 10128......... Benacerraf MR & MRS Ari
New York........................ 10128......... Benjamin MR & MRS Richard D
New York........................ 10128......... Benkard MRS James W B
New York........................ 10128......... Berry MR & MRS Charles G
New York........................ 10128......... Berry MR & MRS Nicholas McG
New York........................ 10128......... Berson MR Joel I
New York........................ 10128......... Bevan MRS David C JR
New York........................ 10128......... Blair MRS George A
New York........................ 10128......... Blanchard MR & MRS Alan F
New York........................ 10128......... Blind MR William C JR
New York........................ 10128......... Boston MR & MRS Hugh C III
New York........................ 10128......... Boyer MRS A Gillian Peterson
New York........................ 10128......... Brainerd MR & MRS Charles C
New York........................ 10128......... Bramwell MR & MRS Austin W
New York........................ 10128......... Brodlieb MR Jeffrey & Ely MS Lyda Barclay
New York........................ 10128......... Brown MR Edward Nicholas
New York........................ 10128......... Brown MS Leelee d'O
New York........................ 10128......... Burch MR & MRS Robert L IV
New York........................ 10128......... Burger MR & MRS (DR) Van Vechten JR
New York........................ 10128......... Cameron MR & MRS Duncan B
New York........................ 10128......... Cannon MISS Jane H
New York........................ 10128......... Caspersen MR & MRS (DR) Samuel M W
New York........................ 10128......... Caspersen MR & MRS Erik M W
New York........................ 10128......... Chapin MR & MRS Edward W
New York........................ 10128......... Chapman MR & MRS Drew G L

New York.......... 10128.......... Cheever MISS Mary C
New York.......... 10128.......... Chen MR & MRS Kimball C
New York.......... 10128.......... Cherna MR & MRS Andrew R
New York.......... 10128.......... Claar MS Alice
New York.......... 10128.......... Clagett MRS Lillian Hill
New York.......... 10128.......... Claghorn MR & MRS John W III
New York.......... 10128.......... Clark MR & MRS Carrington III
New York.......... 10128.......... Clark MR & MRS David C JR
New York.......... 10128.......... Colcord MRS Bradford P
New York.......... 10128.......... Collins MR & MRS Robert M
New York.......... 10128.......... Collinsworth MRS Eden
New York.......... 10128.......... Conrad MR & MRS Jonathan M
New York.......... 10128.......... Conrad MR & MRS Winthrop B JR
New York.......... 10128.......... Cook MR & MRS Stephen A
New York.......... 10128.......... Cooper MR John W W
New York.......... 10128.......... Crary MR & MRS Horace I JR
New York.......... 10128.......... Crawford MR & MRS J Hamilton 3D
New York.......... 10128.......... Crocker MRS Frank L
New York.......... 10128.......... Cunningham MR & MRS Courtland B
New York.......... 10128.......... Cushing MR & MRS R Hunter
New York.......... 10128.......... Cutler MR & MRS Stewart L
New York.......... 10128.......... de Ganay CT Arthur F
New York.......... 10128.......... de Ganay CT Lambert P
New York.......... 10128.......... de Ganay MRS Frances S
New York.......... 10128.......... de Liagre MRS Nicholas
New York.......... 10128.......... de Montebello MR & MRS Charles B L
New York.......... 10128.......... de Montebello MR & MRS Guy-Philippe Lannes
New York.......... 10128.......... de Peyrelongue MR & MRS Guy
New York.......... 10128.......... Dearie MRS Christopher F
New York.......... 10128.......... Delafield MR & MRS J Dennis
New York.......... 10128.......... Denny MR & MRS R Breck
New York.......... 10128.......... Dewey MR & MRS Thomas E L
New York.......... 10128.......... Dick MRS Hilary
New York.......... 10128.......... Dorson MR & MRS William S
New York.......... 10128.......... Drucker MR & MRS Richard A
New York.......... 10128.......... Ducommun MR & MRS Robert C
New York.......... 10128.......... Dunham MR & MRS (DR) Wolcott B JR
New York.......... 10128.......... Dycus MR Gary L
New York.......... 10128.......... Dye MR & MRS Alexander M
New York.......... 10128.......... Egerton-Warburton MR & MRS James W
New York.......... 10128.......... Eichorn MR & MRS Mark D
New York.......... 10128.......... Elliott MR & MRS James D
New York.......... 10128.......... Elmlinger MR & MRS Paul J
New York.......... 10128.......... Embry MR & MRS Talton R
New York.......... 10128.......... Emlen MRS Alan L
New York.......... 10128.......... Evans MR & MRS William J
New York.......... 10128.......... Fahs MRS (DR) Mary Ellen
New York.......... 10128.......... Fichera MR Joseph S
New York.......... 10128.......... Fisher MR & MRS Charles Avery
New York.......... 10128.......... Fisher MR & MRS Philip B JR
New York.......... 10128.......... Flanagan MRS Laura M
New York.......... 10128.......... Forster MRS Christopher A
New York.......... 10128.......... Fowler MISS Angela W
New York.......... 10128.......... Fowler MRS Cruger D G JR
New York.......... 10128.......... Frei MRS Amanda Schuster
New York.......... 10128.......... Frelinghuysen MR & MRS Peter
New York.......... 10128.......... Fremantle MR & MRS Hugh D
New York.......... 10128.......... Fulweiler MISS Pamela S
New York.......... 10128.......... Garrett MR & MRS Johnson
New York.......... 10128.......... Garrett MR Robert JR
New York.......... 10128.......... Garrett MRS Robert
New York.......... 10128.......... George MR Michael M
New York.......... 10128.......... Gerschel MR & MRS Patrick A
New York.......... 10128.......... Gilbane MR & MRS Michael P
New York.......... 10128.......... Giuffra MR & MRS Robert J JR
New York.......... 10128.......... Glazebrook MISS Catherine W
New York.......... 10128.......... Glover MRS Price P
New York.......... 10128.......... Gluck MR & MRS Marshall J
New York.......... 10128.......... Goldstein MR & MRS Bernard L
New York.......... 10128.......... Gonzalez MR & MRS Peter W JR
New York.......... 10128.......... Gooder MR & MRS Grenville MacD JR
New York.......... 10128.......... Gordan MR & MRS John D 3D
New York.......... 10128.......... Grannis MR & MRS Alexander B
New York.......... 10128.......... Green MRS Ashbel
New York.......... 10128.......... Gregory MR & MRS Peter S
New York.......... 10128.......... Griffin MR & MRS William J 4TH
New York.......... 10128.......... Griswold MR & MRS Roger P JR
New York.......... 10128.......... Grosjean MRS Diahne D
New York.......... 10128.......... Gunther MR Jack D JR
New York.......... 10128.......... Hadden MR & MRS Paul J
New York.......... 10128.......... Haggin MR & MRS J Ben Ali
New York.......... 10128.......... Haigney MR Dayton P III
New York.......... 10128.......... Hall MR & MRS Benjamin S
New York.......... 10128.......... Hallen MR & MRS John R
New York.......... 10128.......... Halpin MR & MRS Christopher P
New York.......... 10128.......... Hambrecht MR George A
& Fahnestock MRS Andrea H
New York.......... 10128.......... Hamilton MR Henry D
New York.......... 10128.......... Harman MISS Victoria C
New York.......... 10128.......... Harris MRS Victor S
New York.......... 10128.......... Harrison MR & MRS James B
New York.......... 10128.......... Hass MR & MRS Anthony C
New York.......... 10128.......... Hay MR & MRS Andrew W
New York.......... 10128.......... Heard MR John O
New York.......... 10128.......... Hebard MR & MRS George W III
New York.......... 10128.......... Herron MISS Liza G
New York.......... 10128.......... Hetherington MR & MRS Edwin S
New York.......... 10128.......... Highet MR & MRS Ian D
New York.......... 10128.......... Hoffman MR Nicholas M W
New York.......... 10128.......... Hoffmann MR & MRS John B
New York.......... 10128.......... Hogen MS Elizabeth Laurie
New York.......... 10128.......... Horner MR & MRS Martin
New York.......... 10128.......... Horowitz MR Jonathan R & Wolden DR Suzanne L
New York.......... 10128.......... Howard-Potter MR & MRS Jack R
New York.......... 10128.......... Hoyle MR & MRS Eric L
New York.......... 10128.......... Hunt MR & MRS Ernest E 4TH
New York.......... 10128.......... Hurley DR & MRS Kevin J
New York.......... 10128.......... Inglis DR & MRS Allan E JR
New York.......... 10128.......... Iselin MRS John Jay
New York.......... 10128.......... Isles MRS Alexandra M
New York.......... 10128.......... Ivanoff MR & MRS Ivan V
New York.......... 10128.......... Jackson MRS Katharine E
New York.......... 10128.......... Jacoby MS Elizabeth E
New York.......... 10128.......... Jenkins MR & MRS Robert N
New York.......... 10128.......... Johnson MR & MRS Stuart H 3D
New York.......... 10128.......... Johnston MR & MRS G Sim 3D
New York.......... 10128.......... Jones MR & MRS Peter D
New York.......... 10128.......... Kean MR Nicholas
New York.......... 10128.......... Kean MR Robert W III
New York.......... 10128.......... Kellogg MR & MRS James McN
New York.......... 10128.......... Kelly MR & MRS Caleb
New York.......... 10128.......... Kennedy MISS Lisa B
New York.......... 10128.......... Kennedy MR Alexander S
New York.......... 10128.......... Keough MR & MRS Clarke R
New York.......... 10128.......... Ketner MR & MRS D Scott
New York.......... 10128.......... Kikoski MR Andre B
New York.......... 10128.......... Killian MRS (DR) Marianne L
New York.......... 10128.......... King MR & MRS Bayard LeR 2D
New York.......... 10128.......... King MR & MRS C Lewis
New York.......... 10128.......... Klebnikov MR & MRS Michael
New York.......... 10128.......... Klein MR & MRS Donald R
New York.......... 10128.......... Klopp MR & MRS John R

New York, NY—New York, NY

New York........................ 10128......... Krimendahl MISS (DR) Elizabeth K
New York........................ 10128......... Lambert MR & MRS John C
New York........................ 10128......... Lambert MR & MRS Paul C
New York........................ 10128......... Lange MISS Robin C
New York........................ 10128......... Lanius MR P Baxter 3D
New York........................ 10128......... Laserson MRS Frances G
New York........................ 10128......... Lasry MR & MRS David P
New York........................ 10128......... LeConey MRS Ann S
New York........................ 10128......... Leness MR & MRS John G
New York........................ 10128......... Lewis MR Adam
New York........................ 10128......... Ley MR & MRS Peter D
New York........................ 10128......... LickDyke MRS Jay C
New York........................ 10128......... Liebolt MR & MRS Frederick Lee JR
New York........................ 10128......... Lilien MR & MRS Robert D
New York........................ 10128......... Lindblad MRS Elizabeth T
New York........................ 10128......... Littlefield MR & MRS Durwood E
New York........................ 10128......... Loomis MS Stephanie
New York........................ 10128......... Lord MR & MRS Edward C
New York........................ 10128......... Lorenz MISS Anne E
New York........................ 10128......... Lovelace MISS Caroline S
New York........................ 10128......... Mabon MRS Charles K
New York........................ 10128......... MacDonald MR & MRS Bryce E A
New York........................ 10128......... Macdonald MR & MRS Robert S
New York........................ 10128......... Mackay MRS Jacqueline deF
New York........................ 10128......... Mackenzie MR Charles R
New York........................ 10128......... Mahoney MR & MRS Thomas H IV
New York........................ 10128......... Mallory MR & MRS Clifford D
New York........................ 10128......... Manice MR & MRS Peter B
New York........................ 10128......... May MR & MRS A Cushman
New York........................ 10128......... McDaniel MS Sarah D
New York........................ 10128......... McKenna MRS Elizabeth W
New York........................ 10128......... McLanahan MR & MRS W Alexander
New York........................ 10128......... McPhillips MR & MRS Warren J III
New York........................ 10128......... Medina MRS Standish Forde JR
New York........................ 10128......... Menegon COL David J
New York........................ 10128......... Metcalf MR S Warren
New York........................ 10128......... Metcalf MS Pauline C
New York........................ 10128......... Metcalf MS Teresa D
New York........................ 10128......... Milbank MR & MRS Jeremiah 3D
New York........................ 10128......... Milbank MR & MRS Samuel L
New York........................ 10128......... Milburn MRS Frank H
New York........................ 10128......... Miller MR & MRS Garfield L III
New York........................ 10128......... Miller MR & MRS Robert P
New York........................ 10128......... Miller MR & MRS William J JR
New York........................ 10128......... Miller MRS K Gill
New York........................ 10128......... Mitchell MRS David L
New York........................ 10128......... Montgomery MRS Austin P JR
New York........................ 10128......... Moreland MR W Theodore
New York........................ 10128......... Morgan MRS G Frederick
New York........................ 10128......... Morris MR & MRS John M
New York........................ 10128......... Morris MR Brian E & Coudert MS Cynthia
New York........................ 10128......... Moss MR Peyton H JR
New York........................ 10128......... Mott MR & MRS (DR) Lawrence
New York........................ 10128......... Nagel MR & MRS Jon
New York........................ 10128......... Nicholls MR Samuel S 3D
New York........................ 10128......... Niles MRS William F
New York........................ 10128......... Nixon MISS Diane A
New York........................ 10128......... Noble MRS Joyce G
New York........................ 10128......... Nolen MR & MRS Wilson
New York........................ 10128......... Ogden MRS Susan Clark
New York........................ 10128......... Olive MR & MRS John C
New York........................ 10128......... Oliver MR & MRS Daniel JR
New York........................ 10128......... O'Malley MISS Anne B
New York........................ 10128......... O'Malley MR & MRS John A
New York........................ 10128......... O'Malley MR Hilaire
New York........................ 10128......... Oneglia MR & MRS Daniel S
New York........................ 10128......... Osborne MR & MRS Steven W
New York........................ 10128......... Palmer MR & MRS Philip
New York........................ 10128......... Palmer MR Lucius N & Lederer MS Sloane W
New York........................ 10128......... Palmer MRS F Morgan JR
New York........................ 10128......... Palsgrove MRS James L 3D
New York........................ 10128......... Patterson MR & MRS David S JR
New York........................ 10128......... Pearson MR Harold A
& Osterman MS Jeanne-Marie
New York........................ 10128......... Perkins MR & MRS Roswell B
New York........................ 10128......... Perreten MR & MRS Frederic C
New York........................ 10128......... Pettit MR Jeffrey
New York........................ 10128......... Phyfe MRS Henry Pinkney
New York........................ 10128......... Piper MS Kelly
New York........................ 10128......... Platt MR & MRS Charles A
New York........................ 10128......... Polk MR & MRS F Lyon 3D
New York........................ 10128......... Prout MRS Francis J
New York........................ 10128......... Quinlan MR & MRS Robert C
New York........................ 10128......... Rand MR & MRS William
New York........................ 10128......... Rand MR William M
New York........................ 10128......... Rault MR & MRS Joseph M
New York........................ 10128......... Reese MR & MRS Algernon B 3D
New York........................ 10128......... Reinicke MRS F Rogers
New York........................ 10128......... Riegel MR William M JR & Lyman MS Elizabeth A
New York........................ 10128......... Rittenour MRS Charles A
New York........................ 10128......... Robinson DR & MRS Thomas D
New York........................ 10128......... Rollinson MR & MRS Christopher C H
New York........................ 10128......... Root MR & MRS Gregory C
New York........................ 10128......... Root MRS Pamela P
New York........................ 10128......... Ross MS P Allen
New York........................ 10128......... Rowan MRS Joseph E
New York........................ 10128......... Rudick DR & MRS A Joseph JR
New York........................ 10128......... Rueckert MR & MRS Cleveland D
New York........................ 10128......... Russell MRS D Fenton
New York........................ 10128......... Rutherfurd MR & MRS Guy Christopher
New York........................ 10128......... Rutherfurd MR & MRS Guy G JR
New York........................ 10128......... Rutherfurd MR & MRS Winthrop JR
New York........................ 10128......... Saint-Amand DR Nathan E
New York........................ 10128......... Sanford MRS N MacCowatt
New York........................ 10128......... Saracco MR Anthony I & Price MS Emilie A
New York........................ 10128......... Saurel MISS Christine
New York........................ 10128......... Scarborough MR & MRS Robert H III
New York........................ 10128......... Schiavetta MR & MRS John L
New York........................ 10128......... Schmitt MR Roger M L V
New York........................ 10128......... Scott MR & MRS Christopher G
New York........................ 10128......... Selby MRS Linn Howard
New York........................ 10128......... Shafir MR & MRS Mark G
New York........................ 10128......... Sheehan MR & MRS Robert W
New York........................ 10128......... Sherman MS Wendy
New York........................ 10128......... Sinclair MR & MRS James P
New York........................ 10128......... Singer MR & MRS Oliver G L
New York........................ 10128......... Sipp MR & MRS John A
New York........................ 10128......... Sise MR & MRS John Sewell
New York........................ 10128......... Smilgin MR & MRS Caleb M H
New York........................ 10128......... Smith DR & MRS Barry H
New York........................ 10128......... Smith MR & MRS Blair Webster
New York........................ 10128......... Smith MR & MRS Carter McCook
New York........................ 10128......... Smith MRS Suzette de Marigny
New York........................ 10128......... Southworth MRS Hamilton JR
New York........................ 10128......... Sperry MR & MRS Paul S
New York........................ 10128......... Stanton MRS Gordon R
New York........................ 10128......... Steeger MRS Henry 4TH
New York........................ 10128......... Stewart MR & MRS Thomas A
New York........................ 10128......... Stimpson MR & MRS Phillip E
New York........................ 10128......... Sullivan MR & MRS John W JR
New York........................ 10128......... Sutton MR & MRS Edmund H
New York........................ 10128......... Swett MRS Bradford N

New York........................ 10128......... Taylor MISS Adina V M
New York........................ 10128......... Taylor MR & MRS Kenneth E
New York........................ 10128......... Terry MRS Kathryn Pender
New York........................ 10128......... Thomas MRS Gladys R
New York........................ 10128......... Thompson MR & MRS Philip A
New York........................ 10128......... Tracy MS Virginia S
New York........................ 10128......... Turner MR E Deane
New York........................ 10128......... Utterman MR & MRS Johan
New York........................ 10128......... Van Cott MR & MRS Charles S
New York........................ 10128......... Voehl MRS Patricia S
New York........................ 10128......... von Heisermann MR Julian H
New York........................ 10128......... Vura MR & MRS Gary R
New York........................ 10128......... Wainwright MR & MRS Jonathan M
New York........................ 10128......... Walker MR Bryce S
New York........................ 10128......... Walsh MR & MRS Nelson Salt
New York........................ 10128......... Wareham MR & MRS Raymond N
New York........................ 10128......... Weatherley-White MR & MRS Carl C
New York........................ 10128......... Webster MR & MRS Robert D
New York........................ 10128......... Weld MR & MRS William F
New York........................ 10128......... Welles MR & MRS Jeffrey F
New York........................ 10128......... Werner MR & MRS Charles P
New York........................ 10128......... Werwaiss MR & MRS John A
New York........................ 10128......... White MRS Paul D
New York........................ 10128......... Whiting MR & MRS Gordon J
New York........................ 10128......... Wight MR & MRS Christopher R
New York........................ 10128......... Wilbur MR & MRS Jeffrey F
New York........................ 10128......... Wilcox MR Gordon Cumnock
New York........................ 10128......... Wilson Fromson MS Carmel S
New York........................ 10128......... Winchester MR John G 2D
New York........................ 10128......... Winmill MR & MRS Thomas B
New York........................ 10128......... Winthrop MR & MRS Grant F
New York........................ 10128......... Wood MS Rowena A F & Gibson MR Gene H Sr
New York........................ 10128......... Woods MR & MRS Ward W JR
New York........................ 10128......... Wray MR & MRS T Cecil JR
New York........................ 10128......... Wu MR & MRS Douglas L
New York........................ 10128......... Wyckoff MR & MRS Jeffrey H
New York........................ 10128......... Yates MR L Randall
New York........................ 10128......... Youngman MR & MRS Robert P
New York........................ 10128......... Zacharias MISS Clelia Delafield
New York........................ 10128......... Zilkha MR & MRS Nathaniel M
New York........................ 10150......... Rusch MR Henry A 3D
New York........................ 10162......... Boyce MR & MRS Collis H G
New York........................ 10162......... Edmonds MR & MRS Robert S
New York........................ 10162......... Johnson MR & MRS David C
New York........................ 10163......... Tilney MS Mary A
New York........................ 10167......... Butler MISS Mary M
New York........................ 10185......... De La Poer MISS Marguerite A
New York........................ 10185......... Wham MISS Jane Coleman Cotten
New York........................ 10268......... Williams MR Andrew J
New York........................ 10280......... Bierbaum MR & MRS Richard L
New York........................ 10280......... Clothier MRS J Powers
New York........................ 10280......... Gehring MR Joseph E JR
New York........................ 10280......... Pecnik MR Michael
New York........................ 10280......... Williams MRS C Porter
New York........................ 10282......... Barton MR & MRS William J
New York........................ 10282......... Bramwell MR William M JR
New York........................ 10282......... Donald MRS Douglas D
New York........................ 10282......... Gray MRS John D
New York........................ 10282......... Iselin MR & MRS Charles Oliver
New York........................ 10282......... Scully MRS Erika C
Newburg........................ 12550......... Simmons MR & MRS Tifton JR
Newburgh........................ 12550......... Appleton MISS Wendy Wilcox
Newburgh........................ 12550......... Pontifell MR & MRS Luke Ives
Niscayuna........................ 12309......... Pennington MR & MRS James Sutton 3D
Niskayuna........................ 12309......... Conners MR & MRS Christopher P
North Babylon.............. 11704......... Gordon DR & MRS Thomas T
North Salem.................. 10560......... Bennett MR & MRS A Jeffrey Rives
North Salem.................. 10560......... Cecil MR & MRS Charles G
North Salem.................. 10560......... Eliott DR & MRS (DR) Matthew B
North Salem.................. 10560......... Garnett MR & MRS Bradford L
North Salem.................. 10560......... Grand MR & MRS Gordon 3D
North Salem.................. 10560......... Ivanhoe MR & MRS Brian J
Northport........................ 11768......... Ames DR John Worthington
& Street-Ames MS Lori
Northport........................ 11768......... Ferrell MISS Merri McI
Nyack.............................. 10960......... Kirchner MR & MRS Karl S F
Old Brookville............... 11545......... Dunlaevy MR & MRS Michael A
Old Brookville............... 11545......... Gage MR & MRS John Z JR
Old Brookville............... 11545......... Grant MR & MRS Thomas W JR
Old Brookville............... 11545......... Pell MR & MRS Peter J JR
Old Chatham................. 12136......... Briney MR & MRS Timothy P
Old Westbury................ 11568......... de Roulet MR & MRS Daniel C JR
Old Westbury................ 11568......... Phipps MR & MRS Howard III
Old Westbury................ 11568......... Rinaldini MR & MRS Luis E
Orangeburg.................. 10962......... Douglas MRS Henry B 2D
Orchard Park................. 14127......... Clark MR & MRS Frederick G II
Orchard Park................. 14127......... Cutler MRS Thomas P
Orchard Park................. 14127......... Kimber MR W Lawrence
Orchard Park................. 14127......... Sullivan MR & MRS Mortimer A JR
Ossining......................... 10562......... Cochran MRS George Van B
Ossining......................... 10562......... Cooper MR & MRS Thomas C JR
Ossining......................... 10562......... McLean MR & MRS Brendan M
Ossining......................... 10562......... Sheerin MR Charles M
Ossining......................... 10562......... Van Syckle MR & MRS Lloyd G II
Ossining......................... 10562......... West MRS George P
Oyster Bay...................... 11771......... Alexander MR Lee C
Oyster Bay...................... 11771......... Armstrong MR & MRS James F
Oyster Bay...................... 11771......... Baker MR George D
Oyster Bay...................... 11771......... Benjamin MR & MRS John J
Oyster Bay...................... 11771......... Berens MR & MRS Rodney B
Oyster Bay...................... 11771......... Bostwick MR & MRS Thomas S
Oyster Bay...................... 11771......... Chapman MR & MRS Gilbert W 3D
Oyster Bay...................... 11771......... Clark MR Henry C & Gerard MS Harriet C
Oyster Bay...................... 11771......... Cottafavi MR Francesco L
Oyster Bay...................... 11771......... Cutting MRS George W JR
Oyster Bay...................... 11771......... Davidson MRS Jean R
Oyster Bay...................... 11771......... Evans MR & MRS Samuel S
Oyster Bay...................... 11771......... Geddes MR & MRS E Maxwell JR
Oyster Bay...................... 11771......... Glenn MR & MRS J Wooderson 3D
Oyster Bay...................... 11771......... Grace MR & MRS Howard E
Oyster Bay...................... 11771......... Graham MR & MRS Jeremy M
Oyster Bay...................... 11771......... Heard MISS Susan E
Oyster Bay...................... 11771......... Howard MS Pamela
Oyster Bay...................... 11771......... Hulse MR & MRS R Alexander
Oyster Bay...................... 11771......... Korson MR & MRS B Andrew II
Oyster Bay...................... 11771......... Leib MRS John H
Oyster Bay...................... 11771......... McCurdy MR & MRS Ian A
Oyster Bay...................... 11771......... Meyer MR & MRS Willets Symington
Oyster Bay...................... 11771......... Meyer MR George S
Oyster Bay...................... 11771......... Miller MRS Lindley G
Oyster Bay...................... 11771......... Mitchell MS Tucker
Oyster Bay...................... 11771......... Mooney MR & MRS William G
Oyster Bay...................... 11771......... O'Brien MR & MRS Michael S
Oyster Bay...................... 11771......... Olt MR & MRS Frank J JR
Oyster Bay...................... 11771......... O'Neill MR George D
Oyster Bay...................... 11771......... Paumgarten MR & MRS Nicholas B
Oyster Bay...................... 11771......... Pulling MR & MRS Thomas L
Oyster Bay...................... 11771......... Roll MR & MRS Walter G
Oyster Bay...................... 11771......... Roosevelt MISS Elizabeth E
Oyster Bay...................... 11771......... Russell MISS Diana
Oyster Bay...................... 11771......... Sands MRS Patricia P
Oyster Bay...................... 11771......... Schmidlapp MR & MRS Allan

To nominate a candidate for the Social Register Association, please email: SRCommittee@thesocialregister.org

Oyster Bay, NY—Rye, NY

Oyster Bay........ 11771........ Sheeline MR & MRS William E
Oyster Bay........ 11771........ Shepard MRS Edward M
Oyster Bay........ 11771........ Sherrer MRS Roland C JR
Oyster Bay........ 11771........ Smith MR & MRS Baldwin III
Oyster Bay........ 11771........ Smith MR & MRS John Cram
Oyster Bay........ 11771........ Sutherland MR & MRS Howard R
Oyster Bay........ 11771........ Vaughn MR & MRS Eric T
Oyster Bay........ 11771........ Ward MR & MRS John G
Oyster Bay........ 11771........ Weekes MR & MRS Bradford G III
Oyster Bay........ 11771........ Weir MR & MRS Richard III
Oyster Bay........ 11771........ Williams MR & MRS John M
Palisades........ 10964........ Lalire MR & MRS Rex P
Palisades........ 10964........ Ludington MR & MRS Nicholas S
Palisades........ 10964........ Shrady MRS Henry M 3D
Patchogue........ 11772........ Farr MR James W
Pawling........ 12564........ Chappell MRS William B JR
Pawling........ 12564........ Lester DR & MRS Robin D
Pawling........ 12564........ Smith MR & MRS Archibald A 3D
Peekskill........ 10566........ Clark MR & MRS Christopher R
Pelham........ 10803........ Bos MR & MRS Gerard P
Pelham........ 10803........ Lapey MR & MRS John D
Pelham........ 10803........ Murray MS Melissa
Pelham........ 10803........ Perreten MR & MRS George H
Pelham........ 10803........ Pierce MR & MRS Phillip J
Pelham........ 10803........ Russello MR & MRS Gerald J
Pelham........ 10803........ Tifft MR & MRS William N
Pelham........ 10803........ Withers MR & MRS (DR) H Averell L
Pelham Manor........ 10803........ Emery MR & MRS Andrew C
Pelham Manor........ 10803........ Henningsen MRS Victor W JR
Pelham Manor........ 10803........ Kiernan MR & MRS John S
Pelham Manor........ 10803........ Leckie MR & MRS Gavin F
Pelham Manor........ 10803........ Middleton MR & MRS Thomas S
Penn Yan........ 14527........ Borges MR Bruce S
Penn Yan........ 14527........ Hill MR & MRS Stephen L
Penn Yan........ 14527........ Jensen MR & MRS Peter G
Penn Yan........ 14527........ Jensen MR & MRS Reid B
Penn Yan........ 14527........ Jensen MRS Robert O
Pine Plains........ 12567........ Banning MR & MRS John P JR
Pine Plains........ 12567........ Collins MISS Emily V
Pine Plains........ 12567........ Greenwood MS Edith R
Pine Plains........ 12567........ King MRS Diana N
Pine Plains........ 12567........ Luke MR & MRS Douglas S
Pittsford........ 14534........ Banks MR & MRS John S
Pittsford........ 14534........ Connard MR & MRS Brayton McK
Pittsford........ 14534........ Gibbons MR & MRS David W
Pittsford........ 14534........ Pierson MR & MRS Mitchell 3D
Pittsford........ 14534........ Pierson MR & MRS Mitchell JR
Plandome........ 11030........ Bertrand MR & MRS John T JR
Plandome........ 11030........ Sears MR & MRS Richard M
Plattsburgh........ 12901........ Krueger MR John W
Pleasant Valley........ 12569........ Slagsvol MR & MRS Steven E
Pleasantville........ 10570........ Maldonado MS Sarah T
Pleasantville........ 10570........ Pinkerton MR & MRS Peyton R H
Pleasantville........ 10570........ Seymour MR Peter A
Pleasantville........ 10570........ Sperling MISS Ridley W
Port Chester........ 10573........ McKinlay MRS Ann H
Port Chester........ 10573........ Randell MR & MRS David M JR
Port Chester........ 10573........ Swank MR & MRS Andrew W
Port Jefferson Stations... 11776........ Fish MS Elizabeth L
Port Washington........ 11050........ Barry MRS Caroline P
Port Washington........ 11050........ Du Bois MISS Caroline S
Port Washington........ 11050........ Fiveson MR & MRS Keith W
Port Washington........ 11050........ Grayson MISS Maud M P
Port Washington........ 11050........ McMahon MR & MRS Frederic G
Poughkeepsie........ 12601........ Stillman MR & MRS Peter G
Poughkeepsie........ 12603........ Phyfe MR & MRS Duncan A
Poughquag........ 12570........ Edmonston MR & MRS Charles E
Pound Ridge........ 10576........ Baker MR & MRS Carson T
Pound Ridge........ 10576........ Biddle MS Christine M
Pound Ridge........ 10576........ Clark MS Elisabeth Van C & Tofte MS Laila
Pound Ridge........ 10576........ Gerber MR & MRS Scott L
Pound Ridge........ 10576........ Laird MR & MRS Walter J 3D
Pound Ridge........ 10576........ Litchfield MRS Philip A
Pound Ridge........ 10576........ Lovell MR & MRS A Buffum
Pound Ridge........ 10576........ Parker MR & MRS Foxhall A
Pound Ridge........ 10576........ Taylor MR & MRS Aaron W
Pound Ridge........ 10576........ Ulmann MR & MRS Alexander E JR
Pound Ridge........ 10576........ Woodhull MR & MRS Timothy C
Purchase........ 10577........ Cameron MR & MRS Douglas W
Purchase........ 10577........ Loeb MR & MRS John L JR
Purchase........ 10577........ Reich MR & MRS Christopher V
Putnam Valley........ 10579........ Brigham MR William A
Queensbury........ 12804........ Russell MRS A David
Quogue........ 11959........ Botsford MR & MRS Andrew M
Quogue........ 11959........ Bradley MR & MRS E Michael
Quogue........ 11959........ de Ropp MRS Harald S
Quogue........ 11959........ Demirjian MRS M John
Quogue........ 11959........ Gardner CDR (RET) Richmond
Quogue........ 11959........ Marckwald MRS A Hunt
Quogue........ 11959........ Murray MR & MRS Robert A
Quogue........ 11959........ Wyman MRS Joseph C
Red Hook........ 12571........ Baxter MR Daniel H
Red Hook........ 12571........ Hertz MISS Suzanne E
Rhinebeck........ 12572........ Chanler MRS Bronson W
Rhinebeck........ 12572........ Fowler MR & MRS (DR) Morgan C JR
Rhinebeck........ 12572........ Funkhouser MR & MRS Christopher T
Rhinebeck........ 12572........ Graham MR Gerrit
Rhinebeck........ 12572........ Hill MR & MRS Jefferson B
Rhinebeck........ 12572........ Preston MR & MRS Seymour JR
Rhinebeck........ 12572........ Scott MS Carolyn A
Rhinebeck........ 12572........ Slaby MR & MRS Michael J
Rhinebeck........ 12572........ Thoron MRS J Lloyd
Ridgewood........ 11385........ Brinkley MR Minor Dunbar
Riverdale........ 10471........ Olinger MR & MRS Chauncey G JR
Rochester........ 14610........ McHugh MS Ernestine L
Rochester........ 14618........ Rupp MISS Susan S
Rochester........ 14618........ Spencer MRS H Allen
Rochester........ 14618........ Wisner MR & MRS Todd J W
Rochester........ 14620........ Peltz MR & MRS John S
Rochester........ 14623........ DeYager MR & MRS David R
Rockville Centre........ 11570........ Cobian MRS Rafael R
Rockville Centre........ 11570........ de Jong MR & MRS James M JR
Roosevelt Island........ 10044........ Mackay MISS Melinda L
Roslyn Harbor........ 11576........ McLaughlin MR Timothy R
Roslyn Harbor........ 11576........ McLaughlin MRS Linda Holmes
Rye........ 10507........ Howson MR & MRS Judson T
Rye........ 10580........ Black MISS Elizabeth D
Rye........ 10580........ Boester MR & MRS Gregory J
Rye........ 10580........ Brokaw MR & MRS Carter S
Rye........ 10580........ Cecil MRS Russell C
Rye........ 10580........ Clark MR & MRS Christopher T
Rye........ 10580........ Collins MRS Albert E JR
Rye........ 10580........ Connor MR & MRS Michael B
Rye........ 10580........ Curran MR William E
& Rose MS (REV) Margaret R
Rye........ 10580........ Dannheim MR & MRS William J
Rye........ 10580........ Davidson MR & MRS Marvin H
Rye........ 10580........ de Menocal MR & MRS Daniel C
Rye........ 10580........ Dinger MR & MRS Michael S
Rye........ 10580........ Everett MR & MRS Nicholas S
Rye........ 10580........ Featherston MR & MRS William A JR
Rye........ 10580........ Finley MR John M

Rye, NY—Southampton, NY

Rye	10580	Fraser MRS Richard A R
Rye	10580	Gambee MR & MRS Robert R
Rye	10580	Gerrish MR & MRS Campbell T
Rye	10580	Gray MR John L 3D
Rye	10580	Haneman MRS William F JR
Rye	10580	Hargraves MR & MRS Gordon S JR
Rye	10580	Harris MR & MRS David W JR
Rye	10580	Hester MR & MRS James McN
Rye	10580	Hicks MR & MRS Paul De F JR
Rye	10580	Kahle MR & MRS Jeffrey L
Rye	10580	Kennedy MR & MRS Philip L
Rye	10580	Kourides MR & MRS P Nicholas
Rye	10580	Leonard MR & MRS John D
Rye	10580	Lorono MR & MRS Joseph F
Rye	10580	Mayosmith MR Worthington
Rye	10580	McGrory MR & MRS Glenn P
Rye	10580	McLaughlin MS Mary Jane
Rye	10580	Montgomery MR & MRS John Anthony JR
Rye	10580	Murphy MR Joseph F 3D & Ward MS Hilary H
Rye	10580	Nields MRS Benjamin III
Rye	10580	Parsons MR David McI
Rye	10580	Patricola MRS Lucy B
Rye	10580	Pearson MR & MRS Nathan W JR
Rye	10580	Raynor MR & MRS (REV) Andrew B
Rye	10580	Redican MR & MRS Richard J JR
Rye	10580	Reid MR & MRS Buford Scott
Rye	10580	Sands MR & MRS Geoffrey K
Rye	10580	Skodnick MR & MRS Leif
Rye	10580	Smith MR & MRS (DR) H Oliver IV
Rye	10580	Smith MR & MRS Henry O III
Rye	10580	Smith MR & MRS Nicholas F
Rye	10580	Snyder MRS Mary Kniffin
Rye	10580	Spaeth MR & MRS Otto L JR
Rye	10580	Squires MR Gary W
Rye	10580	Steers MR & MRS William M
Rye	10580	Steers MR Charles R C III
Rye	10580	Steers MRS Charles R C JR
Rye	10580	Steers MRS Diana W
Rye	10580	Steers MRS Judith
Rye	10580	Sullivan MR & MRS Benjamin J JR
Rye	10580	Sutro MR & MRS Porter H
Rye	10580	Sweeny MISS Heather G
Rye	10580	Sweeny MR & MRS Bradley P
Rye	10580	Teillon MR & MRS Geoffrey P
Rye	10580	Vietor MR & MRS Alexander W
Rye	10580	Walker MR & MRS Andrew R M
Rye	10580	Waters MRS Somerset R
Sag Harbor	11963	Evarts MISS Kate L
Sag Harbor	11963	Fenwick MR & MRS Bayard S
Sag Harbor	11963	Grosjean MS Maria Emlen
Sag Harbor	11963	McAuliffe MRS Dorothy Buck
Sag Harbor	11963	Reed MS Susan K
Sag Harbor	11963	Sudler MISS Elizabeth E
Sag Harbor	11963	Watson MS Olive F
Sagaponack	11962	Johnson MR Michael T
Sagaponack	11962	Perlberg MR Edward B
Sagaponack	11962	Polhemus MRS Henry Martin JR
Sagaponack	11962	Taylor MRS Sandra B
Saint James	11780	Coxe MR & MRS Richard B JR
Salem	12865	Satterthwaite MR Sheafe
Salt Point	12578	Atkins MR & MRS Ronald R
Salt Point	12578	Field MR & MRS Marshall 6TH
Salt Point	12578	Pierce MR & MRS Charles E JR
Salt Point	12578	Seaman MR & MRS Bryant W III
Sands Point	11050	Silbersack MR & MRS John W
Saranac Lake	12983	Dame MRS Alexandra J
Saranac Lake	12983	Little MISS Melinda L
Saratoga Springs	12866	Aldrich MR & MRS Alexander
Saratoga Springs	12866	de Wolf MR & MRS Buckmaster
Saratoga Springs	12866	Holmes MR & MRS Timothy A
Saratoga Springs	12866	Moore MR Michael
Saratoga Springs	12866	Stephens MISS Alexandra H
Saratoga Springs	12866	Tower MRS Whitney
Saugerties	12477	Slagsvol MR & MRS Adam T
Scarsdale	10583	Aulisi MR & MRS Andrew C
Scarsdale	10583	Brinckerhoff MRS D Beard
Scarsdale	10583	Daire MRS Sidney Witter
Scarsdale	10583	Gilpin MR & MRS Edward U
Scarsdale	10583	Johnson REV CANON & MRS William Alexander
Scarsdale	10583	Poole MR David D P
Scottsville	14546	Johnson MRS Helen H
Sea Cliff	11579	Pool MR & MRS F W Bouker III
Setauket	11733	Strong MRS Raymond B JR
Shelter Island	11964	Gerard MRS Kathleen R
Shelter Island Heights	11965	Coulson MR & MRS Christopher
Shelter Island Heights	11965	Fischer MR & MRS F Wood
Shelter Island Heights	11965	Tiernan MR & MRS Charles W JR
Skaneateles	13152	Haberstock MRS R Alan
Skaneateles	13152	Haux MR George E
Sleepy Hollow	10591	Pearson MR & MRS Joshua L
Sleepy Hollow	10591	Smythe MR & MRS J L Nevill 3D
Sleepy Hollow	10591	Wood MR & MRS James
Smithtown	11787	Buchet MR & MRS Robert F
Snyder	14226	Muenter MRS Knud B
Somers	10589	Davidson MISS Mary B
Somers	10589	McKone MRS Pope
Somers	10589	O'Boyle MRS Edwards C
South Salem	10590	Biddle MR & MRS Willing L
South Salem	10590	Clark MRS Leah H
South Salem	10590	Cobera MR Luis M & Reisinger Cobera MS Hope B
South Salem	10590	Faraci MR & MRS Giuseppe
South Salem	10590	Foley MRS Gifford T
South Salem	10590	Tiné MR & MRS Harold L
South Salem	10590	Truitt MISS Alexandra
South Setauket	11720	Chubb MR & MRS Charles F JR
South Worcester	12197	Kernan MR Henry S
Southampton	11968	Anton DR John R
Southampton	11968	Bruder MR William B & Shelton-Bruder MRS Frances
Southampton	11968	Bunn MR & MRS George R JR
Southampton	11968	Fagan MR & MRS Paul I III
Southampton	11968	Ferrer MR & MRS James C
Southampton	11968	Fletcher MRS Andrew JR
Southampton	11968	Freeman MRS Elaine Lavalle
Southampton	11968	Haux MISS Heather V
Southampton	11968	Hearst MS Deborah
Southampton	11968	Hentic MRS Yves F M
Southampton	11968	Hoge MR James Hamilton
Southampton	11968	Horn MR & MRS L Stoddard
Southampton	11968	Ingolia MR & MRS Lawrence G
Southampton	11968	Lloyd MRS Grace McG
Southampton	11968	Louthan MR & MRS Thomas C
Southampton	11968	Mathieu MRS Charles L JR
Southampton	11968	McCormack MS Julia J
Southampton	11968	Meehan MR Michael J 2D
Southampton	11968	Meem MR & MRS Gilbert S JR
Southampton	11968	Morrisey MISS Florence Earle
Southampton	11968	Munn MRS Orson D
Southampton	11968	Rice MRS Francis B
Southampton	11968	Schaefer MRS Herman A
Southampton	11968	Schuster MR & MRS Charles B
Southampton	11968	Taft MR Robert W

Southampton, NY—Asheville, NC

Southampton	11969	Benjamin MR Theodore C
Southampton	11969	Brokaw MRS Clifford V 3D
Southampton	11969	Campbell MRS Samuel R
Southampton	11969	Clair MR & MRS Richard L
Southampton	11969	Crocker MRS John Howe
Southampton	11969	Haux MS Suzanne E
Southampton	11969	Havemeyer MR Frederick C III
Southampton	11969	Leonard MR & MRS Craigh
Southampton	11969	McFarland MR & MRS Alan R
Southampton	11969	Mortimer MR Richard
Southampton	11969	Nadal DR Evan C
Southampton	11969	Nadal MR David W
Southampton	11969	Rush MRS Robert
Southampton	11969	Semerjian MR George G
Southampton	11969	Witker MR & MRS James B
Southold	11971	Cox MRS Edward V JR
Southold	11971	Strong MR Raymond B III
Sparkill	10976	Scharf MR & MRS David L
Springfield Center	13468	Clarke MR Arthur R H
Springfield Gardens	11413	Kelly MRS Wilhelmena Rhodes
St James	11780	Coleman MR Leighton H III
St James	11780	Edwards MRS Oliver
St James	11780	Lawrence MISS Allison Paige
St James	11780	Lawrence MR & MRS A Brewster 3D
St James	11780	Miller MR Charles Duncan 3D
St James	11780	Miller MS Guenn S
St James	11780	Mosle MR Edward B
St James	11780	Van Liew MR Jeffere F
St James	11780	Van Praagh DR Ian
St James	11780	White MR Daniel W
St James	11780	White MRS F L Peter
Stanfordville	12581	Blodgett MRS Helen
Stanfordville	12581	Collins MRS Marie-Laure N
Stanfordville	12581	Richards MR & MRS William B
Staten Island	10301	Bramwell MR & MRS George Y
Staten Island	10301	Ellis MR & MRS William H 3D
Staten Island	10310	Buatta MR Mario
Stone Ridge	12484	Walden MRS Charles C 3D
Stony Brook	11790	Poole MR & MRS Hubert E
Stony Brook	11790	Scalogna MR & MRS Salvatore R
Suffern	10901	Gould MRS William S 3D
Syosset	11791	Browne MR & MRS F Sedgwick
Syosset	11791	de Roulet MR & MRS Daniel C
Syosset	11791	Eckelberry MRS John E
Syosset	11791	Howard MR & MRS George H 4TH
Syosset	11791	Ingraham MR & MRS Michael G
Syosset	11791	Kaye MR & MRS Woodward L
Syosset	11791	Lindsay MRS George N
Syosset	11791	Low MR Seth JR
Syosset	11791	Roche MRS Thomas K
Syosset	11791	Rupp MR & MRS Christopher F
Syosset	11791	Schiff MR & MRS Peter G
Syosset	11791	Senior MR & MRS Enrique F
Syosset	11791	Stiger MR & MRS Anthony D
Syosset	11791	Tiernan MR & MRS Bartholomew T III
Syosset	11791	Travis MISS Helen W
Syosset	11791	Weeks MRS Annabel C
Syosset	11791	Whitman MRS Johnston de F
Syracuse	13215	Groat MR & MRS Christopher A
Tarrytown	10591	du Pont MR & MRS Pierre S 5TH
Tarrytown	10591	Sands MR & MRS Benjamin F
Tarrytown	10591	Thomas DR & MRS Henry M III
Ticonderoga	12883	Pell-deChame MR Robert R
Tivoli	12583	Davis MISS F Dennie
Tivoli	12583	Lankenau MRS John C
Troy	12180	Hunn MR & MRS David T
Troy	12181	Gale MISS Jane
Tuxedo Park	10987	Colwell MR Bryan York
Tuxedo Park	10987	Draper MISS Elizabeth P
Tuxedo Park	10987	du Pont MR & MRS David B
Tuxedo Park	10987	Mattes MR Edward C JR
Tuxedo Park	10987	Neuhauser MR & MRS Charles
Tuxedo Park	10987	Rodzianko MR & MRS Paul
Tuxedo Park	10987	Sonne MR & MRS Christian R
Tuxedo Park	10987	Watson MR John J
Unadilla	13849	McDonald MRS Mary M
Upper Brookville	11545	Myles MR & MRS George F
Upper Brookville	11732	Bancroft MR & MRS Thomas M JR
Valatie	12184	Clemence MR & MRS James B
Valatie	12184	De MS (DR) Elise J B
Valley Cottage	10989	Pejoves MR & MRS George A
Valley Stream	11581	Bird DR & MRS Thomas E
Vermontville	12989	Bodine MS Marian Taylor
Vestal	13850	Laserson MR Stephen A
Waccabuc	10597	Hallberg MR Garth R
Waccabuc	10597	Hardy MR & MRS David R
Waccabuc	10597	Henshaw MR & MRS Richard T IV
Waccabuc	10597	Howard MR & MRS Christopher S
Waccabuc	10597	Reid MRS Ogden R
Waccabuc	10597	Reimer MRS J Squier
Wainscott	11975	Holmes MR & MRS Hilary H
Wainscott	11975	Meyer MRS Henry von L JR
Wantagh	11793	Buck MR Harold P JR
Warwick	10990	Ford MR & MRS Christopher Peale
Warwick	10990	LeBrecht MRS Robert
Warwick	10990	McLean MRS Robert 3D
Warwick	10990	Schieffelin MR & MRS Cooper L
Warwick	10990	Winslow MR & MRS Christopher W
Washington Mills	13479	Schafer MR Thomas G
Water Mill	11976	Bogert MR & MRS H Lawrence 3D
Water Mill	11976	Hunnewell MS Sarah F
Water Mill	11976	Lovejoy MRS Sherrylyn P
Water Mill	11976	Mahoney MISS Barbara A
Water Mill	11976	Masters MR & MRS William H III
Watertown	13601	Wells MR & MRS Christopher B
Wesley Hills	10952	Lippincott MR John L
West Kill	12492	Castleton MRS Edward L JR
West Kill	12492	Christ MR Donald C
West Seneca	14224	Larkin MISS Mary
Westbury	11590	Phipps MR & MRS Howard JR
Westhampton	11977	Whitney MR Robert B
Westport	12993	Stephens MRS Simone S
White Plains	10601	Sanford MR William J
White Plains	10603	Marshall MR & MRS Robert Bamber JR
White Plains	10604	Scully MR & MRS Kevin M
White Plains	10605	King MRS David R
Williamsville	14221	Knox MRS Seymour H III
Williamsville	14221	Montgomery MRS Philip S
Williamsville	14221	Wende MR Albert B
Willsboro	12996	Clarke MR & MRS Thurston B
Woodhaven	11421	Lipscomb MR Thomas H III
Woodmere	11598	Dinan MRS Camilla C
Woodstock	12498	Caren MR Eric C
Woodstock	12498	Schauffler MISS Nancy A

NORTH CAROLINA

Apex	27502	Macdonell MR & MRS James T
Arden	28704	Ford MR & MRS James A
Asheville	28801	Howell DR & MRS Lucius A
Asheville	28801	Rivière MR Scott D & Sauer MR Robert O J
Asheville	28801	Stehli MRS Annabel S

Asheville, NC—Fayetteville, NC

Asheville	28803	Bolton MR & MRS Thomas C
Asheville	28803	Capers MR & MRS Rushton T
Asheville	28803	Clark MRS Margaret R
Asheville	28803	Flynn MR & MRS Michael L
Asheville	28803	Heuermann MR William W
Asheville	28803	Huger MR Daniel E
Asheville	28803	Peckham MISS Mary S
Asheville	28803	Vermilye MRS H Rowland 3D
Asheville	28804	Kampmann MR John P
Asheville	28804	Nicoll MISS Margaret
Bahama	27503	Gaither MR & MRS John S
Bahama	27503	Kirkland MR & MRS F Russell JR
Biltmore Forest	28803	Morosani MISS Katherine C
Biltmore Forest	28803	Watson DR & MRS (DR) Donald C JR
Boone	28607	Lewis MISS Molly MacKinnon
Candler	28715	Huger MISS Barbara B
Carrboro	27510	Carpenter MR & MRS Darryl W
Carrboro	27510	Lewis MR Charles W
Cary	27511	Darlington MRS Henry 3D
Cary	27511	Payson MR Eliot K
Cary	27513	Busbice MR & MRS John B
Cary	27513	Perkins MR & MRS L Parker III
Cary	27513	Sellery REV CANON & MRS David F
Cary	27539	O'Connor MR Anthony M JR
Cashiers	28717	Halsey MR & MRS Charles D
Cashiers	28717	Moore MRS John Clark JR
Cedar Point	28584	Fahy MAJ Nathaniel G
Chapel Hill	27514	Allen MR Gordon M JR & Feldman MS (DR) Maryann P
Chapel Hill	27514	Buck MR & MRS Leonard J
Chapel Hill	27514	Collins MR & MRS Bayard Dickens
Chapel Hill	27514	Haynes MR & MRS Harrison E
Chapel Hill	27514	King MR & MRS Kimball
Chapel Hill	27514	Rogers MRS Theodore B 3D
Chapel Hill	27514	Treat MR & MRS Logan P
Chapel Hill	27516	Creissen MR & MRS Alain J
Chapel Hill	27516	Fischer MR P L Charles JR
Chapel Hill	27516	Medearis MRS Donald N JR
Chapel Hill	27516	Paine MS Alix E
Chapel Hill	27516	Reid MRS Bryan S JR
Chapel Hill	27516	Resnik MR & MRS Michael D
Chapel Hill	27516	Wright MRS Barbara Brush
Chapel Hill	27517	Green MR & MRS (DR) Geoffrey F
Chapel Hill	27517	Hill DR & MRS John B
Chapel Hill	27517	Miller MRS Garfield L
Chapel Hill	27517	Tilson DR & MRS Hugh H
Chapel Hill	29716	Wade MR & MRS Edward T
Charlotte	28203	Barlow MR & MRS Malcolm L
Charlotte	28204	Clarke MR & MRS Dumont IV
Charlotte	28205	Townsend MR & MRS David D
Charlotte	28205	Townsend MR & MRS Edward L
Charlotte	28207	Allison MR & MRS Charles S
Charlotte	28207	Cálves MR & MRS Herbert E JR
Charlotte	28207	Clark MR & MRS Christopher R
Charlotte	28207	Elliott MR & MRS Thomas R
Charlotte	28207	Falls MR & MRS Henry L III
Charlotte	28207	Gambrell MRS Charles G
Charlotte	28207	Heyer DR & MRS Robert A
Charlotte	28207	Hinshaw MR & MRS Michael W JR
Charlotte	28207	Knight MR & MRS Steven D
Charlotte	28207	Laporte MR & MRS William F 3D
Charlotte	28207	Leaycraft MR & MRS Timothy W
Charlotte	28207	Lingerfelt MR & MRS Christopher L
Charlotte	28207	Shaw MR & MRS Harry A IV
Charlotte	28207	Smith DR & MRS Henry L II
Charlotte	28207	Willis MR & MRS Christopher H
Charlotte	28208	Lamson MR Clifford D
Charlotte	28209	Oliver MR & MRS Peter A
Charlotte	28209	Rose MR & MRS Whitaker B
Charlotte	28209	Tuttle MR & MRS Howard McD
Charlotte	28209	von Werssowetz MR & MRS Odon F W
Charlotte	28209	Zbinden DR & MRS Louis H III
Charlotte	28210	Cowan MR & MRS William S JR
Charlotte	28210	Gentry MR & MRS Frank L
Charlotte	28210	McGregor MR & MRS William E JR
Charlotte	28210	Prentice MRS Ezra P
Charlotte	28211	Belk MR & MRS Irwin
Charlotte	28211	Bos MRS Harriet
Charlotte	28211	Gilbert MR & MRS J Grant
Charlotte	28211	Holzman MR & MRS R Langdon
Charlotte	28211	O'Leary MR & MRS Brian McA
Charlotte	28211	Phillips MR & MRS John M
Charlotte	28216	McMullan MR & MRS Heath P
Charlotte	28226	Geoghegan MRS M Gilbert
Charlotte	28226	Kent MR & MRS A Atwater 3D
Charlotte	28226	Movius MR & MRS Lee W
Charlotte	28226	Petty MR & MRS Alec W B
Charlotte	28226	Stewart MR & MRS Todd F
Charlotte	28226	Warrick MR & MRS William H III
Charlotte	28226	White DR & MRS Richard L JR
Charlotte	28277	Cronin MR & MRS David R
Charlotte	28277	Dorsel MRS A Clifford
Charlotte	28277	Leber MR & MRS Edward C JR
Charlotte	28277	McCloy MR & MRS John J III
Charlotte	28277	Miller MR & MRS T Wilson C
Charlotte	28277	Stewart MRS Floyd M
Charlotte	28278	Burrows MRS William M
Charlotte	28278	Trowbridge DR & MRS Thomston S
Clayton	27520	Howland MR & MRS Jonathan E
Clemmons	27012	Sortwell MR Daniel R 3D
Columbus	28722	Ely MR & REV CANON DR Duncan Cairnes
Columbus	28722	Pack MR & MRS Lewis Gerald
Columbus	28722	Pomeroy MR William A C
Concord	28025	Lewallen DR & MRS John D
Cornelius	28031	Felix MR & MRS Robert
Cornelius	28031	Henderlite MR & MRS Robert L
Cornelius	28031	Scherbatow PRCSS Alexis
Cornelius	28031	Scott MR Harold W JR
Durham	27701	Hagan MR & MRS John W
Durham	27701	Rand MRS Renée Allen
Durham	27703	Greer MRS Nan E
Durham	27705	Cox MR & MRS Robert E
Durham	27705	Locke MRS (DR) Elizabeth H Hughes
Durham	27705	Rogers DR & MRS (DR) David Price
Durham	27705	Scovil MRS Janet MacL
Durham	27705	Weld DR & MRS William C
Durham	27705	Williams MR & MRS John W
Durham	27706	Sanford MRS Terry
Durham	27707	Fish MR & MRS Jonathan H
Durham	27707	Hanson MR & MRS J Stillman
Durham	27707	Huber MR & MRS Joel C 3D
Durham	27707	James DR & MRS M Lucas
Durham	27707	Rand MR & MRS Richard N III
Durham	27707	Townsend MR & MRS David D JR
Durham	27712	Forbes MRS John Douglas
Durham	27712	Odom LTC (RET) & MRS Charles R
Durham	27713	Tucceri MISS Clive E
Elizabeth City	27909	Caldwell MR William C III
Elkin	28521	Stevenson MR & MRS William H 3D
Enka	28728	Scull MR Nicholas
Fayetteville	28303	Fox MR & MRS Richard L 2D
Fayetteville	28303	Jenkins DR & MRS Joseph McK

Fayetteville, NC—Wilmington, NC

Fayetteville 28303 Vieta DR & MRS Paul A
Fayetteville 28305 Lancaster MR & MRS Kenneth C JR
Fayetteville 28305 McLean MR & MRS James W JR
Fayetteville 28305 Slater MRS John E
Garner 27529 Robinson DR & MRS (DR) Gregory P
Grantsboro 28529 Taylor DR Jeffrey S
Greensboro 27408 Cushman MR & MRS Blinn L
Greensboro 27408 Hartley MR & MRS Garrett A
Greensboro 27408 Klug MR & MRS Darrell T
Greensboro 27408 Preyer MR & MRS Britt A JR
Greensboro 27408 Preyer MR & MRS Britt Armfield
Greensboro 27408 Worth MR & MRS David McAlister
Greensboro 27410 Doughten MS Barbara P
Greensboro 27410 Shelmerdine MISS Susan C
Greensboro 27410 Taft MR & MRS Arthur T
Greensboro 27455 Averitt MR & MRS James I
Greenville 27858 Sparrow MRS Wendall Keats
Henderson 27536 Godfrey MR & MRS Robert H
Hendersonville 28739 Turner MR & MRS J V Peter
Hendersonville 28791 Flowers MR & MRS John Baxton 3D
Hendersonville 28791 Taylor MRS H Furness 3D
Hendersonville 28792 Howe MR Arthur K
Hickory 28601 Blake MR & MRS Robert H III
Hickory 28601 Mills MR & MRS John T
Hickory 28601 Mills MR & MRS John W
Hickory 28602 Regan MR Anthony W
Hillsborough 27278 Franz MRS Whitney R
Hillsborough 27278 Griffin MR & MRS Rex H
Holly Springs 27540 Dean MR Charles W
Huntersville 28078 Zimmermann MR & MRS T C Price
Kernersville 27284 Nelson MR Christopher J & Wheelwright MS Alice
Kill Devil Hills 27948 Woolard MR & MRS John H
Lake Lure 28746 Miller MRS Walter P 3D
Laurinburg 28352 Beales MR James A G 3D
Lewiston-Woodville 27849 Urquhart MR & MRS Burges IV
Lewisville 27023 Dunn MR Noel L
Lewisville 27023 Hall MR & MRS Mark Allen
Matthews 28104 Rundlett MR & MRS Raymond C 2D
Matthews 28105 Carpenter MRS Anne R
Mebane 27302 Bond MR & MRS Calhoun JR
Mooresville 28117 Oldham MR & MRS Terry S
Mooresville 28117 Robinson MRS Charles C
Morehead City 28557 Ballantine MR & MRS William P
Morganton 28655 Collett MR & MRS (DR) J Rountree JR
Morrisville 27560 Oldham DR & MRS Christopher J
Morrisville 27560 Vauclain MRS William E
New Bern 28561 Grainger MISS Jean C
New Bern 28562 Moeller MR Peter S
New Bern 28562 Pogue MR & MRS Shelton L
Pfafftown 27040 Glen DR & MRS Dulaney
Pfafftown 27040 Rutter MRS John A
Pilot Mountain 27041 Kirk MR Robert L JR
Pinehurst 28370 Hall MRS Eloise Joy S
Pinehurst 28370 McKean MR John W
Pinehurst 28370 Meyer MR & MRS Charles G
Pinehurst 28370 Rumery MR & MRS John R
Pinehurst 28374 Borthwick MR & MRS Thomas C
Pinehurst 28374 Hopper MR & MRS Arthur F III
Pinehurst 28374 McLendon MRS Charles A
Pinehurst 28374 Mosbrook MR & MRS Robert C
Pinehurst 28374 Sewell DR & MRS Mark F
Pinehurst 28374 Smith MR Bradley W SR
Pinehurst 28374 Squires MR & MRS Kendall B M
Pinehurst 28374 Thomas MR & MRS Andrew H
Pittsboro 27312 Brown MS Sara E
Pittsboro 27312 Bultman MRS Richard P
Pittsboro 27312 Livingston MR & MRS Philip R JR
Pittsboro 27312 Ravenel MR & MRS Lee B
Pittsboro 27312 Wilkie MR & MRS Peter L
Raeford 28376 Hostetler MR & MRS Charles A
Raleigh 27603 Jones MR & MRS Patrick L
Raleigh 27605 Attride MR & MRS Roy R B 3D
Raleigh 27605 Preston MRS Helen Davis
Raleigh 27607 Liggett MR Frank R IV
Raleigh 27607 Liggett MRS J Edgerley
Raleigh 27607 Lyman MRS Mary S F
Raleigh 27607 Pulsifer MR & MRS William H
Raleigh 27607 Skinner MRS William P JR
Raleigh 27608 Fariss MR & MRS B Anderson II
Raleigh 27608 Harman MR John R JR
Raleigh 27608 Jones REV & MRS S Gregory
Raleigh 27608 Thompson MR & MRS Stuart D
Raleigh 27609 Brown MRS Julia H
Raleigh 27609 Janvier MR & MRS William P
Raleigh 27609 Liggett MR & MRS David K
Raleigh 27609 Liggett MR & MRS Frank R III
Raleigh 27609 Smith MR & MRS George T JR
Raleigh 27609 Smith MRS George T
Raleigh 27612 Hayward MISS Barbara A
Raleigh 27612 Roberts MR & MRS Lee H
Raleigh 27613 Ballantine MR & MRS (DR) W Parke JR
Raleigh 27613 Dalton DR & MRS (DR) Benjamin W
Raleigh 27613 Ecton MR & MRS Thomas Luke
Raleigh 27614 Hepting MR & MRS Dyson D
Raleigh 27615 Bogue MR & MRS R Peter
Raleigh 27615 Davis DR & MRS Glenn M
Raleigh 27615 Sinwell MRS Evelyn
Raleigh 27617 Hepting MR G Carleton
Rocky Mount 27804 Lucas DR Charles Clement JR
Rougemont 27572 Payne MS (DR) Victoria M
Sherrills Ford 28673 Thomas MR & MRS Frederick H
Southern Pines 28387 Ambersley MR & MRS Robert C
Southern Pines 28387 Bushing MRS Farrell W JR
Southern Pines 28387 Cutler MR & MRS Geoffrey I
Southern Pines 28387 Schenkel MRS Suzanne C
Southern Pines 28387 Schwab MRS Gustav 5TH
Southern Pines 28388 Bell MRS Helen S
Southern Pines 28388 Emerson MR & MRS Edward E JR
Southern Pines 28388 Hart MR & MRS Thomas Van Tine
Southport 28461 Malone MRS Frances M
Southport 28461 Randall MRS Lois C
Speed 27881 Urquhart MR & MRS William E JR
Spruce Pine 28777 van der Vorst MR & MRS Stephanus H S
Trent Woods 28562 Moeller MRS Phoebe M
Tryon 28782 Gardner MRS Robert H JR
Tryon 28782 Jetton DR & MRS Robert L
Vilas 28692 Riker CDR (RET) Robert T
Wake Forest 27587 Finke MR & MRS Richard C
Wanchese 27981 Bostwick MRS Laura
Washington 27889 Connard MR & MRS David McK
Washington 27889 Register MR & MRS John M
Waxhaw 28173 Price MR & MRS William J 5TH
Weddington 28104 Oliphant MR & MRS Andrew E
Wilmington 28401 Whitham MR Scott J & Baldridge MS Brooke B
Wilmington 28402 Irvine MR William Burriss III
Wilmington 28403 Baldridge MR & MRS Dickson B
Wilmington 28403 Beane MRS Agnes R
Wilmington 28403 Lewis MRS Patricia
Wilmington 28403 Sprunt MR & MRS David H
Wilmington 28403 Whelpley MISS Mary B B
Wilmington 28403 Whelpley MRS Lamberton
Wilmington 28403 Wright MRS Thomas Henry JR

Wilmington.................. 28405 .... Hale MR & MRS Bradley H
Wilmington.................. 28405 .... Lawrence MR & MRS Robert L
Wilmington.................. 28405 .... Lewis MR Frederick W 3D
Wilmington.................. 28405 .... Logothetis MR & MRS Anestis L
Wilmington.................. 28405 .... Picken MR & MRS E Craig
Wilmington.................. 28405 .... Royce MR & MRS Robert C
Wilmington.................. 28409 .... Lamberton MR Rolland H
Wilmington.................. 28409 .... Merkley MAJ (RET) & MRS Bart N
Wilson .... 27895......... Boykin MR & MRS Jesse R III
Winnabow..................... 28479......... Szalankiewicz MRS Mary W
Winston Salem .... 27114 .... Taquey MR & MRS Antony
Winston-Salem............. 27104......... Cumming MRS Edward G
Winston-Salem............. 27104......... Treadway MRS William L
Winston-Salem............. 27104......... Womble MR William F
Winston-Salem............. 27106......... Hanson MR & MRS William R
Winston-Salem............. 27106......... Medlin MRS John G JR
Winston-Salem............. 27106......... Stewart MRS John E
Winston-Salem............. 27106......... Wilson MR & MRS (DR) Grover Gray

NORTH DAKOTA

Fargo.............................. 58103......... Wilking MR & MRS Leo F J 3D
Grand Forks.................. 58201......... Johnson MOST REV & MRS Rutherford Barry
Valley City..................... 58072......... Smith REV Du Bois T
Williston .... 58801......... Borden REV & MRS (REV) Carleton H

OHIO

Akron............................. 44303......... Mabry MR & MRS Alanson H
Akron............................. 44313......... Marshall MR & MRS (DR) Tucker Hamlin
Akron............................. 44313......... Nelson MRS Pamela E
Akron............................. 44333......... Khan MR & MRS Mohamad W
Albany .... 45710......... McCament MR & MRS Benjamin K
Ashland......................... 44805 .... Flannery MR & MRS Christopher
Athens .... 45701......... Buckley MR & MRS Geoffrey L
Athens .... 45701......... Thibault MRS Roberta L
Athens .... 45701......... White DR & MRS Matthew M
Aurora .... 44202 .... Everett MR & MRS Chandler H
Bay Village.................... 44140......... O'Brien MR & MRS Patrick C 3D
Bentleyville................... 44022 .... Clarke MR & MRS Charles F 4TH
Bratenahl....................... 44108......... Bolton MR & MRS William B
Bratenahl....................... 44108......... Goff MR William H
Burton .... 44021......... Herrick MR William T-P
Camp Dennison .... 45111 .... Farmer MR Scott E
Centerville .... 45458 .... Moland MR & MRS William W
Chagrin Falls................. 44022 .... Alexander MR & MRS Quentin
Chagrin Falls................. 44022 .... Berens MISS Brooke Van A
Chagrin Falls................. 44022 .... Blossom MR & MRS C Perry
Chagrin Falls................. 44022 .... Boles MR & MRS Edgar H II
Chagrin Falls................. 44022 .... Clarke MRS Charles F 3D
Chagrin Falls................. 44022 .... Dempsey MR & MRS James H JR
Chagrin Falls................. 44022 .... Eells MR & MRS Samuel JR
Chagrin Falls................. 44022 .... Gallin MR & MRS Joseph W
Chagrin Falls................. 44022 .... Gratry MR & MRS Jerome R
Chagrin Falls................. 44022 .... Hellmuth MR & MRS Theodore N JR
Chagrin Falls................. 44022 .... Herron MR & MRS Lewis 2D
Chagrin Falls................. 44022 .... Hitchcock MR & MRS John E
Chagrin Falls................. 44022 .... Ingalls MRS David S JR
Chagrin Falls................. 44022 .... Jackson MR & MRS Richard M JR
Chagrin Falls................. 44022 .... Kilroy MR & MRS William S 2D
Chagrin Falls................. 44022 .... Lomas MR & MRS Robert K
Chagrin Falls................. 44022 .... Neville MR & MRS Francis W
Chagrin Falls................. 44022 .... Scovil MR & MRS Alexander C
Chagrin Falls................. 44022 .... Seymour MRS William B
Chagrin Falls................. 44022 .... Shiverick MR & MRS Reginald C
Chagrin Falls................. 44022 .... Shiverick MR David G
Chagrin Falls................. 44022 .... Vilas MR & MRS Malcolm B JR
Chagrin Falls................. 44023 .... Anderson REV DR Philip A
& Anderson MRS (REV) MarySterrett
Chagrin Falls................. 44023 .... Calfee MR & MRS Peter H
Chagrin Falls................. 44023 .... Conway MRS Gerald A
Chagrin Falls................. 44023 .... Gardner MRS Joseph E
Chagrin Falls................. 44023 .... Kilroy MR Gregory T
Chagrin Falls................. 44023 .... Mortimer MR & MRS J Thomas
Chagrin Falls................. 44023 .... Taft MR & MRS William W
Chagrin Falls................. 44023 .... Vail MRS H Lansing JR
Chardon .... 44024 .... Knerly MR Stephen J JR
Chardon .... 44024 .... Roudebush MR George M III
Chesterland .... 44026 .... Herrick MRS Thomas G
Cincinatti....................... 45208......... Bolce MR Earle E III
Cincinnati...................... 45202......... Hall MR Virginius C
Cincinnati...................... 45202......... Laffoon MRS Polk III
Cincinnati...................... 45202......... Lyon MR Edward A
Cincinnati...................... 45202......... Scott MR Daniel W III
Cincinnati...................... 45204......... Brown MR Daniel
Cincinnati...................... 45206......... Chatfield MISS Helen H
Cincinnati...................... 45206......... Holzman MR & MRS Robert S
Cincinnati...................... 45206......... Howard MRS C Alexander
Cincinnati...................... 45206......... Kyte MR & MRS Lawrence H JR
Cincinnati...................... 45206......... Leo MRS James R
Cincinnati...................... 45207......... Warrington MR & MRS George H
Cincinnati...................... 45208......... Bahlman MR & MRS William Ward
Cincinnati...................... 45208......... Baily MR & MRS O Lippincott
Cincinnati...................... 45208......... Baldwin MRS Sally C
Cincinnati...................... 45208......... Barrett MR C Francis
Cincinnati...................... 45208......... Brooks MR & MRS Kyle C
Cincinnati...................... 45208......... Callard DR & MRS George M
Cincinnati...................... 45208......... Campbell MR & MRS Stephen S
Cincinnati...................... 45208......... Coombe MR & MRS Michael A
Cincinnati...................... 45208......... Cox MR & MRS William P JR
Cincinnati...................... 45208......... Davidson MRS Thomas E
Cincinnati...................... 45208......... Dinsmore MR Wiley
Cincinnati...................... 45208......... Elsey MRS Edward C
Cincinnati...................... 45208......... Fath MR & MRS Harry J
Cincinnati...................... 45208......... Good MR & MRS Daniel J
Cincinnati...................... 45208......... Goodman DR & MRS Michael D
Cincinnati...................... 45208......... Hall DR & MRS Edward C IV
Cincinnati...................... 45208......... Hardy MRS Barbro M
Cincinnati...................... 45208......... Hays MS Elizabeth T
Cincinnati...................... 45208......... Hupper MR & MRS David R
Cincinnati...................... 45208......... Johnson MRS Morse
Cincinnati...................... 45208......... Kellar MR & MRS Lorrence T
Cincinnati...................... 45208......... Kellar MS Ainsley
Cincinnati...................... 45208......... Konop MR & MRS Thomas A
Cincinnati...................... 45208......... Konop MR William T
Cincinnati...................... 45208......... Labrot MR & MRS William H
Cincinnati...................... 45208......... Matthews MR A Pierce JR
Cincinnati...................... 45208......... McElroy MRS Malcolm N
Cincinnati...................... 45208......... Motch MRS Arthur E JR
Cincinnati...................... 45208......... Ott MR & MRS Robert B
Cincinnati...................... 45208......... Pugh MR & MRS William W
Cincinnati...................... 45208......... Pugh MRS Charlotte R
Cincinnati...................... 45208......... Randman MR Barry I
Cincinnati...................... 45208......... Russell MR & MRS Francis P
Cincinnati...................... 45208......... Rybolt MR & MRS William C
Cincinnati...................... 45208......... Smith MRS R Witham
Cincinnati...................... 45208......... Stanley MR & MRS Ethan T
Cincinnati...................... 45208......... Taylor MR & MRS William Ernst
Cincinnati...................... 45208......... Vogel MR Cedric W
Cincinnati...................... 45208......... Warrington MR & MRS John W JR
Cincinnati...................... 45208......... Whitaker MRS Caleb C III
Cincinnati...................... 45209......... Carson MR James G

To nominate a candidate for the Social Register Association, please email: SRCommittee@thesocialregister.org

Cincinnati, OH—Gates Mills, OH

Cincinnati	45209	Maxwell MR Stewart Shillito JR
Cincinnati	45220	Johnston DR & MRS Peirce W
Cincinnati	45220	Leo REV & MRS Jason E
Cincinnati	45226	Gerdsen MR & MRS James N
Cincinnati	45226	MacLachlan MR Robert G & Bernard MS Ann Maris
Cincinnati	45226	Todd MR Samuel P III
Cincinnati	45226	Todd MRS Samuel P JR
Cincinnati	45227	Applegate MRS Leslie T
Cincinnati	45227	Beech MR & MRS Joseph III
Cincinnati	45227	Craig MRS Elizabeth R
Cincinnati	45227	Harris MR & MRS John S
Cincinnati	45227	Levick MR & MRS Stephen O
Cincinnati	45227	Maxwell MR & MRS Irving McC
Cincinnati	45227	Sanders MR David I JR
Cincinnati	45227	Tinkham MR & MRS James E
Cincinnati	45230	Bahlman MR & MRS Baker DeC
Cincinnati	45230	Campbell MR & MRS David W II
Cincinnati	45230	Johnson MISS Judith E
Cincinnati	45230	Muhlhofer MR & MRS F William III
Cincinnati	45230	Neely MRS Homer E
Cincinnati	45230	Pratt MR & MRS Carl E
Cincinnati	45230	VanDerzee MR & MRS Douglas S
Cincinnati	45231	Sanford MR & MRS Lawrence H
Cincinnati	45242	Hall MRS Louise S
Cincinnati	45242	Welsh DR & MRS George F
Cincinnati	45243	Allyn MRS Compton
Cincinnati	45243	Anderson MR & MRS (REV) James M
Cincinnati	45243	Applegate MR & MRS L Thomas 3D
Cincinnati	45243	Barrett MR & MRS John F
Cincinnati	45243	Chabris MR & MRS Peter D Jr
Cincinnati	45243	Closson MR & MRS A Burton JR
Cincinnati	45243	Coburn MR & MRS John 3D
Cincinnati	45243	DeWitt MR & MRS William O JR
Cincinnati	45243	Farmer MR & MRS Richard T
Cincinnati	45243	Fleischmann MRS Charles III
Cincinnati	45243	Geier MRS Philip O JR
Cincinnati	45243	Hardigg MR & MRS William B JR
Cincinnati	45243	Higgins MR & MRS William M
Cincinnati	45243	Hirons MRS Frederic C
Cincinnati	45243	Jackson DR & MRS Richard L
Cincinnati	45243	Janson MR Dennis J
Cincinnati	45243	Kelly MRS William Cody
Cincinnati	45243	Lawrence MRS John T JR
Cincinnati	45243	Lippert DR & MRS Wayne A
Cincinnati	45243	Long MR & MRS Phillip C
Cincinnati	45243	Lothmann MR Scott T & Audretch MS Sharon
Cincinnati	45243	Nippert MISS Mary B
Cincinnati	45243	Off MR & MRS Robert B
Cincinnati	45243	Pettengill MR & MRS Charles A
Cincinnati	45243	Rowe MR & MRS Basil H
Cincinnati	45243	Sanders MR & MRS David I
Cincinnati	45243	Schmidlapp MRS Clarinda S
Cincinnati	45243	Selnick MR & MRS R Bruce
Cincinnati	45243	Taliaferro MR & MRS George W JR
Cincinnati	45243	Thomas MR & MRS Charles L III
Cincinnati	45244	Carey MR & MRS George G 4TH
Cincinnati	45244	Stefani MR & MRS Jeffrey J
Cincinnati	45246	Chamberlain MRS Lemoyne R
Cleveland	44106	Garfield MR & MRS Rudolph H JR
Cleveland	44108	Dempsey MRS Bourne P
Cleveland	44118	Davis MR & MRS Aaron W
Cleveland	44118	Sawyer DR Baldwin
Cleveland	44120	Brownell MRS Henry G II
Cleveland	44120	Bruner DR & MRS William E II
Cleveland	44120	Day MRS Rufus S JR
Cleveland	44120	Limbocker MRS John JR
Cleveland	44120	Mecaskey MR & MRS Richard G
Cleveland	44120	Mueller MRS Werner D
Cleveland	44120	Stubbins MRS Sam G
Cleveland	44122	Dunn MRS George J
Cleveland	44124	Downing MR & MRS Thurman
Cleveland	44124	Hondlik MR & MRS Christopher J
Cleveland	44124	Marshall MISS Mary W
Cleveland	44124	Moroscak MR & MRS John M
Cleveland	44124	Neville MRS Robert J
Cleveland	44124	Wilson MR John R
Cleveland	44126	Berens MR Lawrence P
Cleveland Heights	44106	Ayers MR Joseph B 3D
Cleveland Heights	44106	Daley MRS William C JR
Cleveland Heights	44106	Iredell MR & MRS Robert 4TH
Cleveland Heights	44106	Jones MR & MRS Charles W
Cleveland Heights	44106	Tuttle MS Christeen C
Cleveland Heights	44118	Cooley MR & MRS Charles P III
Cleveland Heights	44118	Coughlin MR & MRS Dennis
Cleveland Heights	44118	Hadden MRS John A JR
Cleveland Heights	44118	Hartwell MR & MRS Samuel S
Cleveland Heights	44118	Lloyd MR & MRS Whitney
Cleveland Heights	44118	Marting MR & MRS Michael G
Cleveland Heights	44118	Parkin MR & MRS R Rex JR
Cleveland Heights	44121	McChord MRS John S
Columbus	43202	Allen DR & MRS (DR) Theodore T
Columbus	43206	Sculley MR & MRS Arthur B JR
Columbus	43209	Johnson MR Kiehner
Columbus	43209	Snavely MR & MRS David A
Columbus	43213	Struthers MR & MRS Robert
Columbus	43214	Virgin MR & MRS William P
Columbus	43215	Taft MR & MRS Sheldon A
Columbus	43220	Pernoud MISS (DR) Cathleen
Columbus	43221	Ruxton MISS Mary L
Columbus	43221	Taylor MRS S Mabrey
Columbus	43235	Chesser MRS Don F
Cuyahoga Falls	44221	Munroe MISS Dorothy F
Dayton	45402	Janney MR Jervis S JR
Dayton	45409	Janney MRS Jervis S JR
Dayton	45419	Borneman MS (DR) Katherine L
Dayton	45419	Ohmer MR & MRS Frederic L III
Dayton	45419	Terhune MR Everit B 3D
Dayton	45420	Mitakides MR & MRS Andrew J
Dayton	45429	Bergsten MS Sandra A
Dayton	45429	Greene MRS John B
Dayton	45429	Tschudin MRS Hanspeter
Dayton	45429	Woodward MR & MRS Peirce F
Dayton	45440	Grant MR & MRS Richard R H 3D
Dublin	43017	Quinn MR & MRS Michael K
Dublin	43017	Wise DR & MRS Henry A 2D
East Liverpool	43920	Gaudieri MRS M Hall
Gambier	43022	Hoffmann MR & MRS Thomas J
Gates Mills	44040	Anderson MR & MRS Glenn G JR
Gates Mills	44040	Barnes MS Julia P
Gates Mills	44040	Bole MR & MRS Richard H
Gates Mills	44040	Butler MR & MRS John C JR
Gates Mills	44040	Dautel LT COL REV Terrence P
Gates Mills	44040	Holmes MRS Melinda P
Gates Mills	44040	Humphrey MRS Marguerite B
Gates Mills	44040	Manuel MRS Richard A
Gates Mills	44040	Morris MR & MRS Warren L 2D
Gates Mills	44040	Oppmann MR & MRS Patrick P
Gates Mills	44040	Oppmann MRS Harvey G
Gates Mills	44040	Roulston MR & MRS Scott D
Gates Mills	44040	Scovil MR & MRS Samuel K
Gates Mills	44040	Scovil MR & MRS Samuel K 3D
Gates Mills	44040	Wheaton MR & MRS Gerald R

Glendale	45246	Dunlap MRS John Gaff
Glendale	45246	Hall MR & MRS Joseph L 5TH
Glendale	45246	Hall MR & MRS Thomas Cartwright JR
Glendale	45246	Noone MRS Robert Scott
Granville	43023	Bradley MR & MRS E Tremain JR
Granville	43023	Havill MR & MRS Jessen T
Granville	43023	von Goeben MISS Hedda Windisch
Hamilton	45013	Carruthers MS Sara Procter
Hudson	44236	Caldwell MRS Kenneth S JR
Hudson	44236	Franklin MR & MRS John H JR
Hudson	44236	Girvin MR & MRS Matthew G
Hudson	44236	Pulte MR & MRS Michael L JR
Hudson	44236	Reynolds MR & MRS A William II
Hudson	44236	Ritter MR & MRS (DR) John D
Hunting Valley	44022	Everett MR & MRS Morris JR
Hunting Valley	44022	Hosler MR & MRS Robert M JR
Hunting Valley	44022	Inkley DR & MRS Scott R
Hunting Valley	44022	Lennon MR & MRS William H
Hunting Valley	44022	Vail MR & MRS Thomas Van H
Kettering	45429	Miller MR & MRS William R JR
Kettering	45429	Mitakides DR & MRS John E
Kirtland	44094	Murfey MR & MRS Latham W 3D
Kirtland	44094	Ours MR & MRS Adam S
Loveland	45140	Colbert MR & MRS John P
Loveland	45140	Havighurst MR & MRS Bryan J
Loveland	45140	Miller MR & MRS Robert John
Lyndhurst	44124	Roulston MR & MRS Thomas H 2D
Madison	44057	Broadbent MRS B Holly JR
Maineville	45039	Shebesta MR & MRS Tarry E
Mason	45040	Coombe MR & MRS James M
Maumee	43237	Robinson DR & MRS Howard H JR
Mentor	44060	McConnell MR & MRS F Stevens 3D
Mentor	44060	McConnell MRS Frederick S
Mentor	44060	Seabright MR & MRS Thomas W
Mentor	44060	Vitiello MS (DR) Alice C
Milford	45150	Matthews MISS Mary-Morse
Moreland Hills	44022	Oppmann MRS Lydia B
Moreland Hills	44022	Schenkel MR & MRS John L H JR
Munson	44024	Ours MR & MRS John W JR
New Albany	43054	Lovering MR & MRS Richard S 3D
New Philadelphia	44663	Stoddard MR A Colin Brooks
New Richmond	45157	Morrison MRS M Peters
New Richmond	45157	Steele MR & MRS John F JR
Novelty	44072	Abbott MR & MRS James S 4TH
Novelty	44072	Into MRS J Timberman
Oakwood	45419	Bieser MR & MRS Irvin G JR
Oakwood	45419	Mitakides DR Katherine W
Ostrander	43061	Andrews MR & MRS Alexander McA
Pepper Pike	44124	Converse MR & MRS Chandler B JR
Pepper Pike	44124	Everett MR & MRS Chandler P
Pepper Pike	44124	Jones MR & MRS Clarke Fitz-Gerald
Pepper Pike	44124	King MR & MRS W Griffin 3D
Pepper Pike	44124	Rutter MR & MRS John A JR
Pepper Pike	44124	Taylor MR & MRS T Ryburn
Perrysburg	43551	Merrick DR & MRS Hollis W III
Perrysburg	43551	Williams MR & MRS Thomas A JR
Richfield	44286	Distad MS Marcella A
Rocky River	44116	Barker MR & MRS Mark W
Rocky River	44116	Dempsey MR & MRS Richard B
Rocky River	44116	Engelbert MR & MRS Robert W
Rocky River	44116	Rollinson MR & MRS James H
Russell	44072	Hollister MR & MRS John B 3D
Shaker Heights	44118	Junod MR Henri Pell JR
Shaker Heights	44120	Andrews MR & MRS Oakley VanderPoel
Shaker Heights	44120	Brody DR & MRS Robert
Shaker Heights	44120	Gries MR & MRS Robert D
Shaker Heights	44120	Jones MR & MRS Walter R
Shaker Heights	44120	Roosevelt MISS
Shaker Heights	44120	Rorimer MR & MRS Louis
Shaker Heights	44120	Thalman MR John R
Shaker Heights	44122	Anderson MR Robert F
Shaker Heights	44122	Bauschard MR Richard B
Shaker Heights	44122	Bauschard MS Laura A
Shaker Heights	44122	Berglund DR & MRS Ryan K
Shaker Heights	44122	Bridge MR & MRS Jonathan E
Shaker Heights	44122	Brown MRS Jack L JR
Shaker Heights	44122	Clark MR & MRS Paul G
Shaker Heights	44122	Cockley MR & MRS David H
Shaker Heights	44122	Cronin MR & MRS Daniel C
Shaker Heights	44122	Distad MR R Neall
Shaker Heights	44122	Emmet MR & MRS Robert
Shaker Heights	44122	Girvin MR & MRS Robert N
Shaker Heights	44122	Hollington MR & MRS Richard R 3D
Shaker Heights	44122	Mueller MR & MRS John M
Shaker Heights	44122	Orbach MR & MRS Seth
Shaker Heights	44122	Ott-Hansen MR Henry
Shaker Heights	44122	Randol MR & MRS Mark A
Shaker Heights	44122	Rubin MR & MRS Vaughn P
Shaker Heights	44122	Smith MRS Ralston F
Shaker Heights	44122	Taft MR & MRS Peter G
Shaker Heights	44122	Vail MR & MRS Thomas Van H JR
Solon	44139	Wellman MR & MRS Robert C JR
Spring Valley	45370	Allen MR & MRS Kenneth D
St Louis	63132	Culver MR Bertram B 3D
Sunbury	43074	Mulder MR & MRS Gary C
Terrace Park	45174	DeCamp MRS Johnson
Terrace Park	45174	Long MR & MRS Bruce C
Terrace Park	45174	Robertson MISS Cynthia S
Terrace Park	45174	Sarran MR & MRS William R
Toledo	43614	Metcalf MISS Barbara E
Versailles	45380	Cain DR Marvin J
Waite Hill	44094	Rankin MR & MRS Alfred M JR
West Chester	45069	Tinnin MR Alden & Hackenbracht MS Sarah
Westerville	43081	Board MRS James M
Willoughby	44094	Hatch MR & MRS Henry R III
Willoughby	44094	Murch MR & MRS Creighton B
Willoughby Hills	44094	Howell MR & MRS A Allen
Worthington	43085	Whitman MR & MRS Edouard R F
Wyoming	45231	Celi LT COL & MRS Sean A D
Xenia	45385	Darrow MR & MRS William H II
Yellow Springs	45387	Swetland MRS Frederick L JR

OKLAHOMA

Edmond	73013	Fedor MR & MRS David A
Nichols Hills	73116	Katigan MR & MRS Steven M
Nichols Hills	73116	McCune MR John R 6TH
Nichols Hills	73120	McCubbin MR & MRS David J
Oklahoma City	73103	Griffin MR & MRS Andrew W
Piedmont	73078	Davis MISS Marguerite T
Tulsa	74105	Walter MR Peter M
Tulsa	74114	Holt DR Gregory R
Tulsa	74114	Smith MS Pattiann E G
Tulsa	74114	Winter MRS Thomas G
Tulsa	74136	Carlson MR & MRS Lee R

OREGON

Ashland	97520	Ashbey MR & MRS William N
Ashland	97520	Lincoln MR & MRS Alexander III
Bend	97702	Farwell MR & MRS John V 4TH
Bend	97702	Lyons MR & MRS Donald J

To nominate a candidate for the Social Register Association, please email: SRCommittee@thesocialregister.org

Bend, OR—Ardmore, PA

Bend .... 97702 .... Swindells MR & MRS Theodore H
Bend .... 97703 .... Johnson MR & MRS Roger L
Canby .... 97013 .... Smith MR & MRS Stephen H
Dallas .... 97338 .... Esbenshade DR & MRS John F
Eugene .... 97401 .... Kehl MR & MRS (DR) Jonathan E
Eugene .... 97401 .... Webb MR William B
Eugene .... 97403 .... Harper MR & MRS James G
Eugene .... 97405 .... Hutchings MR Robert E JR
Eugene .... 97405 .... Hutchings MRS Robert E JR
Eugene .... 97405 .... Leavitt MR & MRS W Bradbury
Eugene .... 97405 .... Ryan MRS A Park
Eugene .... 97405 .... Wonham MR & MRS Henry B
Hillsboro .... 97123 .... Day MISS Sylvia C
Jacksonville .... 97530 .... Campbell MR Michael R
Jefferson .... 97352 .... Whitton MR & MRS David P
Klamath Falls .... 97601 .... Martin MR & MRS Eric B
Lake Oswego .... 97034 .... Godfrey MR & MRS Thompson C
Lake Oswego .... 97035 .... Appleton MR Benjamin B
Lake Oswego .... 97035 .... Jakotich MR & MRS John S
Lincoln City .... 97367 .... Plath MR & MRS David C
Medford .... 97501 .... Pepper MR William S JR
Medford .... 97504 .... Francis MR & MRS Sidney R JR
Medford .... 97504 .... Goddard MRS C Convers
Portland .... 97201 .... Cantlin MR & MRS Richard A
Portland .... 97201 .... Drake MR & MRS Matthew B
Portland .... 97201 .... Jorgenson MR & MRS Jeffrey L
Portland .... 97201 .... Lorion MR & MRS Paul A
Portland .... 97201 .... Meier MR & MRS Roger S
Portland .... 97201 .... Munch MR & MRS Ernest R
Portland .... 97201 .... Munch MR & MRS Nicholas R H
Portland .... 97201 .... Robinson MRS Barclay JR
Portland .... 97201 .... Williamson MR & MRS Samuel H
Portland .... 97202 .... Bragdon MR & MRS Paul E
Portland .... 97202 .... Hull MR & MRS David E
Portland .... 97202 .... McKee MR & MRS Richard G
Portland .... 97202 .... Nicholson DR & MRS (DR) Nigel J
Portland .... 97205 .... Warren MRS Robert C
Portland .... 97207 .... Hetherington DR & MRS Arthur F 3D
Portland .... 97207 .... Madden MISS Paula M
Portland .... 97209 .... Abeel MR & MRS Neilson
Portland .... 97209 .... Garrett MR David T
Portland .... 97210 .... Halsey MRS Stephen S
Portland .... 97210 .... Harrison MR & MRS John C
Portland .... 97210 .... MacColl MR & MRS Eugene K JR
Portland .... 97211 .... Mudge MR & MRS Matthew S
Portland .... 97212 .... Corser MR & MRS Nathan C
Portland .... 97212 .... Doubleday MR & MRS Stephen T
Portland .... 97212 .... Jain MR & MRS Raj Van Dusen
Portland .... 97212 .... Leonard MISS Margot D
Portland .... 97212 .... Perkins MR & MRS Luke A
Portland .... 97212 .... Reich MR & MRS Christopher Guittard
Portland .... 97212 .... Terry MR & MRS Stephen W
Portland .... 97212 .... Younes MR & MRS Saleh Tarek
Portland .... 97213 .... Mendenhall DR & MRS Andrew B
Portland .... 97213 .... Schmidt MISS Josie H
Portland .... 97213 .... Tilghman MR & MRS Henry R
Portland .... 97214 .... Collins MRS Alan C
Portland .... 97214 .... McDonald MR & MRS Ryan A
Portland .... 97219 .... Crumpacker MR & MRS James F
Portland .... 97219 .... Gruner DR & MRS Sam E
Portland .... 97220 .... Bowie MR Sean A & Rose MS Mary H
Portland .... 97220 .... O'Brien MISS Welby A
Portland .... 97221 .... Allen MR Philip 3D & Faris MS Kathleen B
Portland .... 97221 .... Dick MR & MRS Spencer B
Portland .... 97221 .... Jubitz MR & MRS M Albin
Portland .... 97221 .... McCall MR & MRS Robert H
Portland .... 97221 .... McCarley MR Thomas P
Portland .... 97221 .... Miller MR & MRS Randolph L
Portland .... 97221 .... Platt MR John W S
Portland .... 97221 .... Pope MR & MRS Guy W
Portland .... 97221 .... Spencer MR & MRS George C
Portland .... 97223 .... McDonald MISS Frances B
Portland .... 97225 .... Daigle MR & MRS James MacL
Portland .... 97225 .... Mead MR & MRS George W
Portland .... 97229 .... Gardiner MR & MRS Allen B
Portland .... 97229 .... Preble MR & MRS Bradley B
Portland .... 97229 .... Preble MR & MRS Wallace L
Portland .... 97229 .... Roome DR & MRS Peter W JR
Portland .... 97231 .... Adamson MR & MRS Peter S
Portland .... 97232 .... Smith DR Eric T & McKee MS Alice M
Portland .... 97239 .... Geoffroy MRS Charles H
Portland .... 97239 .... Hardin MR & MRS B Lauriston III
Portland .... 97239 .... Mack MR & MRS M Wakefield
Portland .... 97239 .... Mann MR & MRS Britton R
Portland .... 97239 .... Shoemaker MR & MRS Peter R
Portland .... 97296 .... Shore DR & MRS Howard Everett IV
Portland .... 97702 .... Reid MR Andrew V
Sherwood .... 97140 .... Metcalf MR & MRS John Brockway
Sherwood .... 97140 .... Van Nice MR & MRS Anthony H
West Linn .... 97068 .... McFarlane MR & MRS Ronn
West Linn .... 97068 .... Ziel MR & MRS John G M
Wilsonville .... 97070 .... Lamberton MR & MRS Richard D
Wilsonville .... 97070 .... Snowden MISS Virginia P

PENNSYLVANIA

Aliquippa .... 15001 .... Lufkin MR Peter W SR
Allentown .... 18103 .... Krogstad MR & MRS Robert B 2D
Allentown .... 18104 .... Lee MRS Lewis H JR
Ambler .... 19002 .... Bast MR & MRS Robert L
Ambler .... 19002 .... Bennett MR & MRS John C JR
Ambler .... 19002 .... Bodine MR & MRS Lawrence D
Ambler .... 19002 .... Bolt MR Eugene A JR
Ambler .... 19002 .... Campbell MR & MRS Ross L
Ambler .... 19002 .... Carey MR & MRS H Augustus
Ambler .... 19002 .... Coxe MISS Caroline T
Ambler .... 19002 .... Coxe MR & MRS Henry B 3D
Ambler .... 19002 .... Cross MR & MRS E George III
Ambler .... 19002 .... Disston MRS Ellen L
Ambler .... 19002 .... Donnon MRS Gwen B
Ambler .... 19002 .... Ervin MR & MRS Robert L
Ambler .... 19002 .... Gast MR & MRS William R
Ambler .... 19002 .... Hart MR Joshua F
Ambler .... 19002 .... Henderson MR & MRS Gerald van S JR
Ambler .... 19002 .... Hipp MR & MRS Lawrence K
Ambler .... 19002 .... Lindemann MR & MRS H Eugene III
Ambler .... 19002 .... Lloyd MR John Strawbridge
Ambler .... 19002 .... Martin MS Laurie S
Ambler .... 19002 .... Nichols MRS George Q
Ambler .... 19002 .... Patton MR & MRS J Stiles
Ambler .... 19002 .... Pepper MR & MRS J Sergeant
Ambler .... 19002 .... Pierce MR & MRS Guy C 3D
Ambler .... 19002 .... Roden MS Robin H
Ambler .... 19002 .... Smith MR & MRS Jeffrey R
Ambler .... 19002 .... Wetherill MR & MRS Stephen H
Ardmore .... 19003 .... Cutler MR & MRS Peter K
Ardmore .... 19003 .... Dillon DR & MRS Richard S
Ardmore .... 19003 .... Fox MR & MRS Reeder R
Ardmore .... 19003 .... Fuller MR Graham C
Ardmore .... 19003 .... Grubb MRS Joseph Spenser
Ardmore .... 19003 .... Hodges MRS Jean G
Ardmore .... 19003 .... Hole DR & MRS Richard W JR

Ardmore, PA—Bryn Mawr, PA

Ardmore	19003	Lewis MRS Joanna McNeil
Ardmore	19003	Parrott MR & MRS John M
Ardmore	19003	Pendergast MR & MRS Jeffrey R
Ardmore	19003	Putnam MR & MRS Alfred W JR
Ardmore	19003	Reed MRS Edward A
Ardmore	19003	Vogt MR Peter A
Aston	19014	Wurts MR Reed M W
Audubon	19403	Huber MS Electa Mary
Audubon	19403	Kratovil MRS Elizabeth S
Audubon	19403	Peck MRS Hubert R
Audubon	19407	Le Boutillier MR Charles P
Avondale	19311	Hutz MR & MRS R Eric
Bala Cynwyd	19004	Clement MR Timothy R
Bala Cynwyd	19004	Gregg MR & MRS Stephen S
Bala Cynwyd	19004	McComb MR & MRS David F
Bala Cynwyd	19004	Nagy MR & MRS Alexander K
Bala Cynwyd	19004	Peters MRS George B
Bala Cynwyd	19004	Post MS Diana & Milroy MS (DR) Elizabeth LaMotte C
Bedford	15522	Roach MR & MRS Lloyd Bankson
Bedminster	18910	Sigety MRS Elizabeth
Berwyn	19312	Arnold MR & MRS James H
Berwyn	19312	Clement MR & MRS Thomas S
Berwyn	19312	Clement MR Samuel B
Berwyn	19312	Clement MRS Charles F 3D
Berwyn	19312	Congdon DR & MRS James B
Berwyn	19312	Cruice MRS John M
Berwyn	19312	Dixon MR & MRS Terence A
Berwyn	19312	Donald MR & MRS Martyn P
Berwyn	19312	Foster MR Daniel W
Berwyn	19312	Gowen MR & MRS James E 2D
Berwyn	19312	Grady MR & MRS Hugh A
Berwyn	19312	Greer DR & MRS William R
Berwyn	19312	Gresh MRS W Perry
Berwyn	19312	Hagar MR & MRS Erik H
Berwyn	19312	Hartman MR & MRS William R JR
Berwyn	19312	Hastings MR & MRS David B JR
Berwyn	19312	Havens MRS Margaret S
Berwyn	19312	Heckscher MR & MRS Benjamin H
Berwyn	19312	Henderson MR & MRS Branton H JR
Berwyn	19312	Hodge MR & MRS John H
Berwyn	19312	Hole MR & MRS James W B
Berwyn	19312	Kraft MR & MRS William B 3D
Berwyn	19312	Leisenring MR & MRS Edward W
Berwyn	19312	Leisenring MRS Edward B
Berwyn	19312	Lyon MR & MRS Jeffrey K N
Berwyn	19312	Madeira MR & MRS Harry R JR
Berwyn	19312	Metcalf MR & MRS Philip A
Berwyn	19312	Moss MRS Arthur H
Berwyn	19312	Rawson MR & MRS David W
Berwyn	19312	Rollins MRS Deborah F
Berwyn	19312	Sadtler MR & MRS Philip B
Berwyn	19312	Snyder MR & MRS Martin C
Berwyn	19312	Thompson MISS Maris Wistar
Berwyn	19312	Tobin MRS Mark C
Berwyn	19312	Tremblay MR & MRS Donald P
Berwyn	19312	Wagner MR & MRS Jeffrey W
Berwyn	19312	Watters MR & MRS Edward McL 3D
Berwyn	19312	Whalen DR & MRS Thomas J
Berwyn	19312	Wickes MR & MRS Schuyler C
Berwyn	19312	Wister MRS E P Benson
Berwyn	19312	Wood MR & MRS Harvard C IV
Berwyn	19312	Young MR & MRS Richard N III
Bethlehem	18015	Hart MR & MRS John H
Bethlehem	18017	Beales MR & MRS Jefferson D
Bethlehem	18017	Dunbar MRS Davis T
Bethlehem	18018	Robinson MRS D Patrick M
Bethlehem	18018	Thayer MRS Frederick M JR
Bethlehem	18018	Vanderbeck MS Ruth
Birchrunville	19421	Levis MRS Frederick H JR
Birchrunville	19421	Quillman MR & MRS R Scott
Birdsboro	19508	Stokes MR Edward B JR
Blue Bell	19422	Beegle MRS Frederick N 2D
Blue Bell	19422	Brown MRS Francis Shunk 3D
Blue Bell	19422	Bryant MR & MRS Stephen C
Blue Bell	19422	Culp MR & MRS Thomas C JR
Blue Bell	19422	Ervin MR & MRS Robert L JR
Blue Bell	19422	Fernley MRS Robert C
Blue Bell	19422	Hunter MRS Andrew McA
Blue Bell	19422	Lawrence MRS Marjorie B
Blue Bell	19422	Lyons MR & MRS George R
Blue Bell	19422	McIlvaine MRS Charles L 3D
Blue Bell	19422	Miller MR Charles F
Blue Bell	19422	Morris MRS Joseph Paul JR
Blue Bell	19422	Newhall MR & MRS Daniel T
Blue Bell	19422	Pearson MRS Corning
Blue Bell	19422	Penniman MRS H Dawson
Blue Bell	19422	Plumb MR & MRS Fayette R 2D
Blue Bell	19422	Rodgers MR & MRS John C
Blue Bell	19422	Schwartz MR & MRS James P
Blue Bell	19422	Sheppard MR Edgar M JR
Blue Bell	19422	Test MR & MRS Alfred L JR
Blue Bell	19422	Wurts MR & MRS Clarence Z
Blue Ridge Summit	17214	Lamberton MR & MRS Harry C JR
Boalsburg	16827	Lee MR Christopher G
Boalsburg	16827	McLaughlin MRS Mary M
Boiling Springs	17007	McLean DR & MRS Donald A JR
Bowmansdale	17055	Nauman MR & MRS Spencer G JR
Boyertown	19512	Leavitt MR Gregory A
Bristol	19007	Melville MRS Charlotte L
Broomall	19008	Bowman MR & MRS Benjamin E
Broomall	19008	Hollingshead MR & MRS Wickliffe Stewart 2D
Broomall	19008	Johnson MRS Allan M
Bryn Mawr	19010	Alexander MR Charles T
Bryn Mawr	19010	Aller MRS Harris Coles JR
Bryn Mawr	19010	Andrews MRS Stuart B
Bryn Mawr	19010	Averill MRS John B
Bryn Mawr	19010	Babka MR & MRS Patrick C
Bryn Mawr	19010	Baird MR John A JR
Bryn Mawr	19010	Baird MRS Samuel B D
Bryn Mawr	19010	Ballard DR & MRS Ian M
Bryn Mawr	19010	Barker MR & MRS Robert P
Bryn Mawr	19010	Biddle MR & MRS Christopher L
Bryn Mawr	19010	Biddle MR & MRS Ernest L JR
Bryn Mawr	19010	Biddle MR & MRS James C
Bryn Mawr	19010	Biddle MRS Edmund Randolph
Bryn Mawr	19010	Bishop MRS Harry C
Bryn Mawr	19010	Bittel MRS Diana H
Bryn Mawr	19010	Blacque MR & MRS Richard E
Bryn Mawr	19010	Blischak MR & MRS Matthew P
Bryn Mawr	19010	Boenning MRS Henry D
Bryn Mawr	19010	Bohlen MISS Priscilla D
Bryn Mawr	19010	Borie MRS H Peter JR
Bryn Mawr	19010	Bright MR & MRS Joseph C
Bryn Mawr	19010	Brown MR & MRS Bruce M
Bryn Mawr	19010	Bullitt MRS Orville H JR
Bryn Mawr	19010	Butterworth MR & MRS David G
Bryn Mawr	19010	Campana MR & MRS Peter M
Bryn Mawr	19010	Campbell MRS Alfred M 3D
Bryn Mawr	19010	Carr MR & MRS Edward W
Bryn Mawr	19010	Catherwood MR & MRS Cummins JR
Bryn Mawr	19010	Chandlee MR & MRS William B JR
Bryn Mawr	19010	Clapham MR & MRS John H

To nominate a candidate for the Social Register Association, please email: SRCommittee@thesocialregister.org

Bryn Mawr, PA—Bryn Mawr, PA

Bryn Mawr	19010	Clothier MR & MRS Isaac H 4TH
Bryn Mawr	19010	Clothier MR & MRS Robert C 3D
Bryn Mawr	19010	Clothier MRS Ann H
Bryn Mawr	19010	Colket MRS Tristram C
Bryn Mawr	19010	Cooke MR & MRS Merritt T JR
Bryn Mawr	19010	Cooke MRS M Todd
Bryn Mawr	19010	Coxe MR & MRS Theodore S JR
Bryn Mawr	19010	Crane MR R Thompson 3D
Bryn Mawr	19010	Cresap MR & MRS Mark W III
Bryn Mawr	19010	Cromwell MR & MRS O Eaton JR
Bryn Mawr	19010	Curran MR D Edward
Bryn Mawr	19010	Curran MRS Ann Pew
Bryn Mawr	19010	Daly MRS Donald F
Bryn Mawr	19010	Davis MR & MRS Christopher S
Bryn Mawr	19010	Davis MR & MRS E Morris 4TH
Bryn Mawr	19010	deForest Keys MR & MRS David
Bryn Mawr	19010	Donaghy MRS Edwin C JR
Bryn Mawr	19010	Drayton MRS John W
Bryn Mawr	19010	Drayton MRS Richard
Bryn Mawr	19010	Earle MR Lawrence W
Bryn Mawr	19010	Eisenbrey MRS J Kenton
Bryn Mawr	19010	Erdman MR Michael P
Bryn Mawr	19010	Ernst MR & MRS Peter A
Bryn Mawr	19010	Farber MRS Brent H JR
Bryn Mawr	19010	Fenstermacher MR & MRS Ronald W JR
Bryn Mawr	19010	Fergusson MR & MRS A Carter
Bryn Mawr	19010	Fowler MR & MRS Gordon B JR
Bryn Mawr	19010	Fraser MR Ronald G
Bryn Mawr	19010	Gay MRS H Burton
Bryn Mawr	19010	Godfrey MR & MRS Peter JR
Bryn Mawr	19010	Godfrey MR Peter
Bryn Mawr	19010	Gowen MRS George F
Bryn Mawr	19010	Haack MR & MRS Frederick L 3D
Bryn Mawr	19010	Hacker MR & MRS A Heathcote 3D
Bryn Mawr	19010	Halpert MR & MRS Samuel R
Bryn Mawr	19010	Hamilton MR & MRS S Matthews V JR
Bryn Mawr	19010	Hancock MRS Charles L
Bryn Mawr	19010	Hanley MR & MRS Christopher D
Bryn Mawr	19010	Harding MR & MRS Robert S O
Bryn Mawr	19010	Harris MRS Gwathmey
Bryn Mawr	19010	Harrity MRS William F JR
Bryn Mawr	19010	Hastings MR & MRS David B
Bryn Mawr	19010	Henderson MRS J Welles
Bryn Mawr	19010	Hippler MR & MRS Cory O
Bryn Mawr	19010	Howard MR & MRS Morton
Bryn Mawr	19010	Hutchinson MR & MRS Daniel L
Bryn Mawr	19010	Hutchinson MR Mahlon 3D
Bryn Mawr	19010	Hyland MR & MRS William S
Bryn Mawr	19010	Ingersoll MR & MRS Daniel W
Bryn Mawr	19010	Ingersoll MRS Henry McK
Bryn Mawr	19010	Irwin MR & MRS Charles D
Bryn Mawr	19010	Jarrett MISS E Jean
Bryn Mawr	19010	Kaltenbach MRS Henry J
Bryn Mawr	19010	Koberg MR & MRS Heino C F
Bryn Mawr	19010	Koons MR Charles B
Bryn Mawr	19010	Le Vine MR & MRS D Christopher
Bryn Mawr	19010	Lincoln MRS George J 3D
Bryn Mawr	19010	Lisle MR & MRS John
Bryn Mawr	19010	Lloyd MR & MRS John S
Bryn Mawr	19010	Lovell MRS Douglas G JR
Bryn Mawr	19010	Machold MR William D
Bryn Mawr	19010	Madara MR & MRS Edward S JR
Bryn Mawr	19010	Madeira MR & MRS Edward W
Bryn Mawr	19010	Manganaro MRS Lynne D S
Bryn Mawr	19010	Markle MR & MRS Alvan III
Bryn Mawr	19010	Marshall MR & MRS Charles N
Bryn Mawr	19010	Marshall MRS Elizabeth R
Bryn Mawr	19010	McAdoo MR & MRS Robert C
Bryn Mawr	19010	McCabe MR & MRS James L
Bryn Mawr	19010	McCauley MR & MRS Hugh J
Bryn Mawr	19010	McMullin MR & MRS Hunter B
Bryn Mawr	19010	McNeely MR George H 3D
Bryn Mawr	19010	Means MR & MRS William M II
Bryn Mawr	19010	Miller MR & MRS George J
Bryn Mawr	19010	Miller MRS Philippus JR
Bryn Mawr	19010	Moffitt MRS George W JR
Bryn Mawr	19010	Monroe REV Elizabeth W
Bryn Mawr	19010	Montanaro MR & MRS Alexander
Bryn Mawr	19010	Morris MR & MRS Christopher A
Bryn Mawr	19010	Morris MR & MRS Roland
Bryn Mawr	19010	Morris MR & MRS Samuel W JR
Bryn Mawr	19010	Morrison MRS Barclay JR
Bryn Mawr	19010	Morsman MR & MRS Kimball H
Bryn Mawr	19010	Mucklé MRS Craig W JR
Bryn Mawr	19010	Neilson MR & MRS Benjamin R
Bryn Mawr	19010	Neilson MRS Harry R JR
Bryn Mawr	19010	Nelson MR & MRS Lathrop B JR
Bryn Mawr	19010	Nemo MR & MRS Jonathan E
Bryn Mawr	19010	Nimick MRS A Corkran
Bryn Mawr	19010	Norris MISS Katharine H
Bryn Mawr	19010	Norris MR Charles C 2D
Bryn Mawr	19010	Oberdorf MR John G
Bryn Mawr	19010	Ogelsby MR & MRS Charles Warwick JR
Bryn Mawr	19010	Osborn MRS O'Neill
Bryn Mawr	19010	Osborne MRS Raymond B
Bryn Mawr	19010	Page MRS L Rodman
Bryn Mawr	19010	Painter MR David L
Bryn Mawr	19010	Pakradooni MRS Dikran S
Bryn Mawr	19010	Pemberton DR & MRS Clifford H
Bryn Mawr	19010	Pew MR & MRS G Thompson JR
Bryn Mawr	19010	Piasecki MR & MRS John W
Bryn Mawr	19010	Pozos MR & MRS Antonio M
Bryn Mawr	19010	Randolph MR & MRS David S JR
Bryn Mawr	19010	Rauch MR & MRS Keith D
Bryn Mawr	19010	Ravenscroft MRS Richard S
Bryn Mawr	19010	Roberts MRS Howard H
Bryn Mawr	19010	Robinette MRS J Todd
Bryn Mawr	19010	Roche MRS Robert P
Bryn Mawr	19010	Rorer MR & MRS Gerald B
Bryn Mawr	19010	Ross MR & MRS Wilson Sharpless
Bryn Mawr	19010	Royer MRS Elizabeth D
Bryn Mawr	19010	Ruthrauff MR & MRS Wilbur Bourne
Bryn Mawr	19010	Saylor MRS Genevieve
Bryn Mawr	19010	Sellers MR & MRS Frank R S JR
Bryn Mawr	19010	Shafer MRS George C JR
Bryn Mawr	19010	Sharp MR & MRS M Rust
Bryn Mawr	19010	Sherwin MRS Robert P
Bryn Mawr	19010	Smythe MRS J L Nevill
Bryn Mawr	19010	Snyder DR & MRS Howard McC III
Bryn Mawr	19010	Starr MRS Edward 3D
Bryn Mawr	19010	Steigerwalt MRS John L
Bryn Mawr	19010	Stetzer MR & MRS John J III
Bryn Mawr	19010	Stewardson MRS Alice
Bryn Mawr	19010	Stokes MR & MRS Peter F
Bryn Mawr	19010	Thayer MRS Edmund JR
Bryn Mawr	19010	Thompson MR & MRS Paul III
Bryn Mawr	19010	Tilghman MR & MRS Richard A
Bryn Mawr	19010	Tilghman MRS Joseph F
Bryn Mawr	19010	Truitt MRS S Stokes
Bryn Mawr	19010	van Beuren MR & MRS Archbold D
Bryn Mawr	19010	Van Dusen MR & MRS Duncan W
Bryn Mawr	19010	Warner MRS Silas L

Bryn Mawr .... 19010 .... Webster MR Maurice A JR
Bryn Mawr .... 19010 .... Wheeler MR & MRS Warwick S
Bryn Mawr .... 19010 .... Wheeler MRS Arthur L
Bryn Mawr .... 19010 .... Williams MRS William L
Bryn Mawr .... 19010 .... Wolcott MRS Robert W JR
Bryn Mawr .... 19010 .... Wood MR Charles R
Bryn Mawr .... 19010 .... Wood MRS Sabina A
Bryn Mawr .... 19010 .... Yarnall MRS Charlton 2D
Bryn Mawr .... 19010 .... Ziesing MRS Robert A
Bryn Mawr .... 19010 .... Zug MR & MRS James W
Camp Hill .... 17011 .... Schoettle MR & MRS Timothy W
Camp Hill .... 17011 .... Vetterlein MR & MRS Frederick S
Canonsburg .... 15317 .... Dodds MRS Robert J JR
Chadds Ford .... 19317 .... Barringer MR C Minor
Chadds Ford .... 19317 .... Bell MR & MRS James E III
Chadds Ford .... 19317 .... Draper MR & MRS Ford B JR
Chadds Ford .... 19317 .... Gow MR Philip R
Chadds Ford .... 19317 .... Gowen MR & MRS George F JR
Chadds Ford .... 19317 .... Hoopes MS Ruth Snowdon
Chadds Ford .... 19317 .... Jordan MR & MRS F Peter JR
Chadds Ford .... 19317 .... May MRS Irénée du P
Chadds Ford .... 19317 .... Reed MR & MRS Austin
Chadds Ford .... 19317 .... Schutt MR & MRS Charles P JR
Chadds Ford .... 19317 .... Shedd MR & MRS Carl B Ely
Chadds Ford .... 19317 .... Timon MR & MRS Philip C
Chadds Ford .... 19317 .... Tobias MR & MRS Terrence A
Chadds Ford .... 19317 .... Waldron MR & MRS Adam A
Chadds Ford .... 19317 .... Walker MR & MRS Bayard JR
Chadds Ford .... 19317 .... Wells MR & MRS Peter Scoville
Chadds Ford .... 19317 .... Witherspoon MR & MRS Andrew J
Chalfont .... 18914 .... Donnon MR Edward D
Chester .... 19013 .... Barrow MR & MRS Kenneth P JR
Chester Springs .... 19425 .... Butler MRS Smedley D 3D
Chester Springs .... 19425 .... Dietrich MR Christian Braun
Chester Springs .... 19425 .... Dunn MR & MRS Thomas L
Chester Springs .... 19425 .... Fox MR & MRS Jarvis P
Chester Springs .... 19425 .... Fox MR Shawhan L
Chester Springs .... 19425 .... Fraley MRS Pierre C
Chester Springs .... 19425 .... Geer MRS R Taggart
Chester Springs .... 19425 .... Gober MR & MRS Robert D
Chester Springs .... 19425 .... Greeney MR & MRS Robert A
Chester Springs .... 19425 .... Hesler MR & MRS David M
Chester Springs .... 19425 .... Hollister MR & MRS A Dunham JR
Chester Springs .... 19425 .... Hornsey MR & MRS John W III
Chester Springs .... 19425 .... Jordan MRS Henry A
Chester Springs .... 19425 .... Judson MR & MRS Arthur 2D
Chester Springs .... 19425 .... Mannix MR & MRS Daniel P 5TH
Chester Springs .... 19425 .... McKechnie MRS Deborah S
Chester Springs .... 19425 .... McNeil MR & MRS Collin F
Chester Springs .... 19425 .... Milne MR & MRS David V
Chester Springs .... 19425 .... Mumma MR & MRS Kenneth B
Chester Springs .... 19425 .... Neilson MRS Lewis L
Chester Springs .... 19425 .... Ouwerkerk MR & MRS Pieter C
Chester Springs .... 19425 .... Richards MR & MRS Alfred N 3D
Chester Springs .... 19425 .... Scott MRS Warren T
Chester Springs .... 19425 .... Umberger MR & MRS Max J
Chester Springs .... 19425 .... Wiederseim MR Theodore E 3D
Chester Springs .... 19425 .... Wurts MR & MRS Christopher C J
Chester Springs .... 19425 .... Zimmerman MR & MRS Peter H
Chesterbrook .... 19087 .... Cauffman MR Philip P & McIlvain MS Marcia Jordan
Chesterbrook .... 19087 .... Eckert MRS Anne P
Chestnut Hill .... 19118 .... Biddle MISS Charlotte Hopkins
Chestnut Hill .... 19118 .... Farnum MRS Edward S W
Chestnut Hill .... 19118 .... Lukens DR & MRS J Nicholas
Chestnut Hill .... 19118 .... Myer MR & MRS Thomas J
Chestnut Hill .... 19118 .... Saylor MR & MRS Peter M
Coatesville .... 19320 .... Bright MR & MRS J Clayton
Coatesville .... 19320 .... Ensor MR & MRS Lawrence E III
Coatesville .... 19320 .... Fisher DR & MRS John R S
Coatesville .... 19320 .... Jenks MR & MRS Anthony W
Coatesville .... 19320 .... Malone MRS Mary Alice
Coatesville .... 19320 .... McNeil MR & MRS Robert D
Coatesville .... 19320 .... Rode MR Stephen W
Coatesville .... 19320 .... Roosevelt MR & MRS Thomas D
Coatesville .... 19320 .... Slater MR & MRS Samuel
Coatesville .... 19320 .... Wood MS Constance C
Cochranville .... 19330 .... Jenney MRS Marshall W
Cochranville .... 19330 .... Saunders MR & MRS Jesse D
Cochranville .... 19330 .... Thompson MR & MRS (DR) Gerald D
Collegeville .... 19426 .... Lamac MR & MRS Austin W
Collegeville .... 19426 .... McNelly MR & MRS Robert J
Collegeville .... 19426 .... Meschter MISS Amanda L
Collegeville .... 19426 .... Parker MR & MRS Garth R JR
Collegeville .... 19426 .... Risell MR & MRS David R
Collegeville .... 19426 .... Stafford MR & MRS Mark MacLeod
Collegeville .... 19426 .... Tenney MISS Elizabeth I
Collegeville .... 19426 .... Tillman MR & MRS Thomas J J
Conshohicken .... 19428 .... Marshall MR Edward S
Conshohocken .... 19428 .... Clark MR & MRS Edward C
Conshohocken .... 19428 .... Frazier MR & MRS B Graeme 4TH
Conshohocken .... 19428 .... MacNeill MR & MRS Fletcher H
Conshohocken .... 19428 .... Marshall DR Edward W 3D
& Bassert MS (DR) Joanna M
Conshohocken .... 19428 .... Sutherland MRS Malcolm J JR
Coopersburg .... 18036 .... Raab MR & MRS Henry Richard
Coopersburg .... 18036 .... Rodgers MR & MRS John L 3D
Danville .... 17821 .... Loughborough REV Robert H R
Denver .... 17517 .... Leach MR & MRS Peter T
Devon .... 19333 .... Baxter MR & MRS Richard B JR
Devon .... 19333 .... Brown MR & MRS W Thacher
Devon .... 19333 .... Butterworth MS Susan C
Devon .... 19333 .... Clement MR John K 3D
Devon .... 19333 .... Clements DR & MRS William W JR
Devon .... 19333 .... Cozens MRS Lee E
Devon .... 19333 .... de Luca MR & MRS Robert N
Devon .... 19333 .... Dewey MR & MRS Frederick N D
Devon .... 19333 .... Fleitas MR & MRS Albury N JR
Devon .... 19333 .... Harkins MR John G JR
Devon .... 19333 .... Harvey MR & MRS C Randolph
Devon .... 19333 .... Herz MR & MRS Frank Frederick IV
Devon .... 19333 .... Hurtado DR & MRS Alex C
Devon .... 19333 .... Ingersoll MRS Marie-Louise G
Devon .... 19333 .... Ingersoll MRS Melissa K
Devon .... 19333 .... Jackson MRS Millard H JR
Devon .... 19333 .... Jaeger MRS Eugene A
Devon .... 19333 .... Klaus MR & MRS Kenneth S
Devon .... 19333 .... Kline MR & MRS (DR) C Tomlinson III
Devon .... 19333 .... Lee MR & MRS Edward F
Devon .... 19333 .... Lewis MRS Howard H
Devon .... 19333 .... Livingston MR & MRS Clayton C
Devon .... 19333 .... Markle MR & MRS Alvan IV
Devon .... 19333 .... Marshall MR William B
Devon .... 19333 .... McCoy MR & MRS David M
Devon .... 19333 .... Neilson MR & MRS Carl L
Devon .... 19333 .... Peterson MRS Eleanor R
Devon .... 19333 .... Picard MR & MRS Daniel J
Devon .... 19333 .... Pierce MRS Cynthia W
Devon .... 19333 .... Preston MR & MRS Eugene C JR
Devon .... 19333 .... Roehrs MRS Walter E JR
Devon .... 19333 .... Rollins MR & MRS Richard II
Devon .... 19333 .... Royer MR Theodore W
Devon .... 19333 .... Steers DR & MRS (DR) John C JR

Devon, PA—Gladwyne, PA

Devon	19333	Stokes MR & MRS Edward B
Devon	19333	Teillon MR & MRS L Pierre JR
Devon	19333	Thacher MR & MRS John Hoover JR
Devon	19333	Todd MRS B Civitella
Devon	19333	Walker MR & MRS William M II
Devon	19333	Wheeler MR & MRS Samuel B 4TH
Devon	19333	Whiteman MR & MRS David B
Devon	19333	Wiederseim MR & MRS William B
Devon	19333	Woodville MR & MRS Richard W
Downington	19335	Fox MRS Brandi L
Downingtown	19335	Lohmann MR & MRS Charles P III
Doylestown	18901	DelPlato MR & MRS H Christopher
Doylestown	18901	Graff MR William E
Doylestown	18901	Lentz DR Charles W & Lentz MR Matthew Malinowski
Doylestown	18901	Neiley MR & MRS Richard B JR
Doylestown	18901	Ramsey MRS Mercy E
Doylestown	18901	Rockafellow MR Daniel B
Doylestown	18901	Warden MRS M Franca
Doylestown	18902	Frazier MR & MRS Christopher S JR
Doylestown	18902	Wells MR & MRS Jonathon H
Dresher	19025	Peirce MR Brian G
Drumore	17518	Gibson MR & MRS Douglas W
Drumore	17518	Gibson MR & MRS John McCullough
Drumore	17518	Gibson MR Christopher M
E Fallowfield	19320	Elkins DR & MRS William L
East Fallowfield	19320	Cauffman MRS Cynthia I
East Fallowfield	19320	Coyne MISS Anna E
East Fallowfield	19320	Rush MISS Deborah N
East Fallowfield	19320	Thorington MR & MRS Milby B
East Norriton	19401	McAtee MRS Swoyer
East Stroudsburg	18301	Doolittle MR William M
East Stroudsburg	18301	Harrison MR & MRS Robert Carter
Easton	18042	Cooke MR & MRS R Caswell III
Easton	18042	Junker MR C Peter
Edgemont	19028	MacDonnell MR & MRS Robert A
Elverson	19520	Brock MR & MRS Charles A
Elverson	19520	Christiansen MR & MRS Stephen B
Elverson	19520	Cochrane MR & MRS William J
Elverson	19529	Bartlett MR & MRS Lincoln R
Erdenheim	19038	Borie MR H Peter III
Erdenheim	19038	Connelly MR & MRS George M
Erdenheim	19038	Dhody MRS Dinesh C
Erdenheim	19038	Gilbert MR & MRS Theodore V JR
Erdenheim	19038	Peterson MRS Charles M JR
Erdenheim	19038	Taylor-Conner MRS Susan D
Erdenheim	19038	Warth MR Robert S
Erdenheim	19038	Whetzel MR & MRS William M
Erdenheim	19038	Worrall MISS Catherine A
Erie	16505	Ashcraft MS Nancy Olson
Erie	16505	McCracken MR David Jackson Beekman
Erie	16505	Murphy MR & MRS Mark
Erie	16505	Parry MR David L
Erie	16507	McCracken MRS Jackson
Erwinna	18920	Dorn MR & MRS John Z
Erwinna	18920	Roberts MR & MRS John L M
Exton	19341	Lukacs MRS Pamela
Exton	19341	Markle MRS John JR
Exton	19341	Saunders MR & MRS W Grier
Exton	19341	Taylor DR & MRS Alexander H
Fairview	16415	Mead THE HON & MRS John J IV
Fleetwood	19522	Schaeffer MR & MRS Daniel A
Flourtown	19031	Baker MR & MRS Newcombe C III
Flourtown	19031	Bast MR & MRS William L
Flourtown	19031	Biddle MR & MRS Livingston L IV
Flourtown	19031	Brady MR & MRS Anthony N
Flourtown	19031	Connell MR George W JR
Flourtown	19031	Cooke MRS S Graff
Flourtown	19031	Coste MRS Nicholas
Flourtown	19031	Daly MRS Joseph A
Flourtown	19031	Forjohn MR & MRS Daniel O
Flourtown	19031	Leininger MISS Linda L
Flourtown	19031	Littleton MR & MRS William H
Flourtown	19031	Low MR David B
Flourtown	19031	Pearson MR & MRS Stephen JR
Flourtown	19031	Randall MR & MRS Peter G
Flourtown	19031	Sheppard MR & MRS Carl F JR
Flourtown	19031	Sommaripa MRS Ann K
Flourtown	19031	Talbot MR & MRS John D II
Flourtown	19031	Thayer MR & MRS David B
Flourtown	19031	Tyson MR & MRS Charles R 3D
Flourtown	19031	Watson MR & MRS Scott M
Fourtown	19031	Raynor-Smith MR & MRS Spencer M
Ft Washington	19034	Robertson MR & MRS Bruce C JR
Ft Washington	19034	Sabo MR & MRS John P
Ft Washington	19034	Day MR & MRS Peter A
Ft Washington	19034	Glendinning MR & MRS R Bruce
Ft Washington	19034	Muir MR Charles G & Perot MRS S Baird
Ft Washington	19034	Sawyer MR & MRS Jonathan S
Ft Washington	19034	Test MS Bettina P
Furlong	18925	St Claire REV & MRS E Kyle JR
Gettysburg	17325	Hallberg LT COL (RET) Budd J & Jess MS Susan L
Gettysburg	17325	Hancock MR & MRS Thomas A
Gettysburg	17325	Henderlite MR & MRS John deS
Gettysburg	17325	Henry MR & MRS Guido Rombauer JR
Gettysburg	17325	Scott MRS Laurence S
Gibsonia	15044	Lloyd MR Charles F
Gladwyne	19035	Adamson MR & MRS L Talbot
Gladwyne	19035	Allen MR & MRS Thomas A
Gladwyne	19035	Annesley MR & MRS William H
Gladwyne	19035	Batt MRS Robert R
Gladwyne	19035	Bevan MRS (DR) Marcy R
Gladwyne	19035	Boenning MRS H Dickson S
Gladwyne	19035	Burch MR & MRS Robert L
Gladwyne	19035	Campbell MR & MRS John C E
Gladwyne	19035	Carr MR & MRS Richard R
Gladwyne	19035	Carson MRS James Tyson
Gladwyne	19035	Churchman MRS William B III
Gladwyne	19035	Clark MRS Frederic W
Gladwyne	19035	Clement MRS Frederick T J
Gladwyne	19035	Colen MR & MRS Joseph E JR
Gladwyne	19035	Collings MR Charles P
Gladwyne	19035	Conway MR & MRS Richard J
Gladwyne	19035	Cornell MISS Amy B
Gladwyne	19035	Cornman MRS Henry D 3D
Gladwyne	19035	Crawford MRS Russell H
Gladwyne	19035	Davis MRS William P 3D
Gladwyne	19035	Davis MS Betsey W
Gladwyne	19035	Dillon MRS Edward V
Gladwyne	19035	Doelger MR & MRS Matthew M
Gladwyne	19035	Edwards MS Mary H
Gladwyne	19035	Fischer MR C Henry 3D
Gladwyne	19035	French MR & MRS Harry B
Gladwyne	19035	Geisel MR C Meade JR
Gladwyne	19035	Getze MISS Susan M
Gladwyne	19035	Guenther MR & MRS Eric Edward L JR
Gladwyne	19035	Hamilton MR Richard 2D
Gladwyne	19035	Harris MR George B
Gladwyne	19035	Henderson MRS Gerald van S
Gladwyne	19035	Hopkins MRS R Stockton B
Gladwyne	19035	Huston MRS P Havemeyer
Gladwyne	19035	Kellett MR & MRS Morris C
Gladwyne	19035	Kirkland MRS Faris Russell

Gladwyne	19035	Lee MR & MRS Robert H JR
Gladwyne	19035	Lee MRS B Herbert
Gladwyne	19035	LeRoux MRS Jacques J
Gladwyne	19035	Lippincott MR & MRS Richard
Gladwyne	19035	Littleton MRS Arthur R
Gladwyne	19035	Lueders MRS Thomas L
Gladwyne	19035	Martin MRS David C
Gladwyne	19035	McCoy MRS John H
Gladwyne	19035	McLean MRS William L III
Gladwyne	19035	Montgomery MR & MRS John Lewis II
Gladwyne	19035	Pendergrass MRS Henry P
Gladwyne	19035	Platt MR & MRS Lucian B
Gladwyne	19035	Read MR & MRS William B III
Gladwyne	19035	Richards MR & MRS John H III
Gladwyne	19035	Rorer MR & MRS Herbert T
Gladwyne	19035	Sands MRS Robert J
Gladwyne	19035	Schneider MR & MRS Richard G
Gladwyne	19035	Schoettle MR & MRS Karl R JR
Gladwyne	19035	Scott MRS Margaret
Gladwyne	19035	Sheehan MR & MRS Mark A
Gladwyne	19035	Simonds MRS Robinson
Gladwyne	19035	Sinwell MR John W
Gladwyne	19035	Stick MR & MRS T Howard F
Gladwyne	19035	Thomas MR & MRS William P
Gladwyne	19035	Toland MRS Richard H R
Gladwyne	19035	Treadway MISS Caroline Worrell Harper Corbett
Gladwyne	19035	Treadway MR & MRS James Crispin Curran Corbett
Gladwyne	19035	Truscott MR & MRS William L
Gladwyne	19035	Tucker MR & MRS Frederick A JR
Gladwyne	19035	Waldron MR & MRS Arthur N
Gladwyne	19035	Wallace MRS Wallace H
Gladwyne	19035	Wessells MRS Daniel B
Gladwyne	19035	Wigton MRS Robert W JR
Gladwyne	19035	Williams MR & MRS Quincy N
Gladwyne	19035	Wood MR & MRS Alan 4TH
Gladwyne	19035	Wrightson MR & MRS William L III
Gladwyne	19035	Zug MR & MRS Thomas V JR
Gladwyne	19035	Zug MRS Sara Griswold
Glen Mills	19342	Willcox MR & MRS Mark III
Glen Mills	19342	Willcox MRS Mark JR
Glen Rock	17327	Ashton MR David A
Glenmoore	19343	Amidon MRS Charles S
Glenmoore	19343	Cochrane MR & MRS James A 4TH
Glenmoore	19343	Dolan MR & MRS Brooke K
Glenmoore	19343	Osborn MR & MRS Henry C 3D
Glenmoore	19343	St Georges MR & MRS Joseph F
Glenmoore	19343	Stevens MRS William J JR
Glenmoore	19343	Zook MR & MRS Dunwoody
Glenside	19038	Disston MR Henry JR
Glenside	19038	Edgar DR & MRS William 3D
Glenside	19038	Gray MRS Peyton Randolph
Glenside	19038	Greenleaf MRS Ellen W
Glenside	19038	Harmar MR & MRS Charles K
Glenside	19038	Lloyd MR & MRS Edward B
Glenside	19038	Saunders MRS E Randolph
Glenside	19038	Tasman MR & MRS W Graham
Greensburg	15601	Walthour MR Marshall B JR
Gulph Mills	19428	Hall MRS Craig M
Gwynedd	19436	Du Bois MRS Frederic M
Gwynedd	19436	Gibian MRS Paul P
Gwynedd	19436	Harper MR & MRS Jonathan M
Gwynedd	19436	Kellogg MR & MRS Howard
Gwynedd	19436	Lennig MR Charles K JR
Gwynedd	19436	Randall MRS Peter
Gwynedd	19436	Simons MRS S Stoney
Gwynedd Valley	19437	Claghorn MR & MRS Frederic S JR
Gwynedd Valley	19437	Harrison MR & MRS Randolph JR
Gwynedd Valley	19437	McAdoo MR Henry M JR
Hanover	17331	Glynn MRS Thomas A JR
Harrisburg	17101	Yellott MRS Anne J
Harrisburg	17102	Morrison MR David J
Harrisburg	17110	Woods MRS Charles A JR
Harrisburg	17112	Hickok MRS Daniel H
Harrisburg	17112	Morrison MRS George Le R
Hatfield	19440	Barclay MR & MRS Charles M
Haverford	15041	Wallick MR & MRS Daniel W
Haverford	19041	Ashton MR & MRS Thomas G JR
Haverford	19041	Baer MRS William G 2D
Haverford	19041	Barnett MRS Benjamin H JR
Haverford	19041	Brown DR & MRS Fraser H
Haverford	19041	Buck MRS J Mahlon JR
Haverford	19041	Burch MR & MRS Charles C
Haverford	19041	Campbell DR & MRS Robert E
Haverford	19041	Classen MRS Charles H
Haverford	19041	Clement MR & MRS Peter Withington
Haverford	19041	Collings MR & MRS Clifford C JR
Haverford	19041	Connell MR & MRS George W
Haverford	19041	Conrad MR & MRS William L
Haverford	19041	Cooke MISS Rebecca C
Haverford	19041	D'Angelo MR & MRS Christopher Scott
Haverford	19041	Daniels MR & MRS William G
Haverford	19041	Dayton MRS Alice S
Haverford	19041	de Rham MRS Charles
Haverford	19041	Devine DR & MRS (DR) John G JR
Haverford	19041	Dodge MR Charles L
Haverford	19041	Donahue MRS Frank R
Haverford	19041	Dunwoody MR & MRS Colin J
Haverford	19041	Egan MR Sean J
Haverford	19041	Ehret MISS Alexandra F
Haverford	19041	Ernst MR & MRS Charles A 4TH
Haverford	19041	Eyre MR & MRS William H JR
Haverford	19041	Fell MR & MRS John R III
Haverford	19041	Fisher MRS Robert M
Haverford	19041	Foster MR & MRS Timothy
Haverford	19041	Funk MRS Elmer Hendricks JR
Haverford	19041	Garno MR & MRS Edmund F III
Haverford	19041	Gill MR & MRS Bruce Cooper
Haverford	19041	Gregg MS Mary H
Haverford	19041	Hagin MR & MRS Robert L
Haverford	19041	Hamilton MR & MRS Nathaniel Peter
Haverford	19041	Harvey MR & MRS John S C 3D
Haverford	19041	Hires MRS William L
Haverford	19041	Hutton MS Carlotta Paxson
Haverford	19041	Jacobs MR & MRS Peter W
Haverford	19041	Justi MR & MRS Henry M
Haverford	19041	Kamp MR & MRS R Stephen
Haverford	19041	Kania MR & MRS Arthur J JR
Haverford	19041	Keene MR & MRS John C
Haverford	19041	Keith MR & MRS Sidney
Haverford	19041	Kennedy MR & MRS Mark B
Haverford	19041	Knight MR & MRS Charles C
Haverford	19041	Knight MRS Roma W
Haverford	19041	Kuensell MRS Scott L
Haverford	19041	La Motte MR & MRS Nicholas H
Haverford	19041	Leary MR H Michael B
Haverford	19041	Lee MR & MRS Stephen S
Haverford	19041	Leto MR & MRS Francis J
Haverford	19041	Lewis MR Andrew L 4TH
Haverford	19041	Lloyd MR & MRS H Gates
Haverford	19041	Marsh MR & MRS Harry A JR
Haverford	19041	Marshall MR & MRS Samuel R
Haverford	19041	Marx MR & MRS Graham A

To nominate a candidate for the Social Register Association, please email: SRCommittee@thesocialregister.org

Haverford	19041	McClenahan MRS John M
Haverford	19041	McFarland MR & MRS George C JR
Haverford	19041	Meschter MR G Andrew
Haverford	19041	Moore MR & MRS J Thomas
Haverford	19041	Newbold MR William T 2D
Haverford	19041	Oberdorf MRS E Joy
Haverford	19041	Piasecki MR & MRS Frederick W
Haverford	19041	Piasecki MRS Frank N
Haverford	19041	Pierce MR & MRS Leo W JR
Haverford	19041	Riley MR & MRS J Barton
Haverford	19041	Saunders MR & MRS Stuart T JR
Haverford	19041	Sayre MR & MRS Robert W
Haverford	19041	Schafer MRS Robert
Haverford	19041	Scullin MR & MRS John G
Haverford	19041	Selway MR & MRS James P III
Haverford	19041	Simpson MRS Zachary A
Haverford	19041	Smith MR & MRS Henry B duP
Haverford	19041	Smith MR & MRS Henry H JR
Haverford	19041	Smith MRS Cabanné C
Haverford	19041	Smith MRS Warren L JR
Haverford	19041	Sperry MR & MRS Richard S
Haverford	19041	St Claire MRS Elbert K
Haverford	19041	Steel MS Anna B
Haverford	19041	Stephanoff MR & MRS Alexander N
Haverford	19041	Stewardson MR Dana H
Haverford	19041	Strong MRS George V III
Haverford	19041	Thomas MR & MRS G Brinton
Haverford	19041	Trump MRS Robert Townshend
Haverford	19041	Vander Zwaag MR & MRS John B
Haverford	19041	Wallace MRS Frank Rich
Haverford	19041	Wallick MR & MRS Philip B
Haverford	19041	Ward MR E Smedley III
Haverford	19041	White MRS A Duritz
Haverford	19041	White MRS William Poe
Haverford	19041	Wilder MRS Diana Ott
Haverford	19041	Woehrle MR & MRS (DR) Christopher P
Haverford	19041	Wolffe MR & MRS Douglas H
Haverford	19041	Worth MRS Theron Huntting
Havertown	19041	Cox MR & MRS Charles H 3D
Havertown	19083	Christoph MR & MRS Blake M
Havertown	19083	Hepburn MRS Marion S
Havertown	19083	Jarvis MISS Sarah P
Havertown	19083	Mackey MR & MRS Michael V
Havertown	19083	Pidot MR & MRS Seth T
Hellertown	18055	Crofoot MRS David L
Hellertown	18055	Ritchey MR & MRS R Julian
Holland	18966	Prestegord MR & MRS Adam
Holland	18966	Van Gulick MRS Robert R
Hollidaysburg	16648	Rothrauff MR & MRS Donald L
Hollidaysburg	16648	Volpe MR & MRS Seth M
Honey Brook	19344	Baines MR Robert A
Honey Brook	19344	Darby MR & MRS D Weston JR
Honey Brook	19344	Gould MRS Curtis E L
Honey Brook	19344	Wilson MR & MRS Frederick E
Huntingdon Valley	19006	Bartlett DR & MRS Frederick H 3D
Huntingdon Valley	19006	Roden MR Lincoln 3D
Jenkintown	19046	Hill MRS Louis G
Jenkintown	19046	Zuccotti MR & MRS J Andrew
Kennett Square	19348	Baines MRS Ann A
Kennett Square	19348	Bowditch MR & MRS Nathaniel R
Kennett Square	19348	Britt MR & MRS Christopher D
Kennett Square	19348	Clarke MRS Bolling B
Kennett Square	19348	Cracknell MRS John V
Kennett Square	19348	Davis MR & MRS Peter D
Kennett Square	19348	Driscoll MRS Lee F JR
Kennett Square	19348	du Pont MR & MRS Alfred B
Kennett Square	19348	Duer MRS (DR) Susan R
Kennett Square	19348	Ervin MR & MRS Spencer JR
Kennett Square	19348	Glass MRS J Hall
Kennett Square	19348	Hutton MR & MRS James A
Kennett Square	19348	Hutz MR & MRS Rudolf E
Kennett Square	19348	Lofting MR & MRS Hugh
Kennett Square	19348	Lofting MRS Wendy W
Kennett Square	19348	Martin MR George W
Kennett Square	19348	Meserve MR & MRS Andrew E
Kennett Square	19348	Meserve MR & MRS Frederick L JR
Kennett Square	19348	Morrow MS Anne P
Kennett Square	19348	Peltz MR & MRS Henry B
Kennett Square	19348	Petersen MR & MRS James L
Kennett Square	19348	Pooley MRS John A
Kennett Square	19348	Rittenhouse MR Peter D
Kennett Square	19348	Rogers MR & MRS Frank H
Kennett Square	19348	Scott MR & MRS Sidney 3D
Kennett Square	19348	Slaymaker MRS R Barrie
Kennett Square	19348	Wagner MR & MRS Samuel
Kennett Square	19348	Wood MISS Elizabeth V
Kennett Square	19348	Ziesing MR & MRS Richard D JR
Kimberton	19442	Holt MR & MRS Stephen W
Kimberton	19442	Meinfelder MRS Edmond L 2D
Kimberton	19442	Scott MR & MRS John T
King of Prussia	19406	Cummin MR & MRS A Bevan
King of Prussia	19406	Dalstrom MR Theodore S & Skillern-Dalstrom MS Lia
King of Prussia	19406	Gibb MR John B
King of Prussia	19406	Leininger MRS Jennifer L
King of Prussia	19406	Wood MS Julianna
Kintnersville	18930	Karr MR & MRS George W JR
Lafayette Hill	19444	Adams MR Ellis C L
Lafayette Hill	19444	Biddle MRS Oliver C
Lafayette Hill	19444	Bonsall MRS Edward H III
Lafayette Hill	19444	Brownell MR & MRS Lawrence D
Lafayette Hill	19444	Crouter MR Henry E
Lafayette Hill	19444	DeMott MRS Richard W
Lafayette Hill	19444	Dinsmore MRS Francis William
Lafayette Hill	19444	Dixon MRS Fitz Eugene JR
Lafayette Hill	19444	Dolan MR Thomas 4TH
Lafayette Hill	19444	Driscoll MRS Sonya D
Lafayette Hill	19444	Du Bois MRS Samuel S M
Lafayette Hill	19444	Ferguson MRS William C
Lafayette Hill	19444	Garvan MRS Anthony N B
Lafayette Hill	19444	Glendinning MRS Robert 2D
Lafayette Hill	19444	Good MRS William F
Lafayette Hill	19444	Hutchinson MR Pemberton
Lafayette Hill	19444	Jenkins MRS Richard
Lafayette Hill	19444	Johnston MRS Hugh McB 3D
Lafayette Hill	19444	Jones MR & MRS Ellwood F JR
Lafayette Hill	19444	Lloyd MR & MRS Thomas
Lafayette Hill	19444	McCurdy MR John G
Lafayette Hill	19444	Murdoch MRS Lawrence C JR
Lafayette Hill	19444	O'Malley MR & MRS Brendan H
Lafayette Hill	19444	Pearson MRS Stephen
Lafayette Hill	19444	Peirce MRS W Grant 3D
Lafayette Hill	19444	Ritchie MR & MRS Thomas M JR
Lafayette Hill	19444	Roberts DR & MRS John M
Lafayette Hill	19444	Saunders MR Morton T
Lafayette Hill	19444	Schaefer MR & MRS Charles H
Lafayette Hill	19444	Sheble MRS John W
Lafayette Hill	19444	Starr MRS I Tatnall
Lafayette Hill	19444	Stewart MRS James M
Lafayette Hill	19444	Strong MR & MRS Newbold
Lafayette Hill	19444	Wallis MR & MRS Robert C
Lafayette Hill	19444	Washburn MR William Bogar
Lafayette Hill	19444	Wetherill MRS Elkins

Lafayette Hill, PA—Nazareth, PA

Lafayette Hill	19444	Williams MRS Matthews
Lafayette Hill	19444	Wistar MR & MRS C Cresson
Lafayette Hill	19444	Wood MR & MRS Theodore V JR
Lafayette Hill	19444	Wright MR Minturn T III
Lahaska	18931	Ray MR E Tinsley JR
Lancaster	17601	Hayward MR & MRS Robert B JR
Lancaster	17601	Slaymaker MR & MRS Samuel Cochran 3D
Lancaster	17601	Slaymaker MRS Samuel R 2D
Lancaster	17602	Farmer MR & MRS C Richard
Lancaster	17602	Hayward MR & MRS John R W
Lancaster	17602	Shafer MR G Carlton 3D
Lancaster	17603	Campbell DR & MRS John B
Lancaster	17603	Waters MR & MRS Thomas J
Landenberg	19350	Austin MRS Roger G J
Landenberg	19350	Jenks MR & MRS Philip V
Landenberg	19350	Marani MR & MRS Paul P
Landenberg	19350	Vetterlein MR & MRS James S
Lansdale	19446	Altemus MRS Edward Lee
Lansdale	19446	Czoernig von Czernhausen MRS Carl E
Lansdale	19446	Greenwood MR & MRS Thomas S
Lansdale	19446	Morris MRS Daniel I
Lansdale	19446	Patterson DR & MRS (DR) Joseph M III
Lansdale	19446	Smith MR Logan M
Laughlintown	15655	Côté MRS Edward T
Laughlintown	15655	Mellon MR & MRS Richard A
Laverock	19038	Biddle MR & MRS Ralph E JR
Lewisburg	17837	Anderson MR Stanley D
Ligonier	15658	Burkland MR & MRS William S
Ligonier	15658	Cathey MR & MRS John M
Ligonier	15658	Curry MRS Albert JR
Ligonier	15658	Elkus MRS Christopher J
Ligonier	15658	Fisher MR & MRS Chester G 3D
Ligonier	15658	Hoffstot MR & MRS Henry Phipps 3D
Ligonier	15658	Knapp MR & MRS William B
Ligonier	15658	McCullough MR & MRS George R
Ligonier	15658	Milbury MR & MRS Edwin Van R
Ligonier	15658	Reed MR & MRS H Mason JR
Limerick	19468	Saylor MR Harold D 2D
Lincoln University	19352	McCammon MR & MRS Joseph K 4TH
Lincoln University	19352	McIlvain MR & MRS J Gibson III
Lititz	17543	Michael MR & MRS Charles A SR
Littlestown	17340	Woodward MR James S JR
Lower Gwynedd	19002	Sargent MR & MRS Hugh A A
Macungie	18062	Berger DR & MRS Paul M
Macungie	18062	Howard MRS Thomas B
Macungie	18062	Sadtler MR & MRS Thomas MacL
Macungie	18062	Wilson MR & MRS William B
Malvern	19355	Borst MR & MRS Robert S
Malvern	19355	Brown MRS Bruce W
Malvern	19355	Cauffman MR & MRS George III
Malvern	19355	Chance MR Samuel K
Malvern	19355	Churchman MR & MRS W Morgan III
Malvern	19355	Claytor DR & MRS R Brannon
Malvern	19355	Claytor MR & MRS Warren Ingersoll
Malvern	19355	Coleman MISS Alexandra K
Malvern	19355	Colket MR & MRS Bryan D
Malvern	19355	Dixon MRS William J 3D
Malvern	19355	Evans MR & MRS James S
Malvern	19355	Francis MR & MRS Bernard A JR
Malvern	19355	Gilpin MRS Vincent JR
Malvern	19355	Gitlin MR & MRS Louis J
Malvern	19355	Howard MR & MRS William T
Malvern	19355	Hundt MR & MRS George S JR
Malvern	19355	Kennedy MR & MRS (DR) Raoul D
Malvern	19355	King MR Harold C
Malvern	19355	Mark DR & MRS W Steven
Malvern	19355	Morsman MS Kristin K
Malvern	19355	Nassau MR & MRS Henry N
Malvern	19355	Neel MISS Cynthia P
Malvern	19355	Newbold MR & MRS Arthur E 4TH
Malvern	19355	Palmer MR & MRS Raymond N
Malvern	19355	Robertson MR & MRS George W JR
Malvern	19355	Shoemaker MR & MRS William Reed
Malvern	19355	Simpson MR & MRS C Morgan
Malvern	19355	Smith MRS Linda Ball
Malvern	19355	Spahr MR & MRS Robert N
Malvern	19355	Sullivan MRS Ward
Malvern	19355	Tasman MRS S Haskins
Malvern	19355	Taylor MR & MRS Wilson H
Malvern	19355	Tyson MR J Gillmur III
Malvern	19355	Wall MR & MRS Michael A M
Malvern	19355	Wetherill MR & MRS Cortright JR
Malvern	19355	White MR & MRS Robert D
Malvern	19355	Williams MRS Alexandra P
Manayunk	19127	Trott MISS Christine A
Maple Glen	19002	Doviak MR Gregory J & Repplier MS (DR) Ann D
Maple Glen	19002	Lizell MR & MRS Paul A
Marcus Hook	19061	Lassen MR Christian K II
Marshallton	19382	Longmaid MRS David D
Mechanicsburg	17055	Pracht MRS Frederick R JR
Media	19063	Boyer MR John W JR
Media	19063	Brooks MR Clinton C
Media	19063	Chittenden MRS George H
Media	19063	Clyde MR & MRS William M
Media	19063	Fikse MR & MRS Andrew J
Media	19063	Gardner MRS Valerie P
Media	19063	Lewis MR & MRS Andrew A
Media	19063	Mitchell MR & MRS James F III
Media	19063	Moore MRS E Townsend
Media	19063	Moran MR & MRS Kevin R
Media	19063	Muhlenberg MR & MRS Kobi
Media	19063	Pepper MRS G Willing
Media	19063	Perry MR & MRS Lyman S A
Media	19063	Peters DR & MRS James C
Media	19063	Saylor MR & MRS J Michael
Media	19063	Schroeder MR N Thayer
Media	19063	Stephenson MRS Robert C
Media	19063	Thompson MISS Sara C
Media	19063	Thompson MR & MRS Fairman R
Media	19063	Wagner MR John
Media	19063	Watson MR & MRS James W
Media	19063	Zug REV & MRS Albert E R
Mendenhall	19357	Gummey MR & MRS Charles F
Merion Station	19066	Leibowitz MR & MRS (DR) Michael H
Merion Station	19066	Lynagh MR & MRS Aloysius P
Merion Station	19066	Pearson MR & MRS Alexander C
Merion Station	19066	Stevens MR & MRS James H
Merion Station	19066	Whelan MR & MRS Richard Q
Middlebury Center	16935	Price MR & MRS Willard L
Morgantown	19543	Neilson MR William H
Muncy	17756	Barlow MR Malcolm B
Murrysville	15668	Silbert REV Marion N
Narberth	19072	Bullitt MR William C
Narberth	19072	Chew MR Richard S JR
Narberth	19072	Harvey MR & MRS W F Atlee
Narberth	19072	Macfarlane MISS Jean P
Narberth	19072	Ravenscroft MR & MRS Philip M
Narberth	19072	Romine MR & MRS David E
Narberth	19072	Wilson DR William W
Narberth	19072	Worth MR Theron Huntting
Nazareth	18064	Connell MRS Robert J
Nazareth	18064	Cox MR & MRS James S

To nominate a candidate for the Social Register Association, please email: SRCommittee@thesocialregister.org

New Hope, PA— Philadelphia, PA

New Hope	18938	Hover MR & MRS John C II
New Hope	18938	Kanovsky MR & MRS Stephen M
New Hope	18938	Mitchell MR & MRS John D
New Hope	18938	Todd MR & MRS Frederic A de P
New Hope	18938	Warden MR & MRS P Jeffrey L
New Oxford	17350	Hardy MR & MRS Randolph Willson JR
Newtown	18940	Bennett MR & MRS (DR) Matthew MacGeorge
Newtown	18940	Bromley MR & MRS Edward P JR
Newtown	18940	Coyne MR & MRS Thomas H
Newtown	18940	Griffith MR & MRS Richard S JR
Newtown	18940	Griffith MR Peter C
Newtown	18940	Kyle DR George Clayton
Newtown	18940	Pennock MRS Caspar W A
Newtown	18940	Rossmassler MR & MRS Peter R
Newtown	18940	Woodger MR Bruce B
Newtown	19073	Wright MRS Margaret Z
Newtown Square	19073	Adams MR Brinton H
Newtown Square	19073	Alford MR & MRS Bryan J
Newtown Square	19073	Batchelder MRS Robert F
Newtown Square	19073	Black MR & MRS William T JR
Newtown Square	19073	Bowden MS Virginia Penniman
Newtown Square	19073	Brandt MS Jessamine
Newtown Square	19073	Cassidy MR & MRS Todd M
Newtown Square	19073	Cauffman MRS George
Newtown Square	19073	Churchman MRS Anne W
Newtown Square	19073	Clothier MR & MRS Isaac H 5TH
Newtown Square	19073	Conlan MRS Walter A JR
Newtown Square	19073	Cox MR & MRS Gary A
Newtown Square	19073	de Dominicis MR & MRS Danilo M
Newtown Square	19073	Devereux MR John C
Newtown Square	19073	Dewey MRS Carpenter
Newtown Square	19073	Doyle MR & MRS Matthew R
Newtown Square	19073	Engelbert MR & MRS Herbert
Newtown Square	19073	Ewing MRS Joseph N JR
Newtown Square	19073	Foreman MR Winfield A 3D & Soloviova MS Marina
Newtown Square	19073	Francis MR & MRS James B JR
Newtown Square	19073	Garson MRS Diana T
Newtown Square	19073	Gibson MR & MRS James E
Newtown Square	19073	Gordon MRS W Richard
Newtown Square	19073	Grace MR & MRS Charles B
Newtown Square	19073	Havens MRS Collier
Newtown Square	19073	Heiserman MRS Hewitt
Newtown Square	19073	Higgins MRS John F
Newtown Square	19073	Howe MRS Edward R JR
Newtown Square	19073	Hunter MR & MRS W Whitney
Newtown Square	19073	Ingersoll MRS Paul M
Newtown Square	19073	Jordan MRS F Peter
Newtown Square	19073	Kneass MRS George B
Newtown Square	19073	Kraftson MR & MRS Donald W
Newtown Square	19073	Lea MRS Francis C JR
Newtown Square	19073	Lerch MR & MRS Dana Thompson
Newtown Square	19073	Lerch MR & MRS Richard Jones T
Newtown Square	19073	Macdonald MR William M
Newtown Square	19073	MacElree MRS Lawrence E
Newtown Square	19073	McMullin MR & MRS David B
Newtown Square	19073	Newman MR & MRS John Winslow
Newtown Square	19073	O'Connell DR & MRS James R
Newtown Square	19073	O'Donnell MR & MRS Francis A JR
Newtown Square	19073	Riley MRS C Madison JR
Newtown Square	19073	Rippel MR & MRS Mark L
Newtown Square	19073	Roberts MRS T Williams JR
Newtown Square	19073	Rorer MR & MRS Jonathan B
Newtown Square	19073	Sellers MR & MRS Frank R S
Newtown Square	19073	Smith MR & MRS Langhorne B
Newtown Square	19073	Spahr MR & MRS C Stewart W
Newtown Square	19073	Thayer MS Margaretta
Newtown Square	19073	Van Alen MR & MRS James L II
Newtown Square	19073	Wadhams MRS Barbara P
Newtown Square	19073	Watson MR & MRS H Ross JR
Newtown Square	19073	Wehle MISS Edith M P
Newtown Square	19073	Wharton MR Heyward M
Newtown Square	19073	Willoughby MR & MRS Alan T
Newtown Square	19073	Wilson MR Scott O & Morse MS Anne S
Norristown	19403	Cadwalader MR Henry JR
Norristown	19403	McDaniel MR & MRS R Chase II
North Huntingdon	15642	Edgerton MR & MRS James P
North Wales	19454	Grove MR & MRS David D
North Wales	19454	Harrison MR & MRS John S
North Wales	19454	Pruitt MR & MRS Matthew T
North Wales	19454	Santa Maria MR Stephen M
North Wales	19454	Van Gulick MR & MRS Robert R JR
Norwood	19074	Greenwood MR Daniel B
Oreland	19075	Gray MR & MRS Robert G JR
Oreland	19075	Hager MR & MRS Alan J
Oreland	19075	Krumbhaar MR Peter D
Oreland	19075	Levy MR & MRS Adam S
Oreland	19075	Seus MR & MRS Thomas E
Oxford	19363	Lewis DR Maria L
Oxford	19363	Roosevelt MR & MRS Nicholas S
Paoli	19301	Auchincloss MR Thomas F D
Paoli	19301	Barnett MRS Elizabeth N
Paoli	19301	Bennett MRS Joseph Smith IV
Paoli	19301	Chaffe MRS John C
Paoli	19301	Chew MR & MRS John T III
Paoli	19301	Colket MR & MRS Tristram C JR
Paoli	19301	Cox MR & MRS Charles H
Paoli	19301	di Stefano MR & MRS Richard R P
Paoli	19301	Fridy MR & MRS John H
Paoli	19301	Gilbert MRS Dorothy P
Paoli	19301	Gresh MR & MRS Perry C
Paoli	19301	Harris MR & MRS W Gibson III
Paoli	19301	Holt MR & MRS Matthew W
Paoli	19301	Lewis MR & MRS Howard H JR
Paoli	19301	McElroy MR & MRS John J 3D
Paoli	19301	McKenna MR William R
Paoli	19301	Miller MR & MRS John A
Paoli	19301	Rollins MR Joseph R III
Paoli	19301	Smith MR & MRS Wilson L
Paoli	19301	Sterling MR & MRS Keith L
Paoli	19301	Stull MRS Lee T
Penllyn	19422	Murdoch MRS Allison H
Penllyn	19422	Stulb MR & MRS Edwin H 3D
Penllyn	19422	Trafford MR Perry
Penllyn	19422	Walbridge MS Elizabeth C
Penn Valley	19072	Purcell MR & MRS Andrew W
Penn Valley	19072	Seltzer DR & MRS Jonathan H
Perkiomenville	18074	Magill MR & MRS Jeffrey L
Philadelphia	19025	Moore MR Philip B
Philadelphia	19102	Campbell MR Angus C
Philadelphia	19102	Eden MR Avi D & Cooke MS Emanuela
Philadelphia	19102	Pilling MS (DR) Lucille B
Philadelphia	19102	Stanley MR Jason M
Philadelphia	19103	Brockway MR Julian S
Philadelphia	19103	Caulk MR & MRS John R III
Philadelphia	19103	Clothier MRS William J
Philadelphia	19103	Day MR Andrew
Philadelphia	19103	de Schauensee MISS Maude T
Philadelphia	19103	Doering MR Albert Lindsay IV
Philadelphia	19103	Domínguez MR & MRS Martín
Philadelphia	19103	Giordano MR & MRS John
Philadelphia	19103	Greene MR Edwin B JR
Philadelphia	19103	Hall MRS Katherine S K

Philadelphia	19103	Horne MRS Lee C
Philadelphia	19103	Jordan MR William J D
Philadelphia	19103	Leidy MR Carter R JR
Philadelphia	19103	Loubier MR & MRS Kirk A
Philadelphia	19103	Minott MR & MRS Joseph O
Philadelphia	19103	Montgomery MR Edward A JR
Philadelphia	19103	Park MR John N
Philadelphia	19103	Penrose MISS Christine
Philadelphia	19103	Randolph MR & MRS John
Philadelphia	19103	Rulon-Miller MR & MRS William L
Philadelphia	19103	Scott MR Ralph M S
Philadelphia	19103	Stuempfig MR Anthony A P
Philadelphia	19103	Terhune MR Andrew S & McMillen MS Janice E
Philadelphia	19103	Turner MR & MRS Evan H
Philadelphia	19103	Warden MR & MRS James Bryce
Philadelphia	19103	Whitehouse MISS Mary E
Philadelphia	19104	Montanaro MR Gregory P
Philadelphia	19104	Rust MR & MRS Langbourne W
Philadelphia	19104	Spears MR Wiley McC
Philadelphia	19104	Verkuil MR & MRS (DR) Paul R
Philadelphia	19106	Armistead MR & MRS Henry T
Philadelphia	19106	Auten MR & MRS David C
Philadelphia	19106	Buck MRS Gladys R
Philadelphia	19106	Davis MR & MRS Charles H
Philadelphia	19106	DeWyngaert MR & MRS Richard A
Philadelphia	19106	Huston MR & MRS Morrison C JR
Philadelphia	19106	Landreth MR & MRS Charles B
Philadelphia	19106	O'Neill DR Hugh
Philadelphia	19106	Riley MR Henry Barton
Philadelphia	19106	Sadtler MRS Samuel B
Philadelphia	19106	Sherk DR & MRS Henry H
Philadelphia	19106	Soutendijk MR & MRS Dirk R
Philadelphia	19106	Strawbridge MR & MRS Francis R 3D
Philadelphia	19106	Wilson MR & MRS G Ross
Philadelphia	19106	Young MS Sherley
Philadelphia	19107	Carr LT CDR DR & MRS (DR) Shamus R
Philadelphia	19107	LaValley MR Frederick M & Whitenight-LaValley MR John
Philadelphia	19107	Wister MS Noelle
Philadelphia	19113	Riley MR & MRS Phelps T
Philadelphia	19118	Agate MR & MRS Williams J JR
Philadelphia	19118	Aimette MR Alexander A M & Wirts MS Jennifer B
Philadelphia	19118	Baker MR James P
Philadelphia	19118	Baltzell MISS Virginia S
Philadelphia	19118	Beck MR & MRS Jeffrey F
Philadelphia	19118	Bell MRS James T
Philadelphia	19118	Betancourt MRS Raul
Philadelphia	19118	Bissell MR & MRS Rolin P
Philadelphia	19118	Boericke MR Gideon F
Philadelphia	19118	Cadwalader MR & MRS Gardner A
Philadelphia	19118	Carey MS Gretchen F
Philadelphia	19118	Claghorn MRS Frederic Strawbridge
Philadelphia	19118	Clark MRS Joseph Sill
Philadelphia	19118	Coates MR & MRS (DR) George G H JR
Philadelphia	19118	Conant MR & MRS Jonathan B
Philadelphia	19118	Converse MS Katherine W
Philadelphia	19118	Cope MRS Paul M JR
Philadelphia	19118	Coste MISS Suzanne Lloyd
Philadelphia	19118	Crimmins MR & MRS Patrick J
Philadelphia	19118	Dickey MR & MRS Robert 4TH
Philadelphia	19118	Diefenbach MR & MRS David P
Philadelphia	19118	Dilks MR & MRS Charles D
Philadelphia	19118	Driscoll MR & MRS Edward C
Philadelphia	19118	Driscoll MR & MRS Joseph E
Philadelphia	19118	Epperly MISS Melissa B
Philadelphia	19118	Ewing MR & MRS John H
Philadelphia	19118	Farnum MR & MRS Peter R
Philadelphia	19118	Fiechter MR & MRS Bayard R
Philadelphia	19118	Fifield MR & MRS Jason H
Philadelphia	19118	Fullerton MR & MRS Stuart L
Philadelphia	19118	Gadsden MR & MRS Christopher H
Philadelphia	19118	Gerbner MR & MRS John C
Philadelphia	19118	Griswold RT REV & MRS Frank T 3D
Philadelphia	19118	Hannafin MRS Frances H
Philadelphia	19118	Hine MR Edwin W 2D
Philadelphia	19118	Hirshorn MR & MRS Ralph S
Philadelphia	19118	Horan MRS Woodward
Philadelphia	19118	Hunter MRS Rosalie L
Philadelphia	19118	Ingersoll MRS Joseph R
Philadelphia	19118	Ingersoll MRS P Brock
Philadelphia	19118	Jarvis MR & MRS J Andrew
Philadelphia	19118	Johnson MR & MRS Craig N
Philadelphia	19118	Kerr MR & MRS Alexander
Philadelphia	19118	Kimberly MR & MRS John R
Philadelphia	19118	King MR & MRS Adrian R JR
Philadelphia	19118	Lee MR & MRS Charles T 3D
Philadelphia	19118	Leininger MRS Robert L
Philadelphia	19118	Lewis MR & MRS J Rodolphe M de S
Philadelphia	19118	Lloyd MRS Barsha B
Philadelphia	19118	Lloyd MRS Morris JR
Philadelphia	19118	Longstreth MR & MRS Peter S
Philadelphia	19118	Loring MR & MRS Thomas Bowen
Philadelphia	19118	Maloumian MR & MRS Royden M
Philadelphia	19118	Marshall MR & MRS George K JR
Philadelphia	19118	Marvin MR & MRS Peter F
Philadelphia	19118	McHugh MR & MRS Burton P JR
Philadelphia	19118	McNeely MR George H 4TH
Philadelphia	19118	Meigs MR & MRS John Forsyth 2D
Philadelphia	19118	Miller MRS M Benson
Philadelphia	19118	Morris MR & MRS Thomas B JR
Philadelphia	19118	Morris MRS James Shepherd
Philadelphia	19118	Moseley MRS Elaine
Philadelphia	19118	Murphy MR Martin N
Philadelphia	19118	Nalle MR & MRS Alexander B
Philadelphia	19118	Oberholtzer MRS Wendell W
Philadelphia	19118	O'Malley MRS Shaun F
Philadelphia	19118	Osborne MR & MRS Minturn S
Philadelphia	19118	Parker MR & MRS Christopher W
Philadelphia	19118	Pearson DR & MRS Philip Y
Philadelphia	19118	Pearson MR & MRS Eric Garfield
Philadelphia	19118	Peck MR & MRS Robert McC
Philadelphia	19118	Polk MR & MRS David C S
Philadelphia	19118	Price MR & MRS Philip JR
Philadelphia	19118	Rawls MR Henry P
Philadelphia	19118	Reichner COL (RET) & MRS Henry H JR
Philadelphia	19118	Reichner MR & MRS Henry F
Philadelphia	19118	Roberts DR & MRS Andrew B
Philadelphia	19118	Ruthrauff MRS L Williams
Philadelphia	19118	Schwartz MR & MRS Marshall L
Philadelphia	19118	Slaughter MR & MRS Frank G JR
Philadelphia	19118	Smith MRS Lewis du P
Philadelphia	19118	Snowden MR Richard Wood
Philadelphia	19118	Soroko MR & MRS John J
Philadelphia	19118	Spaeth MR & MRS Karl H JR
Philadelphia	19118	Stanley MR & MRS Peter G
Philadelphia	19118	Strasbaugh DR & MRS Wayne R
Philadelphia	19118	Taylor MR & MRS Lane JR
Philadelphia	19118	Taylor MR & MRS Nathaniel A
Philadelphia	19118	Taylor MS Abby Paine
Philadelphia	19118	Trayes MS (DR) Kathryn M
Philadelphia	19118	van Rooten MR Courtlandt H K
Philadelphia	19118	Van Sciver MR & MRS Joseph B III

Philadelphia, PA—Pittsburgh, PA

Philadelphia 19118 Vogt MR & MRS Brian J
Philadelphia 19118 Wainwright MR & MRS Robert B
Philadelphia 19118 Walters MR & MRS David L S
Philadelphia 19118 Ward MR & MRS Christopher L
Philadelphia 19118 Watson MS Faith C
Philadelphia 19118 West MR & MRS Ralph E JR
Philadelphia 19118 White MRS Lawrence P
Philadelphia 19118 Wirts DR & MRS Steven B
Philadelphia 19118 Woodward MR & MRS Charles
Philadelphia 19118 Woodward MR George 3D
Philadelphia 19118 Zimmermann MR John E III
Philadelphia 19119 Altemus MR Edward Lee JR
Philadelphia 19119 Barr MR & MRS Albert S IV
Philadelphia 19119 Day MR Christopher A & Lukens MS Elizabeth B
Philadelphia 19119 Dilks MRS Peter D
Philadelphia 19119 Duke MR & MRS Benjamin B
Philadelphia 19119 Emlen MR & MRS Thomas F
Philadelphia 19119 Ewing MR & MRS William H
Philadelphia 19119 Fleming MR & MRS Peter E
Philadelphia 19119 Lawrence MR & MRS Robert S JR
Philadelphia 19119 Lippincott MS Deborah W
Philadelphia 19119 Menocal MRS Alberto V
Philadelphia 19119 O'Malley MR & MRS Andrew W
Philadelphia 19119 Richardson MR & MRS Laurence B II
Philadelphia 19119 Schmidt MISS Elizabeth W
Philadelphia 19119 Swain MR & MRS Clifford H
Philadelphia 19119 Woodruff MRS Allen M
Philadelphia 19119 Wright MR & MRS John B II
Philadelphia 19121 Ashbridge MS Hewett McA
Philadelphia 19124 Read MR E Stoney 3D
Philadelphia 19125 Raynor-Smith MRS Murray
Philadelphia 19127 Pemberton MR & MRS Samuel H
Philadelphia 19128 Ashmead MRS Duffield III
Philadelphia 19128 Ballard MR & MRS Augustus S
Philadelphia 19128 Barton MRS Thomas C JR
Philadelphia 19128 Borden MR Frank H
Philadelphia 19128 Borie MRS A Clay
Philadelphia 19128 Borie MRS J R McAllister
Philadelphia 19128 Brégy MRS Philip A
Philadelphia 19128 Browne MRS Stanhope S
Philadelphia 19128 Congdon MRS James B
Philadelphia 19128 Emmons MRS Thomas P
Philadelphia 19128 Heckscher MRS Sarah S
Philadelphia 19128 Hood MR Clifford C R
Philadelphia 19128 Ingersoll MR Charles J II
Philadelphia 19128 Johnson MRS Lawrence JR
Philadelphia 19128 Jones MR & MRS Loren F
Philadelphia 19128 Latta MRS Cuthbert H
Philadelphia 19128 Lee DR & MRS Charles T JR
Philadelphia 19128 Mallery MRS Bayard M
Philadelphia 19128 Nalle MRS Jesse
Philadelphia 19128 Ripley MRS Edward F
Philadelphia 19128 Roberts MR & MRS George B JR
Philadelphia 19128 Seelye MRS Mary S
Philadelphia 19128 Sheffield MR & MRS Edwin S
Philadelphia 19128 Sinkler MR & MRS David D
Philadelphia 19128 Spaeth MR Karl H
Philadelphia 19128 Starr MR & MRS Harold P
Philadelphia 19128 Torrey MRS Carl G
Philadelphia 19128 Torrey MRS Philip C
Philadelphia 19128 Walton MR & MRS John M 3D
Philadelphia 19128 Wright MRS Spencer D III
Philadelphia 19129 Commons MR & MRS Harold T JR
Philadelphia 19129 Duncan MISS Charlotte D
Philadelphia 19129 Franklin MR & MRS (DR) Oliver St C
Philadelphia 19129 Mather MR & MRS Charles E 3D
Philadelphia 19129 Reifsnyder MR & MRS Henry G
Philadelphia 19130 Carter MR & MRS Samuel M
Philadelphia 19130 Denton MS Elizabeth C
Philadelphia 19130 Fieger MR & MRS Matthew T
Philadelphia 19130 Huber MR Thomas C
Philadelphia 19130 Kaminski MR & MRS Kevin M
Philadelphia 19130 Murphy MR Ryan J
Philadelphia 19130 Rauch MR & MRS Alfred 3D
Philadelphia 19130 Storey MR Bayard T
Philadelphia 19130 Tucker DR & MRS Robertson B
Philadelphia 19131 Rosen MRS M Patiño Treat
Philadelphia 19131 Stineman MRS J Wilbur
Philadelphia 19135 Mannal MRS Janice H
Philadelphia 19143 Rogers MR Bryan T & Whitbeck MS Caroline N
Philadelphia 19144 Adamson MR Ames
Philadelphia 19144 Hepburn MR & MRS Charles McG
Philadelphia 19144 Slaymaker DR & MRS William W
Philadelphia 19146 Benson MR Perry JR
Philadelphia 19146 Berresford MISS Nancy C
Philadelphia 19146 Cadwalader MS Sandra L
Philadelphia 19146 Chambers MR & MRS Michael T E
Philadelphia 19146 Crowell MR & MRS Jonathan L
Philadelphia 19146 D'Angelo MR & MRS J Robert
Philadelphia 19146 Davies MRS Frances R
Philadelphia 19146 Longenecker DR & MRS (DR) Andrew S
Philadelphia 19146 McConnel MISS Mary Blair
Philadelphia 19146 Melby MR & MRS Garrett D
Philadelphia 19146 Pagano MR & MRS Richard F
Philadelphia 19146 Rooney MR & MRS Ronald G
Philadelphia 19146 Rynning DR & MRS (DR) Ralph E
Philadelphia 19146 Willard MR John O
Philadelphia 19147 Angelides MS Marica Pariante
Philadelphia 19147 Edwards MR & MRS Sean C
Philadelphia 19147 Ewing MISS (DR) Madeleine Q
Philadelphia 19147 Geyelin MR Antony L 3D
Philadelphia 19147 Godfrey MISS Marian A
Philadelphia 19147 Keates MR Charles P
Philadelphia 19147 McCabe MR & MRS Thomas B IV
Philadelphia 19147 Rother MRS W Klaus H
Philadelphia 19147 Smith MR & MRS Courtney C JR
Philadelphia 19147 Tucker MR & MRS Matthew H
Philadelphia 19148 McGuinness MR & MRS Trevor S
Philadelphia 19148 Minott MR John H C
Phoenixville 19460 Clement MRS S Beale
Phoenixville 19460 Eddy MR & MRS David A
Phoenixville 19460 Geisel MR G Stuart
Phoenixville 19460 Geyelin MR & MRS Anthony A
Phoenixville 19460 Ghosh MR & MRS Amit
Phoenixville 19460 Illoway MR & MRS L Stockton
Phoenixville 19460 Klotzbach MR & MRS Hans J
Phoenixville 19460 Leith MRS Kelly H
Phoenixville 19460 Morris MRS Galloway C 4TH
Phoenixville 19460 Murphy MISS Virginia M
Phoenixville 19460 Newbold MRS Arthur E 3D
Phoenixville 19460 Riegl MR & MRS Edward J
Phoenixville 19460 Ross MR & MRS Thomas E
Phoenixville 19460 Siolek MR & MRS Raymond S
Phoenixville 19460 Sullivan MR & MRS Robert W
Phoenixville 19460 Tilghman MR & MRS John S
Phoenixville 19460 Tucker MR & MRS William L
Phoenixville 19460 Wood MISS Margaretta D
Pineville 18946 Chandor MR & MRS Christopher B
Pipersville 18947 Sigety MR & MRS Cornelius E
Pipersville 18947 Sigety MR Robert G
Pittsburgh 15201 Fisher MR & MRS Timothy O
Pittsburgh 15201 Porteous MRS Robert E

Pittsburgh........................ 15206.......... Fisher MRS Sheila A
Pittsburgh........................ 15206.......... Moore MR & MRS John T B
Pittsburgh........................ 15206.......... Moore MR G Dwight
Pittsburgh........................ 15206.......... Scott MISS Diana M
Pittsburgh........................ 15206.......... Scott MR & MRS John H
Pittsburgh........................ 15206.......... Slaymaker MR & MRS R Barrie JR
Pittsburgh........................ 15208.......... Bissell MR & MRS G William
Pittsburgh........................ 15208.......... Roberts MR William D
Pittsburgh........................ 15208.......... Wheeler MISS Deirdre W
Pittsburgh........................ 15211.......... Levick MRS Dudley A JR
Pittsburgh........................ 15211.......... Young MRS Ledlie W JR
Pittsburgh........................ 15213.......... Barry DR Herbert III
Pittsburgh........................ 15213.......... Block MR John R
Pittsburgh........................ 15213.......... Ebbert MRS James Kay
Pittsburgh........................ 15213.......... Egbert MR Richard Cook JR
Pittsburgh........................ 15213.......... Hillman MR Henry L
Pittsburgh........................ 15213.......... Hunter MRS James G
Pittsburgh........................ 15213.......... Jannetta MRS Peter J
Pittsburgh........................ 15213.......... Lynch MRS Hilary G
Pittsburgh........................ 15213.......... Read MR & MRS Robert O JR
Pittsburgh........................ 15213.......... Sheehan MR Thomas E
Pittsburgh........................ 15213.......... Smith MR Mark T V O
Pittsburgh........................ 15213.......... Thompson MR & MRS Harry A 2D
Pittsburgh........................ 15215.......... Follansbee MRS N Walton
Pittsburgh........................ 15215.......... Garrett DR & MRS William S JR
Pittsburgh........................ 15215.......... Jones MS Katharine H
Pittsburgh........................ 15215.......... Thompson MR & MRS Douglas A
Pittsburgh........................ 15217.......... Adibi DR & MRS Siamak A
Pittsburgh........................ 15217.......... Brown MR & MRS William J W
Pittsburgh........................ 15217.......... Cox MR & MRS Basil M
Pittsburgh........................ 15217.......... Douglas MR & MRS John W JR
Pittsburgh........................ 15217.......... Duff MRS John M
Pittsburgh........................ 15217.......... Fisher MR & MRS Henry
Pittsburgh........................ 15217.......... Fisher MRS James A
Pittsburgh........................ 15217.......... Love MRS Howard McC
Pittsburgh........................ 15217.......... Robinson MR & MRS Frank Brooks
Pittsburgh........................ 15217.......... Schoyer MR & MRS Edward H
Pittsburgh........................ 15217.......... Stephaich MRS (DR) Peter H
Pittsburgh........................ 15217.......... Stephenson MRS Robert L
Pittsburgh........................ 15217.......... Tucker MRS Richard B
Pittsburgh........................ 15218.......... Mercer MR Richard D JR
Pittsburgh........................ 15224.......... Conrad MR David C
Pittsburgh........................ 15228.......... Smith MR & MRS Templeton JR
Pittsburgh........................ 15232.......... Battle MRS Margaret Ritchie R
Pittsburgh........................ 15232.......... Cheever MR & MRS George M
Pittsburgh........................ 15232.......... Frank MR Alan I W
Pittsburgh........................ 15232.......... Harbison MR & MRS Samuel P 3D
Pittsburgh........................ 15232.......... Hillman MR & MRS David McL
Pittsburgh........................ 15232.......... Hunt MR & MRS Torrence M JR
Pittsburgh........................ 15232.......... Moore MRS J Brodhead
Pittsburgh........................ 15232.......... Moreland MR & MRS W Ford 2D
Pittsburgh........................ 15232.......... Muse MR & MRS Albert C
Pittsburgh........................ 15232.......... Scaife MR & MRS David N
Pittsburgh........................ 15232.......... Schmidt MR Thomas M
Pittsburgh........................ 15232.......... Scott MR & MRS Richard S
Pittsburgh........................ 15232.......... Stephaich MR Peter H
Pittsburgh........................ 15238.......... Coleman MR & MRS Jack H
Pittsburgh........................ 15238.......... Gaier MR & MRS Mark J
Pittsburgh........................ 15238.......... Hansen MRS Stephen C
Pittsburgh........................ 15238.......... Heiner MR & MRS David A
Pittsburgh........................ 15238.......... Heiner MRS William G JR
Pittsburgh........................ 15238.......... McKnight MR & MRS Stephen H
Pittsburgh........................ 15238.......... Mosle MRS William B JR
Pittsburgh........................ 15238.......... Roberts MR & MRS Philip R
Pittsburgh........................ 15238.......... Runnette MR & MRS Robert G
Pittsburgh........................ 15238.......... Thompson MR & MRS Michael A
Pittsburgh........................ 15238.......... Willock MR & MRS George J 3D
Pittsburgh........................ 15243.......... Evans MR & MRS Thomas Goodwin
Plymouth Meeting........ 19462.......... Leininger MR Robert D
Plymouth Meeting........ 19462.......... Peirce MR & MRS Robin J
Plymouth Meeting........ 19462.......... Sheppard MR & MRS Winston C
Plymouth Meeting........ 19462.......... Talbot MR & MRS James M II
Plymouth Meeting........ 19462.......... Thomson MR & MRS Robert G
Pocono Lake Preserve.. 18348.......... Lowry MRS (DR) Barbara S
Pocono Pines................. 18350.......... Robb MR & MRS G B Garrett
Pocono Pines................. 18350.......... Willis MRS Cynthia
Pocopson........................ 19366.......... Roosevelt MR & MRS Henry L
Portland.......................... 18351.......... Walton MRS Henry Foster 3D
Pottstown........................ 19464.......... Hennessey MR Timothy B
Pottstown........................ 19465.......... Hallowell MR Edward R
Pottstown........................ 19465.......... Harvey MRS Gregory M
Pottsville........................ 17901.......... Walsh MRS Basil S 3D
Quakertown.................. 18951.......... La Farge MISS Elizabeth
Quakertown.................. 18951.......... Meredith MR & MRS Charles M III
Quakertown.................. 18951.......... Sinatra MR & MRS Tynan L
Radnor............................ 19087.......... Alexandre MRS Lawrence
Radnor............................ 19087.......... Bentley MR & MRS James A JR
Radnor............................ 19087.......... Chance MR & MRS Steven K
Radnor............................ 19087.......... Chew MR Samuel JR
Radnor............................ 19087.......... Claytor MR & MRS Norris Vaux
Radnor............................ 19087.......... Coffin MRS Susanne M
Radnor............................ 19087.......... Crowell MR & MRS James L
Radnor............................ 19087.......... Forte MR & MRS (DR) Earl M 3D
Radnor............................ 19087.......... Goodman MR & MRS Edward T
Radnor............................ 19087.......... Gray MR & MRS Robert L 3D
Radnor............................ 19087.......... Heintz MR & MRS Paul C A
Radnor............................ 19087.......... Hepburn MR & MRS Austin Barry JR
Radnor............................ 19087.......... Humphrey DR David McC & McCluskey MS Gayla J
Radnor............................ 19087.......... Jennings MR & MRS James W
Radnor............................ 19087.......... Kellett MR & MRS Roderick C
Radnor............................ 19087.......... Krout MRS John E
Radnor............................ 19087.......... Leaman MRS Benjamin F
Radnor............................ 19087.......... MacCain MR & MRS James P 2D
Radnor............................ 19087.......... McAdoo MR & MRS McKinley Campbell
Radnor............................ 19087.......... Moore MRS Rudolph A
Radnor............................ 19087.......... Paul MR & MRS Anthony J D 3D
Radnor............................ 19087.......... Paul MRS Wendy D
Radnor............................ 19087.......... Raymer MR & MRS John Hutcheson
Radnor............................ 19087.......... Riley MR & MRS Thomas A III
Radnor............................ 19087.......... Smartt MR & MRS James M
Radnor............................ 19087.......... Smith MR & MRS H Morgan
Radnor............................ 19087.......... Smith MRS David S J
Radnor............................ 19087.......... Sparkman DR & MRS Thorne JR
Radnor............................ 19087.......... Stengel MR & MRS Geoffrey JR
Radnor............................ 19087.......... Stevenson MISS Annette P
Radnor............................ 19087.......... Stine MR Jonathan E
Radnor............................ 19087.......... Strawbridge MR David W
Radnor............................ 19087.......... Tatnall MR & MRS Francis G
Radnor............................ 19087.......... Williams MR & MRS Carter D
Radnor............................ 19087.......... Witcher MR & MRS Robert L
Reading.......................... 19605.......... Vanderbeck MISS Tabitha
Reading.......................... 19605.......... Vanderbeck MR & MRS Samuel R III
Reading.......................... 19606.......... Mohr MISS Ann
Reading.......................... 19606.......... Ruffing MR John J JR
Reading.......................... 19607.......... Da Costa MR Peter M
Reading.......................... 19610.......... Hildreth DR Eugene A
Rector.............................. 15677.......... Mellon MR & MRS Armour N
Rector.............................. 15677.......... Miller MR & MRS George B B
Rector.............................. 15677.......... Mudge MR & MRS Edmund T 4TH
Rector.............................. 15677.......... Van Ingen MR & MRS William B
Red Lion.......................... 17356.......... Wilson MR Charles W
Revere............................ 18953.......... Carey MISS Emily N

To nominate a candidate for the Social Register Association, please email: SRCommittee@thesocialregister.org

Riegelsville, PA—Villanova, PA

Riegelsville.......... 18077.......... Hutchinson DR & MRS Richard W
Robesonia.......... 19551.......... Altemus MR & MRS Nicholas W
Rosemont.......... 19010.......... Bingenheimer MR & MRS Thomas E
Rosemont.......... 19010.......... Goff MR & MRS Stephen
Rosemont.......... 19010.......... Hodges MR & MRS Thomas V
Rosemont.......... 19010.......... Howard MR & MRS Robert M
Rosemont.......... 19010.......... Kaier MR & MRS Edward J
Rosemont.......... 19010.......... Kirkpatrick MR & MRS Jack H JR
Rosemont.......... 19010.......... Kremer MRS J Lee
Rosemont.......... 19010.......... Laveran-Stiebar DR & MRS Rudolf L
Rosemont.......... 19010.......... Logan MS Virginia A
Rosemont.......... 19010.......... McIlvain MR & MRS Alan JR
Rosemont.......... 19010.......... Mount MR & MRS Jonathan G
Rosemont.......... 19010.......... Packer MRS John B
Rosemont.......... 19010.......... Page MRS P Bradshaw
Rosemont.......... 19010.......... Porter MR & MRS A Hobart
Rosemont.......... 19010.......... Rauch MR & MRS Alfred JR
Rosemont.......... 19010.......... Revell MRS Alexander H III
Rosemont.......... 19010.......... Rogers MR & MRS Robert G JR
Rosemont.......... 19010.......... Souder MISS Margaret L
Rosemont.......... 19010.......... Thompson MR & MRS Radclyffe F
Rosemont.......... 19010.......... Wargo MR & MRS Charles F
Rosemont.......... 19010.......... Weary MRS Thomas S
Rosemont.......... 19010.......... Wermuth MR & MRS William C 5TH
Rosemont.......... 19010.......... Wheelock DR & MRS E Frederick
Roslyn.......... 19001.......... Weiler MR & MRS Joseph F JR
Rydal.......... 19046.......... Hamilton MR & MRS William G 3D
Rydal.......... 19046.......... MacColl MR & MRS Norman A 3D
Rydal.......... 19046.......... Murray MR & MRS Karl S
Saint Davids.......... 19087.......... Knight MR & MRS Mark W
Scranton.......... 18503.......... Freeman MRS Murray F
Sellersville.......... 18960.......... Thompson MR & MRS Henry F
Sewickley.......... 15143.......... Brakenridge MS Bonnie S
Sewickley.......... 15143.......... Brown MRS Fitzhugh L
Sewickley.......... 15143.......... Childs MRS Clinton L JR
Sewickley.......... 15143.......... Davis MR & MRS Stephen C
Sewickley.......... 15143.......... de Haven MR & MRS William T
Sewickley.......... 15143.......... Dodds MR & MRS Anthony J
Sewickley.......... 15143.......... Edson MR & MRS John Joy V
Sewickley.......... 15143.......... Gebhardt MRS Ronald E
Sewickley.......... 15143.......... Haines DR & MRS James B
Sewickley.......... 15143.......... Kipp MISS Donna L
Sewickley.......... 15143.......... Lowe MRS Charles U
Sewickley.......... 15143.......... Macdonald REV CANON DR & MRS John A
Sewickley.......... 15143.......... Merryman MS Frances Love
Sewickley.......... 15143.......... Metcalf MRS William 3D
Sewickley.......... 15143.......... Moorhead MR & MRS Thomas C JR
Sewickley.......... 15143.......... Nichols MRS Clifford JR
Sewickley.......... 15143.......... Porter LT COL DR & MRS Paul S JR
Sewickley.......... 15143.......... Schroeder MR J Howison
Sewickley.......... 15143.......... Schroeder MRS A Reed
Sewickley.......... 15143.......... Sculley MR David W
Sewickley.......... 15143.......... Singer MR G Harton 3D
Sewickley.......... 15143.......... Smith MR & MRS Richard C
Sewickley.......... 15143.......... Snyder MR & MRS J Brandon
Sewickley.......... 15143.......... Snyder MR & MRS William P 3D
Sewickley.......... 15143.......... Sullivan MRS Henry P
Sewickley.......... 15143.......... Tarasi MS Elizabeth M
Sewickley.......... 15143.......... Thompson MRS LeRoy
Sewickley.......... 15143.......... Thomson MRS Leon T
Sewickley.......... 15143.......... Trent MRS Stephane
Sewickley.......... 15143.......... Viall MR & MRS Richmond III
Sewickley.......... 15143.......... Zimmerman MR & MRS John G JR
Shippensburg.......... 17257.......... Brooks DR Clifford W JR
Shrewsbury.......... 17361.......... Hollyday MISS Louise Este
Skytop.......... 18357.......... McHugh MRS Burton P
Solebury.......... 18963.......... Darlington MR & MRS Jesse M
Solebury.......... 18963.......... Downie MRS Dorothy S
Southampton.......... 18966.......... Biddle MR & MRS Stephen A
Spring House.......... 19477.......... Jennings MR Christopher R JR
St Davids.......... 19087.......... Auchincloss MR & MRS Richard S JR
St Davids.......... 19087.......... Confer MR & MRS James M
St Davids.......... 19087.......... Davison MR & MRS John E JR
St Davids.......... 19087.......... Driscoll MR & MRS Robert W JR
St Davids.......... 19087.......... Gaunt MR & MRS William L
St Davids.......... 19087.......... Geyelin MRS Susan H
St Davids.......... 19087.......... Manganaro MR Nicholas W M
St Davids.......... 19087.......... Pelaez MR & MRS Jorge L
St Davids.......... 19087.......... Pendergast MRS Stephen H
St Davids.......... 19087.......... Rogers MR & MRS James G
St Davids.......... 19087.......... Ross MR & MRS Thomas H
St Davids.......... 19087.......... Siedlarz MR & MRS Joseph B 3D
St Davids.......... 19087.......... Spofford MRS Virginia S
St Davids.......... 19087.......... Twitmyer MR & MRS Robert Y
St Davids.......... 19087.......... Tyler MR & MRS Michael E
Stahlstown.......... 15687.......... Armstrong MR & MRS Henry H
Stahlstown.......... 15687.......... Childs MR & MRS Harvey JR
Stahlstown.......... 15687.......... Laskow MR & MRS Mark J
Stahlstown.......... 15687.......... Nelson MR & MRS B Gordon III
Stahlstown.......... 15687.......... O'Neill MR & MRS Bertram L JR
Stahlstown.......... 15687.......... Widing MR & MRS Eric P
State College.......... 16801.......... Rath MR & MRS M Peter
State College.......... 16803.......... Winsor MR & MRS Philip
Strafford.......... 19087.......... Hill MRS J Bennett JR
Strafford.......... 19087.......... Ingersoll MR H Warren
Strafford.......... 19087.......... Irey MRS I Grant JR
Strafford.......... 19087.......... Pearson MR David R
Strafford.......... 19087.......... Young MR & MRS Alexander S
Stroudsburg.......... 18360.......... Walker MR & MRS Graham McK
Swarthmore.......... 19081.......... Greenwood MR & MRS Richardson C
Swarthmore.......... 19081.......... Kent MR & MRS Donald W JR
Swartmore.......... 19081.......... Brien MR & MRS R Frederick JR
Thornton.......... 19373.......... Malloy MRS (DR) Charles B
Trumbauersville.......... 18970.......... McCormick MRS Jane Putnam
Unionville.......... 19375.......... Cadwalader MR Anthony J D
Unionville.......... 19375.......... Coyne MR Charles C
Unionville.......... 19375.......... Fisher DR & MRS (DR) J Rush S JR
Unionville.......... 19375.......... Glaccum MR & MRS Denis M
Unionville.......... 19375.......... Glaccum MRS Anne E
Unionville.......... 19375.......... Reese DR & MRS Charles L 4TH
Unionville.......... 19375.......... Rush DR & MRS Lockwood
Unionville.......... 19375.......... Scott MR Edgar JR
Unionville.......... 19375.......... Slater MS Joy L
Unionville.......... 19375.......... Swett MR Thomas C
Unionville.......... 19375.......... Thayer MR & MRS R Dixon
Unionville.......... 19375.......... Wood MR & MRS Crosby
Valley Forge.......... 19481.......... Drayton MR & MRS Geoffrey W
Valley Forge.......... 19481.......... Taggart MR & MRS Rush 3D
Verona.......... 15147.......... Atwell DR & MRS Robert B
Verona.......... 15147.......... Crandon MRS A Seabury JR
Verona.......... 15147.......... Grimstad MR & MRS Charles M
Verona.......... 15147.......... Hallahan MR & MRS Donald G
Verona.......... 15147.......... McCullough MRS C Hax JR
Verona.......... 15147.......... Page MR & MRS David Arthur
Verona.......... 15147.......... Person MRS Solon A III
Verona.......... 15147.......... Smyth MRS D Grahame
Verona.......... 15147.......... Thornburgh MR & MRS Richard L
Verona.......... 15147.......... Widdoes MRS W Peirce
Villanova.......... 19085.......... Archer MR & MRS Pierce
Villanova.......... 19085.......... Baker MR Harold W 3D
Villanova.......... 19085.......... Bissinger MR Frederick L JR
Villanova.......... 19085.......... Blain MRS Deirdre G

Villanova, PA—Wayne, PA

Villanova ... 19085 ... Blynn MR & MRS H Reid JR
Villanova ... 19085 ... Borda MRS Charles A 3D
Villanova ... 19085 ... Buck MR & MRS William C
Villanova ... 19085 ... Cadwalader MR & MRS R Kent
Villanova ... 19085 ... Carper MR & MRS Nicholas Wood
Villanova ... 19085 ... Chapman MRS E Blackwell JR
Villanova ... 19085 ... Clement MR & MRS Frederick T J JR
Villanova ... 19085 ... Cullen MR & MRS Craig W
Villanova ... 19085 ... Cunningham MR & MRS John J
Villanova ... 19085 ... Curran MR & MRS William T
Villanova ... 19085 ... Davis MRS Murdoch
Villanova ... 19085 ... Dearden MR & MRS Edward C 3D
Villanova ... 19085 ... DuBarry MR & MRS Joseph N V
Villanova ... 19085 ... Duff MR & MRS Richard M III
Villanova ... 19085 ... Farrell MR & MRS Michael J
Villanova ... 19085 ... Frick MR & MRS Benjamin C
Villanova ... 19085 ... Friend DR Theodore W 3D
Villanova ... 19085 ... Graham MR & MRS Philip L
Villanova ... 19085 ... Groome MR & MRS Harry C 3D
Villanova ... 19085 ... Havens MR & MRS Peter H
Villanova ... 19085 ... Hitschler MR & MRS W Anthony
Villanova ... 19085 ... Hoffman MR David F
Villanova ... 19085 ... Houghton MR & MRS Neil L
Villanova ... 19085 ... Humann MR & MRS Francis J
Villanova ... 19085 ... Hummeler MRS Klaus
Villanova ... 19085 ... Jacobs MR Francis B 2D
Villanova ... 19085 ... Keene MISS Katharine
Villanova ... 19085 ... Kraftson MR & MRS Raymond H
Villanova ... 19085 ... Lammers MRS Suzanne K
Villanova ... 19085 ... Lanni MRS Allison D
Villanova ... 19085 ... Laverell MR & MRS Judson D II
Villanova ... 19085 ... Lemmon MR & MRS George B JR
Villanova ... 19085 ... Long MR & MRS Walter T
Villanova ... 19085 ... Mackie MRS Julius A JR
Villanova ... 19085 ... Maner MR & MRS Walter P IV
Villanova ... 19085 ... Marinchak DR & MRS Roger A
Villanova ... 19085 ... Merriman MR & MRS Richardson T
Villanova ... 19085 ... Moneta MISS Judith A
Villanova ... 19085 ... Morris MR & MRS I Wistar 3D
Villanova ... 19085 ... Murdoch MR & MRS Britton
Villanova ... 19085 ... Neilson MR & MRS Lewis L JR
Villanova ... 19085 ... Pew MRS George L
Villanova ... 19085 ... Pilkington MR & MRS Charles F
Villanova ... 19085 ... Porter MR Andrew W JR
Villanova ... 19085 ... Rawlings MR & MRS Peter Sayres
Villanova ... 19085 ... Reed MR & MRS Alan L
Villanova ... 19085 ... Remer MS M Scott
Villanova ... 19085 ... Rittenhouse MISS Kendall A
Villanova ... 19085 ... Roberts MRS Noma Ann
Villanova ... 19085 ... Smith MR & MRS Stockton N
Villanova ... 19085 ... Snyder MR & MRS Martin Avery
Villanova ... 19085 ... Snyder MR John Avery
Villanova ... 19085 ... Steel MRS Howard H
Villanova ... 19085 ... Stokes MRS David B
Villanova ... 19085 ... Talbot MS Mary Wallace
Villanova ... 19085 ... Taylor MR & MRS B Loyall JR
Villanova ... 19085 ... Todd MR J Harrison
Villanova ... 19085 ... Torrey MR & MRS L Russell
Villanova ... 19085 ... Towle MR & MRS John A
Villanova ... 19085 ... Tuten MR & MRS John C JR
Villanova ... 19085 ... Umstattd MRS James M
Villanova ... 19085 ... Warren MRS Andrew C
Villanova ... 19085 ... Wood MR & MRS William P JR
Villanova ... 19085 ... Zelov MR & MRS Peter E
Villanova ... 19087 ... Aronchick MR & MRS Robert N
Wallingford ... 19086 ... Kell MR & MRS John R
Wallingford ... 19086 ... Rogers MR & MRS Benjamin B
Wallingford ... 19086 ... Seltzer MRS C Scott
Warminster ... 18974 ... Baxter MR & MRS George Jaffray
Warrington ... 18976 ... Bergin MR & MRS (DR) John J JR
Washington ... 15301 ... Reed MISS Diana L
Washington Crossing ... 18977 ... Miller MS Mary Richardson
Wayne ... 19087 ... Ballard MR & MRS Ian M JR
Wayne ... 19087 ... Barker MR Nathaniel S
Wayne ... 19087 ... Bennett DR & MRS David S
Wayne ... 19087 ... Bennett MR & MRS Wade K
Wayne ... 19087 ... Beuf MS Helen B & Barnett MR Charles
Wayne ... 19087 ... Bowden MR Francis J III
Wayne ... 19087 ... Broach DR Vance Carter JR
Wayne ... 19087 ... Bullock MR & MRS Thomas F
Wayne ... 19087 ... Butcher MR & MRS McBee JR
Wayne ... 19087 ... Cahill MR & MRS Kevin C
Wayne ... 19087 ... Chance MRS Samuel K
Wayne ... 19087 ... Charrington MR & MRS Arthur M R III
Wayne ... 19087 ... Charrington MR & MRS Peter R
Wayne ... 19087 ... Chew MR John T JR
Wayne ... 19087 ... Claghorn MR & MRS Edward T
Wayne ... 19087 ... Cockman MR Eric W
Wayne ... 19087 ... Conlan MR & MRS William M
Wayne ... 19087 ... Connolly MR & MRS Edward P
Wayne ... 19087 ... Culbertson MR & MRS Timothy R
Wayne ... 19087 ... Ebmeyer MR & MRS Christopher B
Wayne ... 19087 ... Fergusson MR & MRS Jeremy L
Wayne ... 19087 ... Forbes MR & MRS William F
Wayne ... 19087 ... Games MR & MRS Timothy E
Wayne ... 19087 ... Harris MR & MRS Montgomery 3D
Wayne ... 19087 ... Hart MR & MRS Christopher P
Wayne ... 19087 ... Hayes MR & MRS James S III
Wayne ... 19087 ... Henderson MR & MRS Jeffrey S
Wayne ... 19087 ... Henderson MR & MRS William Halstead
Wayne ... 19087 ... Hiestand MRS Harry K
Wayne ... 19087 ... Hollos MR Paul A
Wayne ... 19087 ... Jaeger MR & MRS James R II
Wayne ... 19087 ... Jarrett MRS Richard B
Wayne ... 19087 ... Jones MRS Pansy B
Wayne ... 19087 ... Justi MR & MRS Thomas R
Wayne ... 19087 ... Karnavas MR & MRS Andrew C
Wayne ... 19087 ... Linz MR & MRS Brian J
Wayne ... 19087 ... McCurdy DR & MRS Alexander 3D
Wayne ... 19087 ... Michell MR & MRS Henry F 4TH
Wayne ... 19087 ... Miller MR & MRS Peter M
Wayne ... 19087 ... Mundy MR & MRS William H
Wayne ... 19087 ... Newhall MR & MRS Daniel W
Wayne ... 19087 ... Newman DR Clyde F JR
Wayne ... 19087 ... O'Malley MRS E Campion
Wayne ... 19087 ... Page MR & MRS L Rodman 3D
Wayne ... 19087 ... Pakradooni MR & MRS D Loyd
Wayne ... 19087 ... Paradis MR Douglas & Schoenborn-Paradis MS Jane
Wayne ... 19087 ... Pearson MR & MRS Gardiner P
Wayne ... 19087 ... Peck DR & MRS Robert G
Wayne ... 19087 ... Pratt MR Elisha W
Wayne ... 19087 ... Ringe MR & MRS Thomas B K
Wayne ... 19087 ... Ringe MR & MRS Thomas B K III
Wayne ... 19087 ... Rogers MR & MRS Paul H
Wayne ... 19087 ... Scott MR & MRS Sean D
Wayne ... 19087 ... Scudder MR George W
Wayne ... 19087 ... Slater MR & MRS John G T JR
Wayne ... 19087 ... Slattery MRS Price W
Wayne ... 19087 ... Smith MR & MRS John C 3D
Wayne ... 19087 ... Sommer MR & MRS Sandford S
Wayne ... 19087 ... Spano MR Francis M T III
Wayne ... 19087 ... Spofford MR John L

To nominate a candidate for the Social Register Association, please email: SRCommittee@thesocialregister.org

Wayne, PA—Wyndmoor, PA

Wayne	19087	Stanley MR & MRS John B
Wayne	19087	Stiff MR & MRS S Bertram 3D
Wayne	19087	Sullivan MR Andrew R
Wayne	19087	Todd MRS John Barnes
Wayne	19087	Tyson MR & MRS John II
Wayne	19087	Ulichney DR & MRS Andrew B 2D
Wayne	19087	Vasquez MR & MRS Mark J
Wayne	19087	Vincent MR & MRS Anthony T
Wayne	19087	von Czoernig MRS Mary B
Wayne	19087	Walker MRS Maud T
Wayne	19087	Wallace MISS (DR) Dale H
Wayne	19087	Wampler MR & MRS Fredrick D
Wayne	19087	Weber MR & MRS John C JR
Wayne	19087	Werner MR & MRS David A
Wayne	19087	Wietlisbach MR & MRS Bruce D
Wayne	19087	Willcox DR & MRS Thomas O JR
Wayne	19087	Wister MRS Malcolm L
Wayne	19087	Wolgin MR & MRS Roy D
Wayne	19087	Wood MR & MRS William H
West Brandywine	19320	Hedges MR & MRS Donald W
West Brandywine	19320	Tower MR & MRS James W
West Chester	19380	Anthony MR & MRS Roscoe Tate III
West Chester	19380	Bailey MR & MRS Omar
West Chester	19380	Birney REV & MRS James G
West Chester	19380	Borie MR & MRS William J S JR
West Chester	19380	Church MRS John W JR
West Chester	19380	Crawford MR & MRS Alan III
West Chester	19380	de Bordenave MR & MRS John
West Chester	19380	Driscoll MR & MRS Bernard E 2D
West Chester	19380	Drumwright MR & MRS James R
West Chester	19380	Earle MR & MRS George H V
West Chester	19380	Griffin MR & MRS Samuel W M
West Chester	19380	Griffin MRS J Tyler JR
West Chester	19380	Hall MR & MRS James F
West Chester	19380	Hayes MR & MRS J Stoddard JR
West Chester	19380	Hepburn MRS Austin B
West Chester	19380	Jones MR Arthur E JR
West Chester	19380	Kellogg MR Thomas R
West Chester	19380	LeBoutillier MR C Pierre R
West Chester	19380	Lynch MR & MRS Michael P
West Chester	19380	Markle MRS Mary McL
West Chester	19380	McEvoy MR & MRS Thomas M 3D
West Chester	19380	Morris MR & MRS Anthony
West Chester	19380	Morrison MR & MRS Jason E
West Chester	19380	Moss MISS Margaret P
West Chester	19380	Neilson MRS Winthrop C III
West Chester	19380	Preston MR & MRS Seymour S 3D
West Chester	19380	Rogers MRS Theodore O
West Chester	19380	Russell MRS Nancy Clark
West Chester	19380	Schiffer MRS Herbert F
West Chester	19380	Schiffer MRS Peter B
West Chester	19380	Seeley MR & MRS Franklin M
West Chester	19380	Shafer MRS J MacBean
West Chester	19380	Staller MR & MRS Harry W
West Chester	19380	Stedman MR & MRS Derek C
West Chester	19380	Toland MR & MRS M Keith
West Chester	19380	Wanamaker MRS Daisy C F
West Chester	19380	Webb MR & MRS Charles H
West Chester	19380	Wilson MR & MRS Marvel JR
West Chester	19380	Wood MR & MRS David W JR
West Chester	19380	Young MRS Brinton Coxe
West Chester	19381	Armstrong MRS Richard M JR
West Chester	19382	Armstrong MR & MRS A Joseph 3D
West Chester	19382	Bullitt MR & MRS John S C
West Chester	19382	Bullitt MR & MRS R Thayer
West Chester	19382	Burns MR & MRS Edward P II
West Chester	19382	Dougherty MR & MRS A Webster JR
West Chester	19382	Gilpin MR & MRS David V
West Chester	19382	Hallowell MR & MRS Frederick C III
West Chester	19382	Hanna MR & MRS Colin A
West Chester	19382	Hodges MISS Elizabeth W
West Chester	19382	Johnson MR & MRS W Patrick
West Chester	19382	Leidy MRS Frances A Hufty
West Chester	19382	Odell MRS David Dallas
West Chester	19382	Sargent MR & MRS James C JR
West Chester	19382	Taylor MR & MRS Stewart F
West Chester	19382	Walkup MR & MRS Richard L
West Chester	19382	Wright MRS Louisa W
West Conshohocken	19428	Zug MISS Holly E
West Grove	19390	Bradford MR Seth
West Grove	19390	Devereux MR & MRS Antelo JR
West Grove	19390	Flood MRS E Thomas 2D
West Grove	19390	Gober MRS Glenn D
West Grove	19390	Jackson MR & MRS M Roy
West Grove	19390	Lofting MRS Colin M
West Grove	19390	Sawyer MRS Richard C
West Grove	19390	Stroud MS Anne
West Grove	19390	Wintersteen MR & MRS George F
Westtown	19395	Barber MR & MRS Charles P
Westtown	19395	Manganaro MRS E Morris
Westtown	19395	Morris MR Robert M
Wexford	15090	Henningsen MR & MRS Timothy F
Wexford	15090	Weaver MRS Katherine B
Willow Grove	19090	Day MISS Mary B
Willow Grove	19090	Willis MR Richard S
Willow Street	17584	Leiper MR John A JR
Willow Street	17584	Ritter MR & MRS Philip O
Worcester	19490	D'Lauro MR Frank A JR
Wrightstown	18940	Staub MR John H III
Wrightsville	17368	Clark MR & MRS Clarence H 5TH
Wyncote	19095	Warden MR & MRS Derek P B
Wyndmoor	19038	Baxter MR & MRS Justin M
Wyndmoor	19038	Blankin MRS Grant L
Wyndmoor	19038	Boyd MR & MRS George 5TH
Wyndmoor	19038	Bradley MR & MRS Tyler B H
Wyndmoor	19038	Brown MR J Crosby IV
Wyndmoor	19038	Clattenburg MR & MRS Theodore JR
Wyndmoor	19038	Foulke MR & MRS Walter L
Wyndmoor	19038	Frank MR & MRS Jonathan W
Wyndmoor	19038	Gagné MR & MRS W Roderick
Wyndmoor	19038	Greenwood MR & MRS Thomas S JR
Wyndmoor	19038	Groton MR Nathanael B JR
Wyndmoor	19038	Harmar MR & MRS William 3D
Wyndmoor	19038	Harris MRS Henry F
Wyndmoor	19038	Howe MR & MRS Arthur W 4TH
Wyndmoor	19038	Ix MR & MRS Raymond E JR
Wyndmoor	19038	Larkin MR & MRS Brian M
Wyndmoor	19038	Lennon MRS Kenneth N
Wyndmoor	19038	Lukens MR & MRS Robert A
Wyndmoor	19038	Madeira MR & MRS Andrew M
Wyndmoor	19038	Madeira MR & MRS George W P
Wyndmoor	19038	McNeil MRS Robert L JR
Wyndmoor	19038	Morrow MR & MRS Robert H III
Wyndmoor	19038	Ponce MR & MRS Michael C
Wyndmoor	19038	Roberts MR & MRS Isaac W 2D
Wyndmoor	19038	Ross MRS Robyn
Wyndmoor	19038	Sayer MR & MRS Dorsey T
Wyndmoor	19038	Sheffield MR & MRS David P
Wyndmoor	19038	Simonin MRS Robert W
Wyndmoor	19038	Stout MR & MRS Morris A 4TH
Wyndmoor	19038	Tasman MR James B
Wyndmoor	19038	Tasman MRS William

Wyndmoor .... 19038 .... Toogood MISS Anna Coxe
Wyndmoor .... 19038 .... Tyson MRS Anna Starr
Wyndmoor .... 19038 .... Webster MR & MRS Edward S
Wynnewood .... 19096 .... Baker DR & MRS (DR) Howard S
Wynnewood .... 19096 .... Baker MR Nicholas M
Wynnewood .... 19096 .... Boyd DR Robert L
Wynnewood .... 19096 .... Cuthbert MRS Richard I
Wynnewood .... 19096 .... Finkenstaedt MR & MRS Edward R 2D
Wynnewood .... 19096 .... Harris MR & MRS Jonathan M
Wynnewood .... 19096 .... Kuhnmunch MR & MRS Caleb L
Wynnewood .... 19096 .... Lame MR & MRS Anthony C
Wynnewood .... 19096 .... McConnell MR Edward L III
Wynnewood .... 19096 .... Menocal MR Enrique V
Wynnewood .... 19096 .... Pierce MR Benjamin R
Wynnewood .... 19096 .... Raymer MR John H JR
Wynnewood .... 19096 .... Roberts MR & MRS John S JR
Wynnewood .... 19096 .... Shaver DR & MRS Jeffrey S
Wynnewood .... 19096 .... Shields DR & MRS David A
Wynnewood .... 19096 .... Siedlarz MRS Joseph B JR
Wynnewood .... 19096 .... Smith MR & MRS Sidney V JR
Wynnewood .... 19096 .... Spaeth MR & MRS Christopher P
Wynnewood .... 19096 .... Taylor MR & MRS Charles M
Wyomissing .... 19610 .... Runyeon MRS William K
Wyomissing .... 19610 .... Shaffer MR & MRS David M
Wyomissing .... 19610 .... Widing MR & MRS J William 3D
Yardley .... 19067 .... Callaway MR William T
Yardley .... 19067 .... Meyer DR & MRS Richard W
Yardley .... 19067 .... Plum MISS Nancy T
Yardley .... 19067 .... Wiles MR James G
York .... 17403 .... Currier DR & MRS Charles B JR
York .... 17403 .... Dalby MR & MRS Allen J
York .... 17403 .... Drake MR & MRS Carlos C JR
York .... 17403 .... Shanner MR & MRS Robert W
York .... 17408 .... Ellis MS Marianne Beyea
Zelienople .... 16063 .... Silbert REV John C R

RHODE ISLAND

Adamsville .... 02801 .... Penney MR & MRS John S JR
Barrington .... 02806 .... Fisher MR & MRS Sean H
Barrington .... 02806 .... Fogarty MR & MRS Gerald J JR
Barrington .... 02806 .... Robertson DR & MRS Alexander P III
Barrington .... 02806 .... Townsend MR & MRS Charles Coe 3D
Barrington .... 02806 .... Walsh CAPT (DR) & MRS Eric F
Barrington .... 02806 .... Winfield MRS M Lee
Barrington .... 02806 .... Wiseman MS (DR) Claire V
Barrington .... 02806 .... Zingg MR & MRS Christopher D
Block Island .... 02807 .... Pike MRS Nancy D
Bristol .... 02809 .... de Rham MR & MRS Jeremiah E
Bristol .... 02809 .... Knight MR & MRS C Foster
Bristol .... 02809 .... Sparkman MR & MRS Thorne III
Bristol .... 02809 .... Upton MISS Mary D
Cranston .... 02905 .... Funkhouser MR Stewart M
Cranston .... 02905 .... Phyfe MR & MRS James D III
Cranston .... 02905 .... Satterthwaite MR & MRS Franklin B JR
East Greenwich .... 02818 .... Endicott MR & MRS David S
East Greenwich .... 02818 .... Mali MR & MRS Pierre
East Greenwich .... 02818 .... West MR & MRS George S
Exeter .... 02822 .... Leonard MR Buchanan R
Exeter .... 02882 .... Sinkler MR & MRS R Knowles JR
Jamestown .... 02835 .... Boenning MR & MRS Dickson G
Jamestown .... 02835 .... Bridgham DR Clive W
Jamestown .... 02835 .... Converse MRS Costello C
Jamestown .... 02835 .... Ferguson MR & MRS Scott H
Jamestown .... 02835 .... Fleitas MR & MRS Allison F II
Jamestown .... 02835 .... Gray MR & MRS John B
Jamestown .... 02835 .... Lippincott MR & MRS Bertram 3D
Jamestown .... 02835 .... Outerbridge MRS Yeaton D
Jamestown .... 02835 .... Ross MR & MRS Stuart C
Jamestown .... 02835 .... Schieffelin MR Peter L
Jamestown .... 02835 .... Slingluff MRS Patricia K
Jamestown .... 02835 .... Thomas MRS W G Brooks
Jamestown .... 02835 .... Wharton MR James D
Johnston .... 02919 .... Lenssen MR & MRS Nicholas F 3D
Johnston .... 02919 .... Sage MISS Kristin B
Little Compton .... 02837 .... Angell MR & MRS I Jackson
Little Compton .... 02837 .... Chandor MR & MRS Jeffrey F
Little Compton .... 02837 .... Hagan MR & MRS Brooks W
Little Compton .... 02837 .... Havens MR & MRS Richard W
Little Compton .... 02837 .... McNaughton MR & MRS Donald B
Little Compton .... 02837 .... Merriman MR & MRS David W
Little Compton .... 02837 .... Myrin MR & MRS F A Wilhelm 2D
Little Compton .... 02837 .... O'Hara MRS Charles E
Little Compton .... 02837 .... Page MR & MRS Charles H
Little Compton .... 02837 .... Thomas MRS Samuel P
Little Compton .... 02837 .... Truslow MR & MRS James L
Middletown .... 02842 .... Clark MR & MRS Cameron B
Middletown .... 02842 .... Demy MR & MRS Timothy J
Middletown .... 02842 .... Gray MR & MRS David A
Middletown .... 02842 .... Grosvenor DR & MRS Richard
Middletown .... 02842 .... Jacobs MR Richard S C
Middletown .... 02842 .... Johnson MRS George F B JR
Middletown .... 02842 .... Lewis MR & MRS Perry
Middletown .... 02842 .... Loebs MR Richard C JR
Middletown .... 02842 .... Oberg MR & MRS Nathan T
Middletown .... 02842 .... Peixinho MR John M
Middletown .... 02842 .... Prince MR & MRS William N Wood
Middletown .... 02842 .... Reilly MR & MRS Andrew K
Middletown .... 02842 .... Straus MR & MRS Timothy von F
Middletown .... 02842 .... Strauss MRS Elliott MacGregor
Middletown .... 02842 .... Taylor CAPT (RET) & MRS Le Roy T
Middletown .... 02842 .... van Beuren MRS John A
Middletown .... 02842 .... Van Liew MR & MRS Alfred B II
Middletown .... 02842 .... Van Liew MS Elizabeth B
Middletown .... 02842 .... Willis MRS N O'Donnell
Narragansett .... 02882 .... Earle MRS Eleanor F O
Narragansett .... 02882 .... Fell MR & MRS Ogden M
Narragansett .... 02882 .... Freeman MRS Felix J JR
Narragansett .... 02882 .... Lee MRS Charles P
Narragansett .... 02882 .... Leeson MR & MRS Robert JR
New Shoreham .... 02807 .... Pike MR F Norris
Newport .... 02840 .... Adams MR & MRS Charles S III
Newport .... 02840 .... Adams MRS Charles C 3D
Newport .... 02840 .... Argento MRS Henry F
Newport .... 02840 .... Auchincloss MISS Maya L
Newport .... 02840 .... Baldwin MR W Barton 3D
Newport .... 02840 .... Baldwin MRS V Thomas
Newport .... 02840 .... Beck MR Edward R C
Newport .... 02840 .... Benkhart MRS Carlyne R
Newport .... 02840 .... Benson MR & MRS Daniel M
Newport .... 02840 .... Berl MISS Ahnie Andréa S M
Newport .... 02840 .... Boenning MR David E
Newport .... 02840 .... Briggs MRS Carolyn A V
Newport .... 02840 .... Bruce MR David C
Newport .... 02840 .... Bush-Brown MR & MRS David F
Newport .... 02840 .... Cavanagh MR Roderick A
Newport .... 02840 .... Clews MISS Sylvan
Newport .... 02840 .... Coates MR W Shelby JR
Newport .... 02840 .... Cooper MRS Alletta M
Newport .... 02840 .... Corbin MRS Robert E
Newport .... 02840 .... Cowley MR & MRS Robert W
Newport .... 02840 .... de Ramel CT & CTSS Guillaume H

To nominate a candidate for the Social Register Association, please email: SRCommittee@thesocialregister.org

Newport, RI— Westerly, RI

Newport	02840	Dewey MRS Chauncey F
Newport	02840	Dick MRS C Mathews JR
Newport	02840	Dick MRS Ronald F
Newport	02840	Field MR & MRS Tylor 2D
Newport	02840	Fischer DR & MRS Edwin G
Newport	02840	French MR & MRS John H II
Newport	02840	Gibson MR & MRS James H McM
Newport	02840	Glenn MR & MRS Lawrence R
Newport	02840	Gorham MR & MRS Sidney S III
Newport	02840	Granbery MISS Pamela
Newport	02840	Griscom MR & MRS Lloyd P JR
Newport	02840	Grosvenor MISS Amanda M
Newport	02840	Grosvenor MRS Charles B
Newport	02840	Helme MISS Elizabeth S E
Newport	02840	Herrick MR & MRS George Gardner
Newport	02840	Holloway MRS Leslie G
Newport	02840	Hunnewell MRS Richard F
Newport	02840	Irving MR & MRS Pierre duP
Newport	02840	Irving MR Washington
Newport	02840	Jones MRS Linda R
Newport	02840	Lewis MRS Winslow JR
Newport	02840	Lirakis MISS Isabelle C M
Newport	02840	Lirakis MR & MRS W Stephen
Newport	02840	McMillen MR & MRS Earl III
Newport	02840	Merrill MR & MRS William B II
Newport	02840	Morris DR & MRS David C
Newport	02840	O'Donnell MR & MRS Andrew L
Newport	02840	Oswald MRS Clinton
Newport	02840	Pardee MISS Margaret T
Newport	02840	Pell MR & MRS Christopher T H
Newport	02840	Pell MS Dallas
Newport	02840	Purviance MR & MRS James A
Newport	02840	Randall MR & MRS Jesse F
Newport	02840	Rex MISS Rebecca
Newport	02840	Rhein MISS Jane F
Newport	02840	Richards MR & MRS Anselm T W
Newport	02840	Riggs MR & MRS Benjamin C JR
Newport	02840	Ross MR & MRS Donald O
Newport	02840	Sabin MR & MRS Robert C
Newport	02840	Slocum MRS John Jermain JR
Newport	02840	Smith MISS Virginia L
Newport	02840	Spencer MR William H F
Newport	02840	Spencer MRS Stephen W
Newport	02840	Stone MRS Edward L
Newport	02840	Tower MS (REV) Laurel P
Newport	02840	Tucker MRS Martha M
Newport	02840	Tyler MR & MRS Peter S S
Newport	02840	Weber MR & MRS Paul F
Newport	02840	Wells MR & MRS Roger K
Newport	02840	Wharton MR Charles W III
Newport	02840	Whitehouse MR & MRS Sheldon
Newport	02840	Wilson MRS R Thornton
Newport	02840	Woodhull MR & MRS William T JR
Newport	02840	Yates MR Eames H JR
Newport	02840	Younes MR & MRS Khaled M
Newport	02840	Zwack de Wahl BRIG GEN & MRS Peter B
North Kingstown	02852	Cross MR & MRS Robert A
North Kingstown	02852	Keeler MR Marston W JR
North Kingstown	02852	Tucker MRS N Beverley JR
North Providence	02911	Fearing MRS George R
Pawtucket	02861	Magendantz DR Henry G
Peace Dale	02879	Sage MRS Nathaniel McL JR
Portsmouth	02871	Bidwell MR Miles O JR
Portsmouth	02871	Breyer MR & MRS Henry W IV
Portsmouth	02871	Crimmins MR & MRS Martin L 4TH
Portsmouth	02871	Highley MR Allen C
Portsmouth	02871	Huggins MR & MRS Marshall Gwinn
Portsmouth	02871	McLane MRS Allan
Portsmouth	02871	McLennan MRS Juliette C
Portsmouth	02871	Reaper MR & MRS John Anthony
Portsmouth	02871	Rose MR & MRS Andrew B
Portsmouth	02871	Walk MR & MRS Stephen G W
Portsmouth	02871	Walker MRS (DR) Benjamin Harrison JR
Portsmouth	02871	Wladyka MR & MRS William J
Providence	02903	Brown CAPT (RET) & MRS Nicholas
Providence	02903	Mauran MR Frank
Providence	02903	More MR & MRS (DR) Timothy T
Providence	02904	Girvin MR & MRS Robert
Providence	02906	Bartsch MR & MRS Jeffrey M
Providence	02906	Bilodeau MR & MRS Harrison McC
Providence	02906	Capozzi MR & MRS Edmund F JR
Providence	02906	Craford DR John P E & Lawrence MS (DR) Alexis C
Providence	02906	Cutts MRS Morgan
Providence	02906	Danforth MR & MRS Murray S 3D
Providence	02906	Fleuette MR & MRS Michel J
Providence	02906	Goddard MR & MRS William H D
Providence	02906	Grant MR & MRS David A
Providence	02906	Hallowell MR & MRS Samuel H JR
Providence	02906	Kellogg MR & MRS David W
Providence	02906	Loney MS Susan A
Providence	02906	Mariner MR & MRS Michael H
Providence	02906	Martin MR & MRS Stewart P
Providence	02906	Miller DR & MRS (DR) Kennon S
Providence	02906	Nash MRS F Philip JR
Providence	02906	Nichols MR & MRS John S JR
Providence	02906	Price MR & MRS Philip III
Providence	02906	Reeves MR & MRS William H 4TH
Providence	02906	Riegel MR & MRS John E JR
Providence	02906	Spalter MR & MRS Michael
Providence	02906	Tompkins MR & MRS Christopher P
Providence	02906	Walsh MR & MRS Laurence S
Providence	02906	Warren MRS Simonds
Providence	02906	Westervelt MR & MRS Peter J
Providence	02907	Ruby MR James A & Wolf MS April Harding
Rumford	02916	Dennison DR & MRS (DR) Allen M
Saunderstown	02874	Berl MS Alexandra S
Saunderstown	02874	Davison MR & MRS C Hamilton JR
Saunderstown	02874	Rhein MR & MRS John H W III
Saunderstown	02874	Symonds MS Anne Worthington
Saunderstown	02874	Wheeler MR & MRS Richard R
Tiverton	02878	Stewart MR & MRS David E
Wakefield	02879	Colt MR Zenas M C
Wakefield	02879	Freed MR & MRS Christopher J
Wakefield	02879	Harrah MR Eric
Wakefield	02879	Harrington MR & MRS James A
Wakefield	02879	Saunders MR & MRS Stuart M
Wakefield	02880	McCleary MR & MRS Benjamin W
Wakefield	02880	Taft MR & MRS William H IV
Wakefield	02880	Waterston MR George C JR
Warren	02885	Flanagan DR & MRS Thomas R
Warwick	02888	Harding MRS George R JR
Warwick	02888	McMillen MISS Shelley
Watch Hill	02891	Lloyd MR David H
Weekapaug	02891	Constantine MR & MRS Richard W
Westerly	02891	Anderson MR & MRS Robert P
Westerly	02891	Cooke MR Caswell JR
Westerly	02891	Dewey MR & MRS Paul C G JR
Westerly	02891	Gordon MR & MRS David G
Westerly	02891	Griscom DR & MRS Andrew H
Westerly	02891	Hollos MRS Paul E
Westerly	02891	Kniffin MRS Timothy B
Westerly	02891	Loney MRS Frederick R

Westerly	02891	Rutan MRS Frank E 3D
Westerly	02891	Snowden MRS George G 3D
Westerly	02981	Cooke MR & MRS Caswell
Wickford	02852	Beckwith MR & MRS Henry L P

SOUTH CAROLINA

Aiken	29801	Becker MRS Charles J
Aiken	29801	Bostwick MR & MRS Albert C
Aiken	29801	Botond MS Krisztina L
Aiken	29801	Bransome DR & MRS Edwin D JR
Aiken	29801	Carey MS (DR) Elizabeth P
Aiken	29801	Corey MR & MRS Alan L 3D
Aiken	29801	Davis MRS Frederica
Aiken	29801	King MR & MRS David N
Aiken	29801	Knowles MS Alice R
Aiken	29801	Maurice MISS Kiffin
Aiken	29801	McLean MRS Linda Knox
Aiken	29801	O'Brien MRS Daniel B
Aiken	29801	Pezzano MR & MRS William J
Aiken	29801	Rasmussen MR & MRS Howard L
Aiken	29801	Rutherfurd MR & MRS Alan L
Aiken	29801	Thompson MR & MRS Mark G
Aiken	29801	Ward MR & MRS Nicholas D
Aiken	29801	Wheeler MS Kendall
Aiken	29801	Yarborough MR & MRS Phillip Heyward
Aiken	29802	Aulisi MR & MRS Joseph E
Aiken	29802	Dupee MR & MRS Matthew D
Aiken	29803	Buckley MR & MRS Martin B
Aiken	29803	Filippeli MR & MRS Daniel C
Aiken	29803	French REV & MRS Alan C
Aiken	29803	Gaver MR James M
Aiken	29803	Gunnell MRS Jane R
Aiken	29803	Hamilton MRS John T III
Aiken	29803	Lutterloh MR Karl G
Aiken	29803	Mitsch MRS William G JR
Aiken	29803	Thomas MRS Alexandra Stokes
Aiken	29803	Vance MS Grace R
Beaufort	29901	Claiborne MRS John H
Beaufort	29902	Bowie MR & MRS David C
Beaufort	29902	Kittredge MR & MRS Harvey Gaylord JR
Beaufort	29902	Post MRS George B JR
Beaufort	29906	Born COL (RET) Howard P
Beaufort	29906	Moneta MR & MRS John A
Beaufort	29907	Chatfield MR & MRS William H
Beaufort	29907	Parker MR & MRS Edward A IV
Beaufort	29907	Paschal MR Guy
Bluffton	29910	Ellis MR & MRS J Wiley
Bluffton	29910	Gale MR & MRS Gordon E
Bluffton	29910	Malone MR Stuart H
Bluffton	29910	Van Wagner MR & MRS James R JR
Bluffton	29910	Vaux MR & MRS Roberts
Bluffton	29910	Wendell MR & MRS Harlan L P JR
Bluffton	29910	White MR & MRS Robert L
Bluffton	29910	Williamson MR & MRS Hugh J
Blythewood	29016	Brick COL & MRS Samuel T JR
Camden	29020	Field MRS Augustus B 3D
Camden	29020	Iselin MR & MRS Frederick D
Camden	29020	Lampshire MR & MRS Nicholas P
Camden	29020	Wenman MISS Diana B
Camden	29021	DuBose MRS Charles Wills
Campobello	29322	Parish MISS Linda D
Campobello	29322	Webel MR Richard C
Charleston	29401	Altschul MRS Arthur G
Charleston	29401	Armstrong MS Julia Rea
Charleston	29401	Baldwin DR & MRS J Gilbert JR
Charleston	29401	Battle MRS Elizabeth L
Charleston	29401	Bonsal MR Warwick P
Charleston	29401	Brenizer MR & MRS William S
Charleston	29401	Burnett MR & MRS Robert W
Charleston	29401	Cabot MS Carla P
Charleston	29401	Cameron DR & MRS Joseph Price JR
Charleston	29401	Cay MR & MRS John E III
Charleston	29401	Coker MR & MRS P Cooper IV
Charleston	29401	Cooper MR Thomas H & de la Morandière MS Anne J Potier
Charleston	29401	Cox MRS Thomas R 3D
Charleston	29401	Crone MR Walter S
Charleston	29401	Culver MR & MRS Edward H JR
Charleston	29401	Cutler MRS Richard M
Charleston	29401	Daughtridge MR & MRS John B
Charleston	29401	Donnem MRS Roland W
Charleston	29401	Gale MR & MRS Elbridge StJ
Charleston	29401	Gallagher MR John M
Charleston	29401	Gephart MR & MRS George W JR
Charleston	29401	Griffen MR & MRS J Pennypacker
Charleston	29401	Hamilton MR & MRS T Heyward M
Charleston	29401	Hamilton MRS Daniel H
Charleston	29401	Harrington COL (RET) & MRS Myron C JR
Charleston	29401	Hart MRS Barbara
Charleston	29401	Haythe MR & MR David O
Charleston	29401	Haythe MR & MRS Thomas M
Charleston	29401	Katz MR Al W & Boone-Katz MRS H Suzanne
Charleston	29401	Klietmann MR & MRS Maximilian W
Charleston	29401	Lane MR & MRS Hugh C JR
Charleston	29401	Lenhardt MR & MRS Benjamin F JR
Charleston	29401	Lucas MS Joan B
Charleston	29401	Maybank MR & MRS Francis P
Charleston	29401	McSpadden MR & MRS Jack D JR
Charleston	29401	Merck MR & MRS Antony M
Charleston	29401	Merck MR Elliott H
Charleston	29401	Morrison MR & MRS R Hamilton III
Charleston	29401	Parrish MR Hugh R III
Charleston	29401	Patrick MR & MRS W Reid JR
Charleston	29401	Pelzer MR & MRS Felix C
Charleston	29401	Pinckney MR & MRS Alfred G
Charleston	29401	Prioleau MR & MRS Robert P
Charleston	29401	Pruitt DR Armstead Bert & Brissey MRS Anne Lyons
Charleston	29401	Ravenel MR & MRS Daniel
Charleston	29401	Rees MR & MRS William M JR
Charleston	29401	Rhett REV DR William P JR
Charleston	29401	Rivers MR & MRS John M JR
Charleston	29401	Russell MISS Lesley Carpenter
Charleston	29401	Sherbacow MR Bryan J & Carr MS Ellen K
Charleston	29401	Smith MR & MRS Richard A JR
Charleston	29401	Struthers COL & MRS W Wood
Charleston	29401	Thompson MR & MRS John E JR
Charleston	29401	Tisdale MR & MRS Thomas S JR
Charleston	29401	Utsch MR Hans P & Merck MS Julia H
Charleston	29401	Wagenlander MISS Katherine C
Charleston	29401	Walker MR & MRS Bradford H
Charleston	29401	Walker MR Ian S & Baran MRS Inga L
Charleston	29401	Waring MR & MRS Bradish J
Charleston	29401	Wellin MRS Keith S
Charleston	29401	Weyher MR Harry F III
Charleston	29401	Willis MR & MRS Gardiner F
Charleston	29401	Wittman MR Kent A & Perkins MS Susan A T
Charleston	29401	Wright CAPT (RET) & MRS Richard T
Charleston	29401	Yates MR Jonathan L
Charleston	29401	Young MR & MRS J Rutledge JR
Charleston	29402	Coker MR & MRS Priestley C III
Charleston	29402	Hanahan MRS Roger P

To nominate a candidate for the Social Register Association, please email: SRCommittee@thesocialregister.org

Charleston, SC—Mt Pleasant, SC

Charleston	29402	Kratovil MR & MRS Stephen C
Charleston	29403	Fain MR & MRS Earl IV
Charleston	29403	Grigorieff MR & MRS Alexey V
Charleston	29403	Hooper MS Jill P
Charleston	29403	Kyle DR & MRS (DR) T Rogers III
Charleston	29403	Manigault MR & MRS Pierre
Charleston	29403	Meek MR Kevin A & Van Liew MS (DR) Camilla H
Charleston	29403	Theobald MS Claire E
Charleston	29405	Leland DR & MRS Thomas M
Charleston	29407	Andrews MR & MRS Mark E IV
Charleston	29407	Boulware MR & MRS Thomas McC VI
Charleston	29407	DuBose MR & MRS Brooks Easter
Charleston	29407	Freer MR & MRS Robert E JR
Charleston	29407	Grimball DR & MRS Arthur
Charleston	29407	Lipman MR & MRS Ross E
Charleston	29407	Schaller MR William A
Charleston	29407	Simons MR & MRS Cotesworth P
Charleston	29407	Sterrett MISS Judith C
Charleston	29407	Van Alen MR & MRS James G
Charleston	29410	Cranworth LORD & LADY
Charleston	29410	Farr MRS C Sims
Charleston	29410	Lyman MRS Ronald T
Charleston	29410	Malabre MR & MRS Alfred L JR
Charleston	29412	Brandt MR & MRS Julian V III
Charleston	29412	Chrystie MRS Thomas L
Charleston	29412	Clare MR N Holmes JR
Charleston	29412	Clawson MRS Harry Q M
Charleston	29412	Derrick MR & MRS Butler C III
Charleston	29412	Fair MR & MRS J Henry JR
Charleston	29412	Grimball MRS Richard B
Charleston	29412	Hadley MR & MRS Dakota L
Charleston	29412	Houlihan MR & MRS Raymond D'A
Charleston	29412	Howe MRS Arthur W 3D
Charleston	29412	Johnstone MR & MRS (REV) Robert L III
Charleston	29412	Kemper MR & MRS A Claude
Charleston	29412	Low MRS S Hastie
Charleston	29412	Lucas MRS Marcia C
Charleston	29412	Moss MR & MRS Peter B
Charleston	29412	Parry CDR John C
Charleston	29412	Prioleau MR & MRS Robert M
Charleston	29412	Stewart MR & MRS William A W 3D
Charleston	29412	Webb DR & MRS Charles A JR
Charleston	29412	Westmoreland MRS William C
Charleston	29413	Winthrop MR & MRS John
Charleston	29414	Flaccus MRS Charles L III
Charleston	29414	Hastie MRS J Drayton
Charleston	29414	Mitchell MR Henry B III
Charleston	29414	Moe DR & MRS Christopher B
Charleston	29464	Saal MR & MRS William D JR
Charleston	29492	Hall MR & MRS Gordon B 3D
Chesnee	29323	Woolsey MISS R Audrey
Clemson	29631	Field MR & MRS Jonathan B
Clemson	29631	Henry MR & MRS Douglas C
Clemson	29631	Kaye MR & MRS Nigel B
Clemson	29631	Pollock MRS Thomas Hood
Clemson	29631	Richards MR & MRS Barry G
Columbia	29016	McCallum DR & MRS B James
Columbia	29201	Townsley MR & MRS Peter A
Columbia	29204	Crawford MRS Margaret Weaver
Columbia	29205	Anderson MR & MRS David C
Columbia	29205	Boyd MR & MRS William C
Columbia	29206	Powers MR & MRS Gilbert T III
Columbia	29206	White MR & MRS Frank E JR
Columbia	29209	Finlay MR & MRS Kirkman 3D
Columbia	29209	Jennings MR & MRS W Croft JR
Columbia	29209	Thompson MR & MRS George R 4TH
Columbia	29223	Eddy MR & MRS David C
Columbia	29223	Locke DR & MRS Mark D
Columbia	29223	Lough DR & MRS Lawrence R
Columbia	29223	McCallum MR & MRS Brown JR
Conway	29526	Johnson MR & MRS Richard K
Daniel Island	29492	Neilson MR & MRS Thomas R 3D
Daniel Island	29492	Sands MR & MRS W Page
Daniel Island	29492	Skeele MR & MRS James B
Daniel Island	29492	Thomas MR George C
Darlington	29532	King DR & MRS (DR) Caleb K
Dataw Island	29920	Rutter MR Joseph Wood
Dataw Island	29920	Sloan MRS Robert N
Dataw Island	29920	Warrick MR & MRS William H JR
Folly Beach	29439	Cook MR & MRS Douglas G
Fountain Inn	29644	Sutton MR & MRS David Charles
Ft Mill	29708	Weymouth MR & MRS A Kent JR
Georgetown	29440	Sibley MR & MRS Horace H
Georgetown	29440	Smith MR & MRS Claiborne Alexander Livingston
Georgetown	29440	Topping MRS Sandra E
Greenville	29601	Finch MR & MRS Stephen B JR
Greenville	29601	Weekes MR & MRS Bradford G IV
Greenville	29605	Brett MR & MRS Peter M
Greenville	29605	Kent MRS M Hart
Greenville	29607	Kent MRS W Thompson
Greenville	29609	Kent MR Mark B
Greer	29650	Cook MR & MRS Rodney W
Hilton Head Island	29926	Bennett MR & MRS John T JR
Hilton Head Island	29926	Bransome MR Edwin D III
Hilton Head Island	29926	Currie DR & MRS Richard J
Hilton Head Island	29926	Gaudreau MRS Thomas L
Hilton Head Island	29926	La Motte MR & MRS Louis H 3D
Hilton Head Island	29926	Marshall MR & MRS Allerton D
Hilton Head Island	29926	Page MRS John H
Hilton Head Island	29926	Rose MR & MRS William S JR
Hilton Head Island	29926	Van Winkle MRS Edgar B II
Hilton Head Island	29926	Vogt MR Thomas Bulman
Hilton Head Island	29926	Warren MR & MRS James F JR
Hilton Head Island	29926	Wood MR William R
Hilton Head Island	29928	Churchill MRS Colin W
Hilton Head Island	29928	Evans MRS James D JR
Hilton Head Island	29928	Gillette MR & MRS Richard C
Hilton Head Island	29928	Herron MRS Polly P
Hilton Head Island	29928	Hoag MR & MRS T Denny
Hilton Head Island	29928	Jennings MR & MRS Keith S
Hilton Head Island	29928	McCombs MRS Robert P
Hilton Head Island	29928	Richey MISS Alice M
Hilton Head Island	29938	Smith MRS Margaret Henry
Hollywood	29449	Peake MR & MRS David V
Isle of Palms	29451	Foulke MR & MRS Adam W
Johns Island	29455	Corcoran MR & MRS Thomas A
Johns Island	29455	Freeman MS Ann Mitchell
Johns Island	29455	Morgan MR & MRS Matthew
Johns Island	29455	Van Liew MR & MRS Bradford R
Johns Island	29455	Wick MR & MRS William O JR
Johns Island	29457	Woodbridge MS Calista H
Kiawah Island	29455	Macauley MR & MRS John C W
Kiawah Island	29455	Nigro MR & MRS Robert A
Lady's Island	29907	Goodale MR & MRS Fairfield 3D
Landrum	29356	Fröhlich MRS H L Van Liew
Lexington	29072	Koehler MR & MRS H William D
Little River	29566	Smart MRS Clarke L
Lynchburg	29080	Hurley MR & MRS John D
Mt Pleasant	29464	Ball MRS Barbara E
Mt Pleasant	29464	Cullen MR & MRS Robert Le F
Mt Pleasant	29464	Frenzel MR & MRS Michael A
Mt Pleasant	29464	Goodwin DR & MRS Melvin H 3D

Mt Pleasant	29464	Hanson MR & MRS Christopher M
Mt Pleasant	29464	Humphrey MR R Walker II & Humphrey DR Tricia Dudek
Mt Pleasant	29464	Humphreys MR & MRS A Stephenson 3D
Mt Pleasant	29464	Humphreys MR & MRS Alan S JR
Mt Pleasant	29464	Jackson MR & MRS Orton P JR
Mt Pleasant	29464	Lesesne MR & MRS Eugene F
Mt Pleasant	29464	Lesesne MRS Thomas P 3D
Mt Pleasant	29464	Mundy MR & MRS R Ward
Mt Pleasant	29464	Pigg MR & MRS Michael P
Mt Pleasant	29466	Randolph DR Christopher & Beardsley MS Sarah
Mt Pleasant	29464	Simmons MRS Adele G
Mt Pleasant	29464	Sinkler MR & MRS George Dana
Mt Pleasant	29464	Turner MR & MRS Robert F III
Mt Pleasant	29464	von Werssowetz MR & MRS Richard O
Mt Pleasant	29464	Waddell MR & MRS James M 5TH
Mt Pleasant	29464	Wood MR & MRS C Clark
Mt Pleasant	29465	Porter MR & MRS Dean D
Mt Pleasant	29466	Bodie MR & MRS George J
Mt Pleasant	29466	Ely MR & MRS Penn W
Mt Pleasant	29466	Howell MR & MRS Thomas T A
Myrtle Beach	29572	Drake MISS Daphne J
Myrtle Beach	29572	White MS Susan F
Newberry	29108	Smith MR & MRS Hugh B
North Charleston	29405	Rivière MR Camden S
North Myrtle Beach	29852	Dent MR & MRS John Elliott
Okatie	29909	Childs MR & MRS Richard H L
Okatie	29909	Crossman MR & MRS William L
Okatie	29909	Grassi MR & MRS Edward A
Okatie	29909	Gwathmey MR & MRS Archibald L
Okatie	29909	Henry MR & MRS Richard L
Okatie	29909	Nordmann MR & MRS Gary A
Okatie	29909	Scheetz MR & MRS Edwin F JR
Okatie	29909	Symington MRS Charles H JR
Okatie	29909	Vanderwarker MR & MRS Richard D
Okatie	29909	Webb MR & MRS Samuel B JR
Okatie	29909	Wierdsma MRS John R
Okatie	29909	Wilds MR & MRS Peter G
Pawleys Island	29585	Ashbridge MR & MRS Stephen D
Prosperity	29127	Brown MR Paul C
Ridge Spring	29129	Dane MISS Barbara H
Ridge Spring	29129	Dane MR & MRS Roger
Ridgeland	29936	Powell MISS Jane L
Seabrook Island	29455	Cummin MR & MRS G Jeremy
Seabrook Island	29455	Pettus MR Thruston W
Seabrook Island	29455	Ralph MR & MRS Richard W
Seabrook Island	29455	Sayko MR & MRS Andrew F
Seneca	29672	Jodice MR & MRS Patrick G R
Sheldon	29941	Bradley MR & MRS Robert L
Sheldon	29941	Cutler MR & MRS Nicholas B
Sheldon	29941	Lortz MR & MRS William C
Sheldon	29941	McIlvain MR & MRS Alan
Simpsonville	29680	Cassell MR & MRS Earl E III
Southern Pines	28387	Day MISS (DR) Deborah
Spartanburg	29302	Brannon MR & MRS Robert A
Spartanburg	29302	Dent MR Frederick B
Spartanburg	29302	Hellyer MR & MRS Arthur T
Spartanburg	29302	Manson MR & MRS Tim J IV
Spartanburg	29302	McGehee REV & MRS Stephen Y
Spartanburg	29302	Stone MR & MRS George E
Spartanburg	29306	McGraw MRS Diana Dent
St Helena Island	29920	Clements MR & MRS Robert M
Sullivans Island	29482	McGee MR & MRS Joseph H
Sullivans Island	29482	Simons MR & MRS Julian M
Sullivan's Island	29482	Sedalik MR & MRS Anton J III
Summerville	29483	Aldinger MR & MRS Thomas L
Summerville	29483	Cameron MR Thomas W L
Sumter	29150	Sholtz MR & MRS David R
Sumter	29154	Anderson MRS Richard K
Wadmalaw Island	29487	Hambleton MR & MRS George B E
Wadmalaw Island	29487	Shannon MR John McC & Estes MR Curtis McL
Yemassee	29945	Morrison MR & MRS Mills Lane

SOUTH DAKOTA

Box Elder	57719	Pierce MR Philip C
Rapid City	57701	Barrows MR & MRS Ryan P
Rapid City	57709	Annan MS (DR) Barbara M
Sioux Falls	57103	van Vliet MR John C
Spearfish	57783	Sayler MR & MRS Bentley S

TENNESSEE

Ashland City	37015	Wheelock MRS Thomas G B
Brentwood	37027	Goss MR & MRS Stuart L
Centerville	37033	Vander Horst MR & MRS Allston
Chattanooga	37405	Howe MS Robin
Chattanooga	37405	Stefaniak DR & MRS Gregory
Chattanooga	37405	Williamson MR & MRS B Franklin
College Grove	37046	Delvin MR & MRS C Henry IV
Collierville	38017	Strange MR & MRS Andrew H
Dickson	37055	Huber MR Anthony S
Fairview	37062	Miller MR & MRS David B
Franklin	37064	Evans MR & MRS Thomas G JR
Franklin	37064	Swensson MR & MRS Earl S
Franklin	37065	Haddock MR & MRS David W
Franklin	37065	Roberts MR & MRS Kenneth L
Franklin	37069	Currey MR & MRS Brownlee O JR
Franklin	37069	Currey MR Christian B
Germantown	38138	Steffens MR & MRS George V 3D
Germantown	38139	Schoelkopf MR & MRS Thomas R
Jackson	38305	Grimball MRS Rosanne D
Jamestown	38556	Scott MISS Mary A
Knoxville	37901	Schumacher MRS H Richard
Knoxville	37901	Townsend MRS Rodman
Knoxville	37912	Condon MR Martin J IV
Knoxville	37919	Absher MR & MRS B Steven
Knoxville	37919	Currier MR & MRS Charles G
Knoxville	37919	Smith MR & MRS Bradley W JR
Knoxville	37919	Townsend REV & MRS Bowman
Knoxville	37922	Woodside MR & MRS Joseph R
La Grange	38046	Lockee CAPT (RET) & MRS Garette E
Lookout Mountain	37350	Baker MR & MRS Rush E IV
Lookout Mountain	37350	Caldwell MR Robert H
Lookout Mountain	37350	Caldwell MRS Robert H JR
Lookout Mountain	37350	Laney MR & MRS James C R
Lookout Mountain	37350	Oehmig MR & MRS Daniel West
Lookout Mountain	37350	Pattee MRS W Burleigh
Lookout Mountain	37350	Van Cleave MRS John P
Memphis	38104	Letsou MR & MRS Peter V
Memphis	38107	Barr MISS (DR) Elizabeth H
Memphis	38111	Stark MRS J Edward JR
Memphis	38111	Wade MR & MRS Festus J III
Memphis	38117	Boyd MR & MRS J Hallam III
Memphis	38117	Boyd MR & MRS J Hallam JR
Memphis	38117	Calil MRS Frances C
Memphis	38117	Daughdrill DR & MRS James H JR
Memphis	38117	Dent MR & MRS Elliott Johnstone III
Memphis	38117	Dohan DR & MRS F Curtis JR
Memphis	38117	Humphreys MR & MRS Anderson
Memphis	38117	Weiss MR & MRS William U
Memphis	38120	Bingham MRS C Tiffany JR

To nominate a candidate for the Social Register Association, please email: SRCommittee@thesocialregister.org

Memphis, TN—Austin, TX

Memphis .... 38120 .... Pacheco MR & MRS R Stephen
Memphis .... 38120 .... Watson MISS Susan H
Memphis .... 38120 .... Williams DR & MRS Robert W III
Murfreesboro .... 37130 .... Wheelock MR Thomas G B
Nashville .... 37203 .... Tams MISS Caroline M
Nashville .... 37204 .... Van Riper MRS Susan Evans
Nashville .... 37205 .... Bass MR Jack M III
Nashville .... 37205 .... Bass MRS Edith McB
Nashville .... 37205 .... Bradford MRS James C JR
Nashville .... 37205 .... Caldwell MR & MRS Wentworth JR
Nashville .... 37205 .... Clay MR & MRS John W JR
Nashville .... 37205 .... Clay MR & MRS Stewart C
Nashville .... 37205 .... Coleman MR & MRS Gregory R
Nashville .... 37205 .... Crook MRS George W
Nashville .... 37205 .... Daane MR & MRS J Dewey
Nashville .... 37205 .... Edwards DR & MRS William H
Nashville .... 37205 .... Edwards DR & MRS William H JR
Nashville .... 37205 .... Foote MR & MRS Douglass G JR
Nashville .... 37205 .... Frist MR & MRS Thomas F III
Nashville .... 37205 .... Green MR & MRS Peyton N
Nashville .... 37205 .... Griffin MR & MRS Mark C
Nashville .... 37205 .... Hale MR & MRS R Walter 3D
Nashville .... 37205 .... Heard MRS Edwin Anthony JR
Nashville .... 37205 .... Joyce MR & MRS Alexis J
Nashville .... 37205 .... Kelly MR & MRS L Owen
Nashville .... 37205 .... Kelly MR & MRS Mark H
Nashville .... 37205 .... Knight MR & MRS Richard H JR
Nashville .... 37205 .... Land MR & MRS Thomas W
Nashville .... 37205 .... Landstreet MR & MRS Beverly W IV
Nashville .... 37205 .... Leschen MR & MRS Elliott F
Nashville .... 37205 .... Levi MR & MRS Joseph C
Nashville .... 37205 .... McKelvey MR & MRS Thomas H JR
Nashville .... 37205 .... McLeod DR & MRS Alexander C
Nashville .... 37205 .... Middleton DR & MRS Blackford
Nashville .... 37205 .... Morgan DR & MRS Walter McN 3D
Nashville .... 37205 .... Mulron MR & MRS Timothy K O'T
Nashville .... 37205 .... Nelson MR & MRS Edward G
Nashville .... 37205 .... Noel MR & MRS Lee F
Nashville .... 37205 .... Rhett MR & MRS H Moore 3D
Nashville .... 37205 .... Richardson MR & MRS Henry Hobson IV
Nashville .... 37205 .... Rose MR & MRS Anthony A JR
Nashville .... 37205 .... Saidy MR & MRS John F
Nashville .... 37205 .... Tarkington MRS J Fred JR
Nashville .... 37205 .... Whitson MR & MRS Albert P JR
Nashville .... 37205 .... Whitson MR & MRS Christopher C
Nashville .... 37205 .... Zimmermann MR & MRS Peter J
Nashville .... 37206 .... Stuart MR & MRS James Harrison
Nashville .... 37209 .... Baldassari MRS Jerome H
Nashville .... 37209 .... Iredell MISS Melissa A
Nashville .... 37209 .... Sperow MS Jacqueline Blake
Nashville .... 37212 .... Davis MISS Kate C
Nashville .... 37212 .... Lang DR & MRS (DR) Matthew J
Nashville .... 37212 .... Leonard MR & MRS John J
Nashville .... 37212 .... Wilson MS Celeste Rose
Nashville .... 37214 .... Blankenship MR Edward G
Nashville .... 37214 .... Mathews MR & MRS Stephen S
Nashville .... 37215 .... Anderson MR & MRS William Wallace 5TH
Nashville .... 37215 .... Armistead MR Hunter JR
Nashville .... 37215 .... Armistead MR Robert H F
Nashville .... 37215 .... Campbell MR & MRS John P III
Nashville .... 37215 .... Conner JUDGE & MRS Lewis H JR
Nashville .... 37215 .... Dale MR & MRS Robert V
Nashville .... 37215 .... Goddard MRS George A
Nashville .... 37215 .... Hart MR & MRS Christopher F
Nashville .... 37215 .... Ingram MR & MRS John R
Nashville .... 37215 .... Joyce MR & MRS Douglas Henry
Nashville .... 37215 .... Kryder MRS Patricia Porter
Nashville .... 37215 .... Leap MR & MRS John M
Nashville .... 37215 .... Leschen MR H John IV
Nashville .... 37215 .... Lipman MR & MRS Lawrence M
Nashville .... 37215 .... Lufkin MRS Blakeslee Cook
Nashville .... 37215 .... Maggart MR & MRS William E
Nashville .... 37215 .... Nelson MR & MRS Charles III
Nashville .... 37215 .... Norvell MISS Margaret P
Nashville .... 37215 .... Obolensky MR & MRS David I
Nashville .... 37215 .... Pilling MR & MRS Robert B
Nashville .... 37215 .... Reed MR James H IV
Nashville .... 37215 .... Smith MISS L Amory
Nashville .... 37215 .... Stadler MS Julia Carell
Nashville .... 37215 .... Wills MR & MRS William Ridley 2D
Nashville .... 37220 .... Morris DR & MRS John A JR
Nashville .... 37221 .... Caldwell MR & MRS Kenneth S 3D
Oak Ridge .... 37830 .... Storey MR & MRS John M E
Oak Ridge .... 37830 .... Wurts MR John W JR
Shelbyville .... 37160 .... Smith MR & MRS Gardiner F
Strawberry Plains .... 37871 .... Kramer DR & MRS John F JR

TEXAS

Addison .... 75001 .... Loudon JHR & MRS Gregory J
Addison .... 75001 .... Rhoades MR & MRS James C
Amarillo .... 79102 .... Lovell MRS John J
Amarillo .... 79106 .... Emeny MISS Ruth B
Argyle .... 76226 .... Plate MR & MRS James M
Argyle .... 76226 .... Plate MRS H Robinson
Austin .... 78701 .... Alofsin MR & MRS Anthony M
Austin .... 78701 .... Leonczyk REV CANON Kenneth G JR
Austin .... 78701 .... Lochridge MISS Georgia P
Austin .... 78701 .... Owen MR & MRS James P
Austin .... 78703 .... Burnett DR & MRS Mark G
Austin .... 78703 .... Burnham MR & MRS John S
Austin .... 78703 .... Carpenter MR & MRS Arthur G
Austin .... 78703 .... Drake MR & MRS Brent R P
Austin .... 78703 .... Elliman MS Julia S
Austin .... 78703 .... Foster MR Mark E
Austin .... 78703 .... Hornblower MR & MRS Josiah C
Austin .... 78703 .... Ingram-Eiser MR & MRS Adam S
Austin .... 78703 .... Lochridge MR Lloyd P JR
Austin .... 78703 .... Newman MS Elizabeth Vardin
Austin .... 78703 .... Vineyard DR & MRS John Pendleton JR
Austin .... 78704 .... Miller MR Robert F
Austin .... 78704 .... Olds MR William L JR
Austin .... 78704 .... Richter MR Brian K
Austin .... 78704 .... Todd MR & MRS David A
Austin .... 78704 .... Ziegler MR Timothy O
Austin .... 78705 .... Lehmann MRS Mary L
Austin .... 78705 .... Meyer MS Maria del Carmen J
Austin .... 78731 .... Bell MR & MRS Arch L
Austin .... 78731 .... Hemphill MR & MRS William R JR
Austin .... 78731 .... Lee MR & MRS Chong S
Austin .... 78731 .... Lounsbery MRS DeWitt
Austin .... 78731 .... Winters MR & MRS J Samuel
Austin .... 78731 .... Wood MR & MRS John R
Austin .... 78731 .... Wright MRS Charles A
Austin .... 78732 .... Denebeim MR & MRS Keith Webster
Austin .... 78738 .... Patterson MR & MRS Lloyd A
Austin .... 78738 .... Peniston MR & MRS Nathaniel F
Austin .... 78738 .... Shippey MR & MRS Bryan L
Austin .... 78739 .... Emory MR & MRS Morris S JR
Austin .... 78739 .... Mathews MR & MRS Adam A
Austin .... 78746 .... Parrish MR & MRS David B
Austin .... 78746 .... Rulon-Miller MR & MRS Christopher

Austin 78746 Trabue MS Sarah C
Austin 78749 Emory MS Stephanie Calderón & Emory MS Cathryn Calderón
Austin 78750 Thompson MR & MRS Bruce R
Austin 78750 Van Dusen MR & MRS Duncan P
Austin 78755 Lehmann MR Frederick W 4TH
Austin 78757 Draper MISS Meredith L
Austin 78759 Elliman MR Peter B
Bay City 77414 Runnells MR & MRS John S 3D
Beaumont 77706 Casey LT COL (RET) Lawrence K JR
Beaumont 77706 Selman MR & MRS John B
Bellaire 77401 Hunter DR & MRS Robert L JR
Bellaire 77401 Nelson MR Brendan & Putnam-Farr MS Eleanor L
Brenham 77833 Dippel MR & MRS Tieman H JR
Brenham 77833 Perkins MR Frederic B
Brownsville 78521 Hudson MR & MRS William P C
Brownsville 78521 Yturria MR Fausto JR
Bulverde 78163 English MS Ann C
Coppell 75019 Johnstone MRS James W
Corinth 76210 Hays MR & MRS Geoffrey E S
Corpus Christi 78401 Vogt MR & MRS William T JR
Corpus Christi 78412 Kennedy MR John B
Cypress 77429 Aucoin MR & MRS Chris P
Cypress 77429 Brown MR & MRS Joshua E
Cypress 77433 von Wiesenthal MR & MRS Peter Christian
Dallas 75201 Blanc MRS Elizabeth Hunt
Dallas 75201 Harris MRS Leon A JR
Dallas 75201 Horchow MR S Roger
Dallas 75201 Hsieh MR Jackson & Chen MS Minalie
Dallas 75201 Lemmon MRS Nancy O
Dallas 75201 Manning MR & MRS George T
Dallas 75201 Penn MR Frederick McK & Corbitt MR A Dean
Dallas 75204 Carr MR & MRS William Plack JR
Dallas 75204 Falb MR & MRS H Bentsen
Dallas 75205 Barcus MR & MRS Cyrus E JR
Dallas 75205 Bender MR & MRS Robert G
Dallas 75205 Brown MR & MRS Stuart L
Dallas 75205 Calder MRS Joan N
Dallas 75205 Campbell MR Henry Villard 3D
Dallas 75205 Cathey MRS Molly
Dallas 75205 Cox MR Edwin Lochridge
Dallas 75205 Custard MR & MRS W Allen III
Dallas 75205 Custard MR & MRS William Allen
Dallas 75205 Feld MR & MRS Alan David
Dallas 75205 Fox MR & MRS Rodman R
Dallas 75205 French MRS Marcia M
Dallas 75205 Howland MR & MRS Grafton Dulany
Dallas 75205 Kidd MR & MRS Barron U
Dallas 75205 Lewis MR & MRS George R
Dallas 75205 Lewis MR Millard JR
Dallas 75205 McKenzie MR & MRS Robert Gene
Dallas 75205 McMullin MR & MRS Forbes A JR
Dallas 75205 Mosle MR & MRS John L JR
Dallas 75205 Nelson MR & MRS Paul B
Dallas 75205 Page MR & MRS J Phillip JR
Dallas 75205 Sinwell MR & MRS Andrew E
Dallas 75205 Teller MR & MRS Andrew JR
Dallas 75205 Washburne MR & MRS Ray W
Dallas 75205 Wheeler DR Bonnie
Dallas 75206 Coxe MRS Brinton
Dallas 75206 Strickler MR & MRS William B
Dallas 75208 Lee MR & MRS George Terry JR
Dallas 75209 Boyce MR Sandford C G & Sabin-Boyce MRS Natalie
Dallas 75209 Clark MR & MRS James H JR
Dallas 75209 Clark MRS Anne Kerbey
Dallas 75209 Dow MR & MRS James P
Dallas 75209 Flanigan MR & MRS Andrew A
Dallas 75209 Garrett MRS William Calvert
Dallas 75209 Hart MR & MRS Todd C
Dallas 75209 Henry MR & MRS Edward J
Dallas 75209 Josey MR & MRS Clinton Wiley JR
Dallas 75209 Lemmon DR & MRS Mark L
Dallas 75209 Marsh MR & MRS Tom Fariss
Dallas 75209 Roosevelt MR Elliott III
Dallas 75209 Storey MRS Charles P
Dallas 75209 Taylor MRS Catherine B
Dallas 75209 Thayer MR & MRS Stephen Cook
Dallas 75209 Washburn MISS Sandra L
Dallas 75209 White DR & MRS Charles S III
Dallas 75209 Yandell MR & MRS Lunsford P VI
Dallas 75214 Lippas MISS Alexandra V
Dallas 75214 Rose MR & MRS S Lance
Dallas 75218 Elliott MR & MRS Robert W
Dallas 75218 Sanger MR & MRS Richard H III
Dallas 75219 Buchanan MRS John E JR
Dallas 75219 Caldwell MR & MRS Josef
Dallas 75219 Clark MR & MRS Robert M JR
Dallas 75219 Cullum MS Lee B
Dallas 75219 Gibbons MRS William E
Dallas 75219 Green MR & MRS George Gardiner JR
Dallas 75219 Lapham MRS Roger D
Dallas 75219 Lowdon MS Patty
Dallas 75219 Patterson MRS Patricia M
Dallas 75219 Seale MR & MRS William
Dallas 75219 Wellborn MR & MRS Robert H
Dallas 75219 Wheeler MR George Y IV
Dallas 75220 McGarr MR & MRS Cappy R
Dallas 75220 Seale MR & MRS John Henry B
Dallas 75220 Shutt MRS George Austin
Dallas 75225 Chatham MRS Antoinette Erker
Dallas 75225 Clancy MR & MRS Andrew O
Dallas 75225 Hickox MR Charles R
Dallas 75225 Hurt MR & MRS G Ellison 3D
Dallas 75225 Madina-Gorbea MR Aitor & Taylor MS Katherine C
Dallas 75225 May DR & MRS Reuel
Dallas 75225 Seale MR & MRS William III
Dallas 75225 Sigrist MR & MRS Steven K
Dallas 75225 Siliciano MR & MRS Michael R
Dallas 75225 Trescher MRS Robert L
Dallas 75225 Wildenthal DR & MRS Kern
Dallas 75229 Allison MR & MRS George R
Dallas 75229 Eiseman MR & MRS Richard D
Dallas 75229 Martinez MR & MRS John M 2D
Dallas 75229 Sachs MR & MRS William R JR
Dallas 75229 Silverthorne MRS John H
Dallas 75229 Taylor MRS William Nelson 2D
Dallas 75230 Andrews MR & MRS Prescott R JR
Dallas 75230 Hillier MR Paul W JR
Dallas 75230 Hollingsworth MR Arthur W
Dallas 75230 King MR & MRS Frank-Paul A
Dallas 75230 Lindh MR & MRS Kenneth M P
Dallas 75230 Martin MR & MRS Harry J
Dallas 75230 Oglesby LT COL (RET) & MRS Edward S
Dallas 75230 Ward MRS Anne E
Dallas 75231 Schwarz MS Lesley A
Dallas 75235 Hall MISS (DR) Christiana E Penn-Gaskell
Dallas 75238 McClendon MRS Karen E
Dallas 75248 Hume MR Anthony
Dallas 75248 Moss MR & MRS Michael P
Dallas 75248 Washburne MRS John C
Dallas 75248 Zweig MR & MRS Ivan S

Dallas, TX—Houston, TX

Dallas	75252	Hume MRS Judith H
Dallas	75254	Moore MR & MRS Thomas M
Dallas	75287	Pidgeon MR & MRS (DR) Steven D
Dalworthington Gardens	76015	Reed MS Grace McLain
Denton	76201	Hays DR & MRS Thomas R
El Paso	79902	Etzold MRS David E
El Paso	79902	Lyle MR & MRS James Arthur
El Paso	79912	Hubbard MR & MRS Bruce B
El Paso	79912	MacGuire MR & MRS John T
El Paso	79912	McKnight MRS Frank G
El Paso	79922	Curtis MRS Wickliffe P
El Paso	79922	Hunt MR & MRS Woodley L
El Paso	79934	Bond CAPT & MRS Dale P JR
Fairview	75069	Chambers MR & MRS Matthew M
Farmers Branch	75234	Nelson MRS Lewis C
Flower Mound	75022	Russell MR & MRS Mark J
Flower Mound	75028	Middleton MR & MRS Elliott 3D
Fredericksburg	78624	Parrish MR & MRS Brainerd S
Fredericksburg	78624	Peake MR & MRS David W JR
Fredericksburg	78624	Valentine MISS Sarah McK
Friendswood	77546	Bricker MR Frederick J III
Friendswood	77546	Carter MR Prescott C
Ft Worth	76107	Hudson MR & MRS E Randall 3D
Ft Worth	76107	Bass MR & MRS Robert M
Ft Worth	76107	Blake MR & MRS James R
Ft Worth	76107	Brauer MR Stephen F JR
Ft Worth	76107	Cole MRS Sheila D
Ft Worth	76107	Cutler MRS S Stubbs
Ft Worth	76107	Darden MR & MRS Glenn M
Ft Worth	76109	Devine DR & MRS Robert J
Ft Worth	76107	Ferchill JUDGE & MRS Patrick W
Ft Worth	76107	Gregg MR & MRS Joshua A
Ft Worth	76107	Holmes MRS Larry A
Ft Worth	76107	Hudson MR & MRS Edward R JR
Ft Worth	76107	Key MRS C S King
Ft Worth	76107	Marion MR & MRS John L
Ft Worth	76107	Minton MISS Susan
Ft Worth	76107	Minton MRS Lloyd McKee
Ft Worth	76107	Moncrief MR & MRS Richard W
Ft Worth	76107	Moncrief MR & MRS William Alvin JR
Ft Worth	76107	Pergande MR & MRS John F
Ft Worth	76107	Phillips MR & MRS W Stevenson
Ft Worth	76107	Staniford MR & MRS Foye McK
Ft Worth	76116	Bonnell DR & MRS William Frederic
Ft Worth	76116	Herpin MR & MRS Allen J
Ft Worth	76116	Payne MRS Sophia Yarnall
Ft Worth	76116	Tansill MRS Robert W
Fulshear	77441	Rundlöf MRS Margaret M
Gainesville	76241	Lindh MRS David E P
Garland	75044	Canby MS Joan A
Georgetown	78633	Miller MRS Thomas W C
Heath	75087	Berger MR & MRS Ira S
Hempstead	77445	Dillon MR & MRS Herbert L III
Horseshoe Bay	78657	Schumacher MR & MRS Dick L
Houston	77002	Anderson MRS Thomas D
Houston	77004	Diesel MRS Jan M
Houston	77004	Warren MR & MRS Godfrey B
Houston	77005	Baird MR & MRS James V JR
Houston	77005	Bering MR & MRS Edgar A III
Houston	77005	Colt MR & MRS Richard T
Houston	77005	Gallagher DR & MRS (DR) Matthew W
Houston	77005	Hastings MR & MRS John O JR
Houston	77005	Holzer DR & MRS Shannon
Houston	77005	Kurka MR & MRS George J III
Houston	77005	Mitch DR & MRS William E JR
Houston	77005	Montz MR & MRS Dennis A
Houston	77005	Neuhaus MR & MRS Joseph R JR
Houston	77005	Todd MR & MRS Anderson
Houston	77006	Djerejian MR & MRS Edward P
Houston	77006	Garwood MR & MRS Calvin B 3D
Houston	77006	Goodrich MR & MRS Hart L
Houston	77006	Stevenson MS (DR) Catherine D
Houston	77006	Todd MISS Emily L
Houston	77007	Larkin MR & MRS William V JR
Houston	77007	Phillips MRS Elizabeth B
Houston	77008	Wagner MR & MRS Marcus H
Houston	77009	Laurenzo MR Dante R & Gentry-Laurenzo MS Kimberly
Houston	77018	Hellums MR & MRS Jay D
Houston	77019	Ackerman MR & MRS Asche
Houston	77019	Blake MRS Thomas W JR
Houston	77019	Boesel MR & MRS Peter M
Houston	77019	Bogart MR & MRS Clinton F
Houston	77019	Carter MR & MRS Thomas L JR
Houston	77019	Chapman MR & MRS Max C JR
Houston	77019	Cruse MR & MRS Samuel W 3D
Houston	77019	Elkins MRS James A III
Houston	77019	Estabrook MISS Helen
Houston	77019	Jenney MRS Robert M
Houston	77019	Kilgore MRS Emilie S
Houston	77019	Kilroy MRS William S
Houston	77019	Macpherson MR & MRS Ian
Houston	77019	McFarland MR & MRS Andrew Roberts
Houston	77019	McGregor MRS C Dangerfield
Houston	77019	Mills MR & MRS Bradford Alan
Houston	77019	Negley MRS Nancy Brown
Houston	77019	Neuhaus MR & MRS Charles E
Houston	77019	Prioleau MR & MRS Charles H
Houston	77019	Pyne MR & MRS Joseph H
Houston	77019	Runnells MR & MRS Clive
Houston	77019	Schnitzer MRS Joan W
Houston	77019	Steen MR & MRS John T III
Houston	77019	Symonds MR & MRS Jonathan T
Houston	77019	Vaughn MR & MRS James M JR
Houston	77019	Weekley MR & MRS Richard W
Houston	77019	Weems MISS Alexandra L
Houston	77019	Weems MR F Carrington 2D
Houston	77019	Wise MR & MRS William A
Houston	77019	Wise MS Vivian M
Houston	77019	Young MR & MRS Donald W
Houston	77020	Shearer MRS Hartley P
Houston	77021	Pruden MR & MRS Terry A
Houston	77024	Adams MR & MRS Andrew M
Houston	77024	Crone MR & MRS Walter S JR
Houston	77024	Hirtz MR & MRS William A C
Houston	77024	Kaufman MR & MRS Barry L
Houston	77024	Kelsey DR Mavis P
Houston	77024	Kendall MR John Atterbury
Houston	77024	Lerner MR & MRS Jay B
Houston	77024	Margolis MR Michael A & Mujica-Margolis MRS Mitra
Houston	77024	Murray MR Robert N
Houston	77024	Richey MR Thomas W JR
Houston	77024	Skidmore MR & MRS Christopher A
Houston	77024	Skidmore MR Louis H JR
Houston	77025	Hero MR & MRS Andrew W
Houston	77027	Andrews MR David D
Houston	77027	Brown MR & MRS Joseph Chenoweth
Houston	77027	Casscells MRS S Ward III
Houston	77027	Chapoton MR & MRS O Donaldson
Houston	77027	Firestone MR & MRS Jeffrey B
Houston	77027	Gaunt MR & MRS William H

Houston.......... 77027......... Girard MR & MRS Louis McM
Houston.......... 77027......... Glasgow MR & MRS W Merrill
Houston.......... 77027......... Henry MISS Margaret E
Houston.......... 77027......... Kahle MR & MRS G Kent
Houston.......... 77027......... Kensinger MR & MRS Stuart R
Houston.......... 77027......... Larned MR & MRS David C JR
Houston.......... 77027......... Leonard MRS James H
Houston.......... 77027......... Linbeck MR & MRS Patrick A
Houston.......... 77027......... McLanahan MR & MRS Alexander K
Houston.......... 77027......... McLanahan MR Alexander G
Houston.......... 77027......... Steen MR & MRS James H C
Houston.......... 77027......... Untermeyer MR & MRS Charles G
Houston.......... 77041......... Gray MRS Mark F
Houston.......... 77043......... Nesbitt MR Charles S M
Houston.......... 77043......... Nesbitt MRS Ernest V II
Houston.......... 77043......... Powers DR Francis Persse-Harcourt
Houston.......... 77043......... Storm MR Robert W
Houston.......... 77056......... Armstrong MR & MRS Tobin JR
Houston.......... 77056......... Doubleday DR & MRS Charles W
Houston.......... 77056......... Jewell MRS George H JR
Houston.......... 77056......... Johns MRS Ronald O'N
Houston.......... 77056......... Kelsey MR & MRS Thomas R
Houston.......... 77056......... Lovett MR & MRS H Malcolm JR
Houston.......... 77056......... Manuel MR & MRS William S 3D
Houston.......... 77056......... Moran MR & MRS Alfred Jay JR
Houston.......... 77056......... Passela MR & MRS George W
Houston.......... 77056......... Victor MS Mary Jane
Houston.......... 77057......... Begley MR & MRS William E JR
Houston.......... 77057......... Chapoton MR & MRS John Edgar JR
Houston.......... 77057......... Curlet MR & MRS Nigel W E
Houston.......... 77057......... Curtis MR Robert F
Houston.......... 77057......... DeJarnette MR Edmund T 3D
Houston.......... 77057......... Hanhausen MR & MRS William J
Houston.......... 77057......... Hirsch MR & MRS Duane M
Houston.......... 77057......... Kelly MRS Paul Lance
Houston.......... 77057......... Schrauff MR William P
Houston.......... 77057......... Tilney MR & MRS Schuyler M
Houston.......... 77059......... Green MR & MRS David W
Houston.......... 77059......... Hillman MR & MRS Gilbert R
Houston.......... 77062......... Farmer MRS William H
Houston.......... 77063......... Diesel MR & MRS John H 2D
Houston.......... 77063......... Fowler MR & MRS William H II
Houston.......... 77069......... Augustus MS Juanita
Houston.......... 77079......... Colt MR & MRS S Sloan II
Houston.......... 77079......... Kernan MISS Sheilah E
Houston.......... 77079......... Lamberton MR & MRS Harry C III
Houston.......... 77079......... Robins MRS Alfred LeC
Houston.......... 77096......... Cook DR Richard G & Cook DR Susan Wray
Houston.......... 77096......... Gryska MR & MRS Peter H
Houston.......... 77098......... Bienvenu MR & MRS Brandon B
Houston.......... 77098......... Howe MR & MRS George E
Houston.......... 77098......... Kelsey MR & MRS Mavis P JR
Houston.......... 77098......... Murray MR & MRS R Nelson JR
Houston.......... 77098......... Walker MR & MRS J Ewing JR
Houston.......... 77098......... Wilcox MR & MRS Benjamin D W
Houston.......... 77219......... Peake MISS Susan S
Houston.......... 77227......... Kelsey MR Henry B
Irving.......... 75063......... McCandless MRS Rosemary Van L
Katy.......... 77450......... Nat MR & MRS Andrew A JR
Katy.......... 77494......... Mixter MS Nancy W
Keller.......... 76262......... Tatum MR & MRS John P
Kerrville.......... 78028......... Forbes MRS Erica L
Kerrville.......... 78028......... Nomer MRS Howell F
Kingwood.......... 77339......... Easterby MR & MRS Stewart D 3D
Kingwood.......... 77339......... Parrish MS Christine H
Kingwood.......... 77339......... Tourais MR & MRS Patrick R
Kingwood.......... 77339......... Viault MRS George B
Kingwood.......... 77345......... Easterby MR & MRS David E
Kingwood.......... 77345......... Talbot MR & MRS Fraser H
Laredo.......... 78043......... Curtis MRS McCall
Laredo.......... 78043......... Mills MR & MRS Gordon Lawrence
Longview.......... 75605......... Hull MR & MRS Jeffrey R
McAllen.......... 78501......... Havens MR & MRS Timothy M
McAllen.......... 78502......... Link MRS Edwin Cary
McKinney.......... 75070......... Covington MR Bentley M
McKinney.......... 75070......... Lafferty MR & MRS F Wayne JR
McKinney.......... 75070......... Wellborn MR & MRS Robert H JR
Midland.......... 79701......... French MR & MRS L Robert JR
Midland.......... 79701......... Ritchie MRS James M C
Mission.......... 78572......... Link MR & MRS Theodore C
Missouri City.......... 77459......... Chapman MR & MRS James A B
Missouri City.......... 77459......... Morton MR & MRS Thomas M
Missouri City.......... 77459......... Smith MR & MRS Anderson P
Murphy.......... 75094......... Schrauff MR & MRS Christopher W
New Braunfels.......... 78130......... Schlumberger MR & MRS Pierre Marcel
Pipe Creek.......... 78063......... Leonard MR Nicholas A
Plano.......... 75025......... Conner MR & MRS Stephen P
Plano.......... 75075......... Radtke MR & MRS Timothy L
Plano.......... 75093......... Taylor MR & MRS Nicholas Van Campen
Plano.......... 75093......... Wollenberg MRS Katrina M
Princeton.......... 75407......... Kilborne MS Frances McD
Prosper.......... 75078......... Ford MR H Ross 3D
Richardson.......... 75080......... Succop MR John C
Richardson.......... 75082......... Schrauff MR & MRS Hamilton P
Rockport.......... 78382......... Clark MR & MRS Benjamin L
San Antonio.......... 78204......... Butt MR Charles C
San Antonio.......... 78204......... Wiederhold MR & MRS Michael L
San Antonio.......... 78209......... Carleton MR & MRS James E
San Antonio.......... 78209......... Clement MISS Leslie L
San Antonio.......... 78209......... Davidson MR & MRS (DR) Robert L
San Antonio.......... 78209......... Dowler MR & MRS Moulton Shreve JR
San Antonio.......... 78209......... Farrimond MR & MRS Brent T
San Antonio.......... 78209......... Foultz MR & MRS Eric S
San Antonio.......... 78209......... Fuhrmann MR & MRS Charles J 2D
San Antonio.......... 78209......... Garcia MR & MRS Luis A
San Antonio.......... 78209......... Holt MR & MRS Benjamin D JR
San Antonio.......... 78209......... Johnson MRS Belton Kleberg
San Antonio.......... 78209......... Kelso LT COL & MRS Robert Earl
San Antonio.......... 78209......... Kimbro MRS Robert Willis
San Antonio.......... 78209......... Lahourcade MR & MRS J Lance
San Antonio.......... 78209......... Lange MR & MRS Richard A
San Antonio.......... 78209......... McAllister MRS Walter W JR
San Antonio.......... 78209......... McGaughy MR & MRS Thomas Elkin
San Antonio.......... 78209......... Meyer MR & MRS Vaughan B
San Antonio.......... 78209......... Petty MR & MRS Scott JR
San Antonio.......... 78209......... Rockwood MRS William R
San Antonio.......... 78209......... Rodriguez MR Benjamin E & Beretta MS Jacqueline R
San Antonio.......... 78209......... Sanders MR & MRS David R
San Antonio.......... 78209......... Sheerin MRS J Laurence
San Antonio.......... 78209......... Shields MISS Jennifer A
San Antonio.......... 78209......... Spiro MR & MRS Herbert J
San Antonio.......... 78209......... Steen MR & MRS John T JR
San Antonio.......... 78209......... Steves MR & MRS Albert 4TH
San Antonio.......... 78209......... Vaughan MR & MRS Curtis T 3D
San Antonio.......... 78209......... Vaughan MR & MRS Robert L
San Antonio.......... 78209......... Ward MR & MRS Joseph B
San Antonio.......... 78209......... Zbinden REV & MRS Louis H JR
San Antonio.......... 78212......... Campbell MR William T
San Antonio.......... 78212......... Carson MR Chris
San Antonio.......... 78212......... Newton MR & MRS Howard Pardue
San Antonio.......... 78212......... Oppenheimer MR & MRS Jesse H
San Antonio.......... 78212......... Rentschler MR & MRS Charles F

San Antonio, TX—Manchester Center, VT

San Antonio 78212 Ridenhower MISS Elizabeth Miller
San Antonio 78212 Romano MR Todd A
San Antonio 78216 Rorem DR & MRS David A
San Antonio 78217 Leeper MR & MRS Harry G JR
San Antonio 78218 Montemayor MR & MRS Carlos R
San Antonio 78227 De Young MRS Guy O JR
San Antonio 78227 Wheelis MRS Reuben E
San Antonio 78230 Norman DR & MRS Ruskin C
San Antonio 78230 Senseman DR & MRS David M
San Antonio 78232 Benoist MRS Howard 3D
San Antonio 78232 Miller MR Marshall B JR & Huntington MS Claudia P
San Antonio 78232 Mitchell DR & MRS George W JR
San Antonio 78240 Schoyer MR Timothy R
San Antonio 78240 Wimpress DR & MRS G Duncan JR
San Antonio 78249 Sands MR & MRS William D
San Antonio 78254 Harvey TSGT & MRS David W III
San Antonio 78255 Cox MAJ & MRS Mark A
San Antonio 78258 Coffee MR & MRS Todd B
San Antonio 78258 Giffin RT REV & MRS Robert T
San Marcos 78666 Earle MR & MRS Louis McK
Seabrook 77586 Emanuelsen MR & MRS Mads
Southlake 76092 Cooney MR & MRS Philip A
Southlake 76092 Curtis MR & MRS Wickliffe P JR
Spring 77379 Ivancevich MRS John M
The Woodlands 77375 Blake MR & MRS Robert W
The Woodlands 77375 Mark MR & MRS W Steven JR
The Woodlands 77381 Griffith MR James W JR
The Woodlands 77381 Hutchinson MRS (DR) Stephanie R
The Woodlands 77381 Lipscomb DR & MRS A Brant JR
The Woodlands 77381 Ohlms MR & MRS James H
Trophy Club 76262 McCulloch MR & MRS Owen
University Park 75205 McWilliams MR John L IV
Waco 76712 Sudderth MR & MRS Joe R
Weatherford 76085 Melvin DR Norman C III
Webster 77598 Haugen MS Ann Sims
West Lake Hills 78746 Burke MR & MRS P Gibbons JR
West Lake Hills 78746 Stegeman MR William J & Gill MR Robert Scott

UTAH

Bountiful 84010 Burnley COL & MRS Todd W
Eden 84310 Fowler CAPT (RET) & MRS Charles W III
Millcreek 84109 Cook CAPT & MRS Glen A
Oakley 84055 Victor MR & MRS David
Park City 84060 Jensen MR & MRS Frode 3D
Park City 84060 MacDonald MRS Robert I
Park City 84060 Sturges MR George David
Park City 84098 Graff MR & MRS Robert T
Park City 84098 Hunt MR & MRS Alastair J
Salt Lake City 84101 Lambert DR & MRS Brent W
Salt Lake City 84103 Classen DR & MRS David C
Salt Lake City 84103 Corroon MR & MRS Peter M
Salt Lake City 84103 Magee MISS Daisy M
Salt Lake City 84106 Grandy MR & MRS Edward B
Salt Lake City 84108 Smith MR & MRS Leonard Bacon
Salt Lake City 84121 Fernow MR Steven D
Salt Lake City 84124 Ligget MR & MRS Robert C
Salt Lake City 84124 Wurts MR & MRS Henry C

VERMONT

Arlington 05250 Allen MR Brian T & Horsch MR Steven D
Arlington 05250 Bennett MRS Sandra Skinker
Ascutney 05030 McNabb MR & MRS Alan C JR
Barnard 05031 Field MR & MRS Daniel
Bellows Falls 05101 Read MRS Alexander D
Brandon 05733 Morris MISS Deirdre L E
Brattleboro 05301 Butler MR Sidney M G
Brattleboro 05301 Howat MISS Laura A
Brattleboro 05301 Lenssen MS Isabel B
Brattleboro 05301 Porter REV CANON & MRS Nicholas T
Burlington 05401 Colburn MR & MRS Michael G
Burlington 05401 Freeman MR & MRS John L
Burlington 05401 Motch MR & MRS Elton F JR
Burlington 05401 Murray MR & MRS William T III
Burlington 05408 Shaw MRS Phyllis E
Burlington 05408 Walsh MS Samantha A
Charlotte 05445 Braun DR & MRS John T
Charlotte 05445 Davis MR & MRS Christopher W
Charlotte 05445 Davis MR Jonathan B & Iglehart MS Laura C
Charlotte 05445 Kiernan MR & MRS Stephen P G
Charlotte 05445 Spencer MR & MRS Kenneth W
Chester 05143 Johnson MR Timothy Swaim
Colchester 05446 Couture MR & MRS Joseph E
Colchester 05446 Lamontagne MR & MRS Michael A
Cornwall 05753 Rumbough MR & MRS Douglas M
Craftsbury 05826 Ulman MRS Cornelius M
Craftsbury Common 05827 Schmitt MR & MRS Michael A 3D
Dorset 05251 Ashton MRS David G JR
Dorset 05251 Atwill MS Elena M
Dorset 05251 de Rham MR & MRS Abbott B
Dorset 05251 Faesy MR & MRS A Robert
Dorset 05251 Gilbert MR Clinton JR
Dorset 05251 Lee MR & MRS Henry C
Dorset 05251 Marshall MR Alexander R
Dorset 05251 Melhado MR & MRS William A
Dorset 05251 Phillips MS Wendy L
Dorset 05251 Read MISS Sandra L
Dorset 05251 Reed MR & MRS Pendennis W JR
Dorset 05251 Rollinson MRS Simeon H 3D
Dorset 05251 Taylor MR Frederic F
East Calais 05650 Jacobsen MR & MRS Rowan J
East Calais 05650 Low MR & MRS Anthony
East Dorset 05253 Wise MR & MRS Charles W W
East Dummerston 05346 Montgomery MR & MRS Neil M
East Montpelier 05651 Rauh MR & MRS Stephen S
East Montpelier 05651 Wanzer MR Charles T & Faesy MS (DR) Lydia
East Randolph 05041 Wheelock MR William H JR
Glover 05839 Knowlton MISS Lindsay
Grafton 05146 Evans MR & MRS Thomas M JR
Grand Isle 05458 Graves MR & MRS Harry Hammond
Hardwick 05843 Auchincloss MR Gordon B & Gardner MS Melissa D
Hartland 05048 Hamilton MISS Deborah B
Hartland 05048 Jeffries DR & MRS (DR) Peter F
Hartland 05048 Marrin DR & MRS (DR) Charles A S
Hartland Four Corners 05049 Luquer MR & MRS Peter Van C
Jamaica 05343 Todd MR & MRS James de P
Jericho 05465 Martin MR & MRS Peter R
Jericho Center 05465 Minot MR & MRS David T W
Killington 05751 McKenna MR & MRS Andrew S
Londonderry 05148 Stock MR & MRS Peter D
Lyndon Center 05850 Fischer MR & MRS Heinz G
Lyndonville 05851 Richwien MR & MRS Barry A
Manchester 05254 McCormick MR & MRS Levering
Manchester 05254 Olcott MRS A Van Santvoord JR
Manchester 05254 Peltz MRS Henry S
Manchester 05254 Wilbur MRS James B 3D
Manchester 05255 King MR & MRS Andrew L
Manchester Center 05255 Auchincloss MR & MRS Edgar S 4TH
Manchester Center 05255 Baurmeister MR & MRS Hans U
Manchester Center 05255 du Pont MR & MRS Anthony A
Manchester Center 05255 Howard MR George

Manchester Center, VT—Worcester, VT

Manchester Center........05255.........Kingery MR & MRS Thomas D 3D
Manchester Center........05255.........McCormick MR & MRS John S
Manchester Center........05255.........McGrail MR William P 3D
Manchester Center........05255.........McMillan MRS H George JR
Manchester Center........05255.........Miller MRS Frederick R
Manchester Center........05255.........Philip MR Peter V N
Manchester Center........05255.........Pribble MR & MRS Robert
Manchester Center........05255.........Victor MS Martine V
Manchester Village.......05254.........Ross MR & MRS H Lawrence 3D
Marshfield.......................05658.........Farmer MRS Patrick A
Middlebury......................05753.........Drake MRS Francis A
Middlebury......................05753.........Hiland MR & MRS R Bruce
Middlebury......................05753.........Pierce MRS Norman
Middlebury......................05753.........Stetson MRS Charlotte M
Middlebury......................05753.........Van Tuyl MRS Harry E JR
Montpelier.......................05602.........Castle MR & MRS D Lyman
Montpelier.......................05602.........Durrance MR & MRS John R JR
Montpelier.......................05602.........Scharnberg MR James Fagan
Montpelier.......................05602.........Sease MR Stephen B & Naquin MS Carole J
Montpelier.......................05602.........Woodward MR Bruce A
Moretown........................05660.........McCloy MR & MRS John J II
Morrisville.......................05661.........Bovey MRS William K
Morrisville.......................05661.........Cushman MR John M
Morrisville.......................05661.........Merrill MR & MRS Peter K
Newbury..........................05051.........Grove CAPT (RET) George S
North Bennington.........05257.........Buckley MRS Amelia B
North Bennington.........05257.........Richardson CAPT & MRS
Northfield.......................05663.........McVickar MRS Grenville K
Norwich..........................05055.........Gillotti MR & MRS Albert F
Norwich..........................05055.........King DR Charles III
Norwich..........................05055.........Metcalf MRS Michael P
Norwich..........................05055.........Milliken MR & MRS Peter H
Norwich..........................05055.........Russell MRS Angus M
Norwich..........................05055.........Simmers MR & MRS Clayton R II
Norwich..........................05055.........Simpson MR & MRS Michael H
Norwich..........................05055.........Stetson MR & MRS Eugene William 3D
Orwell.............................05760.........Carpenter MR & MRS David G
Pawlet.............................05761.........Beer MR & MRS John W
Pawlet.............................05761.........Rockwell MR & MRS Charles E
Peacham.........................05862.........Woods MISS Frances S
Perkinsville....................05151.........Clattenburg DR & MRS Richard N JR
Peru................................05152.........Morgan MR & MRS Jeffery B
Putney.............................05346.........Campman MR & MRS Finn T
Putney.............................05346.........Shumlin MR & MRS Jeffrey P
Quechee..........................05059.........Gray MRS Harvey L
Quechee..........................05059.........Scott MR & MRS Philip W
Richmond........................05477.........Filkorn MR & MRS Erik W
Rupert.............................05768.........Trachte MR & MRS David C II
Rutland............................05701.........McCall MRS S Carter JR
Rutland............................05701.........Shinn MRS George Latimer
Rutland............................05701.........Stafford MR & MRS Robert T
Sandgate.........................05250.........Brinckerhoff MRS Starr E JR
Sandgate.........................05250.........de Peyster MISS Suzanne
Shaftsbury......................05262.........Putnam MR & MRS Bruce M
Shelburne........................05482.........Brownell MR & MRS Kenneth Hyde
Shelburne........................05482.........Carstensen MR & MRS Hans L III
Shelburne........................05482.........Davis MR & MRS J Staige III
Shelburne........................05482.........Edgerton MRS Philip
Shelburne........................05482.........Everett MR & MRS Andrew B
Shelburne........................05482.........Gignoux MR & MRS Reginald
Shelburne........................05482.........Hammer CAPT (RET) & MRS John L 3D
Shelburne........................05482.........Hasen MR John H
Shelburne........................05482.........Hollister MR & MRS Buell 3D
Shelburne........................05482.........Miller MRS Susan W
Shelburne........................05482.........Morgan MR & MRS Frederick C
Shelburne........................05482.........Parsons MRS Marselis C 3D
Shelburne........................05482.........Rianhard MR & MRS Perry D JR
Shelburne........................05482.........Roberts MRS Bruce L
Shelburne........................05482.........Vaughan MR & MRS C Wheaton
Shelburne........................05842.........Lishnak DR & MRS Timothy S
Shoreham........................05770.........Jenks MR & MRS T Story JR
Shoreham........................05770.........Maguire MR & MRS J Robert
Shrewsbury.....................05738.........Barclay MR & MRS J Randell
South Burlington...........05403.........Cady MRS K McCarthy
South Burlington...........05403.........Emery DR & MRS Edward S 3D
South Burlington...........05403.........Gray MR & MRS Elliot W
South Burlington...........05403.........King MR & MRS Jeremy W
South Burlington...........05403.........McIlvaine MISS Allan
South Burlington...........05403.........Thompson MR & MRS David R
South Hero......................05486.........Bass MRS Jean M
South Londonderry.......05155.........Barry MR John L 3D
South Londonderry.......05155.........Hunnewell MR & MRS John C
South Londonderry.......05155.........Sherrer MR & MRS Christopher C
South Pomfret................05067.........Thacher MR & MRS Anthony
South Strafford..............05070.........Ray MR & MRS Dustin S
Springfield.....................05156.........Weeks MR & MRS Gerald C
St Johnsbury..................05819.........Amos MR & MRS Robert C
Starksboro......................05487.........Faesy MR & MRS Richard
Starksboro......................05487.........Harris MR Spencer K & Plimpton MS Medora A
Starksboro......................05487.........Mott MR Garret III
Stowe.............................05672.........Brown MR & MRS Courtney W P
Stowe.............................05672.........Brownell MRS Conchessa M
Stowe.............................05672.........Duke MR & MRS A Biddle JR
Stowe.............................05672.........Genung MR & MRS Alexander M
Stowe.............................05672.........Goodson DR & MRS Gregg W
Stowe.............................05672.........Peterkin MRS Jennifer W
Stowe.............................05672.........Tagatac MR & MRS Christopher J
Stowe.............................05672.........Taylor DR & MRS Richard G
Stowe.............................05672.........Wheelwright MRS George W IV
Strafford.........................05072.........Emerson MR Edward E III
Strafford.........................05072.........Hemenway MR John T
Sudbury..........................05733.........Roberts MR & MRS Stephen F
Sutton.............................05867.........Parker MR & MRS Henry S III
Thetford Center.............05075.........Reeves LT COL (RET) Laurence E 3D
Townshend.....................05353.........Jameson MISS Adair
Underhill Center............05490.........Diffenderffer MR & MRS Michael K
Underhill Center............05490.........Diffenderffer MR C Rich
Waitsfield.......................05673.........Haynes MR & MRS Robert B
Waitsfield.......................05673.........Huggins MRS Kenneth R
Waitsfield.......................05673.........Kiendl MR & MRS Philip R JR
Waitsfield.......................05673.........Kiendl MRS Philip R
Wallingford....................05773.........Ryan MR & MRS Thomas R
Warren............................05674.........Cormier MR Clayton P
Warren............................05674.........von Moschzisker MR Felix
West Danville.................05873.........Roosevelt MR & MRS Michael A
West Pawlet...................05775.........Dubois MRS Christina
Weston............................05161.........Ehrhard MR & MRS Louis E JR
Weston............................05161.........Frick MR & MRS Richard T JR
Weston............................05161.........Hoyt MR William W
Weston............................05161.........Neff MRS W Perry
Weston............................05161.........Rosengarten MR & MRS Peter K
Weybridge......................05753.........Hill MRS Robert W JR
Williston.........................05495.........Curtis REV DR & MRS Lawrence R
Windsor..........................05089.........Appleton MRS Benjamin B
Windsor..........................05089.........Smith MR & MRS Bayard W
Woodstock.....................05091.........Debevoise MRS Thomas M 2D
Woodstock.....................05091.........Edmunds MRS Elizabeth P W
Woodstock.....................05091.........Emmons MRS William B JR
Woodstock.....................05091.........Gottsegen MR Daniel A & Jackson MS Margaret
Woodstock.....................05091.........Hoyt MR & MRS Coleman W
Woodstock.....................05091.........Noble MR & MRS Daniel S
Worcester.......................05682.........Shedd MISS Elisabeth H Ely

To nominate a candidate for the Social Register Association, please email: SRCommittee@thesocialregister.org

Accomac, VA—Arlington, VA

VIRGINIA

Accomac	23301	Conrad MR & MRS Barnaby III
Aldie	20105	Morison MR & MRS C Dulany
Aldie	20105	Morison MR & MRS George H
Aldie	20105	Twining MR & MRS Edmund S 3D
Alexandria	22301	Muckerman MR & MRS Peter M
Alexandria	22301	Pelliconi MR & MRS Richard Reydel
Alexandria	22301	Treadway MR & MRS Alexander McC
Alexandria	22302	Batten MR Bruce W & Smith MS Elizabeth Curtiss
Alexandria	22302	Goldsmith MRS John M JR
Alexandria	22302	Hauhart CDR (RET) & MRS James N
Alexandria	22302	Hornung MR & MRS Stephen J
Alexandria	22302	Martin MR & MRS David B H JR
Alexandria	22302	Minor MISS Ann N
Alexandria	22302	Murray MR & MRS Thomas A
Alexandria	22302	Philbrick MR & MRS J Alden IV
Alexandria	22302	Reynolds MR & MRS R Roland
Alexandria	22302	Rodgers MR & MRS Clifton E JR
Alexandria	22302	von Guggenberg MRS Nicholas M
Alexandria	22302	Willard MR & MRS Timothy H
Alexandria	22303	Bruen MR Alexander H
Alexandria	22303	Long MR & MRS Robert E
Alexandria	22303	Rea MRS Elizabeth Beach
Alexandria	22304	Bakewell MR & MRS Charles Adams
Alexandria	22304	Bartol CDR (RET) & MRS John H JR
Alexandria	22304	Blair MR & MRS Duncan W
Alexandria	22304	Kling DR & MRS John D II
Alexandria	22304	Norman MR & MRS James T
Alexandria	22304	Sensenbrenner MR & MRS F James JR
Alexandria	22304	Tabor MR & MRS William H
Alexandria	22305	Davis MR & MRS Joseph H
Alexandria	22305	Dickey MR Alexander G
Alexandria	22305	Greenleaf MISS Allison McC
Alexandria	22305	Krueger MR & MRS Christopher C
Alexandria	22305	Meath Baker MR & MRS H Lysander L
Alexandria	22305	Richey MR & MRS Sheffield C JR
Alexandria	22305	Wise MR & MRS Parker S III
Alexandria	22306	Carter MR & MRS Francis M
Alexandria	22307	Bavin MR & MRS Clark R JR
Alexandria	22307	Cobb MRS Richard
Alexandria	22307	Jones MR & MRS Freeman E
Alexandria	22307	Lamb MR & MRS Faron C
Alexandria	22307	Murray MS Kathryn K
Alexandria	22307	Richards MR & MRS John T L JR
Alexandria	22308	Brown DR Barrett B JR
Alexandria	22308	Burke MR & MRS C S Taylor III
Alexandria	22308	Gebhard MR Russell D
Alexandria	22308	Kennedy MR & MRS David B
Alexandria	22308	Livingston MR & MRS Robert L JR
Alexandria	22308	Longman MR & MRS Tremper 3D
Alexandria	22308	Pyle MR & MRS Mark C
Alexandria	22308	Richards MRS John T L
Alexandria	22308	Sturtevant MISS Brereton
Alexandria	22309	Muir MRS Jo-Ann McNally
Alexandria	22310	Wilson MR & MRS Richard C
Alexandria	22311	Jaeger DR Boi Jon & Corson-Jaeger MRS Ann D
Alexandria	22311	Knowlton MRS William A
Alexandria	22311	Williams MRS Thomas J C
Alexandria	22312	Vanderpoel CAPT (RET) & MRS Eric II
Alexandria	22312	Webb CAPT & MRS T Ladson JR
Alexandria	22314	Bader MR & MRS William B
Alexandria	22314	Barker MR & MRS Michael
Alexandria	22314	Bauer DR & MRS Charles A
Alexandria	22314	Brownell MRS Nora Mead
Alexandria	22314	Burke MRS G Anderton
Alexandria	22314	Cooper MRS Richmond J
Alexandria	22314	Cox MRS H Bartholomew
Alexandria	22314	Crabb MR & MRS David L
Alexandria	22314	Drewry MS Virginia W
Alexandria	22314	Garrison MR William B JR
Alexandria	22314	Montague MR & MRS Robert L 4TH
Alexandria	22314	Montague MR Robert L 3D
Alexandria	22314	Murray MRS Russell 2D
Alexandria	22314	Orr MISS Jean A
Alexandria	22314	Paul JUDGE & MRS Michael T
Alexandria	22314	Peters MISS Marjorie S
Alexandria	22314	Simmons MR & MRS Richard De L
Alexandria	22314	Simonds MRS Albert Rhett JR
Alexandria	22314	Smith MR & MRS Joseph J III
Alexandria	22314	Stevens MISS Larkin E
Alexandria	22314	Thomas MRS Roberta S
Alexandria	22314	Tucker MR & MRS Howard McK
Alexandria	22314	Tyler MR John R
Alexandria	22314	von Raab MRS William C
Alexandria	22315	Stocker MISS Eve M
Amissville	20106	Hall MR H Seymour JR
Annandale	22003	Holmes COL (RET) Frederick S JR
Arlington	22201	Brunton MR & MRS Charles A
Arlington	22201	Davis MR & MRS C Austin
Arlington	22201	Hinzman MR & MRS Joel P
Arlington	22201	Jenks COL (RET) & MRS John P
Arlington	22201	Martin MISS Josephine C
Arlington	22201	Pratt MISS Christine S
Arlington	22201	Redmond MR Sean P
Arlington	22201	Smythe MS Christine L
Arlington	22201	Tibbs MR Eugene E JR & Ortbals-Tibbs MRS Stephanie M
Arlington	22201	von Nirschl MR David A
Arlington	22202	Astigueta MRS Fernando D
Arlington	22202	Bradley MR & MRS J Douglas
Arlington	22202	Carney MRS Robert B JR
Arlington	22202	Perry MR & MRS Ross G
Arlington	22202	Roberts MRS J Milnor JR
Arlington	22202	Smith MR & MRS Andrew L
Arlington	22202	Wright MR William M III
Arlington	22203	Boswell MR Jackson C
Arlington	22203	Buzby MR & MRS George H
Arlington	22203	Dorn MRS Carl S
Arlington	22203	Mann MR William T
Arlington	22203	Openchowski MR Kenneth F A
Arlington	22203	Wilson MRS Dennis K
Arlington	22204	Roach CAPT J Ashley
Arlington	22204	Whalen MR Edward Holmes
Arlington	22205	Chew MRS H Richard
Arlington	22205	Hemingway MS Barbara
Arlington	22205	Lewis MISS Joan K
Arlington	22205	Radcliffe MR Byron W & Tallarico MR Patrick M
Arlington	22205	Shumate MR John T M
Arlington	22205	Wilmer MR & MRS Richard H 4TH
Arlington	22206	Coste MISS Sarah P
Arlington	22206	Deeken DR & MRS John F
Arlington	22206	Etter MR & MRS Thomas C JR
Arlington	22206	Henry MR S Morgan 3D
Arlington	22206	Rhodes MR & MRS Geoffrey P
Arlington	22206	Tulloch MRS Marshall E
Arlington	22207	Bellinger COL (RET) & MRS John B JR
Arlington	22207	Bellinger MR & MRS John B 3D
Arlington	22207	Boggs MR & MRS G Trenholm JR
Arlington	22207	Boggs MR & MRS George T
Arlington	22207	Chubb MR & MRS Talbot Spence
Arlington	22207	Curran MR & MRS Denis A

Arlington .... 22207 .... Donovan MR & MRS (DR) Brian P
Arlington .... 22207 .... Edgar MR & MRS George L
Arlington .... 22207 .... Glaccum MR & MRS John-Amory
Arlington .... 22207 .... Kidder MR & MRS Howard C
Arlington .... 22207 .... Leisenring MR & MRS John
Arlington .... 22207 .... Mabry MR Brian K & Ort-Mabry MRS Catherine E
Arlington .... 22207 .... Moore MR & MRS J Hunter
Arlington .... 22207 .... Roberts MR Jared I
Arlington .... 22207 .... Scarborough VICE ADM (RET) & MRS Robert H JR
Arlington .... 22207 .... Smith MR & MRS David L
Arlington .... 22207 .... Stieglitz MR & MRS Albert B JR
Arlington .... 22207 .... Wells MAJ & MRS Edward F
Arlington .... 22207 .... Wheelock MR & MRS Austin W
Arlington .... 22209 .... Finley MRS William T JR
Arlington .... 22209 .... Goodwyn MR Scott M
Arlington .... 22209 .... Wallop MRS French Carter
Arlington .... 22213 .... Peltier MR & MRS Alec M
Aroda .... 22709 .... Leonard MR & MRS Nicholas A JR
Ashburn .... 20147 .... Everett MR Francis D JR
Ashburn .... 20147 .... Mattingly MISS (DR) Elizabeth H
Ashburn .... 20148 .... Legg MR Eugene Monroe
Ashland .... 23005 .... DeJarnette MR & MRS Edmund T JR
Bacova .... 24412 .... Haynes MR & MRS Patrick R JR
Barhamsville .... 23011 .... Brown MR Michael C
Bentonville .... 22610 .... Dusenbury MR & MRS Donald S
Berryville .... 22611 .... Heilman MR & MRS W Strickland
Berryville .... 22611 .... Henderson MR & MRS Joseph W III
Berryville .... 22611 .... Watkins MRS W Bell IV
Blacksburg .... 24060 .... Young MRS Garrett S
Bluemont .... 20135 .... Foster MRS Rockwood H
Bluemont .... 20135 .... Johns MR & MRS F Winston
Boyce .... 22620 .... Underwood DR Frederic B
Boyce .... 22620 .... Van Wyck MR E Hawley 3D
Bristol .... 24201 .... Goodpasture MR Frank III
Bristol .... 24202 .... McGlothlin MR & MRS James W
Broad Run .... 20137 .... Hazel MR & MRS John T JR
Burke .... 22015 .... Genné MR & MRS Douglas M
Burke .... 22015 .... Hoff MR Henry B
Burke .... 22015 .... Hunt CDR & MRS C Lansdowne
Burke .... 22015 .... Paris COL (RET) & MRS William F 2D
Burke .... 22015 .... Phommachanh MR & MRS Titou P
Castleton .... 22716 .... Taylor MR & MRS Robert E L 3D
Catawba .... 24070 .... Steele MISS Linda F
Centreville .... 20120 .... Whiteley MR & MRS Richard Peyton
Charlottesville .... 22901 .... Achilles MRS Jonathan N
Charlottesville .... 22901 .... Baxter MRS C McGhee JR
Charlottesville .... 22901 .... Beisswanger MR & MRS William J
Charlottesville .... 22901 .... Bishop MR & MRS Thomas B JR
Charlottesville .... 22901 .... Bowen MR & MRS John de K III
Charlottesville .... 22901 .... Bowen MR & MRS John deK IV
Charlottesville .... 22901 .... Darrell MR John Stewart
Charlottesville .... 22901 .... Dudley MR & MRS E Alexander JR
Charlottesville .... 22901 .... Easter MR Peter
Charlottesville .... 22901 .... Edgerton DR Milton T
Charlottesville .... 22901 .... Emery MRS Rose B
Charlottesville .... 22901 .... Ford MR & MRS F Richards 4TH
Charlottesville .... 22901 .... Gammon MR Blair C
Charlottesville .... 22901 .... Gillespie MR & MRS W Scott
Charlottesville .... 22901 .... Jordan MR & MRS David C
Charlottesville .... 22901 .... Lancaster MRS Henry Carrington JR
Charlottesville .... 22901 .... Lewis MR & MRS H Hunter
Charlottesville .... 22901 .... Martin MS Sabina R
Charlottesville .... 22901 .... Milbank MR & MRS Joseph H SR
Charlottesville .... 22901 .... Peters MISS Julie
Charlottesville .... 22901 .... Powers MR & MRS Evan J
Charlottesville .... 22901 .... Sheehan MR & MRS Thomas V
Charlottesville .... 22901 .... Short MR & MRS R Carter N
Charlottesville .... 22901 .... Slaughter MR & MRS D French 3D
Charlottesville .... 22901 .... Strickler MR & MRS Richard S JR
Charlottesville .... 22901 .... Thompson MR & MRS W McIlwaine JR
Charlottesville .... 22901 .... Trinkle MR William F & Granados MR Juan M
Charlottesville .... 22901 .... Vest MR & MRS Charles T
Charlottesville .... 22901 .... Williams MR & MRS Richard K JR
Charlottesville .... 22901 .... Worthington MRS Sarah G
Charlottesville .... 22901 .... Wright MR & MRS Charles P JR
Charlottesville .... 22902 .... Ascher MR James P
Charlottesville .... 22902 .... Bearns MRS Wendy H
Charlottesville .... 22902 .... Brewster MR & MRS Benjamin
Charlottesville .... 22902 .... Gignoux MR & MRS Frederick E III
Charlottesville .... 22902 .... Jordan MR & MRS Daniel P JR
Charlottesville .... 22902 .... Reback MR & MRS Forbes R
Charlottesville .... 22903 .... Agee MR Willard Curtis
Charlottesville .... 22903 .... Ayres MR & MRS H Fairfax 3D
Charlottesville .... 22903 .... Ballantine MR & MRS Martin D
Charlottesville .... 22903 .... Behr MR Richard P
Charlottesville .... 22903 .... Bolus MR & MRS Jay J
Charlottesville .... 22903 .... Bowen MR Howell L
Charlottesville .... 22903 .... Brookfield MR & MRS Christopher M
Charlottesville .... 22903 .... Brown MR & MRS John K
Charlottesville .... 22903 .... Coolidge MRS Francis L
Charlottesville .... 22903 .... Du Bose MR & MRS Charles F
Charlottesville .... 22903 .... Epstein DR & MRS Steven E
Charlottesville .... 22903 .... Fauth MRS Gerald W JR
Charlottesville .... 22903 .... Fearey MR & MRS Christopher L
Charlottesville .... 22903 .... Flood MISS Mary E G
Charlottesville .... 22903 .... Gaston MR John JR
Charlottesville .... 22903 .... Gordon MR & MRS Robert H
Charlottesville .... 22903 .... Hammond MS Helen J
Charlottesville .... 22903 .... Henneman MR & MRS Charles C
Charlottesville .... 22903 .... Keyser MRS Campbell Dirck
Charlottesville .... 22903 .... Lang MRS Cecil Y
Charlottesville .... 22903 .... McLean MR & MRS Stephen T
Charlottesville .... 22903 .... Mirkil MS Sandra I
Charlottesville .... 22903 .... Nolting MRS Frederick E JR
Charlottesville .... 22903 .... Pearson MR & MRS Eric Garfield JR
Charlottesville .... 22903 .... Pollock MR & MRS Eugene P
Charlottesville .... 22903 .... Scott MR & MRS James H III
Charlottesville .... 22903 .... Speidel MR & MRS Russell F 2D
Charlottesville .... 22903 .... Stamp MR J Andrew
Charlottesville .... 22903 .... Stevenson MRS Virginia J
Charlottesville .... 22903 .... Stevenson MRS William W
Charlottesville .... 22903 .... Stoner MR & MRS Frank R 4TH
Charlottesville .... 22903 .... Strauch MR & MRS Joel E
Charlottesville .... 22903 .... Terry MR & MRS Michael Whitelaw
Charlottesville .... 22903 .... von Thelen MR & MRS Alexander C
Charlottesville .... 22903 .... Ziegler MRS Carter C
Charlottesville .... 22905 .... Scott MS E Lee
Charlottesville .... 22905 .... Scripps MRS Betty Knight
Charlottesville .... 22905 .... Tilney MRS Anne Cutler JR
Charlottesville .... 22906 .... Crawford MRS S Coleman
Charlottesville .... 22906 .... Crosby DR & MRS Everett U
Charlottesville .... 22911 .... Catlin MRS Avery
Charlottesville .... 22911 .... Gilbert MR & MRS Jackson B
Charlottesville .... 22911 .... Howell MR & MRS Douglas E
Charlottesville .... 22911 .... Hoyt MR & MRS William V
Charlottesville .... 22911 .... Johnson MR & MRS Harald
Charlottesville .... 22911 .... Maroney MR & MRS Samuel P JR
Charlottesville .... 22911 .... Matheson MR & MRS J Murdoch B
Charlottesville .... 22911 .... Minich CANON & MRS Henry N F
Charlottesville .... 22911 .... Phillips MRS Aubrey
Charlottesville .... 22911 .... Scott MRS James H JR
Charlottesville .... 22911 .... Wist MR & MRS Andrew L

Charlottesville, VA—Lorton, VA

Charlottesville	22911	Worthington MR George M G & Mowat MR Cameron D
Chatham	24531	Miller MR & MRS Harry S
Chesapeake	23328	Evans MR Christopher J
Chesterfield	23832	Heck MR & MRS George C 3D
Clifton	20124	Gardiner MR & MRS Richard E
Clifton	20124	Holmes MR & MRS Douglas E
Coles Point	22442	Rager MS Susan Godman
Crozet	22932	Fox MR & MRS (LT COL) John MacRae
Crozet	22932	Gilliam MS Louise B
Crozet	22932	Harrison MR & MRS Robert C
Crozet	22932	Heppner COL DR (RET) & MRS D Gray JR
Crozet	22932	Rosenblum MR & MRS John W
Crozier	23039	Burgess MR & MRS Richard B
Crozier	23039	Meyer MR & MRS Charles G III
Culpeper	22701	Clark MR & MRS John Sheldon
Dahlgren	22448	Gammon MR & MRS John Lea 2D
Delaplane	20144	Carroll DR & MRS Charles 4TH
Delaplane	20144	Chester MR & MRS George M JR
Delaplane	20144	de Give MRS David de B
Dulles	20189	Hannafin MR & MRS Mark S
Dulles	20189	Smith MR Jeffrey A & Melville MS Ann S
Dulles	80129	Symington MR & MRS W Stuart
Dunn Loring	22027	El-Yacoubi MR & MRS Salime H
Earlysville	22936	Caplow MRS Theodore
Earlysville	22936	Clarke MR & MRS Stephen M JR
Earlysville	22936	Mellinger MR & MRS Larry K
Earlysville	22936	Myers MR & MRS James A
Esmont	22937	Duke MR & MRS Nicholas Rutgers
Esmont	22937	Miller MR & MRS Edward M
Esmont	22937	Sargent MISS Sarah B
Esmont	22937	Tunner DR & MRS William S
Fairfax	22030	DiTeresi MR & MRS Christopher A
Fairfax	22030	Lindsley MR Winston J
Fairfax	22030	Ross MISS Vanessa M
Fairfax	22031	Armentrout MR & MRS Edward J
Fairfax	22031	Dupuy MR & MRS Arnold C
Fairfax	22032	Bassert COL (RET) & MRS David E
Fairfax Station	22039	Buick MR & MRS Timothy M
Fairfax Station	22039	Combe CAPT (RET) Andrew J
Fairfax Station	22039	El-Yacoubi MR & MRS Abd Al-Bary H
Fairfax Station	22039	El-Yacoubi MR & MRS Abdallah H
Fairfax Station	22039	El-Yacoubi MR & MRS Muhssin H
Fairfax Station	22039	El-Yacoubi MRS (DR) Hassan H S
Fairfax Station	22039	Hasan MR Danny S & El-Yacoubi MS Fatimah H
Fairfax Station	22039	Kratovil MRS (DR) Stephen Carr JR
Falls Church	22041	Brinton MR Fullerton
Falls Church	22041	Phillips MRS Donald B
Falls Church	22042	Farnam MR William D
Falls Church	22042	Lenihan MR & MRS Sean P
Falls Church	22043	Ernst MR & MRS Christopher G
Falls Church	22043	Hayes MR & MRS Timothy E
Falls Church	22043	Johnson MR & MRS Parker W
Falls Church	22044	Timashev DR & MRS Sviatoslav A
Falls Church	22046	Marshall MRS Thurgood
Falls Church	22046	Mayhew MR & MRS Aaron C
Falls Church	22046	Sutton MR & MRS Richard D
Flint Hill	22627	Renzy MR & MRS Bernard T III
Flint Hill	22627	Thieriot MS Julia D
Floyd	24091	Bright MR & MRS Lawrence L
Fredericksburg	22401	Meyer MR Richard W III
Fredericksburg	22401	Sheffield MR & MRS Walter J
Fredericksburg	22401	Wilberger MR & MRS Joshua S
Free Union	22940	Hilliard MR & MRS David S
Free Union	22948	Uihlein MISS Linda R
Front Royal	22630	von Gontard MR & MRS Adalbert 3D
Ft Belvoir	22060	Abell MR & MRS Richard Bender
Gainesville	20155	Bailey MR & MRS James MacK
Gainesville	20155	McCawley DR & MRS Austin
Glen Allen	23059	Burger MR & MRS Richard L
Glen Allen	23059	Sadtler MR & MRS Benjamin B
Glen Allen	23060	Swainston MR & MRS Rolf K
Gordonsville	22942	Drew MRS Thayer Hoffstot
Gordonsville	22942	Longaker MS Bettina G
Gordonsville	22942	Regan MR Gordon B
Great Falls	22066	Davis MR Christopher L
Great Falls	22066	de Wolf MRS Bradford C
Great Falls	22066	Dougherty MR & MRS Daniel F
Great Falls	22066	Guthrie MR & MRS Philip H
Great Falls	22066	Huffman MR & MRS Byron K JR
Great Falls	22066	Keating MR & MRS Perry E
Great Falls	22066	Maxwell MR & MRS David B
Great Falls	22066	Rollow MR & MRS William E
Great Falls	22066	Seyfert MR & MRS William H 3D
Great Falls	22066	Simonds MR & MRS William H JR
Great Falls	22066	Treco MR & MRS Gordon D
Greenwood	22943	Peyton MR & MRS Scott B
Hamilton	20159	Haight MRS Sherman P JR
Hampton	23661	Borland MS Susan M
Hampton	23661	O'Reilly MRS Nicholas S
Henrico	23228	Scott MR Charles A
Henrico	23238	Dimond MR & MRS Renwick De G JR
Herndon	20170	Alexander CDR (RET) & MRS John W
Hot Springs	24445	Shriver MRS Beverley Randolph JR
Hot Springs	24445	Smithers MISS M Vey
Hudgins	23076	Story CAPT & MRS William F
Irvington	22480	Agnew MR & MRS James Q
Irvington	22480	French MRS Edward D
Irvington	22480	James MR & MRS Leland T
Irvington	22480	Kuper MR & MRS George Henry
Irvington	22480	Lay MRS David
Irvington	22480	Little MR & MRS Henry A III
Irvington	22480	Stephens MR & MRS Bradley H
Irvington	22480	Williams DR & MRS M Lee
Ivy	22945	Gibson MR & MRS Mark De W
Ivy	22945	Sinks DR & MRS Lucius F
Jeffersonton	22724	Bailey MR & MRS James P JR
Jeffersonton	22724	Burnett MR & MRS Robert R
Keene	22946	Gordon MR & MRS William S
Keswick	22947	Gay MR & MRS Peter A
Keswick	22947	Hoffmann MR & MRS James E
Keswick	22947	Jenks MRS John Story
Keswick	22947	Parker MR & MRS Thomas J
Keswick	22947	Scalise MR & MRS Michael J
King George	22485	Guest MR & MRS Achille M
Laurel Fork	24352	Dick MS Eleanor S
Leesburg	20175	Hunt MR & MRS William H G
Leesburg	20175	Orme MRS Edgar J JR
Leesburg	20175	Sturdevant MR & MRS David C
Leesburg	20176	Rust MR & MRS John M
Leesburg	20176	Spradling MR & MRS Brock A
Leesburg	20176	Walker MR & MRS Wirt D 3D
Leesburg	20178	Jones MRS Benjamin C 3D
Lexington	24450	Baker MRS Gordon McA
Lexington	24450	Henneman MR & MRS Edward O
Lexington	24450	Ingersoll MR & MRS Daniel W IV
Lexington	24450	Rathbun MRS Dean A
Lexington	24450	Rumford MISS Beatrix T
Lexington	24450	Tucker DR & MRS (DR) Spencer C
Lexington	24450	Turbeville CDR & MRS Daniel W
Locust Grove	22508	Colby MR & MRS George H
Lorton	22079	Darling MRS Joseph W McNab
Lorton	22079	Thayer MR Robert H JR

Louisa.......23093.......Wade MR & MRS Troy J
Lynchburg.......24503.......Withington MISS Ann Fairfax
Lyndhurst.......22952.......Bierman MR & MRS Brock D
Manakin Sabot.......23103.......Jones MR & MRS James A III
Manakin-Sabot.......23103.......Reichel MR & MRS Frank H 3D
Manassas.......20112.......Koch DR Henry T 3D
Manassas.......20112.......Reilly MR Christopher C
Mappsville.......23407.......Seybolt MR & MRS Calvert H
Markham.......22643.......Clark MR & MRS P Hamilton III
Markham.......22643.......Drowne MR Bradley C
Markham.......22643.......Leachman MRS William H 3D
Marshall.......20115.......Bedford MRS Erskine L
Marshall.......20115.......Bond MR & MRS Langhorne McC
Marshall.......20115.......Bunting MR & MRS Josiah III
Marshall.......20115.......Ennis MR & MRS David F
Marshall.......20115.......Hunter MRS Phelps Stokes
Marshall.......20115.......Marr MR J Stewart
Marshall.......20115.......Potter MR Trevor A McC & Westring MR Dana S
Marshall.......20115.......Randolph MRS Archibald Cary JR
Marshall.......20115.......Young MRS James L
Martinsville.......24112.......McClain MR & MRS Allan
Mattaponi.......23110.......Light MRS Deborah F
Maurertown.......22644.......Clark MRS Walter D JR
McLean.......22101.......Aquino MR & MRS Sixto F
McLean.......22101.......Bowman MRS A Smith
McLean.......22101.......Carter MISS Lee C
McLean.......22101.......Collins MR & MRS Steven F
McLean.......22101.......Cook MR & MRS H Clayton JR
McLean.......22101.......Coolidge MR & MRS Thomas L
McLean.......22101.......Coyne MR & MRS James K 3D
McLean.......22101.......Darman MRS Richard G
McLean.......22101.......Dewar MR & MRS James M
McLean.......22101.......DuVal MR & MRS Daniel H
McLean.......22101.......Faulks DR & MRS (DR) Craig R
McLean.......22101.......Fritz MR & MRS Jerald N
McLean.......22101.......Gerber MR & MRS George C
McLean.......22101.......Gerber MR & MRS John D T
McLean.......22101.......Henry MR & MRS H Alexander
McLean.......22101.......Hicks MRS James D
McLean.......22101.......Keith CDR (RET) & MRS James
McLean.......22101.......Kirk MR & MRS Alan G II
McLean.......22101.......Kloman MR & MRS Christopher R
McLean.......22101.......Lay MR & MRS Mark P
McLean.......22101.......Martin MR & MRS Middleton Ansley
McLean.......22101.......Motley MR & MRS John L III
McLean.......22101.......Nimick MR & MRS C Lockhart Howe
McLean.......22101.......Noell MR Charles Preston 3D
McLean.......22101.......Noreika MR & MRS (DR) Keith A
McLean.......22101.......Parker MRS Robert Meade JR
McLean.......22101.......Peacock MR & MRS Glen M
McLean.......22101.......Pendleton MRS Edmund E
McLean.......22101.......Prouty MR & MRS J Reid
McLean.......22101.......Riedel DR & MRS Charles J
McLean.......22101.......Robb MR & MRS Charles S
McLean.......22101.......Rodocanachi MR & MRS Stephen J
McLean.......22101.......Rose MR & MRS Jonathan Chapman
McLean.......22101.......Ruffin MR & MRS Nicholas C
McLean.......22101.......Snyder MR & MRS F Eckert
McLean.......22101.......Sutton MR & MRS Charles S
McLean.......22101.......Symington MR & MRS James McKim JR
McLean.......22101.......Talbot MR & MRS Lee M
McLean.......22101.......Thompson MR & MRS (DR) David H
McLean.......22101.......Walker MRS John H
McLean.......22101.......Walton MR & MRS James J
McLean.......22101.......Wilton MR & MRS Frank S
McLean.......22102.......Allen MR & MRS Yorke IV
McLean.......22102.......Arnold COL (RET) & MRS Joseph C
McLean.......22102.......Bedell MR & MRS Kevin B
McLean.......22102.......Bozarth MR & MRS H Austin
McLean.......22102.......Cummings MR & MRS Edward McL
Mclean.......22102.......Cummings MR & MRS Ogden E
McLean.......22102.......Darlington MR & MRS Christopher N
McLean.......22102.......Davidge MS Dorsey
McLean.......22102.......Farnum MR & MRS Michael
McLean.......22102.......Hackett MR & MRS Lance B
McLean.......22102.......Jewett MR & MRS Freeborn G JR
McLean.......22102.......Lovejoy DR Thomas E
McLean.......22102.......Marshall MISS Peyton M
McLean.......22102.......Marshall MR & MRS John R
McLean.......22102.......Marshall MR Fielding C
McLean.......22102.......Mattingly MR Richard V JR
McLean.......22102.......Monroe MR & MRS Michael A
McLean.......22102.......Morgan MR & MRS Junius S II
McLean.......22102.......Simpson MR & MRS Harry J
Merry Point.......22513.......Nuckols MR & MRS Samuel C 3D
Middleburg.......20117.......Burden MR & MRS Childs F
Middleburg.......20117.......Burke MR & MRS John W III
Middleburg.......20117.......Courts MRS Frank J
Middleburg.......20117.......Goltra MR & MRS Peter Seipp
Middleburg.......20117.......Ryan MR C Gregg
Middleburg.......20117.......White MR A Ridgely
Middleburg.......20118.......Cronin MR Paul D
Middleburg.......20118.......Dove MR & MRS Guy O III
Middleburg.......20118.......Fleming MRS R Walton JR
Middleburg.......20118.......Gunnell MR T Nelson
Middleburg.......20118.......Jenkins MRS Virginia W
Middleburg.......20118.......Kaye MRS Howard
Middleburg.......20118.......Mason MRS W Beverley JR
Middleburg.......20118.......Matheson MR & MRS Charles T
Middleburg.......20118.......Murdock MISS Catherine C
Middleburg.......20118.......Ramsay MRS Robert McL
Middleburg.......20118.......Thorndike MR & MRS David N
Middleburg.......20118.......Van Metre MR & MRS Albert G JR
Middleburg.......20118.......Weed DR Timothy
Midlothian.......23112.......Hardy MR & MRS William R JR
Midlothian.......23112.......Hilbert MISS Corinne W
Midlothian.......23112.......Hilbert MR & MRS Samuel R
Midlothian.......23113.......Bland MR & MRS Michael G
Midlothian.......23113.......Clifford MR & MRS Henry F S
Midlothian.......23113.......Dixon MR & MRS Harold G
Midlothian.......23113.......Gilbert MR & MRS Joseph A
Midlothian.......23113.......Knowles MR & MRS Peter I C III
Milford.......22514.......Ferrer MR & MRS Robert N JR
Millboro.......24460.......Reagan MR William R & McGuire MS Amanda K
Millwood.......22646.......Gilpin MR & MRS Thomas T
Millwood.......22646.......Williams MRS Debora W
Mt Sidney.......24467.......Bailey MR & MRS Charles W JR
New Market.......22844.......Ragan MR & MRS Dennis O
Newport News.......23602.......Williams DR & MRS McKim
Newport News.......23606.......Welsh MRS Charles Wesley II
Newport News.......23607.......Vose MRS Frederic H E
Norfolk.......23503.......Jones MR Landon H
Norfolk.......23505.......Chappell MRS John Wade
Norfolk.......23505.......Chase MR & MRS David M JR
Norfolk.......23505.......Grimball MR & MRS William H III
Norfolk.......23505.......Harris MR & MRS Henry P U 3D
Norfolk.......23507.......Johnson MR & MRS (DR) Edward M
Norfolk.......23507.......Pardee MR S Trevor JR
Norfolk.......23510.......Furr MR & MRS Carter B S
North.......23128.......Ashton MR & MRS William H JR
North Garden.......22959.......Moses DR & MRS Hamilton III
Oak Hill.......20171.......Corser MR & MRS Russell E

Oak Hill, VA—Roseland, VA

Oak Hill.......... 20171.......... Doolittle MR & MRS Michael L
Oakton.......... 22124.......... Kennedy MR & MRS Thomas W
Onancock.......... 23417.......... Wadhams MR Edmund Lee
Orange.......... 22960.......... Carter MR & MRS L H Sullivan
Orange.......... 22960.......... Porter MR & MRS J Ridgely 3D
Orange.......... 22960.......... Richards MR Eben
Orange.......... 22960.......... Shackelford MR & MRS Virginius R 3D
Orange.......... 22960.......... Snyder MR & MRS John H
Orange.......... 22960.......... Wiley MR & MRS Justin H
Orlean.......... 20128.......... Hinckley MR Albert P JR
Orlean.......... 20128.......... Lindsay MR & MRS Dale A
Orlean.......... 20128.......... Wise MS Katherine P
Palmyra.......... 22963.......... Cochran MISS Catherine
Palmyra.......... 22963.......... Crowther MR & MRS F Bosley 3D
Palmyra.......... 22963.......... Valentine MR & MRS M Pratt
Petersburg.......... 23805.......... Martin MR & MRS Brandon C
Portsmouth.......... 23704.......... Bielenstein MISS Danielle E M
Portsmouth.......... 23704.......... Bielenstein MRS Hans
Potomac Falls.......... 20165.......... Day MR & MRS Charles W
Potomac Falls.......... 20165.......... Geiger RR ADM (RET) & MRS Robert K
Potomac Falls.......... 20165.......... Haynes MR & MRS James M JR
Potomac Falls.......... 20165.......... Hollister MR & MRS Buell 4TH
Powhatan.......... 23139.......... Jeffress MR Alan S
Pulaski.......... 24301.......... Jeanes MR Isaac W 3D
Pungoteague.......... 23422.......... Sadtler MR & MRS Stephen C
Purcellville.......... 20132.......... Lyon MR & MRS Robert B
Purcellville.......... 20132.......... Trapnell MS Emily M
Purcellville.......... 20134.......... van der Burgh MR & MRS Charles E 3D
Randolph.......... 23962.......... Newcombe MR J Shane
Rectortown.......... 20140.......... Beyer MR & MRS E Charles
Rectortown.......... 20140.......... Lavine MR & MRS Henry W
Reston.......... 20191.......... Allen MRS Helen
Reston.......... 20191.......... Chew MR H Richard JR
Reston.......... 20191.......... Hurd MR & MRS Benjamin N
Reston.......... 20191.......... Maniha MR & MRS John K
Reston.......... 20194.......... Dickey MS Kimberley Anne
Richmond.......... 23220.......... Allen MR Francis O V & Towers MS Laura R
Richmond.......... 23220.......... Blundon MR & MRS Carroll M
Richmond.......... 23220.......... Lowsley-Williams MR & MRS Paul J
Richmond.......... 23220.......... Romaine MR David F
Richmond.......... 23220.......... Scott MR & MRS Gerald W
Richmond.......... 23220.......... Vance MR & MRS Thomas G
Richmond.......... 23221.......... Collin MR & MRS William E
Richmond.......... 23221.......... Finton MR & MRS Timothy C
Richmond.......... 23221.......... Hager MR & MRS John H
Richmond.......... 23221.......... Kirby MR & MRS Roger H W
Richmond.......... 23221.......... McGuire DR & MRS Hunter H JR
Richmond.......... 23221.......... Proctor MR & MRS Robert A 3D
Richmond.......... 23221.......... Reed MR & MRS John M R
Richmond.......... 23222.......... Buchanan MS Mary
Richmond.......... 23222.......... Monroe MRS Mary S G
Richmond.......... 23223.......... Pickering REV & MRS William
Richmond.......... 23225.......... Bozarth MR & MRS Robert S
Richmond.......... 23225.......... Knowles MR & MRS A Stuart Bolling
Richmond.......... 23225.......... Peyman DR & MRS Douglas A R
Richmond.......... 23226.......... Agnew MR Lawrence R
Richmond.......... 23226.......... Bedell MR & MRS Henry A
Richmond.......... 23226.......... Bergner CAPT (RET) & MRS Robert Brewster
Richmond.......... 23226.......... Bowers MR & MRS J Ros JR
Richmond.......... 23226.......... Carter MR & MRS Hugh D
Richmond.......... 23226.......... Clarkson MR & MRS Miles H
Richmond.......... 23226.......... Damgard MR & MRS Michael T
Richmond.......... 23226.......... Davis MR & MRS Mark A H
Richmond.......... 23226.......... Davis MRS Geraldine Hempel
Richmond.......... 23226.......... Fisher DR & MRS (DR) G Hunt
Richmond.......... 23226.......... Hogan MR & MRS Michael Joseph
Richmond.......... 23226.......... Hunton MR & MRS Eppa 5TH
Richmond.......... 23226.......... Krusen MR & MRS William A III
Richmond.......... 23226.......... Mercer MRS Dale Tatum
Richmond.......... 23226.......... Merriman MR Charles H III
Richmond.......... 23226.......... Moore MRS Sumner Kittelle JR
Richmond.......... 23226.......... Perkins MRS Chiswell D L
Richmond.......... 23226.......... Randolph MR & MRS Malcolm M
Richmond.......... 23226.......... Riddle MR & MRS Gary L
Richmond.......... 23226.......... Rise MR & MRS P Carter
Richmond.......... 23226.......... Saffelle MR & MRS Robert N
Richmond.......... 23226.......... Scott MR & MRS S Buford
Richmond.......... 23226.......... Smith MR & MRS R Gordon
Richmond.......... 23226.......... Switz DR & MRS Donald MacL
Richmond.......... 23226.......... Tunner MR & MRS William W
Richmond.......... 23226.......... Valentine MRS E Massie
Richmond.......... 23226.......... Whisnand MR & MRS Carter van A
Richmond.......... 23226.......... Williams MRS John D
Richmond.......... 23227.......... Brandt MRS Paul E
Richmond.......... 23227.......... Dozier MRS O Kemp
Richmond.......... 23227.......... Gates MR & MRS Peter P McN
Richmond.......... 23227.......... Martinez MR & MRS James M JR
Richmond.......... 23227.......... Maxwell MR & MRS John C JR
Richmond.......... 23227.......... Wray MS Mary Denny
Richmond.......... 23228.......... Rugg DR & MRS Robert D
Richmond.......... 23229.......... Adams MR & MRS Brian R M
Richmond.......... 23229.......... Brown MR & MRS Brewster J
Richmond.......... 23229.......... Goodall MR & MRS Robert D
Richmond.......... 23229.......... Greenwood MR & MRS Douglas
Richmond.......... 23229.......... Hutchinson MR & MRS S Pemberton III
Richmond.......... 23229.......... Loree MR & MRS Leonor F 3D
Richmond.......... 23229.......... McConnel MR & MRS W Bruce JR
Richmond.......... 23229.......... McGehee MRS Margaret F V
& Owens MRS Marianne E
Richmond.......... 23229.......... Meigs MRS S Willis
Richmond.......... 23229.......... Penhallow MRS David P
Richmond.......... 23229.......... Price MR & MRS T Winston
Richmond.......... 23229.......... Price MR & MRS Theodore W
Richmond.......... 23229.......... Reed MR & MRS Charles L III
Richmond.......... 23229.......... Reed MR & MRS Charles L JR
Richmond.......... 23229.......... Rogers MR & MRS Christopher C
Richmond.......... 23229.......... Rogers MR & MRS N Pendleton
Richmond.......... 23229.......... Schultz MR & MRS John F
Richmond.......... 23229.......... Scott MR Michael T
Richmond.......... 23229.......... Stauffer MRS Sherryn K
Richmond.......... 23229.......... Sterling MRS Keir B
Richmond.......... 23229.......... White MR & MRS L Lawrence III
Richmond.......... 23230.......... Reichel MRS Frank H JR
Richmond.......... 23233.......... Diffee MR & MRS Craig W
Richmond.......... 23233.......... Dillon DR Edward C
Richmond.......... 23233.......... Norton MR & MRS Marshall L
Richmond.......... 23235.......... Beebe MRS John H JR
Richmond.......... 23235.......... Price MR & MRS F Ransone
Richmond.......... 23235.......... Travis MR & MRS Lionel M III
Richmond.......... 23238.......... Anderson MR & MRS Robert E III
Roanoke.......... 24014.......... Biddle MR & MRS Peyton R 3D
Roanoke.......... 24014.......... Burns MR & MRS R Webb
Roanoke.......... 24014.......... Mortlock DR David H JR
& Mortlock MRS (REV) Elizabeth
Roanoke.......... 24015.......... Schuyler MR Peter G
Roanoke.......... 24018.......... Biddle MR & MRS Compton M
Roanoke.......... 24018.......... Crawford MR & MRS Steven C
Roanoke.......... 24018.......... Grannis MRS Dustin
Roanoke.......... 24018.......... Poland MR Charles B
Rochelle.......... 22783.......... Hammond MS Jane W
Rockville.......... 23146.......... Pell MS Angelene V
Roseland.......... 22967.......... Josephson MR & MRS Wayne A

Roseland, VA—Yorktown, VA

Roseland	22967	Wallace MR Richard S
Ruckersville	22968	Waterbury LT COL & MRS Timothy B
Salem	24153	Elliott MR & MRS Jonathan B
Salem	24153	Newsom MR & MRS Samuel B
Salem	24153	Nordt MR & MRS Paul W 3D
Salem	24153	Turner MS Elisabeth R G
Scottsville	24590	Winsor MRS Curtin
Somerset	22972	Collins MR & MRS James C
Somerset	22972	Dulaney MRS Frances Massey
Somerset	22972	Grennan MR & MRS Edward S III
South Boston	24592	Gillespie CAPT DR & MRS Cameron A Kress
South Riding	20152	Sterling MR & MRS Warner S
Springfield	22150	Blunt MR & MRS William W JR
Springfield	22151	White MR & MRS Richard D
Springfield	22152	Hurst MR Byron W
Springfield	22152	Wiles MR & MRS Ellis W
Springfield	22153	Stratz CAPT & MRS Brandon M
St George	22935	Denkinger MRS M Esty
Stafford	22554	Hoyt MR & MRS William H
Stanardsville	22973	Carpenter MRS Dorr B
Staunton	24401	McDaniel MRS Nancy M
Staunton	24401	White MRS M Brannan
Strasburg	22657	Bancroft MISS Elizabeth A
Strasburg	22657	Greeff MR & MRS Pieter
Tazewell	24651	Olmsted MR Garrett S
The Plains	20198	Carter MRS Robert Lee
The Plains	20198	Chapman MR Henry O III
The Plains	20198	Fleischmann MRS Dorette L
The Plains	20198	Higginson MR & MRS Thomas L JR
The Plains	20198	Lefferts MRS Leffert
The Plains	20198	Lewis MISS Joan P
The Plains	20198	Ohrstrom MR & MRS Christopher F
The Plains	20198	Ohrstrom MR & MRS Mark J
The Plains	20198	Ohrstrom MRS George L JR
The Plains	20198	Ohrstrom MRS Ricard R
The Plains	20198	Turner LT COL (RET) & MRS Robert F III
The Plains	20198	Turner MR Clifford O
The Plains	20198	van Roijen MISS Laura W
The Plains	20198	Wheelwright MR & MRS Henry C
The Plains	22198	Twiss MRS John R JR
Upperville	20184	Gable MR & MRS James S
Upperville	20184	Horkan MRS George A JR
Upperville	20184	Stettinius MRS Joseph JR
Upperville	20184	Young MRS Robert Winthrop JR
Upperville	20185	Bortz MR Richard C
Upperville	20185	Gebhard MRS Karl T E
Upperville	20185	Hood MR Jeffrey J
Upperville	20185	Smart MR & MRS S Bruce JR
Upperville	20185	Spencer MRS Frederick L
Upperville	20185	Stokes MRS William S 3D
Vienna	22180	Burke MR & MRS William S
Vienna	22180	Nelsen MR & MRS Peter R
Vienna	22181	Armstrong MR & MRS Robert S
Vienna	22181	Bochner MR & MRS Richard J
Vienna	22181	McKalip MR & MRS (DR) Frederick D
Vienna	22182	Cooper MR & MRS Joshua J
Vienna	22182	Locke MR John S
Vienna	22182	Mathews MR & MRS Charles P
Virginia Beach	23451	Daniel MRS Robert W JR
Virginia Beach	23451	Devereux MRS Lelia W
Virginia Beach	23451	Ill MR & MRS Peter M
Virginia Beach	23451	Mason MR & MRS Scott C
Virginia Beach	23451	Putney MR & MRS Lacey E JR
Virginia Beach	23451	Turpin MR Carter M JR
Virginia Beach	23451	Wood DR & MRS G Thomas
Virginia Beach	23452	Grimes MRS Thomas J
Virginia Beach	23452	Stahl MR & MRS William C
Virginia Beach	23452	Werth MR Matthew F M JR
Virginia Beach	23453	Logan MR & MRS Frank G 2D
Virginia Beach	23454	Fowler LT COL (RET) & MRS C Worthington 2D
Virginia Beach	23454	Mentz MR George F M JR
Virginia Beach	23455	Culbertson CDR & MRS William J
Virginia Beach	23456	Logan MR & MRS Frank G III
Virginia Beach	23462	Stallard MS Jean M
Ware Neck	23178	Smith MR James R & McClintic MS Miranda P M
Warm Springs	24484	Kirby MISS Annette Sutherland
Warrenton	20186	Nevill MR & MRS Hugh E C
Warrenton	20186	Nevill MR & MRS Lowell S Wells
Warrenton	20188	Cooper MR & MRS Rex S
Warrenton	20188	Greene MISS Stuart T
Warrenton	20188	Jenkins MISS Lora H
Warrenton	20188	Jenkins MR & MRS T Christopher
Warrenton	20188	Nevill MR & MRS Hugh T A
Warrenton	20188	Porter MRS S Prentice
Warrenton	20188	Spencer MRS Harold R
Warsaw	22572	Wellford MR & MRS R Carter 4TH
Washington	22747	Babcock MISS Susan C
Washington	22747	Coulter MR & MRS James R
Washington	22747	Sullivan MR & MRS John Fox
Waterford	20197	Gibson MR & MRS J Chester 3D
Waterford	20197	Smith MRS Ruth Urban
Waynesboro	22980	Nichols MS Vernette
Waynesboro	22980	White MS Lorre L
White Post	22663	Mitchell MISS Virginia P
White Stone	22578	Lee MRS A Carter
White Stone	22578	Marsh MS Ann Carter
Williamsburg	23185	Armour MR & MRS Peter H
Williamsburg	23185	Blow MR & MRS George
Williamsburg	23185	Brown MRS Barrett B
Williamsburg	23185	Davis DR & MRS (COL) Paul B JR
Williamsburg	23185	Davis MR G Vietor JR
Williamsburg	23185	Dudley MR & MRS Wesley C
Williamsburg	23185	Ebersole MR & MRS R Bruce
Williamsburg	23185	Ford MRS H Ross
Williamsburg	23185	Hemphill MR & MRS David Van S
Williamsburg	23185	Kendrick MRS M Hayne
Williamsburg	23185	Krebs MR & MRS William E
Williamsburg	23185	Lashley MRS William A
Williamsburg	23185	Le Gouellec de Schwarz BRN Yann A & BRNSS
Williamsburg	23185	Nicholson BRIG GEN (RET) & MRS John W
Williamsburg	23185	Peters MRS Jane H
Williamsburg	23185	Todd MR & MRS Richard P
Williamsburg	23185	Whitbeck MR & MRS B Hunt JR
Williamsburg	23187	Curtis MR & MRS John R JR
Williamsburg	23187	Roberson MR & MRS Robert S
Williamsburg	23188	Newbold MRS FitzEugene D JR
Williamsburg	23188	Phillips MR Jeffrey B JR
Williamsburg	23188	Phillips MRS Jeffrey B
Williamsburg	23188	Powell DR & MRS Taylor C
Williamsburg	23188	Rork MR & MRS Allen Wright
Williamsburg	23188	Weaver MR Craig H
Winchester	22601	Dame MR & MRS Thomas J
Winchester	22601	Rhein MRS Francis B
Winchester	22601	Williams MR Ian R D
Winchester	22603	Doyle MR & MRS David S
Winchester	22603	Hammond REV & MRS James A
Woodville	22749	Cadwalader MR John
Woodville	22749	McKee MR & MRS Robert E
Woodville	22749	Walker MR & MRS Thomas G JR
Wytheville	24382	Formato MR Richard A JR
Yorktown	23692	Henney LT COL (RET) & MRS Frederic A
Yorktown	23692	Kane MRS John Kent 2D

To nominate a candidate for the Social Register Association, please email: SRCommittee@thesocialregister.org

Anacortes, WA—Seattle, WA

WASHINGTON

Anacortes ... 98221 ... Fairbarns MR & MRS Timothy J D
Auburn ... 98002 ... Pendleton MR & MRS Brian G
Bainbridge Island ... 98110 ... Evans MRS Tilghman B
Bainbridge Island ... 98110 ... Ferrin MR & MRS Allan H
Bainbridge Island ... 98110 ... Fritts MRS J Nunnelee
Bainbridge Island ... 98110 ... Powel MRS John Hare
Bellevue ... 98004 ... Holman MRS William M
Bellevue ... 98004 ... Nordstrom MR & MRS John N
Bellevue ... 98004 ... Pitarys MR & MRS Peter S
Bellevue ... 98004 ... Steele MR Crittenden P
Bellevue ... 98004 ... Wilson MRS Alec MacLaine
Bellevue ... 98005 ... Pero MRS Roderick E
Bellevue ... 98006 ... Dunn MR Reagan B
Bellevue ... 98006 ... Konig MR & MRS Stephen J
Bellevue ... 98006 ... Schmidt MR & MRS Robert E JR
Bellevue ... 98006 ... Tudor MR John H
Bellevue ... 98008 ... Pitts MR & MRS Paris T
Bellingham ... 98226 ... Heisinger MR & MRS Scott David
Bellingham ... 98229 ... Foote MISS Marion R
Blaine ... 98230 ... Johnson MR & MRS A Bryan 3D
Bothell ... 98011 ... Herrlinger MR Berton H
Bothell ... 98012 ... Fadely MR & MRS Brian S
Brush Prairie ... 98606 ... Sharples MR & MRS Hendrik J W
Burien ... 98166 ... Cochran MR & MRS John C
Camano Island ... 98282 ... Rawls MR & MRS Timothy F
Camano Island ... 98282 ... Rawls MR & MRS William H
Clinton ... 98236 ... Henny MR & MRS David C 3D
Clyde Hill ... 98004 ... Wood MRS Carolyn E
Deer Harbor ... 98243 ... Vetterlein MRS Millicent L
Edmonds ... 98020 ... Barber MR & MRS David H
Edmonds ... 98020 ... Lund MR & MRS Theodore M
Edmonds ... 98020 ... Odell MR & MRS Henry R
Edmonds ... 98026 ... Guthrie MR & MRS Bruce MacC
Friday Harbor ... 98250 ... Earle MR & MRS Francis 3D
Issaquah ... 98027 ... Ferrarini CAPT (RET) & MRS Richard L
Issaquah ... 98027 ... McCulloh MR & MRS Hamilton
Issaquah ... 98029 ... Mygatt MRS Donald L
Kirkland ... 98033 ... Griffin MR & MRS J Tyler III
Kirkland ... 98033 ... Hartman MR & MRS Alan E
Kirkland ... 98033 ... Smith MR & MRS Norris M
Kirkland ... 98034 ... Youtsey MR & MRS Thomas H
La Conner ... 98257 ... Dugaw DR & MRS John E JR
Lacey ... 98503 ... Sharp MR & MRS George B
Lake Forest Park ... 98155 ... Lewis MR & MRS Jonathan D
Lakewood ... 98498 ... Rand MRS Frank C III
Langley ... 98260 ... Low MR J Gilman
Malo ... 99150 ... Sims MISS Diana M
Medina ... 98039 ... Biglow MRS Lucius H JR
Medina ... 98039 ... Reider MR & MRS Dennis W
Mercer Island ... 98040 ... Lorenzen MRS Phillip H JR
Nine Mile Falls ... 99026 ... Davis MR & MRS Scott L
Nordland ... 98358 ... Denniston DR George C JR
Normandy Park ... 98166 ... Wallingford MR & MRS Peter A
North Bend ... 98045 ... Master MR & MRS William O JR
Oak Harbor ... 98277 ... Goodhue MR Edmund M
Olympia ... 98506 ... Haws MR & MRS Jason A
Olympia ... 98512 ... Wilson MR & MRS Harvard E
Paulsbo ... 98370 ... Forbes MR Alexander J
Port Angeles ... 98363 ... Dowling MR & MRS Joseph J JR
Poulsbo ... 98370 ... Baldwin MRS L Grant III
Poulsbo ... 98370 ... Chew MR David G
Poulsbo ... 98370 ... Newbold MRS Richard C
Puyallup ... 98374 ... Killion MRS Marion P
Redmond ... 98052 ... Brown MR & MRS James Fearon 2D
Redmond ... 98052 ... Pennington MR & MRS Stuart W
Renton ... 98059 ... Everett MR Alexander U
Ridgefield ... 98642 ... Fahnestock MR & MRS Sheridan Z
Seattle ... 54165 ... Markunas MR & MRS Paul J 3D
Seattle ... 98101 ... Campbell MRS Daniel S
Seattle ... 98101 ... Simons MR & MRS Langdon S JR
Seattle ... 98102 ... Donahue MISS Elizabeth A
Seattle ... 98102 ... Sarkowsky MR & MRS Herman
Seattle ... 98102 ... Stroble MR & MRS Peter A
Seattle ... 98102 ... Vera-Gutiérrez MR Sergio O A & Howe MS Margaret S
Seattle ... 98103 ... Cannell MISS Isabelle B
Seattle ... 98103 ... Clark MR Christopher W & Greenberg MS (DR) Kathryn L-Z
Seattle ... 98103 ... Kellison MRS J Bruce
Seattle ... 98103 ... Nickerson MR & MRS Thomas M
Seattle ... 98103 ... Page MR & MRS Charles 3D
Seattle ... 98103 ... Taylor MS Kathleen B
Seattle ... 98103 ... Townes MR & MRS Charles H
Seattle ... 98104 ... Evans MRS John A
Seattle ... 98104 ... Rinkema MR & MRS Richard A
Seattle ... 98105 ... Kimmey MR & MRS Michael B
Seattle ... 98105 ... Neilson MRS John F JR
Seattle ... 98105 ... Robins MR & MRS Thomas III
Seattle ... 98105 ... Wilgis MR & MRS Herbert E III
Seattle ... 98107 ... Beall MISS Charlotte Ashley
Seattle ... 98107 ... Rava MR & MRS William C
Seattle ... 98107 ... Turner MR Howard M JR
Seattle ... 98107 ... White MR & MRS Charles S IV
Seattle ... 98109 ... Faerber MR & MRS Marc A
Seattle ... 98109 ... Gault MISS (DR) Rosette F
Seattle ... 98109 ... Griffin MR & MRS Sherman G
Seattle ... 98112 ... Andrew MRS Lucius A D 3D
Seattle ... 98112 ... Caner DR & MRS John E Z
Seattle ... 98112 ... Dickey MR & MRS Charles D 3D
Seattle ... 98112 ... Dunley MR & MRS Timothy J
Seattle ... 98112 ... Gardiner MR & MRS Gordon A
Seattle ... 98112 ... Green MR & MRS Joshua 3D
Seattle ... 98112 ... Greer MS Elizabeth
Seattle ... 98112 ... Hinds MR & MRS Bruce J
Seattle ... 98112 ... Morse MR & MRS Charles H IV
Seattle ... 98112 ... Rush MR & MRS R Stockton 3D
Seattle ... 98112 ... Yarington DR & MRS Charles T JR
Seattle ... 98112 ... Yerkes MRS Leonard A III
Seattle ... 98115 ... Early MISS Elizabeth
Seattle ... 98115 ... Feldt MR & MRS William S
Seattle ... 98115 ... Halsey MS Alexandra S
Seattle ... 98115 ... Pew MR & MRS Joseph N V
Seattle ... 98116 ... Thayer MR Meade B
Seattle ... 98116 ... Weld MR & MRS David L
Seattle ... 98118 ... Treat MR & MRS Noel R
Seattle ... 98119 ... Benvenuto DR & MRS John A
Seattle ... 98119 ... Burden MR & MRS Henry S
Seattle ... 98119 ... Carlstrom MR & MRS Robert A
Seattle ... 98119 ... Gidding MR Joshua W & Gilmour MS Julie T
Seattle ... 98119 ... Kiefer MR & MRS (DR) William F III
Seattle ... 98119 ... Willett MR Benjamin C
Seattle ... 98119 ... Young MR & MRS Nathaniel A
Seattle ... 98122 ... Bigham MRS T James
Seattle ... 98122 ... Cantlin MR & MRS Alan R
Seattle ... 98122 ... Palmer MRS Jane S
Seattle ... 98125 ... Beatt MR & MRS Samuel M
Seattle ... 98125 ... Brown MR Cyrus Winthrop 2D
Seattle ... 98127 ... Hale MR & MRS Prentis C IV
Seattle ... 98127 ... Laird MRS Edith R
Seattle ... 98136 ... Curtin MR Mark A & Bennett MS Grace R
Seattle ... 98136 ... Dohan MR Michael B

Seattle 98144 Plumb MISS Suzanna A
Seattle 98144 Stanton MR & MRS L Lee 3D
Seattle 98155 Reagan MR & MRS Bruce V 3D
Seattle 98177 Barry MR & MRS Daniel T
Seattle 98177 Blair MR & MRS Watson B
Seattle 98177 Cobb DR & MRS Oliver E
Seattle 98177 Delafield MR & MRS John Dennis JR
Seattle 98177 Kestenbaum DR Bryan R & Ware MS (DR) Elisabeth P
Seattle 98199 Bowen MISS Zoë R
Seattle 98199 Mott MR & MRS Colter W
Seattle 98199 Pough MRS Edward W
Seattle 98199 Van Liew MRS Marcia
Sequim 98382 Taylor MR & MRS William R
Shaw Island 98286 Robertson MRS Philip McR
Shelton 98584 Willard LT COL (RET) William B JR
Shoreline 98133 Craig MR & MRS James L
Shoreline 98177 Lewis MR & MRS Joseph W 3D
Snohomish 98296 Downs MR & MRS John T
South Bend 98586 Guyer DR Grant P
Spokane 99203 Ambrose MR & MRS Christopher J
Spokane 99203 Hasen MISS (REV) Elizabeth S
Spokane 99223 Greer DR & MRS Alexander P
Tacoma 98407 Mail MISS (DR) Patricia D
Tumwater 98501 Wilcox MS Patricia L
Twisp 98856 Hooper MR Lawrence D
Vancouver 98664 Sharples MRS Thomas D
Vancouver 98683 Dick DR & MRS H Lenox H
Woodinville 98077 Fowler MR & MRS George A JR
Yarrow Point 98004 Green MS Paige C
Yarrow Point 98004 Peters MR & MRS Thomas S

WEST VIRGINIA

Bluefield 24701 Olmsted DR Charles M
Frankford 24938 Kibler MR & MRS Ned A
Harpers Ferry 25425 Johnson DR Hardwick Smith JR
Martinsburg 25401 Cox MR & MRS Louis A
Morgantown 26501 Osborne MISS Caroline L
Morgantown 26505 Schwab DR & MRS Larry
Renick 24966 Zogbaum MRS Ferdinand 3D
Ronceverte 24970 Henneman MRS Nuncia Digges
Shepherdstown 25443 Scott MRS Henry P 3D
Williamstown 26187 Silman MRS Richard C

WISCONSIN

Appleton 54915 McKinney MR & MRS W Richardson
Delafield 53018 Twining MRS Robert C
Egg Harbor 54209 Hellyer MR & MRS Walter 2D
Egg Harbor 54209 Warren MRS Geoffrey S
Fish Creek 54212 Baumgarten MR Frederic K
Fox Point 53217 Schmid MRS Johannes A
Hales Corners 53130 Burnham MR Robert Bailey
Hartland 53029 Wilkey MR & MRS Richard L
Kimberly 54136 McKinney MR Richardson
Lake Geneva 53147 Fritz MR C Andrew IV
Lake Geneva 53147 Rasin MRS Rudolph S
Lake Nebagamon 54849 Khalar MR & MRS Charles S
Madison 53704 Grannis MRS Adrienne E
Madison 53704 Porter MISS Linda M
Madison 53705 Coyne MR & MRS John E 3D
Madison 53711 Hay MS Miranda P
Madison 53711 Kester MR & MRS Gregory B
Madison 53711 Stanley MISS (DR) Emily H
Mayville 53050 Murray MISS Olivia A
Mayville 53050 Murray MRS Jayne B
Menomonee Falls 53051 Curtis MR & MRS Thomas Pelham II
Mequon 53097 Sprague MRS Charles W
Milwaukee 53202 Harrington MR John T
Milwaukee 53202 Levit MR & MRS William H JR
Milwaukee 53211 Hass MR & MRS D Winthrop
Milwaukee 53211 Huston MRS Harland W JR
Milwaukee 53211 Ogden MR & MRS John
Milwaukee 53211 Slaughter MR & MRS William C
Milwaukee 53211 Tallmadge MRS Edward S
Milwaukee 53211 Todryk MR & MRS Luke C
Milwaukee 53217 Carpenter MISS Carol A
Milwaukee 53217 Walcott MRS George
Muskego 53150 Allen MR & MRS John D
Nashotah 53058 Stark MR & MRS Edward B
Neenah 54956 Brownell MR & MRS George S
Pleasant Prairie 53158 Keller MR & MRS Peter J
Racine 53402 Fischer MR & MRS George W
Racine 53402 Ware MR & MRS Thomas E JR
Racine 53402 Williams MR & MRS David D
Rosendale 54974 Erskine MR & MRS James S
Shorewood 53211 Kohler MR & MRS Timothy J
Sturtevant 53177 McKay MR Robert B
Whitefish Bay 53211 Locke MR & MRS T Ferguson JR
Whitefish Bay 53217 Davis MR & MRS John C
Whitefish Bay 53217 VandenBerg MR & MRS Peter H

WYOMING

Buffalo 82834 Gray MRS Cynthia Chace
Cody 82414 Collier MR & MRS Barron G II
Cody 82414 Draper MISS Nancy-Carroll
Cody 82414 Flynn MS Dorothy E Logan
Cody 82414 Mallamo MR & MRS Peter J
Cody 82414 Model MR Robert
Cody 82414 Nielson MR James E & Young MRS Anne N
Cody 82414 Stratford MRS Herbert R
Dayton 82836 Rose MR & MRS James S R
Jackson 83001 Cannell MR J Carlo
Jackson 83001 Cushman MR & MRS Roderick H
Jackson 83001 Moyer MR & MRS Peter F
Jackson 83001 Schmidt MR & MRS Eric C
Jackson 83001 Weiss MR & MRS William D
Jackson 83001 Wyckoff MS Shelby L
Jackson 83002 Carleton MS Heather T
Jackson 83002 Ryan MR & MRS Brandon P
Jackson 83014 Lewis MR & MRS Jason P
Kaycee 82639 Gordon MR & MRS Crawford
Sheridan 82801 Crosby MR & MRS (DR) B Taylor F
Sheridan 82801 Klapp MR Wilbur P 2D
Sheridan 82801 Love MISS Mary Christine
Teton Village 83025 Cowles MR & MRS James C
Wheatland 82201 Landen MR & MRS Gerald C
Wilson 83014 Bradford DR & MRS Williamson Z III
Wilson 83014 Brown MISS Laurie S
Wilson 83014 Chidsey DR & MRS Charles A 3D
Wilson 83014 Coelho DR & MRS Bill J
Wilson 83014 Fossel MR & MRS Scott G
Wilson 83014 Oliver MRS Charlotte O'N
Wilson 83014 Parker MRS Dorothy S
Wilson 83014 Pellet MR & MRS Benoit J F X
Wilson 83014 Phocas MR & MRS George A
Wilson 83014 Rauch MS Susan P
Wilson 83014 Stout MR & MRS John S JR
Wilson 83014 Strawbridge MR Robert E III

To nominate a candidate for the Social Register Association, please email: SRCommittee@thesocialregister.org

Puerto Rico—Canada

Commonwealth & Territories

PUERTO RICO

Mayaguez 00682 .... García MR Adolfo L
Rio Grande 00745 .... Keenan MR & MRS Walter C IV
Rio Grande 00745 .... Wilson MISS Pamela S
San Juan 00907 .... Guthrie MRS Jo Carol
San Juan 00907 .... Prouty MR & MRS Nicholas A
San Juan 00913 .... Swanson MR & MRS Todd Q
San Juan 00927 .... Febbo MR & MRS William J

VIRGIN ISLANDS

Christiansted 00824 .... Hollister MR & MRS Robert Dewey
Cruz Bay 00831 .... Bakewell MISS Jane A

MILITARY

APO AA 34037 .... McHenry MR & MRS William H
APO AE 09046 .... Wheeler LT & MRS A Nicholas
APO AE 09180 .... Unruh MAJ & MRS Charles L
APO AP 96208 .... Senseman MAJ David C T
DPO AE 09744 .... Dorn MR & MRS (DR) Christopher H
DPO AE 09825 .... García Zuñiga MR Sergio A & Buddenhagen MS Caroline R
DPO AE 09836 .... Dean MR & MRS Nathaniel P

International Listings

ANTIGUA & BARBUDA

Antigua .... Morrill MR Amos

ARGENTINA

7630 Necochea, Buenos Aires .... Whitney MR & MRS Francis H

AUSTRALIA

Altona, Victoria 3018 .... Daniel-Dreyfus MR & MRS Marc A
Altona, Victoria 3018 .... Power MR & MRS Timothy L
Bentleigh East, Victoria 3165 .... Robbins MS Katherine D
Brisbane, Queensland 4067 .... Paul MR & MRS Anthony M
Denistone, NSW 2114 .... Mundy MR & MRS (DR) Philip G
Fitzroy, Victoria 3065 .... Fitzgerald MR & MRS Peter
Hawthorn East, Victoria 3132 .... Hedges MR & MRS Scott A
Loftus, NSW 2232 .... Hoyt MR & MRS Edward P
Mermaid Waters, Queensland 4218 .... Johnson MRS Steven B
Mosman, NSW 2088 .... Drayton MR & MRS Whitney
Mosman, NSW 2088 .... Ranck MR & MRS J Hutchison
Mountain River, Tasmania 7109 .... Baehr MR & MRS T Peirce
Sydney, NSW 2093 .... Haskins MR & MRS Craig O
Tamworth, NSW 2340 .... Warden MR & MRS Stephen A
Toorak, Victoria 3142 .... Stratmann DR & MRS Peter F
Vaucluse, NSW 2030 .... Selby MR & MRS Christopher H M F

AUSTRIA

1040 Vienna .... von Waldow MRS Bernd
1050 Vienna .... Auersperg-Breunner PRC & PRCSS Franz-Joseph
1190 Vienna .... Witton MR & MRS Karl A
2345 Brunn Am Gebirgeienna .... Keimpema MR & MRS Erik

BAHAMAS

Nassau .... Disston MRS Jacob S 3D
Nassau .... Disston MS Sarah M
Nassau .... Jones MR & MRS Roger M
Nassau .... Meade MR & MRS Okla B JR
Nassau .... Peterson MR & MRS Nicholas H

BAHRAIN

Manama .... Potter MR & MRS John D

BELGIUM

1050 Brussels .... Delori MRS Philippe P
1050 Brussels .... Ferrante di Ruffano MCHSE Antonio & MCHSA
Brussells 1050 .... Roché MR & MRS Bernard P D

BELIZE

Ambergris Caye .... Fox MR & MRS Charles Clayton

BERMUDA

Hamilton .... Tolaram MR Raj
Hamilton HM GX .... Riker MR & MRS Andrew E
Hamilton HS 02 .... Hutchings MR & MRS George F
Hamilton Parish CR 04 .... Hutchings MRS C H Ford
Hamilton Parish CR BX .... Riker MRS Samuel 3D
Paget DV 04 .... Toogood MR & MRS G Chase
Paget PG 01 .... Berg MR & MRS John R
Paget PG 02 .... Humann MRS Edgar
Paget PG 03 .... Wardman MR & MRS George A
Paget PG 06 .... Pearman MR & MRS R Scott
Paget PG BX .... Lynn MRS Hélène Martin
Pembroke HM 01 .... Freisenbruch MR & MRS Michael D
Smith's FL 08 .... West MR & MRS N Britten B
Smith's Parish FL 05 .... Parker MRS George M
Warwick WK 04 .... Gould MRS Martha Thorson

BORNEO

93050 Kuching Sarawak .... McGuigan MR & MRS Scott J

BRAZIL

Florianopolis, SC 88050-400 .... Marshall MR & MRS Robert B
Morro Agudo, SP 14640-000 .... Knapp MR & MRS Lawrence W 3D
Rio de Janeiro, RJ22210-030 .... Smith MRS W Watt
Salvador, Bahia 40015-160 .... Moskey MR Stamatis
Sao Bonificio, Santa Catarina .... Penrose MR Timothy
Sao Paulo, 04080-13 .... Newcomb MR J Stephen
Sao Paulo, SP 04538 082 .... Wood MR & MRS Richard H M
Sao Paulo, SP 04645-000 .... Winter MR Thomas A & de Almeida Ribeiro MS Sirlene

CANADA

Ancaster, Ontario L9G 2E7 .... Barbour MR & MRS David A
Burlington, Ontario L7R 3X4 .... Douglas MR & MRS Roderick McI
Calgary, Alberta T3P 1K6 .... Smith MR & MRS Chadbourne T
Comox, BC V9M 4H4 .... Harrower MRS Lyle
Dundas, Ontario L9H 2B8 .... Ker MRS David S I
East York, Ontario M4G2H1 .... McLeod MR & MRS James W
Hammonds Plains, Nova Scotia B4B 1K4 .... Buxton MR & MRS Nicholas W

Kitchener, Ontario N2M 2H9	Watson MR & MRS Warwick G
Lunenburg, Nova Scotia B0J 2C0	Andrews MR & MRS Schofield JR
Mississauga, Ontario L5A 3Y4	Laidler MR James R
Montreal, Quebec H3B 1H9	Escobar MR Miguel
Mt Royal, Quebec H3R 1W4	Morgan MR & MRS Robert F JR
Nanaimo, BC V9T 1J8	Benedict MR & MRS John T JR
Nelson, BC V1L 1X3	Hemphill MR & MRS John E S
New Germany, Nova Scotia B0R 1E0	Hare MR & MRS Emlen G
Oakville, Ontario L6J 2E3	Flemington MR & MRS Jeffrey R
Oakville, Ontario L6J 4R9	Peek MR & MRS Dennis R
Ottawa, Ontario K1M 1W5	Wilson MR & MRS Andrew Bruce
Ottawa, Ontario K1N 5J5	Carter MR & MRS Charles N
Plessisville, Quebec G6L 2G2	Pichette MRS Diane
St Andrews, NB E5B 2L4	Hodgson MRS Howard B
Surrey, BC V4A 3J4	Stewart MRS John G
Toronto, Ontario M4G 1B5	Fischer MR & MRS Lindsay K
Toronto, Ontario M4G 1W4	Ishiguro MR & MRS Ken
Toronto, Ontario M4N 2E5	Kilbourne MRS Susan L
Toronto, Ontario M4S 2X3	Meynell MISS Andrea M
Toronto, Ontario M4T 2Y4	McKinnon MR & MRS Ian Neil
Toronto, Ontario M4V 1J5	Dingle MR & MRS Christopher B
Toronto, Ontario M4V 1K6	Aimers MR John L
Toronto, Ontario M4V 2L6	Hammoud MR & MRS (DR) Tawfik
Toronto, Ontario M4V 2R5	Doherty MR & MRS D'Arcy R
Toronto, Ontario M4W 2Y3	Meynell MR & MRS Robert A S
Toronto, Ontario M4X 1S5	Gibson MRS (DR) Sarah S
Toronto, Ontario M54 1B7	Hero MS Eleanor R
Toronto, Ontario M5M 1S9	Silver MR & MRS Adam W
Toronto, Ontario M5N 1M2	McLeod MR & MRS Wallace E
Toronto, Ontario M5P 1A4	Watson MRS Nina V M
Toronto, Ontario M5P 1M3	Lindsey MISS Anne Y
Toronto, Ontario M5R 3T3	Meynell MRS David B
Toronto, Ontario M6K 3L9	Doherty MR D'Arcy P
Toronto, Ontario M6M 5A2	Brown REV & MRS P Schuyler
Toronto, Ontario M9A 4A2	Keilty MR & MRS Robert A
Vancouver, BC V6G 3E9	Cecil MR & MRS Robert S
Vancouver, BC V6H 3N8	Forbes MISS P Seton
Vancouver, BC V6K 2X2	Lewis MR & MRS R Brian
Victoria, BC V8R 5E8	Archer MR & MRS Geoffrey R
Victoria, BC V8S 4R6	Hemphill MR & MRS Tybring M
Westmount, Quebec H3Z 2T2	Coolidge MR Robert T
Wolfville, Nova Scotia B4P 1Z6	Alden MR & MRS John J W

CHILE

Lo Barnechea, Santiago	Missana MR & MRS Sergio
Santiago	Cist MISS (DR) Dorothea B
Vitacura, Santiago	Newbold MR & MRS James F

CHINA

Beijing 100020	Landreth MR & MRS Jonathan S
Beijing 101300	Hurd MR & MRS David P
Beijing 101302	Atkeson MR & MRS Mark G
Hong Kong, Central	Bispham MR & MRS Thomas P
Hong Kong, The Peak	Brown MR & MRS Charles N A
Hong Kong	Chen MR & MRS Alan X
Hong Kong	Ernst MR & MRS Graham S
Hong Kong	Heckscher MR & MRS Christopher D
Hong Kong, North Point	Hilton MR & MRS Samuel A
Hong Kong	Marin MR & MRS Todd R
Hong Kong	McAfee MR & MRS W Gage
Hong Kong, The Peak	Pratt MR & MRS Jon V M
Hong Kong, Stanley	Root MR & MRS Anthony
Hong Kong, Discovery Bay	Wong MR & MRS Sam J
Shanghai 200041, Jing'an District,	Granger MISS Amanda C
Shanghai 200020	Colcord MR & MRS Avery J

COLOMBIA

Bogota	Cashman MR & MRS Eugene R JR

CZECH REPUBLIC

16200 Prague 6	Newbold MR & MRS Thomas Day

ECUADOR

Quito	Dupuy MR & MRS Fielding D
Quito	McLaughlin MR & MRS George H 3D

ENGLAND

Alresford, Hampshire SO24 9HB	Mackintosh MR & MRS Ian
Amesbury, Wiltshire SP4 7DP	Westley MS Thea
Ashbourne, Derbyshire DE6 2DR	Boileau MR & MRS Nicholas P
Bath BA2 9EY	Claydon MR & MRS David J
Brancaster, Norfolk PE31 8AG	Thompson MR & MRS Mark J
Bungay, Suffolk NR35 2HN	Crisp MR J Edward
Cambridge CB1 1JX	Butterfield LADY
Coventry, Warwickshire CV5 6NQ	Miller MISS Sonia H
Devon EX16 9ET	Colvin MRS Monica Van Dusen
Eastbourne, East Sussex BN21 2LU	Moore MR Michael B
Edenbridge, Kent TN8 6QE	Wellesley MR & MRS Robin A
Elstead, Surrey GU8 6DR	McGleughlin MR & MRS Peter T
Elstree, Hertfordshire WD6 3RG	Massey MR Jay Richardson JR
Esher, Surrey KT10 8QA	Bramah MR & MRS Jeremy L
Godalming, Surrey GU8 6NT	Feld MR & MRS David
Hadley Wood, Hertfordshire EN4 0JP	Mackay REV & MRS Rupert
Harrogate, North Yorkshire HG3 2WY	Adams MISS Judith
Henley-on-Thames, Oxfordshire RG9 2NH	Benster MR & MRS Michael I W
Hertfordshire SG8 8LL	Macdonald MR & MRS Samuel H J
Hurst, Berkshire RG10 0BP	Follett MRS (DR) Nancy E
Itchen Abbas, Hampshire SO21 1BA	Terhalle DR & MRS Maximilian P J
Kent TN29 9TR	Velge MR & MRS Bertrand R
Kew, Surrey TW9 2AH	Lamberton MR & MRS Benjamin Paulding 3D
Leatherhead, Surrey KT22 0HR	Kirwan MR & MRS Ian
Lindfield, West Sussex RH16 2NL	Stabler MR & MRS C Norman 3D
London 5W1W 8UP	Kaempfer MR Joseph W JR
London E1 1EQ	Yassukovich MR & MRS Nicholas A
London E8 1AB	Drew MR & MRS John G
London EC2 5DV	McFadden MR John H
London EC2Y 8NJ	Burbank MR Peter A
London N1 8HQ	Grew MR & MRS Christopher A
London N1 OHT	Childs MR & MRS Thomas C C
London N10 3QG	Smith MR & MRS Zimri Luce JR
London N6 5XR	Tilden DR & MRS William M
London N6 5XR	Tilden MR Victor M
London NW1 7TU	Bicket MR & MRS Harry A C
London NW1 8LH	Stanger MISS Jean H
London NW10 5QR	de Zwart MR Paul A & Childs MS Ariel M
London NW3 3AT	Kremer MR & MRS John 4TH
London NW3 3RP	Cox DR & MRS Edward V III
London NW3 4UH	Choa MR & MRS Christopher J
London NW3 5RL	Lamberton MR & MRS Derek H R
London NW3 5UJ	Fink MR & MRS Geoffrey D
London NW3 6UR	Michael MR & MRS Henry B
London NW6 2PY	Parsons MR & MRS Timothy St J
London NW6 5LA	Sargent MR & MRS Rider W
London NW8 6AF	Marsh MR & MRS Alan R JR
London NW8 9AT	Lambert MISS Sophie
London SE10 9UR	Bate MR & MRS Russell

England—England

London SE15 5AR	Haines REV Stephen D
London SE15 5PA	Moles MR & MRS Michael J A
London SE22 0PS	Vine MR & MRS Charles E
London SE24 0BG	Durham MR & MRS John A D B
London SW1	Fellowes-Gordon MR Timothy S
London SW10 0JW	Hammond Alatas MRS Madeleine DeG L
London SW10 0PR	Petó MR & MRS Alexander T
London SW10 9AD	de Rougé CT Aymeric & CTSS
London SW10 9TB	Ingraham MS Cynthia
London SW11 1JH	Jackson MR & MRS Paul J
London SW11 3DR	Adamson LADY Campbell
London SW11 4BL	Thompson MR & MRS Christopher G A
London SW11 4EX	Holland MR & MRS Charles J T
London SW11 6PZ	de Give MISS Ghislaine
London SW12 8BW	Kresler MR & MRS Philip A
London SW13 9PW	Boericke MR & MRS J Bradley
London SW13 9QJ	Pinnington MR & MRS Clive M
London SW14 0AU	Moukheiber MR & MRS Kamal H
London SW15 6DU	Gray MR & MRS Robert B
London SW17 8EP	Hill MR & MRS Jonathan J
London SW17 8RR	Gray MR & MRS Julian C M
London SW17 8RS	Potter MR & MRS John H N 2D
London SW18 2QP	Turcan MR & HON MRS Jake W
London SW18 2RE	Diacre de Liancourt MR & MRS Piers L
London SW18 3BQ	Peace MR & MRS William H 3D
London SW19 5AH	de Boer MR & MRS Klaas
London SW19 5PW	Sodi MR & MRS Marco
London SW1E 6HR	Khairallah MR & MRS Karim M
London SW1P 4QA	Dixon MR & MRS Piers
London SW1V 2AL	Bigbie MR John-Eric de C & de Croy-Solre PRCSS M Eleanore
London SW1V 2DB	Kidder MR & MRS Christopher H
London SW1V 2HF	Baxter MR & MRS Edward D A
London SW1V 4LS	Stanley MR Paul M
London SW1W 8EU	Elbrick di Belmonte MR & MRS Tristan C J
London SW1W 8JU	Quillen MR & MRS Cecil D III
London SW1W 8PQ	Yates MRS C Michael
London SW1W 8TR	Stafford MR & MRS G M Graham JR
London SW1W 8TZ	Agnew SIR Rudolph I J & LADY
London SW1W 9AP	Shanker MR & MRS Mark E
London SW1W 9DF	Walker MR & MRS Richard W
London SW1W 9HJ	Bowes MS Elena
London SW1X 0DY	Wood MR John Walter
London SW1X 8BT	Marano MR Peter D
London SW1X 9HE	Schabacker MRS C Hendy
London SW1Y 6RE	Kent MR Geoffrey J W
London SW20 0QU	Wickes MR & MRS W Forman IV
London SW3 5BB	Franklin MR & MRS Jonathan M
London SW3 2AE	Morris MR & MRS S Houston S
London SW3 3TR	Snowdon MRS Philippa C J
London SW3 4BT	Allen MR & MRS Julian M C H
London SW3 4JR	Cheshire MR & MRS Kevin D
London SW3 5JB	McFadden MRS George
London SW3 5JS	Thorne MRS A Hagan
London SW3 5RA	Vere Nicoll MR & MRS Roderick I
London SW3 6 DT	Parkinson MR & MRS James T IV
London SW3 6AX	Moffett MRS James A
London SW3 6HA	Zirinis MR & MRS Basil
London SW4 0LP	Chandler DR & MRS (DR) Christopher L
London SW4 6HR	Thomson SIR Mark & LADY
London SW4 8QE	Speck MR & MRS Adam
London SW5 0DT	Clive CAPT & MRS Dominic R H
London SW6 2LG	Keilty MR John B
London SW6 3RY	Blenk MR & MRS Peter C
London SW6 3TQ	Reynolds MR & MRS Nicholas J
London SW6 4DJ	Howard MR & MRS Christopher T
London SW6 5BG	Stonor HON Julia M C M Camoys
London SW6 7DB	Carse MR & MRS Donald R JR
London SW7	Michotte MR & MRS Eloy U P G
London SW7 1BH	Summers MR & MRS S Martin
London SW7 1EF	Wilbur MR & MRS Andrew Packer
London SW7 1JE	Prentice MR & MRS Sheldon E
London SW7 2NP	Hudson MR Manley O JR
London SW7 3BD	Licata MR & MRS Brian L
London SW7 3EG	Wells MR Christopher J
London SW7 3LX	Merrill MISS Jane M
London SW7 3NJ	Kramer MR & MRS Mark A
London SW7 4AP	Hayes MRS Hilary
London SW7 4AP	Hinton MISS Marianne
London SW7 4LS	Sellman MR Michael B & Grace MS Amy E
London SW7 4QF	Llewellyn MR & MRS Timothy D
London SW7 5RR	Singer MR & MRS F R Forbes
London SW9 6UW	Brooks-Baker MRS Harold
London W10 6EF	Tiffin MR Edward J S
London SW10 0SS	Foley HON Alexandra M
London W11	Friend MISS Ann G
London W11 1BW	Pakenham SIR Michael Aidan & LADY
London W11 1NY	Kannengieser MR Martin W
London W11 2JH	Kryca MR & MRS Igor F
London W11 2LG	Ponti MR & MRS Andrea
London W11 2PT	Greenough MR & MRS Lawrence R
London W11 3AL	Ylvisaker MRS Jane P M
London W11 3BY	Salmon MR & MRS J Morgan
London W11 3ND	Clark MR & MRS James R
London W11 3PR	Cunningham MR & MRS Mark V
London W11 3PY	Buchanan MR & MRS James A S
London W11 4NP	Medeiros MR & MRS David W
London W12	Willetts MR & HON MRS David L
London W14 0HU	Walker MR & MRS David M
London W14 0HZ	Robson MR & MRS Rupert W
London W14 0QD	Campos MR & MRS Juan A
London W14 0RR	Gignoux MR P Alan
London W14 9HB	Grose MR & MRS Thomas Pierpont
London W1K 1NA	Griffiths LADY
London W1K 2HL	Bowden MRS Adrian H H
London W1U 4PJ	Broderick MR McPharlin L
London W2 1QP	Steavenson MRS David H M J
London W2 2BE	Macpherson MR & MRS Duncan C S
London W2 4AT	Fritze MR & MRS Johannes P
London W2 5NA	Amor MR & MRS Yacine
London W2 6DA	Manheim MR Grant C
London W5 2DJ	Brooke MR & MRS Robert Z
London W6 8HF	Corkhill MR & MRS Jeremy M
London W6 8RN	Henault MR & MRS Damien
London W8 4AH	Cunynghame SIR Andrew D F & LADY
London W8 4NA	Briance MR & MRS Richard H
London W8 4PD	von Thelen MR Christopher M
London W8 5QG	Jennison MR & MRS David R
London W8 6QX	Downing MR & MRS James B 3D
London W8 7BU	Dargan MR & MRS R Alan
London W8 7HX	Darwin MRS George P
London W9 1AB	Jess MR & MRS Adrian
Lymington, Hampshire SO41 5SH	Bicket MR & MRS Robert M
Newick, East Sussex BN8 4JX	Boileau MR & MRS Samuel E
North Cadbury, Somerset BA22 7BW	Wiseman MR & MRS John S
Norwich, Norfolk NR12 8YS	Dorsey MR & MRS William H JR
nr Horsham, West Sussex RH12 3AA	Beckwith-Smith MR & MRS John S M
Osney Island, Oxford OX2 0BQ	Beaty MISS Nancy W
Oundle, Northamptonshire PE8 4EJ	Huntington MR & MRS Anthony P
Oxford OX2 6SH, Oxfordshire	Parshall MR C Ward
Oxford OX2 8DT	MacFarlane DR & MRS S Neil
Oxford, Oxfordshire OX2 7QF	Farr MR & MRS (DR) Charles Sims JR

Oxfordshire OX10 6QS ... Chatwin MRS C Bruce
Pampisford, Cambridgeshire CB22 3ET ... Barclay MR & MRS Brewster F
Pitchcombe, Stroud GL6 7QN ... Thorne MR & MRS Daniel K
Ramsgate, Kent CT11 9SR ... Jeanrenaud MR & MRS Pierre M
Rickmansworth, Hertsfordshire WD3 7EH ... Johnson MR & MRS Ridgely C
Ringwood, Hampshire BH24 1AW ... Bunting CDR Geoffrey C II
Rushden, Hertfordshire SG9 0SS ... James MR & MRS Alexander N
Sevenoaks, Kent TN13 1EL ... Gore MRS Humphry G N
Sevenoaks, Kent TN15 0QA ... Schabacker MR Peter H
Sheffield S6 6GA ... Miller MISS Jennifer D
Stratford-upon-Avon, Warwickshire CV37 8BB ... Horton MR & MRS George S II
Suffolk IP13 9AA ... Adams MR John T
Suffolk IP13 OLW ... Peel MR & MRS Giles D A
Tiverton, Devon EX16 PLY ... Pulver MRS George M
Tunbridge Wells, Kent TN2 5SY ... Douglass MRS William A
Twyford, Berkshire RG10 9EY ... Chonavel MR Sylvain R
Uckfield, East Sussex TN22 1NS ... White MR & MRS Nathaniel T
Wallingford, Oxfordshire OX10 6QN ... Bakewell MR & MRS Anderson D
Walton-on-Thames, Surrey KT12 5BP ... Hay MR & MRS Richard J
Warnham, West Sussex RH12 3RN ... Gordon MRS Lewis H JR
Warwickshire CV9 2HG ... Dugdale SIR William Matthew S & LADY Paige
Westerham, Kent TN16 1UB ... Culbert MISS Laura A
Winchester, Hampshire SO21 2BY ... Wellesley MR & MRS Gerald G

FRANCE

03500 Verneuil-en-Bourbonnais ... Schiffeler MR & MRS (DR) John Wm
06000 Nice ... Forani-Rhein MRS Ludmilla
06130 Grasse ... Veit MR & MRS E Alexander
06140 Vence ... White MR & MRS Michael M
06250 Mougins ... Royce MR & MRS Stephen W 2D
16300 Charente ... Ryan MRS Christopher W
22270 Dolo ... Colas MR & MRS Josselin C
24510 Limeuil, Perigord ... Adda MR Michael E S
28190 St-Luperce ... Cossé Brissac CT Charles L de
30700 Aigaliers ... Hyde MISS Caroline S
31830 Plaisance-du-Touch ... Tricot MR Sylvain P L
45510 Tigy ... Delapalme MRS Alexandra M
50460 Urville-Nacqueville ... Carse MS Shirley D
56740 Locmariaquer ... de Lyrot MR Antoine
60300 Senlis ... Carter MRS David R
61230 La Fresnaie Fayel ... Kyle MR Louis F
62170 Montreuil-sur-Mer ... Knight MRS Ridgway B
64350 Corbere-Aberes ... Kinslow MRS Pamela M S
69370 St-Didier-au-Mt-d'Or ... Marzin MRS Jean E
75001 Paris ... Soulé MR Jean-Luc & Labourdette MRS Marie-Christine
75002 Paris ... Vivaux MR & MRS Laurent E P M
75003 Paris ... McKeon MR & MRS Robert M
75006 Paris ... d'Arnoux CTE Edouard
75006 Paris ... de Bresson VCTE Edgar & VCTSSE
75006 Paris ... Hobson REV DR & MRS George H JR
75007 Paris ... Assouline MR & MRS Jerôme V
75007 Paris ... de Beistegui MR & MRS Charles
75007 Paris ... de Broglie PRC François & PRCSSE
75007 Paris ... de Liagre MS Christina
75007 Paris ... Edwards MR Hilary G
75007 Paris ... Grassi MR & MRS Matteo
75007 Paris ... Jaffer DR Amin
75007 Paris ... McCabe MRS Robert K
75007 Paris ... Mitch MISS Eleanor B
75007 Paris ... Rawson MR & MRS Ramsay C
75007 Paris ... Sadron MR & MRS Jean-Philippe
75007 Paris ... Sainty MR Guy S
75007 Paris ... Trincal MR & MRS Alain J
75007 Paris ... Turchi MR & MRS P Arthur
75007 Paris ... van Marken MR & MRS Bernard
75007 Paris ... Whitbeck MR & MRS John V
75008 Paris ... de Lyrot CTE Alain & CTSSE
75008 Paris ... de Vienne CT Arnaud G
75008 Paris ... Dubout MR & MRS Didier M Y
75008 Paris ... Vilariño MR & MRS Jorge
75009 Paris ... Whitman MR & MRS Alfred B
75011 Paris ... Ryan MISS Jessica F
75014 Paris ... Blewer MISS Evelyn MacGregor
75014 Paris ... Surer MR & MRS Thibault M
75015 Paris ... de Lyrot MRS Hervé J
75015 Paris ... Michelet MR & MRS Bertrand M J L
75015 Paris ... Wright MRS Jefferson C
75016 Paris ... Anathan MISS Leah K
75016 Paris ... Anglès MRS Jean-Paul
75016 Paris ... Auerbach MR & MRS Philip Hone
75016 Paris ... Baldwin MR & MRS Lawrence T
75016 Paris ... Dequesne MR & MRS Maxime
75016 Paris ... Gardiner MR & MRS E Nicholas P
75016 Paris ... Pierce MR & MRS Stephen B
75016 Paris ... Zuber MR & MRS Jean P
75017 Paris ... de Sambucy de Sorgue BRN François-Xavier & de France HRH PRCSS Chantal
75017 Paris ... Galazommatis MR & MRS Jean
75019 Paris ... Burnett MRS Judith E
75116 Paris ... Bingham MRS Holleman
75116 Paris ... de Meaux VCTE & VCTSSE Marc
75116 Paris ... de Seze MR & MRS Ghislain
75116 Paris ... Delapalme MR David
75116 Paris ... Emmet MR & MRS Edouard C
75116 Paris ... La Haye Jousselin MR & MRS Edmond de
75116 Paris ... McGovern MR David T
75116 Paris ... Messiqua MRS Gail P
75116 Paris ... Whitman MR Ian M
78000 Versailles ... Deniau MR & MRS François X
83300 Draguignan ... Crimmins MRS (DR) Jennifer M
85360 La Tranche sur Mer ... Beekman MRS Danièle M
89240 Egleny ... Owen MR & MRS William H
91370 Verrieres-le-Buisson ... Pradier MR & MRS Laurent S
92100 Boulogne ... de La Rochefoucauld CTE Patrice & CTSSE
92200 Neuilly ... Ressler MR & MRS Harold Kirkby
92340 Bourg-la-Reine ... Smadja MR & MRS David

GERMANY

10439 Berlin ... Dellenbaugh MISS Mary H
14129 Berlin ... von Alvensleben-Glauchau MR & MRS Busso H G B
14163 Berlin ... Defty MR Stephen C
14169 Berlin ... Cörper DR & MRS Alexander
22415 Hamburg ... Bölke MR & MRS Urs-Alexander M U
26160 Bad Zwischenahn ... Brown DR & MRS Clifford C
40667 Meerbusch ... Scott MR & MRS Jeffrey F
60596 Frankfurt am Main ... Pennoyer MR & MRS William M
69151 Neckargemund ... Crooker MR & MRS Robert M JR
70597 Stuttgart ... Armstrong MR Edward McP JR
80807 Munich ... Seggerman MRS Frederick E
82049 Pullach i Isartal ... Jaeger MR & MRS Florian P

Greece—Peru

GREECE

Athens 10675 .... Contomichalos MR & MRS Gerassimo
GR 10676 Athens .... Caskey MRS John L
10676 Athens .... Clark MS Helen Remsen
11635 Athens .... Conroy MRS Sheila C
11636 Athens .... Venizelos MR Nikitas
14561 Athens .... Barrett MR & MRS Rafael C
15452 Athens .... Melas MR & MRS George L
GR 16673 Athens .... Church MRS Dimitra T
16121 Kaisariani .... Morgan MISS Josephine M

GUATEMALA

Guatemala City .... Phillips MRS Frances H L

HUNGARY

H-1039 Budapest .... Beck MR & MRS Robert L

IRELAND

Blackrock, Co Dublin .... Moltke MISS Victoria A
Dundalk, Co Louth .... Oakes MR & MRS Daniel J P
Johnstown Bridge, Co Kildare A83 N478 .... Ryan MS Cynthia Fortune

ITALY

00060 Formello, RM .... McAdoo MS Anne B
00152 Rome .... Ponti MRS Ettore
00187 Rome .... Bonmartini Fini CT & CTSS Giovanni W
00191 Rome .... Tanfani DR & MRS Giuseppe
00197 Rome .... Ortona MR & MRS Lorenzo
00197 Rome .... Pizzicaria MRS Jean H
00197 Rome .... Schley MRS Diana R
00197 Rome .... Usai MR & MRS Sergio
00198 Rome .... de Sanctis MR Francesco M
06014 Montone .... Hellyer MRS Eloise LeG
06024 Gubbio, Perugia .... Abbot MRS John
06059 Todi, Perugia .... Caracciolo di Forino CTSSE
18035 Apricale, IM .... Cheney MRS Middleton
20149 Milan .... de Vargas-Machuca DUCA Diego
20149 Milan .... Donà dalle Rose CTE Alvise & CTSSE
30126 Lido, Venice .... Lombardo MR & MRS Fabio
40050 Monteveglio, Bologna .... Mugnaini MR & MRS Enrico
40124 Bologna .... Poggi-Cavalletti MRS Antonio
40137 Bologna .... Penna MR & MRS Antonio
50018 Florence .... Poccianti CT Guido
50022 Greve-in-Chianti, FI .... de Peverelli Luschi MR & MRS Filippo
50055 Lastra a Signa, Fl .... Mugnaini MR & MRS Daniele
50124 Florence .... Mugnaini MR & MRS Renzo
50125 Florence .... Forbes MR Peter
50125 Florence .... Griccioli della Grigia MR & MRS Francesco C
51039 Quarrata, Pistoia .... Reali MR & MRS Michael
53035 Siena .... Casini MR & MRS Nicolò
53043 Chiusi, SI .... Casini MR & MRS Clemente C
53100 Siena, SI .... Barabino Zondadari MR & MRS Giannandrea
5902 Vaiano .... Reinecke MR & MRS Robert Mattison

JAPAN

Tokyo 106-0043 .... Miller MR & MRS Jason E B

LITHUANIA

Vilnius, LT-11350 .... Wilbur MR & MRS Thomas S

MALTA

Molina MDN 1083 .... Atwell MRS William H

MEXICO

Ajijic, Jalisco 45920 .... Wolf MR & MRS René A
Cuernavaca, Morelos .... McNally MRS Frederick G
Guanajuato, GTO 36082 .... Rodriguez MR & MRS Enrique
Merida, Yucatan .... Smith MR Antony C
Mexico City, DF 11000 .... Wadsworth MRS George
Puerto Vallarta .... Drum MR John
Punta Mita, Nayarit .... Warren MR & MRS Frederick J
San Miguel de Allende, CP, GTO 37700 .... Obregón-Peña MR & MRS Eduardo
San Miguel de Allende, GTO 37700 .... Clement MR & MRS Richard M
San Miguel de Allende, GTO 37700 .... Downer MRS H Draper
San Miguel de Allende, GTO 37700 .... George MR William D 3D
San Miguel de Allende, GTO 37700 .... Scott-Paine MRS Elizabeth B
San Miguel de Allende, GTO 37700 .... Truitt MRS James McC
Todos Santos, Baja California Sur .... Buckley MR & MRS Douglas E

MONACO

Monte Carlo 98000 .... Vincent MRS A W Bourn

MOROCCO

40000 Marrakech .... Ayer MR & MRS Frederick III

THE NETHERLANDS

1071 ZR Amsterdam .... de Kock MR & MRS Robert H C
2585 DK Den Haag .... Moore MR & MRS Arthur B
2585 SR The Hague .... Fairbank MRS Kellogg 3D
6226 BK Maastricht .... Kroon MR Johannes A
6287 NB Eys .... Hopkins MRS Erica B

NEW ZEALAND

Christchurch .... Wardman MR John B
Karori, Wellington 6005 .... Pearce DR Euan I F & Fuller MRS Jane G
Nelson .... Armstrong MR & MRS Kevin J
Wairarapa, North Island .... Crofoot MR & MRS Anders N

NORTHERN IRELAND

Belfast BT9 6GB .... Aiken MR & MRS K Dax

NORWAY

2860 Hov .... Nordling MS Seija Kaarina
4950 Risor .... Ertman MR & MRS C Eric

PANAMA

Panama City .... Prout MR & MRS John R

PERU

Lima 18 .... Sears MRS Alexandra W
Lima 27 .... Waller MR & MRS Harold E JR
San Isidro, Lima .... van Ronzelen y de Villarreal MRS M Violeta

PORTUGAL

2775-598 Carcavelos .... Behn MRS Sosthenes 2D
4150-553 Porto .... Illing MR & MRS (DR) Robert Frederick

REPUBLIC OF SINGAPORE

Singapore 049909 .... McCormack MR & MRS William A
Singapore 148954 .... Doherty MR & MRS Manning L
Singapore 248669 .... Poli MR & MRS Peter K
Singapore 249570 .... Blair MR & MRS Edward McC 3D
Singapore 257818 .... Reiser MR & MRS Jasper K
Singapore 298810 .... Experton MR & MRS Gregory M P
Singapore 587758 .... McMahon MR & MRS Frederic C

REPUBLIC OF SOUTH AFRICA

Wynberg 7800 .... Yassukovich MR & MRS Stanislas M

SAUDI ARABIA

Riyadh 11492 .... Barnes MR & MRS John A M

SCOTLAND

Auchterarder, Perthshire PH3 1HP .... Jardine Paterson MR & MRS Andrew
Edinburgh EH16 5AA .... Rodner MR & MRS James O
Edinburgh EH16 5QH .... Vosburgh MS Caroline C
Edinburgh EH4 1DN .... Wood DR & MRS W Duncan
Elie, Fife KY9 1AD .... Harvie-Watt MR Euan
Nairn IV12 5RB .... Baker MR Ian A

SPAIN

03599 Altea La Vieja, Alicante .... Hinckley CAPT (RET) Robert M JR
08034 Barcelona .... Cauro MR & MRS Olivier A
08036 Barcelona .... Saurí-Marchán MR & MRS Sergi
28002 Madrid .... Llopis MR & MRS Jose Maria
28004 Madrid .... Gómez-Acebo de Borbón MR & MRS Juan
28010 Madrid .... Biddle MRS Nicholas D
28014 Madrid .... Fernãndez-Longoria MR & MRS Pablo
28668 Madrid .... San Román MR & MRS Jose L
46010 Valencia .... Dewar MR & MRS Alec Livingston

ST KITTS & NEVIS

Nevis .... Parry MRS Beverley W

ST VINCENT & THE GRENADINES

Bequia .... Brewer MR & MRS Charles H

SWEDEN

S 23940 Falsterbo .... Eckerberg MR & MRS C Lennart

SWITZERLAND

1203 Geneva .... Chatelain MR & MRS Denis A
1204 Geneva .... Dike MISS Deborah A
1204 Geneva .... Saman MR & MRS Alain-Constantin
1206 Geneva .... Doriel MR & MRS Alexandre
1223 Cologny, Geneva .... Saurel MR Paul L
1236 Cartigny .... McClintic MR & MRS Richard D
1292 Chambesy .... Carmalt MR & MRS Samuel W
1659 Flendruz .... Youmans MR & MRS Craig C
1659 Rougemont .... Walker MR William B
1659 Rougemont .... Youmans MRS Scott A
1854 Leysin .... Ware MR & MRS Lawrence P
1874 Champery .... Merryman MRS Frances McL
1874 Champery .... Walker MR & MRS Benjamin
1936 Verbier .... Farrand MRS John E
1936 Verbier .... Farrand MS Laura
3011 Bern .... Turner MRS Louise E
3775 Lenk .... Curtis MR & MRS John N JR
8032 Zurich .... Wehrli MR & MRS (DR) Johann C
8037 Zurich .... McGleughlin MR & MRS William R III
8800 Thalwil .... Curry MR & MRS C MacNeil III
CH 1005 Lausanne .... Servien DR Louis-Marc
CH 1007 Lausanne .... Decazes CTE Edouard E & CTSSE
CH 1224 Chene-Bougeries .... Spiess MR & MRS Dominik F
CH 1226 Thonex .... Hyde MR & MRS Alexis L
CH 1291 Commugny .... Atkinson-Topping MRS Josephine
CH 8802, Kilchberg .... Stump MR & MRS Henrik J
CH 8804 Au Zurich .... Meyer MR & MRS Ulrich D
Martigny 1928 .... Yates MS Megan R
St Sulpice 1025 .... Binz MR & MRS Urban G
Zurich 8002 .... Cahn von Seelen MR & MRS Ulf M

TAIWAN

Taipei City 112 .... Kikoski MR & MRS John N

TANZANIA

Majengo, Moshi .... Rueter MR Matthew C

THAILAND

Bangkok 10120 .... Stent MR James P
Bangkruay, Nontha Buri 11130 .... du Pont DR & MRS Peter T
Surin 32000 .... Fay MR Edward H JR

TURKEY

Emirgan, Istanbul 34450 .... Şenocak DR Dogan
& Thys-Şenocak DR Lucienne M

UNITED ARAB EMIRATES

Abu Dhabi .... Evarts MR & MRS Daniel W

UNITED KINGDOM

Douglas, Isle of Man IM1 3LS .... Boersma MR Frederick L
Broadford IV49 9AA .... Reeves MR & MRS Van Kirk
Broadford, Isle of Skye IV49 9AA .... Reeves MR Evander J
Douglas, Isle of Man IM1 3LS .... Leeds MR & MRS Anthony R L
Douglas, Isle of Man IM1 3LS .... Leeds MR & MRS Roland O

VENEZUELA

Caracas .... Lameda MR & MRS Daniel E
Caracas .... Rodner MRS Henry F JR

VIETNAM

Ho Chi Minh City .... Henriques MR & MRS Peter G

Holidays

Observance	2019	2020
New Year's Day	January 1	January 1
Martin Luther King Jr	January 21	January 20
Lunar New Year	February 18	January 25
Lincoln's Birthday	February 12	February 12
Valentine's Day	February 14	February 14
President's Day	February 18	February 17
Washington's Birthday	February 22	February 22
Ash Wednesday	March 6	February 26
St. Patrick's Day	March 17	March 17
Palm Sunday	April 14	April 5
Passover	April 20	April 8
Good Friday	April 19	April 10
Easter Sunday	April 21	April 12
Mother's Day	May 12	May 10
Armed Forces Day	May 18	May 16
Ramadan (U. S.)	May 6	April 23
Memorial Day	May 27	May 25
Flag Day	June 14	June 14
Father's Day	June 16	June 21
Independence Day	July 4	July 4
Labor Day	September 2	September 7
Rosh Hashanah	September 30	September 18
Yom Kippur	October 9	September 27
Columbus Day	October 14	October 12
Halloween	October 31	October 31
Election Day	November 6	November 3
Veteran's Day	November 11	November 11
Thanksgiving Day	November 28	November 26
Chanukah	December 23	December 10
Christmas Day	December 25	December 25
Kwanzaa	December 26	December 26

Birthstones & Flowers

Month	Stone	Flower
January	Garnet	Carnation
February	Amethyst	Primrose
March	Aquamarine	Violet
April	Diamond	Daisy or Lily
May	Emerald	Lily-of-the-Valley
June	Pearl or Moonstone	Rose
July	Ruby	Sweet Pea
August	Peridot	Gladiolus
September	Sapphire	Aster
October	Opal	Dahlia
November	Topaz or Citrine	Chrysanthemum
December	Turquoise or Lapis	Poinsettia

Zodiac Signs

Dates	Sign	Symbol
Dec. 22 - Jan. 19	Capricorn	Goat
Jan. 20 - Feb. 18	Aquarius	Water Bearer
Feb. 19 - Mar. 20	Pisces	Fish
Mar. 21 - Apr. 19	Aries	Ram
Apr. 20 - May 20	Taurus	Bull
May 21 - June 20	Gemini	Twins
June 21 - July 22	Cancer	Crab
July 23 - Aug. 22	Leo	Lion
Aug. 23 - Sept. 22	Virgo	Virgin
Sept. 23 - Oct. 22	Libra	Scales
Oct. 23 - Nov. 21	Scorpio	Scorpion
Nov. 22 - Dec. 21	Sagittarius	Centaur

Anniversaries

Year	Symbol	Year	Symbol
1st	Paper	13th	Lace
2nd	Cotton	14th	Ivory
3rd	Leather	15th	Crystal
4th	Books	20th	China
5th	Wood or Clocks	25th	Silver
6th	Iron	30th	Pearl
7th	Copper, Bronze or Brass	35th	Coral or Jade
8th	Electrial Appliances	40th	Ruby
9th	Pottery	45th	Sapphire
10th	Tin, Aluminum	50th	Gold
11th	Steel	55th	Emerald
12th	Silk or Linen	60th	Diamond

Birthdays & Anniversaries

Date	Name	Occasion

New Members

"New Members," printed on blue stock in this book, includes all new members admitted within the last six months—as well as members previously listed whose status has changed, such as those who have recently married, or who are now for the first time listed separately from their parents—along with their listings as they appear in this winter edition. The summer listings of those who have provided this information will be found in the summer book, to be published in May.

The Social Register Association maintains its membership base at approximately 25,000, the same number as in 1934. As with any thriving association, club or organization, new members are its lifeblood and nominations are always welcome.

To nominate a candidate for the Social Register Association, please email: SRCommittee@thesocialregister.org.

A

Adams MR Ellis C L
(484) 213-0026
frandam59@comcast.net
801 Ridge Pike, Apt 36
Lafayette Hill, PA 19444
(484) 351-8634
Ul.Sar.Colo'59.Rol'72

Adelaar MR Jesse D & Thomas MR Corrin
(212) 288-6320
jesse@adelaar.us
200 Mercer St, Apt 4B
New York, NY 10012
(212) 204-4680
LirAcad'14.WakeF'96

Allen-Hornblower DR Emily
see Hornblower MR Samuel R

Annesley MR & MRS William H
(Rogers Sandra)
(610) 613-0540 . . Mr
(610) 613-0541 . . Mrs
1339 Beaumont Dv
Gladwyne, PA 19035
Penn'80.Ac.W&J'77.Drex"80

Audretch MS Sharon
see Lothmann MR Scott T

B

Bate MR & MRS Russell
(Wilking Nina D)
nwilking120@gmail.com
14 Tuskar St
London SE10 9UR England
Cl'98.Bklyn'03

Bauer MR & MRS Ernst S (Schriver Leslie)
(415) 716-6680 . . Mr
(415) 716-6749 . . Mrs
bauer.ernst@gmail.com
211 Ninth Av
San Francisco, CA 94118
(415) 221-1214
PugetS'84.Dt.Fmy.Ark'83

Baxter MS Barbara L
(Hall Barbara)
(513) 703-2708
bbaxter1@fuse.net
1 Riverside Place, Unit 104
Covington, KY 41011
(859) 431-1902
Dar.

Beard MR Robert R
& Mohapatra MR Bibhudutta
(646) 234-2552
rrbeard@me.com
bibhu@bibhu.com
344 W 72 St, Apt 5M
New York, NY 10023
(212) 874-2552
FIT'99.C.Ga'81

Beer MR David W
120 E 90 St, Apt 14E
New York, NY 10128
(212) 860-8490
C.K.Mto.H'56.H'59

Benedict MR & MRS Charles P (Walker Blair)
(917) 449-7906 . . Mr
(847) 341-2331 . . Mrs
charles.p.benedict@gmail.com
blair.w.benedict@gmail.com . . Mrs
88 Leonard St, Apt 1019
New York, NY 10013
Wisc'09.Rc.Rh.U'07

Benjamin MR & MRS Richard D
(English Mary Anne)
(917) 370-5937 . . Mr
(917) 319-4686 . . Mrs
rbenjamin@axiomcapital.com . . Mr
benjamin.marianne@gmail.com . . Mrs
500A E 87 St, Apt 11E
New York, NY 10128
(212) 535-7262
V'64.OState'65.C.Gr.Cs.Ncd.H.'59.H'62

Berardocco MS Laura F
see Lamonia MR Anthony J

Bernard MS Ann Maris
see MacLachlan MR Robert G

Berson MR Joel I
(917) 373-2970
ajberson@verizon.net
180 East End Av
New York, NY 10128
(212) 879-3762
56 Thunderbird Terr
Windham, NY 12496
(518) 734-3210
C.Dth'48.Y.'51

Black MS Alexandra C
(917) 613-9763
alexandra.c.black@gmail.com
1838 Broadway St
San Francisco, CA 94109
Bost'11.Sfy.

Bland MR & MRS Frederick A
(Thomson Morley)
26 Pierrepont St
Brooklyn Heights, NY 11201
(718) 596-3792
Bnd'69.C.Y'68.Y'72

Bleich MR & MRS Jeffrey L (Pratt Rebecca)
(510) 452-7314
jlbleich@gmail.com
109 Monte Av
Piedmont, CA 94611
(510) 655-2192
MtH'84.Geo'91.Aht'83.H'86.Cal'89

Borst MR & MRS Alan W JR
(Angell Marilyn)
(914) 261-9076 . . Mr
(914) 329-2502 . . Mrs
abjr57@gmail.com . . Mr
maaborst@gmail.com . . Mrs
743 The Parkway
Mamaroneck, NY 10543
(914) 698-6559
Dt.Cw.Rv.Ay.Mich'80.Md'83

Boudin HON Michael & Field MS Martha A
(857) 270-8764 . . Hon
(617) 820-4246 . . Ms
81 Irving St
Cambridge, MA 02138
(617) 864-5118
Rdc'65.Ch'68.C.Mt.Sb.Tv.H.'61.H'64

Boyd MISS Brooke W
(703) 618-6817
brookewboyd@hotmail.com
29 Charles St, Apt 1A
New York, NY 10014
NCar'00.Nu'17

Bramwell MR & MRS George Y
(Hoehl Patricia A)
(917) 213-6099 . . Mr
(917) 371-7264 . . Mrs
george9337@yahoo.com . . Mr
peacepat1@yahoo.com . . Mrs
45 Park Lane
Staten Island, NY 10301
(718) 442-3105
Ursinus'61.Dt.Fairf'59

Brawer MR & MRS Nicholas A
(Davis Meredith)
(914) 552-7303
11 Leafy Lane
Larchmont, NY 10538-2217
(914) 833-7377
Ws'97.Uv.Cw.Myf.Sar.Cl'91
JUNIORS MISS Charlotte A
JUNIORS MR Nicholas A JR
JUNIORS MR Timothy W

Bristol MR & MRS Brian T
(Woolley Susannah B)
(917) 902-9845 . . Mr
(917) 860-3948 . . Mrs
bbristol@boxwoodadv.com
1165 Fifth Av
New York, NY 10029
(212) 722-5259
Wms'76.Cl'80.K.Uv.Cly.Y'74.P'78.Cl'79

Broach DR Vance Carter JR
(215) 749-2406
broach@udel.edu
290 Iven Av, Apt 3C
Wayne, PA 19087-4906
(610) 687-3031
USA.Pe.R.Cspa.Fw.Rv.Sar.W'minster'62.
Nw'66.MichSt'88

Brodsky MR James S
see McCarthy MR Philip E II

Brown MR & MRS Charles D
(Emery Beth A)
(617) 645-3356 . . Mr
(617) 501-4424 . . Mrs
chuckbrown222@gmail.com . . Mr
babrown0910@gmail.com . . Mrs
18 Hancock St, Apt 3
Boston, MA 02114
Mo'97.McG'00.Ub.Btn.Dar.NCar'89.Va'97

Burdine MS Mary Catherine
see Hurrion DR James R

C

Cahn von Seelen MR & MRS Ulf M
(Smith Kristin)
(011-41-79) 220-15-51 . . Mr
(011-41-79) 222-25-98 . . Mrs
ulfcvs@gmail.com . . Mr
kristincvs@gmail.com . . Mrs
Lavaterstrasse 103
Zurich 8002 Switzerland
(011-41-44) 281-93-30
Pa'91.Ac.Dar.Ncd.Bmc.Karlsruhe'88
JUNIORS MISS Helena M
JUNIORS MISS Susanna M
JUNIORS MISS Celia F

Cappello MR & MRS Juan C
(Forrester Jean)
(917) 923-3335 . . Mr
(908) 803-5830 . . Mrs
14 E 75 St, 10 Floor
New York, NY 10021
(212) 570-5433
Rut'87.Rut'93.Bg.Mt.Ncd.UChile'63.Nw'66

Cappello MR Juan Pablo & Getty MS Christina
(305) 793-7414
jp@jpc.vc
600 Brickell Ave, Ste 1725
Miami, FL 33131
(786) 292-1599
Rc.T.Duke'89.Nu'92
MISS Alessandra
JUNIORS MISS Susana
JUNIORS MISS Adriana

Celi LT COL & MRS Sean A D
(Gouedy Sara)
(318) 518-4188 . . Lt Col
(318) 780-0707 . . Mrs
sac9m@alumni.virginia.edu . . Lt Col
saragceli@gmail.com . . Mrs
551 Compton Rd
Wyoming, OH 45231
235 Sunrise Av, Apt 2003
Palm Beach, FL 33480
WKy'04.Jl.Va'97

Chabris MR & MRS Peter D JR
(Rielly Lynn H)
(513) 703-7000 . . Mr
(513) 400-7621 . . Mrs
lynnchabris@gmail.com
7400 Brill Rd
Cincinnati, OH 45243
Cal'98.Geo'96
JUNIORS MISS Sophia E S H
JUNIORS MR Christopher R

Chenault Minot MRS Marilyn
see Minot MR Winthrop G

Codraro MR & MRS Lawrence F JR
(Meade E Alexandra)
(212) 365-8474 . . Mr
(917) 912-3477 . . Mrs
lcodraro2@gmail.com . . Mr
acodraro@gmail.com . . Mrs
43 Pecksland Rd
Greenwich, CT 06831
(203) 661-6475
Va'99.Rc.Cly.Geo'96.Cl'01
JUNIORS MISS Mary W G
JUNIORS MISS Nina L H

Colbert MR & MRS John P
(Smith Andrea)
(513) 600-5258 . . Mr
(513) 608-6859 . . Mrs
jcolbert@cinci.rr.com . . Mr
acolbert@cinci.rr.com . . Mrs
563 Belle Meade Farm Dv
Loveland, OH 45140
(513) 683-0077
OState'93.Day'96.O'93.Day'96
JUNIORS MR Bradley D
JUNIORS MR Zachary A

Coles MR & MRS Andrés (Vollmer Beatriz)
(646) 244-8310 . . Mr
(646) 322-9799 . . Mrs
agcoles@hotmail.com . . Mr
beatrips@hotmail.com . . Mrs
420 E 55 St, Apt 11A
New York, NY 10022
(212) 244-8310
PontGreg'94.Ri.Bab'94
JUNIORS MISS Helena
JUNIORS MISS Leonor
JUNIORS MR Alberto
JUNIORS MR Eduardo
JUNIORS MR Daniel

Contiguglia MR & MRS Carl A
(Hensel Caroline C)
(917) 693-2045
henselcontiguglia@hotmail.com
171 W 71 St, Apt 9E
New York, NY 10023
(212) 799-2330
MtH'88.Pa'93.Un.Msq.Why.
Jl.Dar.Ncd.Cr'89.Cr'90
JUNIORS MISS Emma G
JUNIORS MISS Courtney A

Conway MR & MRS Elliot S
(Dau Ann)
(917) 744-8841
econway@optonline.net . . Mr
adconway@optonline.net . . Mrs
549 Chicken Valley Rd
Locust Valley, NY 11560
(516) 676-7825
Nw'81.B.Bhm.Lic.Ng.Pr.Rc.Cly.Cr'72.H'74

Coogan MR & MRS David F
(McGirr Pamela)
(617) 974-5698 . . Mr
(617) 840-5953 . . Mrs
david_coogan@yahoo.com . . Mr
backbay0@hotmail.com . . Mrs
40 Saint Botolph St, Apt 21
Boston, MA 02116
NEng'86.Uv.NEng'85
JUNIORS MR Hunter W

Cook CAPT & MRS Glen A
(Waters Melody)
cookslc@aol.com
3742 Twinbrook St
Millcreek, UT 84109
(801) 554-4154

Cook DR Susan Wray
(713) 907-3110
scook913@gmail.com . . Dr (Mrs)
5739 Jason St
Houston, TX 77096
(713) 541-3859
Tex'75.Jl.Cda.Occ.Odcc.Omd.

Cook DR Susan Wray
see Cook DR Richard G

Cummins MR & MRS Thomas B F
(Huffman Jane K)
(773) 590-5214 . . Mr
(617) 620-2050 . . Mrs
cummins@fac.harvard.edu . . Mr
jkhuf@yahoo.com . . Mrs
25 Ellsworth Av
Cambridge, MA 02139
(617) 497-0688
NMex'74.Gr.Denis'73

Curran MR & MRS Mortimer F
(Cottrell Charlotte M J)
(561) 506-9031 . . Mr
(561) 346-8178 . . Mrs
7007 S Flagler Dv
West Palm Beach, FL 33405
IntHospMgt'02.Evg.Geo'95.Tul'00
JUNIORS MISS Sophia M
JUNIORS MISS Serena G
JUNIORS MR Preston M
JUNIORS MR Parker F

Curry MR & MRS (DR) John M
(Buckley Margretta)
((561) 762-0499 . . Mr
(561) 758-3869 . . Dr
jcurry1@gmail.com . . Mr
grettac@fastmail.fm . . Dr
12150 Captains Landing
North Palm Beach, FL 33408
(561) 626-6264
(561) 626-6265
Emman'70.Mass.Cc.Cw.Sar.Hb.SFr'68.H'70

D

Damon MR Sloan F
(415) 307-2841
sloan.damon@gmail.com
635 W 42 St, Apt 38F
New York, NY 10036
Van'17

Darden MR & MRS Glenn M
(Williamson Kimberly)
(817) 475-1917 . . Mr
(817) 233-9016 . . Mrs
54 Valley Ridge Rd
Ft Worth, TX 76107
Cr'79.Ny.Dbl.Srb.Tul'79

Davidson MR & MRS Benjamin Q
(Biddle Philippa L)
(224) 717-2104 . . Mr
(914) 409-7245 . . Mrs
benjaminqdavidson@gmail.com . . Mr
philippa.biddle@gmail.com . . Mrs
10 Church Av
Germantown, NY 12526
(518) 537-3548
Cl'16.B'gton'14

de Castro MR Peter R
(415) 699-6071
1274 Filbert St
San Francisco, CA 94109
(415) 292-5230
Uv.Clare'72.Geo'76
JUNIORS MISS Phoebe C
JUNIORS MR Philip C

de Koning MR & MRS Kendrik J JR
(Kramer Melyora E)
(917) 642-3057 . . Mr
(917) 657-7193 . . Mrs
kendrik@transwestcap.com . . Mr
melyora.dekoning@gmail.com . . Mrs
507 Monroe St
Denver, CO 80206
Va'93.B.Mb.Nrr.Rcn.Srb.Ind'89.JM'93
JUNIORS MISS Everdina W
JUNIORS MR Hendrik W
JUNIORS MR Joost P

D'Elia MR Gregory W
(561) 531-3365
gregwd5@yahoo.com
3800 Washington Rd, Apt 603
West Palm Beach, FL 33405

Doering MR Albert Lindsay IV
(215) 840-1364
lindsaydoering@yahoo.com
2305 Delancey Place
Philadelphia, PA 19103
Rv.SqA.Pa'92

Dougherty MR Marcus J
(917) 297-7832
mdougherty@milbank.com
209 E 56 St, Apt 11PQR
New York, NY 10022
(212) 530-5323
Dt.UnivColLond'94

Doughty MR & MRS Jeffrey C
(Pope Lucy C)
(757) 268-6786 . . Mr
(704) 692-3134 . . Mrs
jcdoughty87@gmail.com . . Mr
lucypdoughty@gmail.com . . Mrs
3700 Massachusetts Av NW, Apt 129
Washington, DC 20016
WakeF'10.Mt.Cc.Cw.VPI'10

E

Edwards MR & MRS Sean C
(Ganczarz Kelly C)
(610) 202-6531 . . Mr
(215) 278-3820 . . Mrs
sean.edwards@rittenhousecom.com . . Mr
kellycgedwards@gmail.com . . Mrs
618 Carpenter St
Philadelphia, PA 19147
SUNY'08.SUNY'10.Ul.Ac.Penn'04

Epperly DR Corinne D
(609) 213-4541
corinne.epperly@gmail.com
1304 River Rd
Titusville, NJ 08560
Va.NCar.NCar.Ncd.

Epperly MISS Melissa B
(646) 554-6816
melissa.epperly@gmail.com
101 West Hampton Rd
Philadelphia, PA 19118
Va.H.Uv.Ncd.

Evans MR & MRS James S
(Ingraham Kimberly)
(917) 763-1539 . . Mr
(917) 797-8531 . . Mrs
jsevans4@hotmail.com . . Mr
kimberlyingraham@hotmail.com . . Mrs
1 Firethorn Lane
Malvern, PA 19355
Duke'00.Un.Cw.Me.Pr.Duke'00.Cl'07
JUNIORS MR James G
JUNIORS MR Carter W
JUNIORS MR Penn H

F

Fairbank MR David Ezekiel
& Smith DR Judith W
(228) 363-3683 . . Mr
(228) 234-3954 . . Dr
zfairbank@gmail.com . . Mr
jwsmithmd@gmail.com . . Dr
20014 Patton Rd
Long Beach, MS 39560
P'79.Cl.Emory.USMM'81.Nu'88

Farmer MR Scott E
(513) 702-3806
sef299@gmail.com
10155 Lincoln Rd
Camp Dennison, OH 45111

Felton MRS Henry D IV
(Oakes Pamela Vanderbilt)
(410) 382-4103
pamela.felton@gmail.com
13001 Dover Rd
Reisterstown, MD 21136
(410) 252-2811
Gchr'65

Field MS Martha A
see Boudin HON Michael

G

Gaston MR & MRS John E
(Morphy Katherine W)
(203) 561-8871 . . Mr
(203) 918-6881 . . Mrs
350 Thunderbowl Lane
Aspen, CO 81611
Colo'09.Hbc.Colo'09
JUNIORS MR Will M

Getty MS Christina
see Cappello MR Juan Pablo

Glover MR & MRS Thomas S
(Kemp Karen)
(917) 226-2400 . . Mr
(917) 324-3300 . . Mrs
tom@tglover.com . . Mr
karenkempglover@gmail.com . . Mrs
829 Park Av, Apt 8A
New York, NY 10021
(212) 737-1575
Duke'85.BtP.Nyc.Ri.Cc.Cly.
Ncd.Va'81.Pa'87
JUNIORS MISS Eugenie M K
at Phillips Andover
JUNIORS MR Thomas B
at U of Chicago

Glueck MR William C
(917) 826-9004
billconnington@gmail.com
123 W 93 St, Apt 5G
New York, NY 10025
Pl.Chr.StG.LondDrArt'89

Gutowski DR Andrew
see Provost MR N Thomas

H

Hackenbracht MS Sarah
see Tinnin MR Alden

Halferty MR & MRS James F
(Livingstone Pamela F)
(213) 447-1770 . . Mr
(626) 437-4770 . . Mrs
jhalferty@lee-associates.com . . Mr
pamelahalferty@yahoo.com . . Mrs
2825 Thorndike Rd
Pasadena, CA 91107
(626) 792-6060
Jon.Vh.
JUNIORS MISS Cornelia S
JUNIORS MISS Adelaide F
JUNIORS MR James C

Hansell MR & MRS (DR) Robert L
(Shanley Phyllis)
(973) 222-8441 . . Mr
(973) 202-1940 . . Dr
hansellrobert@yahoo.com . . Mr
phyllis.hansell@shu.edu . . Dr
18 Brunswick Rd
Montclair, NJ 07042-3013
(973) 746-8527
Fiy.

Hardigg MR & MRS William B JR
(Bobrink Margi A)
(513) 477-0820
mhardigg@hotmail.com
6750 Drake Rd
Cincinnati, OH 45243
(513) 271-5740
Ind'65.Ncd.NotreD'63

Hare MR & MRS Eugene T
(Warner Sharon)
(630) 549-5684 . . Mr
(630) 853-7990 . . Mrs
haregt5@yahoo.com . . Mr
sharon110r@yahoo.com . . Mrs
41 N 12 Av
St Charles, IL 60174
Cda.Dar.Dh.Lewis'75

Harman MR & MRS Daniel H III
(Chapman Beverly J)
(917) 573-0686 . . Mr
(609) 665-9660 . . Mrs
dhnassau@gmail.com . . Mr
leigh886@yahoo.com . . Mrs
168 Copperfield Dv
Lawrenceville, NJ 08648-2583
(609) 882-3128
1065 Park Av
New York, NY 10128-1001
Bost'70.H.'74.Mit'78.Cw.Jts.Rv.Cda.Dar.Myf.
Plg.P'69.Cl'71

Harman MISS Victoria C
(917) 573-0686
vc1harman@gmail.com
1065 Park Av, Apt 9B
New York, NY 10128
(212) 860-8804
Stan'09.Camb'11

Harness MR & MRS Charles R
(Grant Barbara)
(941) 302-0946 . . Mr
(941) 402-5850 . . Mrs
chuck.harness@gmail.com . . Mr
bhar184071@comcast.net . . Mrs
5340 Greenbrook Dv, Legacy Estates
Sarasota, FL 34238
(941) 921-0563
FerrisSt'69.Cda.Dar.Dh.FerrisSt'68

Harrell MR & MRS Cecil Stanford
(Garner Frances G)
(813) 245-3634 . . Mr
(813) 310-2767 . . Mrs
csh912@tampabay.rr.com . . Mr
fgh381040@gmail.com . . Mrs
5125 S Nichol St
Tampa, FL 33611
(813) 254-1527
USA.Cw.Ht.Jts.Rv.Sar.AlaPoly'58

Hartnett MISS Elizabeth A
(917) 576-2970
419 E 57 St, Apt 10E
New York, NY 10022
(212) 644-8109
VillaN'94

Harvey MS Christina McCarron
(646) 573-6634
chrissiemccarron@gmail.com
903 Park Av, Apt 11C
New York, NY 10075
(212) 861-1046
Vt'95.Bm.Dbl.
JUNIORS MR John S

Haugen MS Ann Sims
(713) 204-7020
houston.debutante@gmail.com
3118 FM 528, No 282
Webster, TX 77598
Houst'05

Hawley mr & mrs Shervin B
(Saalfield Carolyn W)
(617) 939-8066 . . Mr
(617) 866-0117 . . Mrs
shervin@sbhawley.com . . Mr
chawley@hlblighting.com . . Mrs
250 Old Sudbury Rd
Sudbury, MA 01776
(617) 244-1778
MiamiU'93.Rens'95.Cc.Cw.Ofp.Rv.Sb.Wt.
Dar.Myf.Ncd.Houst'87
miss Anisa A
miss Ariana D
juniors miss Windley V Knowlton

Heath mr Andrew G B
(914) 299-0463
agbheath@gmail.com
43 E 67 St, Apt 4A
New York, NY 10065
(212) 879-2402
Dbl.Un.Char'ton'05.Char'ton'08

Heathwood mr & mrs Desmond
(Stockman Dorothy Ann)
(617) 460-2775
djh@comcast.net . . Mr
aheathwood@comcast.net . . Mrs
300 Clarke Av
Palm Beach, FL 33480
(561) 366-8387
BtP.Evg.Cl'63

Heisel mr John Kurtland
(310) 600-1623
kurtheisel123@gmail.com
611 Ocampo Dv
Pacific Palisades, CA 90272
Cal'83
juniors miss Annabelle J
juniors miss Maia C

Hollister mr & mrs Robert Dewey
(Harris Lisa)
(859) 468-7402 . . Mr
(513) 207-0630 . . Mrs
deweyhollister@gmail.com . . Mr
twinbridgefarm@aol.com . . Mrs
PO Box 25375
Christiansted, VI 00824
Skd'79.Capital'86.Cw.Cin'85

Hornblower mr Samuel R
& Allen-Hornblower dr Emily
(646) 255-2001 . . Mr
(617) 899-9663 . . Dr
sam.hornblower@icloud.com . . Mr
allen.emilym@gmail.com . . Dr
26 Winthrop St
Brooklyn, NY 11225
(718) 513-0023
EcoleNS'02.H'09.B.Mt.H'02
juniors miss Dune M Allen-Hornblower
juniors miss Jane S Allen-Hornblower

Horowitz mr Jonathan R
& Wolden dr Suzanne L
(917) 696-0523 . . Mr
(347) 982-7830 . . Dr
jonathan.r.horowitz@gmail.com . . Mr
woldens@mskcc.org . . Dr
15 E 91 St, Apt 10B
New York, NY 10128
(212) 472-3023
Stan'90.Cs.Stan'92
juniors miss Hailey S
juniors miss Heidi L
juniors miss Brooke H

Hsieh mr Jackson & Chen ms Minalie
(917) 860-2911 . . Mr
(917) 710-6591 . . Ms
jacksonhsieh@aol.com . . Mr
minaliechen@icloud.com . . Ms
1918 N Olive St, Apt 2202
Dallas, TX 75201
H'87.B.Bac.Rh.Cal'83
mr Nicholas J
mr Cameron C

Hurrion dr James R
& Burdine ms Mary Catherine
(646) 508-1360 . . Dr
(662) 425-2392 . . Ms
mc.burdine@gmail.com
34 W 12 St, PH
New York, NY 10011
W&L'08.Jl.Ox'96.Ox'02

I

Ingraham mr & mrs John W
(Barker Barbara G)
(917) 297-8179
nytuxedo@aol.com
25 Sutton Place, 3 Fl
New York, NY 10022
(212) 861-3152
Maisonette 8 North, 6880 N Ocean Blvd
Ocean Ridge, FL 33435
Mich'56.Un.Cw.Evg.Pr.Cs.H'52.H'57

J

Jackson dr & mrs Richard L
(Doench Kimberly L)
(513) 703-5576 . . Dr
(513) 703-5577 . . Mrs
6620 Madeira Hills Dv
Cincinnati, OH 45243
(513) 321-2071
MiamiU'79.Cw.Jl.MiamiU'79.OSt'83

Jacoby ms Elizabeth E
(917) 592-1202
1230 Park Av, Apt 9D
New York, NY 10128
(212) 722-2726
(212) 722-1112
Emory

Jones mr & mrs James Gregory
(Smith Becky)
(859) 802-7047
445 General Dv
Fort Wright, KY 41011
(859) 341-2279
MorehSt'83.Xav.WKy'77.NKy

K

Kloter mr Owen A
(860) 833-0305
owen.a.kloter@gmail.com
316 E 55 St, Apt 5B
New York, NY 10022
(212) 223-2586
Ul.Ne.Rv.CtColl'05.Conn'08

Klotzbach mr & mrs Hans J
(Mercadante Felicia)
(484) 686-4888 . . Mr
(215) 272-0425 . . Mrs
113 Westridge Place S
Phoenixville, PA 19460
M'vian'09.An.Fw.StG.
juniors mr Conrad D

Knutsen mr & mrs Ragnar M
(Stanton Laureen)
(516) 305-7950 . . Mr
(516) 551-0325 . . Mrs
7 Valley Rd
Locust Valley, NY 11560
(516) 676-5546
(516) 922-6526
480 Park Av
New York, NY 10022
Cr'65.Ny.S.Cs.NorwNavAcad'67

Krebs—May

Krebs MR & MRS William E
(Clark Alice A)
(443) 255-7676 .. Mr
(443) 255-8889 .. Mrs
4krebs@gmail.com
213 Warehams Point
Williamsburg, VA 23185
So.JHop.Ay.Jts.Ncd.Md
MISS Margaret A Martien
W&M'15.Y'22
MISS Augusta G Martien
W&M'16.Y'20

Kromelow MR & MRS Justin M
(Bellis Alexandra C)
(650) 219-3397 .. Mr
(650) 201-9664 .. Mrs
justin@kromelow.com .. Mr
alexandra@kromelow.com .. Mrs
2621 Adeline Dv
Burlingame, CA 94010
(650) 347-0157
Cal'91.Bur.Sfy.Tcy.Myf.Dar.V'87.Ill'90
MR Nicholas C
JUNIORS MISS California V
JUNIORS MR Kirby C

L

Lader MR & MRS Paul J
(Scheurenbrand Sandra L)
(609) 760-1750 .. Mr
(609) 941-7902 .. Mrs
paullader@gmail.com .. Mr
scheurenbrand@voorhees.k12.nj.us .. Mrs
8 E Cherry St
Wenonah, NJ 08090
(856) 468-1413
Eastern'92.Marygr"08.Ll.Penn.Ph.Bmc.
Dar.Ncd.W.StJos'87.VillaN'90
JUNIORS MR Tennyson J

Lamonia MR Anthony J
& Berardocco MS Laura F
(312) 415-0123 .. Mr
(646) 261-4032 .. Ms
tlamonia@uirc.com .. Mr
laurab@coinusa.com .. Ms
5 E 14 Place, Apt 1203
Chicago, IL 60605
FIT'08.DePaul'97

Lentz DR Charles W
& Lentz MR Matthew Malinowski
navyboy80@verizon.net
mjrmalinowski@gmail.com
8 Kirkbride Lane
Doylestown, PA 18901
(267) 809-0082
HolyC'98.Ul.StG.StJ.IndPa'94.Gratz'98.
Arcad'02.Wid'12

Lentz MR Matthew Malinowski
see Lentz DR Charles W

Leone MR & MRS Charles D II
(Castrow Sharon)
(312) 330-7788 .. Mr
(404) 242-0809 .. Mrs
cdleone2@yahoo.com .. Mr
sharon.leone@yahoo.com .. Mrs
3335 W Andrews Dv NW
Atlanta, GA 30305
(404) 377-7788
Van'90.Van'92
JUNIORS MR Charles D III

Ley MR & MRS Peter D
(Harvey Janet M)
(929) 287-5171 .. Mr
(917) 428-1491 .. Mrs
pleypley@gmail.com .. Mr
janetley@gmail.com .. Mrs
1070 Park Av
New York, NY 10128
(212) 722-1698
Dick'91.Un.Dth'81.H'85
JUNIORS MISS Lucille M
JUNIORS MR Carter E
JUNIORS MR Henry P W

Lippas MISS Alexandra V
(214) 289-3551
alexandralippas@gmail.com
6926 Rockview Lane
Dallas, TX 75214
(214) 821-8988
(214) 368-1192
Smu'11

Lippert DR & MRS Wayne A
(Drimal Lynn)
(513) 703-2913 .. Dr
(513) 919-6375 .. Mrs
walmd@fuse.net
7630 Given Rd
Cincinnati, OH 45243
(513) 272-1400
Cin'68.Cw.OState'65.Cin'69

Lothmann MR Scott T
& Audretch MS Sharon
(513) 678-2321 .. Mr
(513) 312-5773 .. Ms
scott.lothmann@hcpoc.com .. Mr
sharon.audretch@hcpoc.com .. Ms
6450 Given Rd
Cincinnati, OH 45243
(513) 271-0506
CinSt'11.Cin'96
JUNIORS MR William P
JUNIORS MISS Madeline G Audretch
JUNIORS MR Aiden P Audretch

Lyman MR & MRS R Jeffrey
(Schnurr Leslie A)
Roseledge, 852 Hale St
Beverly Farms, MA 01915
(978) 927-7707
Sth'85.Sm.My.Tv.Ub.H'86.Vt'93

Lynch MR John J
see Wehland MR Matthew H C

M

McCarthy MR Philip E II
& Brodsky MR James S
(917) 721-6982
(917) 327-5544
785 Park Av, Apt 14B
New York, NY 10021
2150 Ibis Island Rd, Apt 14
Palm Beach, FL 33480
Br'90.Dbl.Mt.Cr'86.Duke'89.Ch'95

McRae MR John Ashton
(229) 220-5613
j.ashton.mcrae@gmail.com
4573 MacArthur Blvd NW, Apt 102
Washington, DC 20007
Sar.So'08

MacLachlan MR Robert G
& Bernard MS Ann Maris
(513) 383-8415 .. Mr
(513) 315-0399 .. Ms
563 Stanley Av
Cincinnati, OH 45226
Cin'78.Kent'74.Loy'81

Marsh MR & MRS Colin W
(Nelson Katelyn R)
349 Grapevine Rd
Wenham, MA 01984
B'gton'12.B'gton'11

Matuschak MR & MRS Mark G
(Hutchins Kate)
(617) 512-7492 .. Mr
(917) 968-5468 .. Mrs
mark.matuschak@gmail.com .. Mr
kate.matuschak@gmail.com .. Mrs
115 Norfolk St, Apt 604
New York, NY 10002
35 Roosevelt Av
Marblehead, MA 01945
Mich'97.Y'00.Dt.Dth'81.Cl'84

May MISS Jennie W
(904) 210-8558
jennie.may@att.net
11 St John St, Apt D-1
North Haven, CT 06473
Syr'17

Mead THE HON & MRS John J IV
(Currie Blair)
(814) 881-5664 .. Hon
(814) 460-8107 .. Mrs
jmead85@aol.com .. Hon
blaircmead@gmail.com .. Mrs
800 Dutch Rd
Fairview, PA 16415
(814) 474-3617
Geo'98.P'80

Meade MR & MRS Winston D
(Sheen Caroline Y)
(917) 484-1369 .. Mr
(703) 801-2554 .. Mrs
meadewi@gmail.com .. Mr
carolineymeade@gmail.com .. Mrs
333 E 66 St, Apt 12J
New York, NY 10065
Va'03.B.Rc.Ri.Va'00
JUNIORS MISS Evelyn M
JUNIORS MISS Georgina P
JUNIORS MR Winston D JR

Meschter MISS Amanda L
(610) 761-5918
mandym1212@yahoo.com
222 W Fifth Av
Collegeville, PA 19426
Pierce'12

Meschter MR G Andrew
(610) 322-0112
g.andrew@meschter.com
215 Winsor Lane, The Cottage
Haverford, PA 19041
Rv.Millers'99.Durham'01

Minot MR Winthrop G
& Chenault Minot MRS Marilyn
(617) 775-0856 .. Mr
(617) 335-3113 .. Mrs
win@minotslight.co .. Mr
marilyn.minot@mcmdm.com .. Mrs
42 Nichols Rd
Cohasset, MA 02025
(781) 383-6611
OklaSt'70.Err.Sm.Eyc.H'73.Ox'75.H'79

Mohapatra MR Bibhudutta
see Beard MR Robert R

Moland MR & MRS William W
(Robinson Janet)
(937) 499-4984 .. Mr
(937) 657-5391 .. Mrs
bwmoland@gmail.com .. Mr
molandcabo@gmail.com .. Mrs
5005 Rhine Way
Centerville, OH 45458
OWes'68.BaldW'53

Moore MR Charles
(347) 957-0137
charles.moore662@gmail.com
7 E 35 St, Apt 6A
New York, NY 10016
P.H.'19

Moran MR & MRS Kevin R
(Corbett Allaire V)
(610) 716-9177 .. Mr
(484) 620-3146 .. Mrs
kmoran559@gmail.com .. Mr
allaire.corbett@gmail.com .. Mrs
7 Brewerytown Court
Philadelphia, PA 19121
Pa'09.Ph.Ul.VillaN'04

Moreau MS Lynda P A
see Walgamotte MR Shannon R

Morris MR & MRS John M (Wilde Jennifer E)
(786) 521-2385
15 E 93 St
New York, NY 10128
(212) 410-7771
Stan'15.Dth'11

Mosse MR & MRS (DR) Peter J C
(St Preux Christine M)
(917) 825-9830
pjcm@att.net
353 E 72 St, Apt 33D
New York, NY 10021
(212) 734-3673
Noreste'86.Plg.StG.Ox'69.Pa'71

Muller MR Daryl A & Reynolds MR William J
(202) 903-1051
(914) 474-1852
darylamuller@gmail.com
reynoldswj@gmail.com
1722 Varnum St NW
Washington, DC 20011
GeoW.UMiami.GeoW

N

Nalywajko MS Katerina L
(917) 696-9872
klnalywajko@yahoo.com
305 E 40 St, Apt 14P
New York, NY 10016
(212) 810-1920
Bnd'83.Cl'97
JUNIORS MISS Andrea J

Neary MR & MRS Victor J (Constable Ashley A)
(917) 741-4484 .. Mr
(646) 387-3639 .. Mrs
vjneary@gmail.com .. Mr
ashleyaconstable@gmail.com .. Mrs
1218 Cordova Blvd
St Petersburg, FL 33704
Nu.SAfr
JUNIORS MISS Sheridan E C

Newcombe MR J Shane
(434) 603-1021
shane@accessoriesabroad.com
2300 Carwile Springs Rd
Randolph, VA 23962
(434) 454-6219
(434) 392-9367
Ofp.StJ.HampSydney'02

Newell MS Valerie L
see Smith MR Timothy A

O

O'Donnell MR & MRS Andrew L
(Varr Meredith A)
(845) 270-1915 .. Mr
(401) 741-2105 .. Mrs
andrewladson@gmail.com .. Mr
merryodonnell1@gmail.com .. Mrs
43 Bull St
Newport, RI 02840
Bost'09.Ny.Hob'09

Oglesby LT COL (RET) & MRS Edward S
(Moore Wendy)
(214) 418-7227
edwardoglesby@gmail.com
7419 Mason Dells
Dallas, TX 75230
USMC.
JUNIORS MISS Katherine L
JUNIORS MR Samuel S

O'Leary MR & MRS Brian McA
(Smith Denise C)
(704) 661-9310
dennyoleary@me.com
1844 Pinewood Circle
Charlotte, NC 28211
(704) 367-1097
Denis'94.Denis'92
JUNIORS MR Smith C
JUNIORS MR Christopher McA

Osborne MISS Caroline L
(540) 319-3474
osbornecl@me.com
224 Park St
Morgantown, WV 26501
NCar'88.Rich'91.Emory'92.NCar'03.Ncd.

Osterman MS Jeanne-Marie
see Pearson MR Harold A

P

Patterson MR & MRS Mark
(Agostinis Elena)
(917) 969-7335 . . Mr
(914) 282-0015 . . Mrs
exracermp@gmail.com . . Mr
elenaapatterson@gmail.com . . Mrs
799 Lord Byron Trail
Hamilton, MT 59840
Stellen'73.B.Uv.Stellen'74.Nu'86

Pearson MR Harold A
& Osterman MS Jeanne-Marie
(917) 881-0773
pearsonah@aol.com . . Mr
4osterman@gmail.com . . Ms
1192 Park Av
New York, NY 10128
(212) 828-1374
Gonz'74.SFrSt'79.B.Y.Cal'63

Peterson MR & MRS Jeffrey R F
(Ergul Eda)
(203) 921-6134 . . Mr
(203) 921-6136 . . Mrs
jeffreypeterson@optonline.net . . Mr
pmpawpet@optonline.net . . Mrs
303 E Middle Patent Rd
Greenwich, CT 06831
(203) 274-7206
Franklin'83.Cw.Sar.Myf.Dar.Ncd.V'79.
Pace'83.Pace'01
MISS Melanie T F
Belm'18.Dar.Myf.Ncd.
MR Randolph E F
Cw.Myf.Sar.VPI'16

Pidgeon MR & MRS (DR) Steven D
(Klein Leslie)
(972) 333-0400 . . Mr
(214) 563-4752 . . Dr
spidgeon@starpower.com . . Mr
lpidgeon@me.com . . Dr
17408 Pauma Valley Circle
Dallas, TX 75287
(972) 380-5940
(972) 504-6671

Piette MS Lyssa
(Mashek Lyssa)
(312) 608-0650
lmpiette@icloud.com
118 E Erie St, Apt 31F
Chicago, IL 60611
(312) 643-3886
Walnut Ridge, 5867 W Kruger Rd
Three Oaks, MI 49128
(269) 756-3232
Bost'72.Mid'73.Sc.Uv.Wa.

Provost MR N Thomas
& Gutowski DR Andrew
(781) 366-7161
(508) 274-7866
rttom@comcast.net
andrew.gutowski@comcast.net
510 Clapboardtree St
Westwood, MA 02090
(781) 329-8316
StMich'80.Rowan'90.Colg'85.Bost'91

Pyne MR & MRS Joseph H
(Bodin Christine)
(713) 817-1261 . . Mr
(713) 517-7555 . . Mrs
joe.pyne@kirbycorp.com . . Mr
tinapyne555@gmail.com . . Mrs
2121 Kirby Dv, 12 South
Houston, TX 77019
Ny.NCar'70
JUNIORS MISS Cameron B

Q

Quinn MR & MRS Daniel L
(Nehila Claudia M)
(781) 718-8616 . . Mr
(339) 222-9195 . . Mrs
dan.quinn@rathstrong.com . . Mr
claudiaqnn@aol.com . . Mrs
243 Meadowbrook Rd
Weston, MA 02493
(781) 894-9799
Fairf'76.Cy.Sm.Chi.BostColl'76

R

Rault MR & MRS Joseph M
(Donnelly Celeste)
(917) 592-9935
Celesterault@gmail.com
1130 Park Av, Apt 52
New York, NY 10128
(212) 996-1657
Scripps'76.Ri.Jl.Pa'77.H'81

Regan MR W Deering
(843) 576-9866
455 W 23 St, Apt 14A
New York, NY 10011
Nu'08

Reibel MISS Katherine G
(203) 606-2851
133 W 22 St, Apt 6C
New York, NY 10011
Dth.Cl.Cly.Dbl.Ri.

Reiss MR & MRS Michael B (Priest Ashley K)
(305) 588-8448 . . Mr
(813) 786-2414 . . Mrs
mbrstuff@mac.com . . Mr
aprunner80@icloud.com . . Mrs
2716 W Jetton Av
Tampa, FL 33629
FlaSt'98.Roch'93.Hof'98
JUNIORS MISS Ruby A

Reynolds MR William J
see Muller MR Daryl A

Richardson GOV & MRS William B
(Flavin Barbara)
governor.richardson@gmail.com
216 Washington Av
Santa Fe, NM 87501
(505) 988-7140
Wheat'71.B.Mt.Tufts'70.Tufts'71

Rooks MRS Valerie
(631) 255-3939
rooksvalerie@aol.com
3800 Washington Rd, Apt 801
West Palm Beach, FL 33405
Dbl.Uv.

Rybolt MR & MRS William C
(Wersel Nancy)
(513) 284-3121 . . Mr
(513) 833-7667 . . Mrs
wrybolt@gmail.com . . Mr
nrybolt@gmail.com . . Mrs
4 Hampton Lane
Cincinnati, OH 45208
(513) 321-4211
USA.Bmc.Cw.Jts.Occ.Sar.Jl.Dar.

S

Salyer MR & MRS Stephen S
(Harrell Catherine C)
(202) 352-3611 . . Mr
(917) 566-7738 . . Mrs
46 Quail Rd
Greenwich, CT 06831
(203) 489-3000
NCar'03.B.Un.L.Tul'03
JUNIORS MISS Catherine C
JUNIORS MISS Evelyn S
JUNIORS MR Joseph A

Sanders MR David I JR
(513) 708-0524
dsanders.a2z@gmail.com
3944 Miami Rd
Cincinnati, OH 45227
Eyc.Xav'95

Scharf MR & MRS Andrew Z
(Schlaff Naomi)
(917) 446-0000 . . Mr
(917) 680-0001 . . Mrs
200 E 65 St, Apt 17C
New York, NY 10065
Nu'15.B.Pa'07
JUNIORS MR Aaron W
JUNIORS MR Henry S

Schell MR Richardson W
(203) 470-3667
rwschell@gmail.com
Kent School, PO Box 2006
Kent, CT 06757
(860) 927-6010
(860) 927-6014
Nrr.H.'73.Y'76

Seaman MR & MRS Bryant W III
(Martin Rebecca J)
(917) 215-3840 . . Mr
(845) 702-5110 . . Mrs
bwseaman3@gmail.com . . Mr
rebofsff@aol.com . . Mrs
Summer Fox Farm, 67 Robinson Rd
Salt Point, NY 12578
(845) 266-4129
Kas'77.Smu'80.B.Cly.Stan'75.Cl'81

Senseman MAJ David C T
trevor.senseman@gmail.com
CMR 388, Box 193
APO, AP 96208
USA.Tex'06

Shaffer MR & MRS David M (Vermilye Shelley)
(484) 793-1503 . . Mr
(828) 989-8232 . . Mrs
svshaffer@me.com
1164 Old Mill Lane
Wyomissing, PA 19610
Hl'ns'88.Il'87

Shen MR Jeff & Yu MS Sally
(917) 224-2129 . . Mr
(646) 263-0233 . . Ms
yuqingshen@yahoo.com . . Mr
sallyxunyu@hotmail.com . . Ms
550 Davis St, Unit 21
San Francisco, CA 94111
Mit'00.Nu'05.Hob'94.Mass'95.Nu'00
JUNIORS MISS Sophia
JUNIORS MISS Serena

Shultz MS Susan (Fried Susan K)
(480) 363-8344
sshultz@theboardinstitute.com
6001 E Cactus Wren Rd
Paradise Valley, AZ 85253
(480) 948-7214
(480) 998-1082
Ariz'64

Shyer MR Christopher D
70 E 10 St, Apt 16-S
New York, NY 10003
(212) 982-1022
Dt.Vt'83.Cl'87

Smith MR & MRS Jeffrey R
(Rose Katrina C)
(215) 620-3784 . . Mr
(267) 625-1256 . . Mrs
55 Hendricks St
Ambler, PA 19002
Cc.Cspa.Cw.Fw.Rv.Sar.Del'03
JUNIORS MISS Nikoline C
JUNIORS MISS Charlotte R
JUNIORS MR William J

Smith DR Judith W
see Fairbank MR David Ezekiel

Smith MR & MRS Patrick D
(Sinko Kristin L)
(646) 740-1535 . . Mr
(203) 249-3750 . . Mrs
patricksmith1223@gmail.com . . Mr
25 Davenport Av
Greenwich, CT 06830
W&M'14.Ihy.Cw.Myf.StJ.Snc.GeoW'14

Smith MR Timothy A & Newell MS Valerie L
(513) 293-8666 . . Mr
(513) 290-4612 . . Ms
timsmith@mac.com
valerie.newell@marinerwealthadvisors.com
312 E 2 St
Covington, KY 41011
BowlG'75.MiamiU'74.Cin'78

Speck MR & MRS Adam
(Gignoux Camilla E)
(011-44) 78-1577-7239
camillaspeckuk@gmail.com
27 Elms Crescent
London SW4 8QE England
Durham'98.Exeter'98
JUNIORS MISS Allegra
JUNIORS MR Rupert

Spencer MR & MRS Jack
(Fay Kelly)
(202) 257-3146 . . Mr
(917) 553-8019 . . Mrs
jack@bsp-nyc.com . . Mr
kellyfspencer@gmail.com . . Mrs
6 Russell Court
Montville, NJ 07045
Nu'00.Bm.GeoW'04
JUNIORS MISS Olivia Fay
JUNIORS MR Henry J

Strasbaugh DR & MRS Wayne R
(Taylor Carol L)
(215) 864-8328 . . Dr
(215) 813-3087 . . Mrs
139 W Springfield Av
Philadelphia, PA 19118
(215) 242-9534
V'74.Ph.R.Ul.Cw.Sar.Bow'70.H'76.H'79

Sutherland MS Maria
(415) 216-6841
maria@mariasutherland.com
PO Box 613
Carmel-by-the-Sea, CA 93921
NewSch'01

T

Tatosian MR Oscar S
(312) 215-0092
oscar@isberian.com
2013 S Prairie Av
Chicago, IL 60616
(312) 467-1212
(312) 467-1616
Art.Un.TCU'83

Thayer MR & MRS David B
(Steffens Laura)
(484) 343-0222 . . Mr
(484) 683-5324 . . Mrs
dbt007@icloud.com . . Mr
laurathayer@me.com . . Mrs
Balinor, 740 Hunt Lane
Flourtown, PA 19031
VillaN'95.Ph.Rv.Pc.Sg.Pa'87.LondEc'90.Ch'99
JUNIORS MR Seamus P Golden

Thomas MR Corrin
see Adelaar MR Jesse D

Thompson MS Samantha J
see Tomazos MR Anastasios

Tiné MR Christopher R
(917) 328-7580
chris@christophertine.com
360 W 55 St, Apt 5K
New York, NY 10019
Pan.Bates'96.Camb'99.Cl'11

Tiné MR Matthew D
(917) 902-5998
535 W 49 St, Apt 2FW
New York, NY 10019
ColC'99

Tinnin MR Alden & Hackenbracht MS Sarah
(937) 499-4104 .. Mr
(216) 903-2069 .. Ms
sarah.hackenbracht@gmail.com
5638 Eagle Nest Court
West Chester, OH 45069
WrSt'03.WrSt'04

Tomazos MR Anastasios
& Thompson MS Samantha J
(312) 315-2315 .. Mr
(312) 560-4989 .. Ms
anastasios.tomazos@gmail.com .. Mr
thompssj@georgetown.edu .. Ms
159 Fuller Lane
Winnetka, IL 60093
Geo'00.FIT'03.McG'95.Ottawa'01.Cl'06
JUNIORS MISS Persephone E J

Tschudin MRS Hanspeter
(Borton Sharon A)
(937) 271-0217
sherry.tschudin48@gmail.com
5507 Tall Trees
Dayton, OH 45429
(937) 298-8256
Louis'70

Tunney MR & MRS Jay R
(Smith Kelly)
(312) 771-7751 .. Mr
(917) 414-0849 .. Mrs
tunneyjay@gmail.com .. Mr
wildtunney@gmail.com .. Mrs
55 E Pearson St, Apt 4804
Chicago, IL 60611
(312) 929-4112
Bhm.Art.Ft.Stan'62

Turner MR E Deane
edeaneturner@gmail.com
1120 Fifth Av, Apt 1-A
New York, NY 10128-0144
(212) 876-5735
(212) 427-2787
Cw.Myf.Un.P'50.H'53

Tyree MR & MRS William B
(George Kathryn C)
(646) 574-9620 .. Mr
(516) 220-4757 .. Mrs
williambtyree@gmail.com .. Mr
kathtyree@gmail.com .. Mrs
108 E 65 St
New York, NY 10065
(212) 517-2151
Ty'86.Rc.Ln.Ng.Dt.Bcs.Ck.Mb.Mcs.Dbl.
Ri.Dth'85.Pa'93
MR William B JR
Dth'18
MR Quintin H
at Dartmouth
JUNIORS MISS Delia D'A
at Dartmouth

W

Walgamotte MR Shannon R
& Moreau MS Lynda P A
(504) 251-8800 .. Mr
(504) 296-8800 .. Ms
walgamotte.shannon@gmail.com .. Mr
dustbuny@ix.netcom.com .. Ms
4009 Green Acres Rd
Metairie, LA 70003-1301
(504) 888-9288
NewOrl.Sar.Wt.Jl.Bmc.Cda.Dar.Jts.NewOrl

Walton MR & MRS David B II
(Delfino Majandra)
(917) 509-7703 .. Mr
(310) 770-1907 .. Mrs
137 N Larchmont Blvd
Los Angeles, CA 90004
B.Bac.Cy.Br'01
JUNIORS MISS Cecilia D
JUNIORS MR Louis A

Ward MR & MRS Eric N
(Rainwater Sarah E)
13 Walker St
Cambridge, MA 02138
(617) 576-0203
DePauw.Cw.Neh.Sar.Dth.Ind
JUNIORS MR Charles V R
JUNIORS MR Henry N R

Weeks MS Patricia M
(212) 472-2421
125 E 78 St
New York, NY 10021
M'mack'73.Dbl.Nyc.P.

Wehland MR Matthew H C & Lynch MR John J
(202) 302-3069
(202) 302-3068
3892 College Av
Ellicott City, MD 21043
(410) 461-6164
Ofp.Sar.Cw.Md'91

Welsh DR & MRS George F
(Dahlen Rosemary)
(513) 519-9100 .. Mr
(513) 535-7585 .. Mrs
fwelsh@aol.com .. Mr
welshro@aol.com .. Mrs
Pentagon Place, 8660 Hopewell Rd
Cincinnati, OH 45242
(513) 791-8883
USAF.GAdolp'70.Cw.H.Carl'62

Wetmore MR & MRS David Harding
(Emre Deniz T)
(202) 210-2955 .. Mr
(202) 384-9329 .. Mrs
1906—16 St NW
Washington, DC 20009
LeesMcR.Mt.Cw.Ofp.Rv.MiamiU.GeoW
JUNIORS MISS Ayla E
JUNIORS MR Alexander L E

Weyand MR William J
(513) 485-3637
williamjweyand@gmail.com
1810 Gulf Shore Blvd N, Apt 302
Naples, FL 34102

Whalen MR Edward Holmes
(202) 210-8609
1400 S Edgewood St, Apt 536
Arlington, VA 22204
Smu'06.OklaCity'11

Wheat MR & MRS John H P
(Cronin Karen)
(860) 508-3185 .. Mr
(860) 508-3490 .. Mrs
john.wheat@sbcglobal.net .. Mr
wheatassoc@icloud.com .. Mrs
23 Carnoustie Circle
Bloomfield, CT 06002
(860) 286-9718
Wes'71.Cl'84

Wick MR & MRS Jared K
(Thieme Victoria M)
(314) 202-3075 .. Mr
(602) 750-5699 .. Mrs
jaredwick86@gmail.com .. Mr
vicwick215@gmail.com .. Mrs
23050 N 94 St
Scottsdale, AZ 85255
Nw'12.Cc.Dar.Pep'09

Wilberger MR & MRS Joshua S
(Schoonover Erika J)
(804) 921-3226 .. Mr
(804) 337-3609 .. Mrs
wilbergerjs@alumni.vcu.edu
823 Cobblestone Blvd, Apt 308
Fredericksburg, VA 22401
Ahca.Cc.Cw.Jts.VaCmth'09.VaCmth'14.
VaCmth'15

Williamson MR & MRS Hugh J
(Mason Mary R)
(843) 290-0135 . . Mr
(843) 295-9343 . . Mrs
marymwilliamson@msn.com
26 Halsey Circle
Bluffton, SC 29910-7868
(843) 815-9376
Wisc'73.Cda.Myf.Syr'71

Wolden DR Suzanne L
see Horowitz MR Jonathan R

Wolf MR & MRS David D (Jackson Virginia)
(404) 229-8917 . . Mr
(404) 790-5393 . . Mrs
ddvjwolf@comcast.net . . Mr
vjwolf@comcast.net . . Mrs
2361 DeFoors Ferry Rd
Atlanta, GA 30318
Cda.Dar.Ht.Jts.Ga'68

Wood MR & MRS Keith S
(Bolce Rebecca)
(925) 683-2998 . . Mr
(925) 683-2997 . . Mrs
2151 Gulf Shore Blvd, Condo 207
Naples, FL 34102
Van'84.Cin'94.Cal'77

Y

Yates MR Jonathan L
(843) 813-0103
jly@hellmanyates.com
2 Prioleau St
Charleston, SC 29401
(843) 414-9754
Cay.Cw.Ne.StA.Char'ton'83.SCar'90
JUNIORS MISS St Julien L
JUNIORS MR Jonathan L JR

Yates LT CDR Richard M
(410) 279-1898
richard.m.yates@gmail.com
1030 Broadwater Rd
Churchton, MD 20733
An.Sar.USN'06.Md'14

Yu MS Sally
see Shen MR Jeff

"He's very much like Leo Tolstoy, except he doesn't write."

— Original cartoon by William Hamilton, courtesy of Lucy Young Hamilton —

Notes